Approaches to Paleoecology

Approaches to Paleoecology

EDITED BY

John Imbrie

Professor of Geology, Columbia University
Research Associate
The American Musuem of Natural History

Norman Newell

Curator of Fossil Invertebrates
The American Musuem of Natural History
Professor of Geology, Columbia University

John Wiley and Sons, Inc., New York · London · Sydney

Library of Congress Catalog Card Number: 64-17143
Printed in the United States of America

Preface

Scientific treatises are published for many reasons. This book is essentially a collection of case histories by experts on work done within the broad spectrum of subjects currently encompassed by the term "paleoecology." In many cases original data are given in depth rather than the customary summaries of literature characteristic of textbooks. Thus it is designed for and appropriate to advanced university seminars. It may also be used as a reference handbook for professional geologists.

This book is the result of a symposium on the principles of paleoecology, which we conceived and organized for the annual meeting of the Paleontological Society at Cincinnati, Ohio, November 2, 1961. Authors' royalties that may derive from the sale of the book will be turned over to the Society's publication fund.

During the past few years, there has been a conspicuous burgeoning of interest and activity in interpreting the history of sedimentary rocks and fossils as deduced from the stratigraphic record. Geologists have necessarily turned to the study of recent marine sediments and organisms for uniformitarian clues about geological history. Increasingly, attempts are being made to coordinate overlapping disciplines in the search for knowledge of the past: paleontology, stratigraphy, sedimentology, petrology, and geochemistry. It is the synthesis of these fields, together with the materials of ecology, that permits paleoecologic interpretations. Hence, paleoecology is an interdisciplinary subject, not a separate field with its own set of methods and principles. Nevertheless, the great petroleum companies and certain universities are adding "paleoecologists" to their staffs, and seminars on the subject are now popular in the universities.

The present book is a natural outgrowth of a need for a progress report on this rapidly evolving area of historical geology. It provides source material on diagenesis, relations between sediment type and organism distribution, and on the historical continuity of community organization.

The treatment necessarily is uneven and there are certain outstanding omissions. For example, paleobotany and significant aspects of organic geochemistry, isotope chemistry, and work on trace elements are either omitted or not sufficiently covered because papers on these topics were not available to us. In spite of this, we believe that the book illuminates well some of the modern trends and complexities of modern paleoecology. It is evident that much more is involved than the ecology of ancient organisms.

We wish to acknowledge financial aid from the National Science Foundation (Grant NSF-G19250), which permitted us to invite such outstanding overseas authorities as B. Kurtén, A. Seilacher, and E. R. Trueman to travel to Cincinnati from Europe in order to participate in our symposium. Also, we wish to thank our publisher, John Wiley and Sons, for editorial counsel and aid.

John Imbrie
Norman D. Newell

June 1964
New York City

Contents

Introduction: The Viewpoint of Paleoecology

by John Imbrie and Norman D. Newell
Columbia University and The American Museum of Natural History, New York

Definitions and Viewpoints

Ecology is a branch of biology devoted to the understanding of relationships between living organisms and their environments. Paleoecology is a branch of geology devoted to the understanding of relationships between ancient organisms and their environments. Although the two disciplines have parallel aims and invoke many of the same principles, they are characterized by substantial differences in points of view and working methods. These differences result from three simple facts of paleoecology:

1. The living organisms now preserved as fossils cannot be observed.
2. Physical and chemical attributes of ancient ecosystems cannot be studied directly.
3. The fossil record is strongly influenced by post-mortem and post-depositional processes.

One conclusion we may draw from these facts is that the level of precision and amount of detail obtainable in paleoecology are far lower than in ecology. These limitations, which will be discussed in more detail, should not discourage effort in this field. Results which *can* be obtained are both valid and useful in spite of their relatively gross character.

The second conclusion following from the special character of paleoecology is that the subject is necessarily more inclusive than ecology. This point is emphasized in Figures 1 through 6, in which the viewpoints of paleoecology and related disciplines are illustrated. In Figure 1 the basic observational data of geology are represented in terms of the facies concept. Organic and inorganic aspects of rocks vary from specimen to specimen, and the aim of geology may be defined as an understanding of these variations. Three sets of causal influences may be identified:

1. Biological materials and processes present and acting at the time the sediment was formed.
2. Inorganic materials and processes of the primary depositional environment.
3. Post-depositional (diagenetic) changes.

The interrelationships between factors (1) and (2) are the concern of the ecologist, who dignifies them by the name *ecosystem* (Figure 2). The action and interaction of the three sets of materials and processes to produce the final fossiliferous rock record is the *paleoecosystem,* the study of which is the main task of paleoecology (Figure 3).

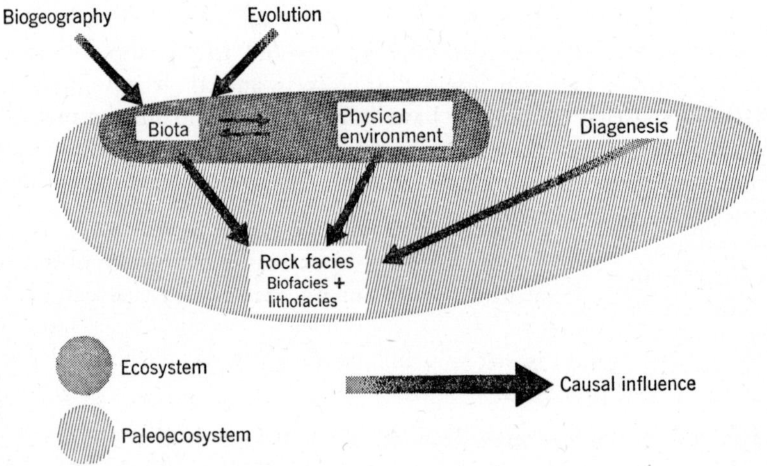

Fig. 1 Causal relationships in biology and geology pertinent to ecology and paleoecology.

Biogeographic and evolutionary processes, although pertinent to paleoecology, are here considered to be outside of its main concern (Figure 4). Petrologic and geochemical studies, also pertinent to

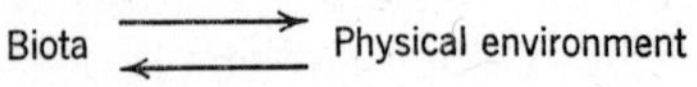

Biota ⇄ Physical environment

Fig. 2 Ecosystem point of view in ecology. Symbols as in Figure 1.

paleoecology, have as their primary objective the understanding of sedimentary rocks considered as products of primary and secondary physical and chemical processes (Figure 5). Paleontology is concerned with explaining the fossil record in terms of evolutionary, biogeographic, and ecologic processes and is only secondarily concerned with diagenesis and the influence of organisms on the physical environment (Figure 6).

Paleoecology deals with fossil organisms. Consequently, sound taxonomy and an appreciation of evolutionary processes are required for documentation and for thorough analysis (see papers by Hedgpeth and Whittington, in this book, pp. 11 and 19). Taxonomy, in turn, must be based on meticulous studies of morphology. This is not only true of population dynamics or functional anatomy of a specific animal or plant which must be accurately identified, but it applies equally well to community studies. The various interactions between organisms and their environment are stronger at the level of subspecies and species than at the levels of higher categories. Useful descriptive work may be done at the taxonomic level of genera, families, orders, etc., in which adaptation is more generalized than it is at the species level. For example, we may recognize ecological zones that include most of the niches of antelopes, starfish, or oak trees, but these do not as closely define or limit habitats as do communities of species. Furthermore, it is ecologically more meaningful to analyze communities by species rather than from the artificial point of view of their quantitative significance as sedimentary constituents.

The geographical distribution of living organsms is determined mainly by availability of habitat, in which such factors as climate, food, and substrate play leading roles. Consequently, it has long been known that maps showing the distribution of habitats and organism communities show close similarities in pattern. Likewise maps rep-

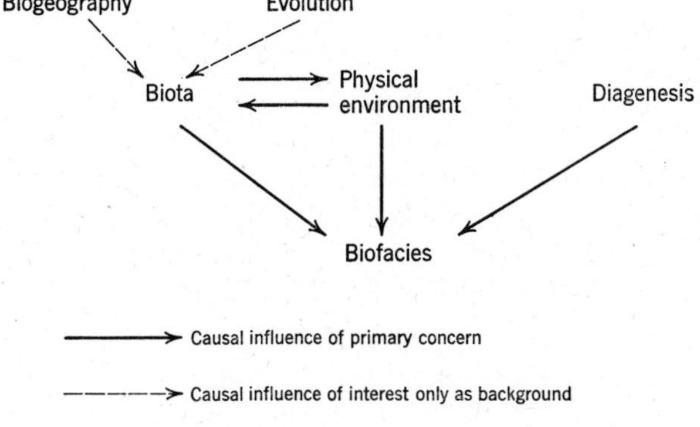

Fig. 3 Paleoecological point of view.

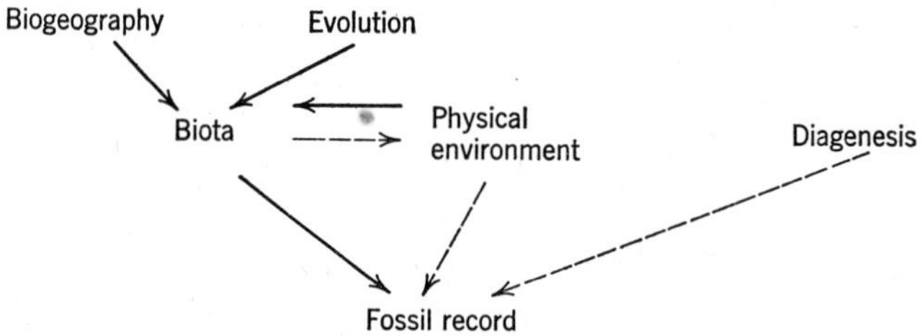

Fig. 4 Point of view in historical biogeography. Symbols as in Figure 3.

resenting lithologic facies in the stratigraphic record are essentially habitat maps of distinctive communities of organisms. This is the area of overlap between paleoecology and paleobiogeography (see Durham's paper, pp. 28–31).

Approaches to Paleoecology

From the definition of paleoecology just put forth, it is clear that methodological approaches to the subject are necessarily varied. It is this theme which has been stressed in organizing this volume. Particular attention has been given (1) to biologic approaches, ranging from interpretations of the morphology of individual specimens (Bandy, Trueman) to broader studies of entire faunas (Shotwell); and (2) to diagenetic approaches. Two papers survey inorganic and biogenic sedimentary structures as an approach to paleoecological problems. Stratigraphic and statistical approaches are covered by one paper each. Geochemical approaches to paleoecology have not been treated, although Bathurst's survey paper provides an excellent review of pertinent literature.

History of Paleoecological Investigation

Because of the wide scope of paleoecology, it has meant different things to different investigators. The uniformitarian interpretation of fossils as indicators of ancient environments goes back as far as Xenophanes and Herodotus, who inferred the former existence of vanished seas from fossils found far inland. In Europe, it has long been customary to exclude from paleoecology the post-mortem history of fossils and their enclosing sediments, but the view is prevalent in America that paleoecological interpretations must take into account the entire history of fossils and rock matrix, not simply their early history. The sedimentary processes by which organic remains become buried are termed *biostratinomy* by many European geologists, and the entire post-mortem history, including burial and diagenesis, is known as *taphonomy* (Müller, 1957).

As with living organisms, paleoecological studies may be devoted to single species, usually stressing the mode of life, functional morphology, population structure, and adaptation to environment. This dominantly biological mode of approach, pioneered by W. O. Kowalewsky (1874) in his classic studies of fossil horses may be termed *paleoautecology*. To many of the German paleontologists, following O. Abel, this line of inquiry is *paleobiology*, but paleobiology is more generally used for the biological aspects of paleontology.

The study of communities of fossil organisms, their interrelations, and ecological distributions is *paleosynecology*. Here, there may be greater emphasis on physical factors of the environment. Consequently, studies of fossil communities commonly are geologically oriented. Edward Forbes (1843, 1844) was one of the earliest investigators to advocate paleoecological studies of marine communities.

Paleoecology has received great impetus under the influence of Johannes Walther (1860–1937), Rudolph Richter (1881–1957), T. Wayland Vaughan (1870–1952), W. H. Twenhofel (1875–1957), F. E. Clements (1874–1945), R. W. Chaney (1890–), O. Abel (1875–1946), Edgar Dacqué (1878–1945), Louis Dollo (1857–1911), J. Weigelt (1890–1948), and many others too numerous to cite here.

The most important recent development is the long-delayed general recognition and acceptance of Gressly's (1838) theory that lithologic and paleontologic facies were influenced by many of the same environmental controls; hence, they tend to vary together. Stratigraphic facies provide valuable clues about the nature and distributions of past environments and virtually all geologists who would understand the genesis of fossiliferous rocks now give attention to the ecological implications of their evidence. Fossils and rock matrix are now studied together in the context of a common environmental framework.

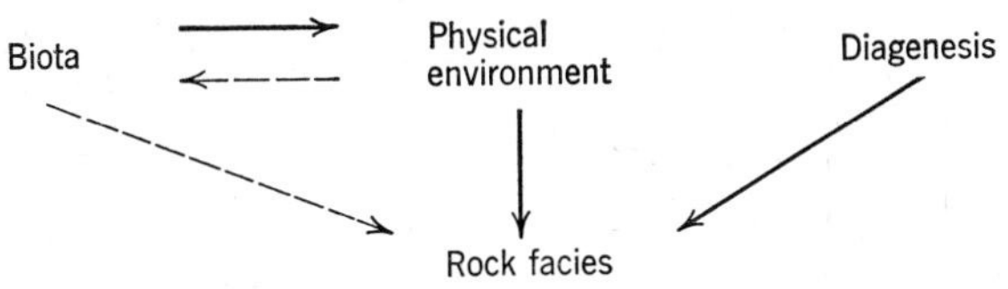

Fig. 5 Point of view of sedimentary petrology and geochemistry. Symbols as in Figure 3.

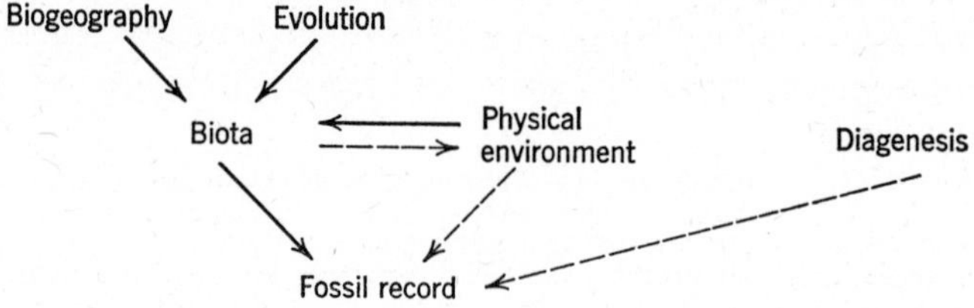

Fig. 6 Point of view of paleontology. Symbols as in Figure 3.

This kind of study has been variously designated as biofacies analysis, biostratigraphy, stratigraphy, and sedimentology, but it falls within the scope of paleoecology.

Increasing interest in environmental interpretations of fossils and rocks has given rise to the great *Treatise on Marine Ecology and Paleoecology,* published by the Geological Society of America and edited by Ladd and Hedgpeth (1957). Excellent textbooks on paleoecology have been published recently by Hecker (1960) and Ager (1963).

Limitations of Paleoecology

Many important elements of environment do not leave an unequivocal record in the rocks. Temperature, humidity, topography, depth of water, and many other factors of physical environment are difficult to reconstruct, and the former existence of soft-bodied elements in an ancient biota usually may only be guessed at. Sediments teach us something about chemical factors of the environment, past climates, and the general nature of transporting agents, but fossils are much more revealing. Even the simple distinction between marine rocks and those formed in lakes and streams may be very difficult in the absence of ecologically distinctive fossils.

In general, organisms are excellent indicators of environments, but adaptations are much more generalized in some than in others, and it may not be at all clear just what environment characterized a particular fossil biota. The fossil record is strongly biased by selective and uneven preservation, and it is clear that many important habitats are poorly if at all represented by fossils (Newell, 1959). It has been estimated that not more than one per cent of the species of some diversified communities are likely to be preserved in the fossil record. Hence, a fossil assemblage is not in itself a community or biocoenose; it is a strongly biased sample from which some of the characters of former communities may be inferred. All fossil assemblages are death assemblages; that is, thanatocoenoses. The use of the term biocoenose for an assemblage of fossils is not justified.

REFERENCES

Ager, D. V., 1963, Principles of Paleoecology, McGraw-Hill.

Forbes, Edward, 1843, Report on the Mollusca and Radiata of the Aegean Sea: *British Assoc. Adv. Sci.*, Rept. 13, pp. 130–193.

——— 1844, On the light thrown on geology by submarine researches: *Edinburgh New Phil. J.*, v. 36, pp. 318–327.

Gressly, Amanz, 1838, Observations géologiques sur le Jura Soleurois, pt. 1: *Schweizer Gesell. Naturwiss. N. Denkschr.*, Bd. 2, pp. 1–112.

Hecker, R. F., 1960, Bases de la paléoécologie: *An. Serv. Information Géologique*, No. 44, Éditions Technip, 98 pp. (Translation of Russian work publ. in 1957.)

Kowalewsky, W. O., 1874, Monographie der Gattung *Anthracotherium* Cuv. und Versuch einer naturlichen Classification der fossilen Hufthiere: *Paleontographica, N. F.*, Bd. 2, pp. 133–285.

Ladd, H. S., and Joel W. Hedgpeth (eds.), 1957, *Treatise on Marine Ecology and Paleoecology:* Geol. Soc. America, Mem. 67, New York City, v. 1, 1296 pp.; v. 2, 1077 pp.

Müller, A. H., 1957, *Lehrbuch der Paläozoologie*: Bd. 1, Jena, Veb Gustav Fisched Verlag, 322 pp.

Newell, N. D., 1959, The nature of the fossil record: *Am. Phil. Soc.*, v. 103, pp. 264–285.

Foundations of Paleoecology

Evolution of Community Structure

by Joel W. Hedgpeth

The origin of the interrelationships of living matter, like that of life itself, is a subject in which opinion takes precedence over authority. The current fashionable thinking is that life originated in some sort of open inorganic system of colloids, co-acervates of complex molecules, and the like in an interface or boundary situation. J. D. Bernal (1961) suggests that things began in the surface-active foam on estuary muds, that "life, like Aphrodite, was born of the sea foam." Darwin long before had suggested that conditions in small rocky pools would be most favorable for the beginning of things, although our present knowledge indicates that such a system would be too small and impermanent. In any event, we cannot easily conceive of a situation favorable to the origin of life which does not involve some sort of precursory system (for example, see Bernal, 1960). It looks as if life had an ecology before it had an individuality.

Conditions must have become established that stimulated the development of life with rapidity after a critical stage. While there may have been a single point of origin, this may have had the effect of one more grain added to a supersaturated mixture. As Teilhard de Chardin put it, "Life no sooner began than it swarmed," for in these early stages the "earth was in a state of biological supertension." In other words, there may have been niches before organisms, and the appearance of organisms in turn brought about new niches. The process has been summarized by Hutchinson as follows:

> Early during evolution, the main process from the standpoint of community structure was the filling of all niche space potentially available for producer and decomposer organisms and for herbivorous animals. As the latter, and still more as carnivorous animals began to appear, the persistence of more stable communities would imply splitting of niches previously occupied by single species as the communities became more diverse (1959, p. 155).

Logically, this would call for an original community of perhaps one organism or type of organism. We have not found and probably never will find, a record of a monospecific system (and because of the limitations of the fossil record, we would never be certain anyhow). Nor does it seem likely that a monospecific system could have been more than a transitory state of affairs. Figuratively speaking, it was probably but a moment of time before complexities set in and we had the beginnings of an ecosystem, an interrelated complex of the abiotic environment with the organic community: essentially a complex of two interrelated systems transferring energy and processing matter. The earliest fossils we know of appear to be some sort of algae, but we cannot be sure, given plants of this level of complexity, that there were not also herbivores of some sort to eat them. Possibly the first herbivores were little more than protoenzymes, breaking up the plant matter. Thus the earliest communities may have been more of an interrelated system of the living and the nonliving than those of the present time; and, as Pirie (1960) remarks, "even with existing organisms and systems, a rigid division into the living and nonliving is not possible." In these early systems, there may of course have been very small consumer organisms, possibly of some complexity, that have left no record or whose remains are yet to be discovered, as Axelrod (1958) has suggested.

The oldest community sample we now have that includes metazoan consumers is that of the allegedly pre-Cambrian Ediacara beds of South Australia (see Glaessner, 1961; Glaessner and Daily, 1959). The fossil material from this site represents a fairly well-developed community, certainly of abundant planktonic forms and possibly of macroscopic plants, producing edible detritus (although sandy bottoms are not too favorable for such plant growth, so this material may have come from neighboring regions, as it does in analogous modern situations), and a variety of filter, detritus, and deposit feeding invertebrates. No large, specialized predatory organisms are recognized, and the only hard parts seem to have been the spicules of some of the colonial coelenteroids.

It seems unlikely that macropredators were absent from such a community as that represented by the Ediacara beds, or that predation as such is dependent on the development of grasping and tearing organs, such as arthropod appendages and molluscan radula. There may well have been flatworms and large nemerteans, whose modern representatives are efficient and voracious predators, which would have left no trace in the record. Nor can one assume that apparent microfeeders were incapable of predatory habits; stalked barnacles, for example, can and do capture fairly large, active animals on occasion (Howard and Scott, 1959). Some evidence of predation by larger animals may indeed be present in the form of lesions or excised parts of soft-bodied animals, and paleontologists should examine their material critically for such signs. One would not expect such organisms as flatworms and nemerteans to be preserved at all, since they disintegrate easily, perhaps because of their loosely organized mesenchyme, whereas the comparatively stiff-jellied body of a coelenterate can obviously persist long enough to form a mold in sediments.

There are certain superficial similarities between the fauna of the Ediacara beds and the modern deep sea benthos: colonial and solitary coelenterates, some large oval-shaped detritus or deposit-feeding organisms (*Dickinsonia* in the Ediacara, holothurians in the deep sea) and worm-like organisms. In the modern deep sea, we have arthropods and apparently some fish. These fish are morphological and possibly ecological types not represented in the Precambrian.

Glaessner's description of the upside-down manner of fossilization of some of the medusoids suggests that they may have been similar in habit to the sedentary rhizostome *Cassiopea.* One of the most common fossils is *Dickinsonia,* an oval form with transverse structures. Could this perhaps be an example of a stock representing the ancestor of both annelids and mollusks? If so, its presence, along with apparent polychaetes but not well-defined mollusks, suggests that mollusks may indeed be a later offshoot of this great invertebrate stock. Perhaps the enigmatic *Pavancorina* represents some sort of limpet-like protomollusk which had instead of a shell a thick tunic-like mantle similar to that of the modern *Onchidiella* or *Tylodina.*

The occurrence in the Ediacara beds of apparent representatives of such quasi-individual but colonial organisms as sea pens indicates that this alternative approach to the efficiency of handling small particles or organisms is as equally old as the development of a large complex organism. Both types are responses to an ecological problem, and both types still prevail in the present environment. It seems unlikely that the complex metazoan could have evolved from anything like sea pens, and indeed the modern compound ascidian appears to be a new —and successful—attempt at filter-feeding specialization.

Neither "pre-Cambrian" nor deep-sea community is a simple, uncomplicated system, and it is probable that the early community was also dependent on the production from another community, such as the deep-sea and sandy shallow-bottom communities are today. The original communities involving complete organisms in a system of transfer of matter from inorganic matrix were probably composed of very small creatures living in interface habitats of "perhaps somewhat variable salinity" (Hutchinson, 1961). Not only are such environments chemically and physically active, but the possible small size of early organisms would have made them much more susceptible to the genetic effects of radiation than later, larger organisms (see Folson, 1958). Unfortunately, most of the organisms represented as microfossils are already too large and well-protected by armor to provide material to test this hypothesis: perhaps early shells and tests, at least those of microorganisms, were protective devices that slowed down radiation effects. Modern microorganisms are also poor material for study; algae, protozoa, and bacteria are capable of withstanding massive doses of radiation under experimental conditions (see Donaldson and Foster, 1957). Evidently, resistance to radiation was acquired or selected for fairly early in the history of these organisms. Perhaps, as our knowledge of this subject increases, comparative radiosensitivity may provide some further clue to the relative ages of organisms.

It seems likely that, under such conditions of living in active interface conditions and possible vulnerability to radiation, early ecosystems were comparatively unstable or rapidly responsive to environmental changes. Occurrence of organisms in fossil beds suggests abundance in the community represented—a well-diversified and probably stable community—although the circumstances that led to its death and preservation may have been marked by environmental instability.

Uniformitarian conditions can be as catastrophic as Krakatoa, and Cloud's (1959) neo-Cuvierian copper may not be as wild as it sounds at first. However, our problem is to consider how communities developed, not how they died.

It has been suggested that abundance of individuals combined with a paucity of species is an indication of a comparatively youthful community (Hutchinson, 1955, 1959; Dunbar, 1960), or of a community limited or restricted by environmental stress (see Odum et al., 1960, for the most recent statement). Both suggestions of course imply that this extreme ratio of individuals-to-species abundance is a sign of a comparatively uncomplicated community, whatever the reasons for such lack of complication may be. A simple community structure does not necessarily mean that the community is primitive or at an early stage of evolution, however.

Some of the simpler communities or systems now in existence may be very old, and their members have developed resistant stages and resting eggs to insure perpetuation of the community against environmental vicissitudes. Perhaps the best example of this is the community of salterns or brine springs, which consists of flagellates (the producers), *Artemia* (the consumer), and probably bacteria (as decomposers). This appears to be a stable community, especially at certain salinities, with little opportunity for new niches to be developed or exploited. A few insects may invade this system at certain stages as predators, but this community is not to be confused with a somewhat similar one of saline lagoons (see Hedgpeth, 1959).

Other such communities are vernal ponds and hot springs. The latter (see Vouk, 1950) are similar in composition to the shallow flats of bays where the system in hot shallow water is reduced to a culture of blue-green algae and microbes thriving in an anaerobic condition. Such circumstances may produce, under favorable conditions, structures resembling stromatolites (Logan, 1961). In these shallow flats there is produced a considerable quantity of organic matter that is not recycled. Although such algal mat communities may be a phenomenon of restricted, hypersaline areas, the conditions favoring their development appear to have occurred from the beginning of the fossil record.

MacArthur (1955) has suggested that the stability of a community increases as the number of links in its food web increases. There are obvious limits to this, as Hutchinson (1959) pointed out, since if sizes were to increase in proportion up the food chain, a series of fifty would require more space than exists in the oceans. Instead, we have the increase of kinds of smaller animals and a "blurring" of food chains. The tendency of natural systems toward stability through increased complexity has been discussed in some detail by Dunbar (1960); the subject was almost simultaneously reviewed by Bates (1960) for a similar occasion. Dunbar suggests that selection acts in favor of stability, producing mature, diversified communities that resist wide oscillations of the producers and primary predators or consumers. Under environmental stress, however, the younger, oscillating communities would be more adaptable according to Dunbar's thesis, and he cites high latitude or Arctic communities as immature but adaptable communities that have developed since the ice age. According to this criterion of increased complexity, Antarctic communities must be older than Arctic communities (if we restrict the comparison to marine communities). Certainly there are remarkable differences in speciation of similar invertebrate groups in the two regions.

It appears that some communities which are part of larger ecosystems go against the trend of multiplication of links in the food chain by developing extremely large primary consumers or predators relying directly on comparatively small consumers. Such systems are represented in the sea by baleen whales. One wonders how vulnerable such "short circuited" communities are, with the withdrawal of mass from the system represented by large populations of enormous individuals. Perhaps this is why the life span of whales appears to be relatively short for animals of such size. Perhaps for theoretical purposes, we ought not to consider man—the most rapacious predator in the history of the earth—in this context, but nevertheless we can upset populations of whales without much difficulty. Such apparently simple systems may be easily endangered by changes in the larger system or by invasion of unexpected predators. It would be useful if we had data on the life span of the larger dinosaurs; they may have been victims of community instability.

The idea of stability as a process in evolution is of course not a new one (see Holmes, 1948), and its application to ecology appears to have been first made by Lotka (1925), as pointed out by Odum and Pinkerton (1955). According to these ideas, natural systems tend to exploit their energy resources to the maximum. Thus, what we interpret as stability may simply be the mechanism for maintaining the optimum rate of environmental utilization by the living matrix. As Bates (1960) remarks: "The over-all impression one gets in looking back over much of the geological record is of the stability of the system, even though the parts of the system are frequently changed. It is impossible to be sure, because of the nature of the fossil record, but it looks as though the total biomass and the total number of organisms have remained about the same for a very long time, possibly from the beginning of the Mesozoic and quite probably through the Cenozoic."

While obviously not a simple system, since the variety of fossils suggests a fair range of niches, the system represented by the Ediacara fossils lacks apparent predators and organisms with heavy shells. Hutchinson (1959, 1961) has suggested that the development of heavy shells in Cambrian times was a response to the appearance of predators. While this explanation is debatable, the appearance of possibly massive numbers of organisms with hard parts is one of the central problems of paleoecology. Hutchinson calls attention to the change of carbon content of Paleozoic as compared with Mesozoic and Tertiary rocks as suggesting that the Paleozoic period was more productive: "more organic carbon per gram of argillaceous matter was deposited in the Paleozoic than at a later date" (Hutchinson, 1948). It is also possible that this represents not so much a more productive period as one in which carbon was not recycled by the ecosystems involved as actively as in later periods. This could be the case where consumer levels had not developed or where consumers did not have ready access, as in shallow, hypersaline algal flats.

We do not, of course, have any unequivocal data about such matters as the efficiency and stability of extinct communities. One of the few paleoecological studies that bears on the problem of community stability and evolution is that of Olson (1952). The evidence presented by Olson suggests that, once established, a community may maintain itself for long periods of time under moderate changes of the environment, and that effective occupation of the niches may inhibit evolutionary changes. On the other hand, a change affecting one or two species may upset the internal balance of the community and set in motion major evolutionary and ecological changes. Although these inferences are based on vertebrates in a delta region, they are in substantial agreement with the theoretical discussions reviewed above.

While it is obvious that Herbert Spencer, writing a hundred years ago, would have felt quite at home with current thinking about ecosystems, the paleontologists and many biologists of his day lagged somewhat behind. We have, however, become more aware of the significance of the interrelationships of the organic and inorganic environment as a geological as well as ecological process, and while the origin of community complexity may be lost in the record of the rocks, this awareness should lead to a fuller understanding of the past.

REFERENCES

Axelrod, Daniel I., 1958, Early Cambrian marine fauna: *Science,* v. 128, n. 3314, pp. 7–9.

Bates, Marston, 1960, Ecology and evolution, *Evolution after Darwin:* University of Chicago Press, v. 1, pp. 547–568.

Bernal, J. D., 1960, The problem of stages in biopoesis, *Aspects of the Origin of Life:* ed. by M. Florkin, New York, Pergamon Press, pp. 30–45.

———— 1961, Origin of life on the shore of the ocean. Physical and chemical conditions determining the first appearance of the biological processes: *Oceanography,* pp. 95–118, 2 figs., Am. Assoc. Adv. Sci., Publ. 67.

Cloud, Preston E., 1959, Paleoecology—retrospect and prospect: *J. Pal.,* v. 33, n. 5, pp. 926–962, 16 figs.

Donaldson, Lauren R., and Richard F. Foster, 1957, Effects of radiation on aquatic organisms, *The Effects of Atomic Radiation on Oceanography and Fisheries,* pp. 96–102: National Academy of Sciences-National Research Council Publ. 551.

Dunbar, M. J., 1960, The evolution of stability: natural selection at the level of the ecosystem, *Evolution: Its Science and Doctrine:* University of Toronto Press, pp. 98–109.

Folsom, Theodore H., 1958, Approximate dosages close to submerged radioactive layers of biological interest: *Proc. Ninth Pacific Science Congr.,* v. 16, pp. 170–175, 5 figs.

Glaessner, Martin F., 1961, Pre-Cambrian animals: *Scientific Amer.*, v. 204, n. 3, pp. 72–78, illus.

Glaessner, Martin F., and B. Daily, 1959, The geology and late pre-Cambrian fauna of the Ediacara fossil reserve: *Records So. Austr. Mus.*, v. 13, n. 3, pp. 369–401, plates xlii-xlvii, 2 text figs.

Hedgpeth, J. W., 1959, Some preliminary considerations of the biology of inland mineral waters: *Arch. Oceanogr. Limn.*, v. II, Suppl., pp. 112–141, 5 figs.

Holmes, S. J., 1948, The principle of stability as a cause of evolution: A review of some theories: *Quar. Rev. Biol.*, v. 23, n. 4, pp. 324–332.

Howard, Galen Kent, and Henry C. Scott, 1959, Predaceous feeding in two common gooseneck barnacles: *Science*, v. 129, n. 3350, pp. 717–718, 1 fig.

Hutchinson, G. E., 1948, Circular causal systems in ecology: *Ann. N. Y. Acad. Sci.*, v. 50, n. 4, pp. 221–246, 4 figs.

———— 1953, The concept of pattern in ecology: *Proc. Acad. Nat. Sci. Phila.*, v. 105, pp. 1–12, 3 figs.

————, 1959, Homage to Santa Rosalia or why are there so many kinds of animals? *Am. Nat.*, v. 93, n. 870, pp. 145–159.

———— 1961, The biologist poses some problems: *Oceanography*, pp. 85–94, Am. Assoc. Sci., Publ. 67.

Hutchinson, G. E., and R. MacArthur, 1959, A theoretical ecological model of size distribution among species of animals: *Am. Nat.*, v. 93, pp. 117–126, 4 figs.

Logan, Brian W., 1961, *Cryptozoon* and associate stromatolites from the Recent, Shark Bay, Western Australia: *J. Geol.*, v. 69, n. 5, pp. 517–533.

Lotka, Alfred J., 1925, *Elements of Physical Biology;* Baltimore, Williams and Wilkins, xxx + 460 pp., illus.

MacArthur, R. H., 1955, Fluctuations of animal populations and a measure of community stability: *Ecology*, v. 35, pp. 533–536.

Odum, Howard T., John E. Cantlon, and Louis S. Kornicker, 1960, An organizational hierarchy postulate for the interpretation of species-individual distributions, species entropy, ecosystem evolution, and the meaning of a species-variety index: *Ecology*, v. 41, n. 2, pp. 395–399, 3 figs.

Odum, Howard T., and Richard C. Pinkerton, 1955, Time's speed regulator: the optimum efficiency for maximum power output in physical and biological systems: *Am. Sci.*, v. 43, n. 2, pp. 331–343, 12 figs.

Olson, Everett C., 1952, The evolution of a Permian vertebrate chronofauna: *Evolution*, v. 6, n. 2, pp. 181–196, 5 figs.

Pirie, N. W., 1960, Chemical diversity and the origin of life: *Aspects of the Origin of Life*, ed. by M. Florkin, New York, Pergamon Press, pp. 55–62, fig. 1.

Teilhard de Chardin, Pierre, 1959, *The Phenomenon of Man:* New York, Harper and Row, 318 pp.

Vouk, Vale, 1950, *Grundriss zu einer Balneobiologie der Thermen;* Basel, Verlag Birkhäuser, 88 pp., 22 figs.

Taxonomic Basis of Paleoecology

by H. B. Whittington *Museum of Comparative Zoology at Harvard College and Department of Geological Sciences, Harvard University, Cambridge, Mass.*

The extent to which progress in ecology depends upon accurate identification, and upon the existence of a sound systematic groundwork for all groups of animals, cannot be too much impressed upon the beginner in ecology. This is the essential basis of the whole thing; without it the ecologist is helpless, and the whole of his work may be rendered useless, or at any rate of far less use than it might otherwise have been, by errors such as including several species as one, or using the wrong names for animals. The result of such errors is endless misinterpretation of work, especially by people in other countries. It is possibly to this danger that we must attribute a certain lack of sympathy for ecological work, politely veiled or otherwise, which is sometimes met with among systematists. They realise that ecological observations are dependent upon correct nomenclature, and are therefore to some extent ephemeral, in cases where the latter is not yet finally settled. Added to this is the feeling that ecologists are rather parasitic in their habits and are to some extent using other people (systematists) to do their work! (Elton, 1927, pp. 164–165.)

The necessity for identifying as accurately as possible all fossils dealt with in a paleoecological study could hardly be better expressed than in Elton's warning to ecologists. The dangers of ignoring this necessity are made equally clear—the work will be of less use than it might have been, open to misinterpretation, and liable to bring paleoecology into disrepute. There are already too many studies, purportedly in paleoecology, that deal with stratigraphy and sedimentation, but only cursorily with fossils named by class, order, or broadly conceived genus. Many of the "Selected analyses from the geologic record," forming chapters 7 to 23 of Volume 2, *Treatise on Marine Ecology and Paleoecology* (Ladd, 1957) are studies of facies and interpretations of environment, and not examinations of relations of

I am indebted to Drs. R. Cifelli, G. Arthur Cooper, and W. D. Ian Rolfe, as well as the editors, for suggestions and criticism during the preparation of this essay.

fossil species to these environments. It is evident in many cases that knowledge of the fossils is too inadequate to attempt any such examination. A similar lack of taxonomic work, despite the "abundant, diverse, and exceptionally well preserved" fauna (p. 650), detracts from the value of Imbrie's (1955) study of the Florena shale. Paleontologists know that it is all too easy to make such criticism and how difficult identification of species may be. Many groups of fossils are receiving scarcely any attention today, supposed "common" and abundant fossils are in reality poorly known, and the relevant literature is vast and scattered. Authors contributing to the *Treatise on Invertebrate Paleontology* know that we are far from having a "sound systematic groundwork" for all the kinds of fossils so far discovered. Paleontologists are striving to cope with this task, as well as deal with the constant flood of new material. The recent estimate that ten millions of fossil species of animals and plants are awaiting discovery (Teichert, 1956; see, also, Simpson's comments, 1960, pp. 135–136) shows the magnitude and complexity of the work that lies ahead.

Taxonomy cannot be avoided because it is too difficult, nor ignored as "out-of-date" in the flush of enthusiasm for the present fashion for paleoecology. Here, the term "taxonomy" means a classification of fossils resulting from detailed morphological studies of carefully collected material that has been prepared with the utmost care and thoroughness—we cannot afford to neglect any information that new or old techniques may derive from fossils. The aim of systematic paleontology is a classification of fossils embodying knowledge of morphology, ecology, geographical distribution, and evolution. Thus systematic and paleoecological work are not separate disciplines; they must go hand-in-hand, and one cannot be done effectively without the other. To some extent the present enthusiasm for paleoecology is a reaction against a type of descriptive paleontology that treats a fossil more or less as an inorganic object, unrelated to other fossils and the rocks that contained it. Such a reaction is as ill-conceived as its cause.

In the passage quoted earlier, Elton refers to the "beginner in ecology." Can there be a beginner in paleoecology in the sense of a graduate student beginning his research on some problem in this field? Granted that sound taxonomy is necessary to progress in paleoecology, it means that such a student must identify the fossils himself or seek the aid of experts, that is, adopt a somewhat parasitic habit that may not prove practical for a beginner. If he is to identify the fossils himself, he can, in the present state of knowledge, make a beginning on the systematics of only one class of organisms in the fauna. To become competent requires experience, and as three recently published doctoral dissertations show (Yochelson, 1956; Batten, 1958; Finks, 1960), the taxonomic work on such faunas is more than sufficient for a beginning problem in research. All three comment briefly and valuably on paleoecology, but emphasize the tentative nature of their conclusions. In the present state of our knowledge of fossil faunas, with a few notable exceptions from Mesozoic and Tertiary rocks, we contend that the "systematic route" is the sound way for a beginner to approach paleoecology. This route leads to an expertness in taxonomy, which gives the basis for worthwhile observations on relations to environment. Paleoecological work on an entire fauna clearly demands teamwork, of the kind exemplified by Coope, Shotton, and Strachan (1961) on a Pleistocene deposit.

If we turn to consider what is known of the ecology of particular fossil species, it is abundantly clear that the information has come from detailed studies of carefully collected, well-preserved fossils. Such studies have commonly been undertaken with description and classication as the main aims, and paleoecological observations as by-products. Fossils are the remains of dead animals, and their daily habits cannot be observed. Further, they may or may not be preserved in or near their original habitat. Few clues to this habitat and the food they ate are preserved in the surrounding rock. But some parts, usually the hard parts, of the animal are preserved, and it is primarily on these findings that paleoecological speculation is based.

The habits, relation to environment, and distribution of many living animals are poorly known. Where information is available, it may be used in the interpretation of the paleoecology of Cenozoic fossil species that appear identical with living ones. As this knowledge is extrapolated to interpret extinct species of living genera, inferences from it become more tenuous, but still appear valuable (see the example by W. Walton, p. 151, and the work of Bandy and Arnal, 1960). As we go back in time to the Mesozoic era the difficulties in interpretation intensify as we attempt to deal with extinct genera and higher categories of living groups. The different forms of the irregular echinoid *Micraster,* and their distribution in the Upper Cretaceous of Britain have attracted attention since the work of Rowe (1899). A biometrical study by Kermack (1954) showed that Rowe's interpretations could be upheld in the main. Recently Nichols (1959*a, b*) investigated living spatangoid sea urchins and showed the relation between mode of life and various characters of the test. Using these findings he was able to functionally interpret test characters used in the taxonomy of *Micraster* and to shed a flood of new light on the paleoecology, evolution, and taxonomy of the Cretaceous fossils. Nichols' synthesis of zoology and paleontology is exemplary.

Interpretations of form and function in Paleozoic fossils are notoriously difficult, since we are dealing almost entirely with merely the hard parts of extinct categories of animals distantly related to living forms. Here everything depends on thoroughness in collecting and technique in preparing the fossils, combined with an alertness, almost an intuition, that discovers and exploits a previously unknown wealth. Among examples one may cite Holm on *Eurypterus* (1898), Walcott's discovery and exploitation of the Burgess shale, work by many authors on pyritized fossils of the Hunsrück shale, and more recently Kozlowski's monograph (1949) on Polish graptolites, and Wills' work (1959, 1960) on Carboniferous "scorpions." All these men have shown, by ingenious preparation and illustration of the highest quality, what the animals were like, and thus given the basic information for paleoecological speculation. Dr. G. Arthur Cooper's leadership in the discovery and study of silicified fossils has opened up entirely new possibilities for understanding the mode of life and mutual relations of Permian marine invertebrates, as descriptive work on gastropods and sponges (Yochelson, 1956, 1960; Batten 1958; Finks, 1960) is beginning to show. When such work on the abundant brachiopods, pelecypods, bryozoa, echinoderms, and other groups is completed, it will, in combination with environmental studies (Newell et al., 1953; Newell, 1957), make possible paleoecological interpretations of a far more advanced character than is now possible in any Paleozoic deposit. An exceptional example of deductions on life habits of fossils deriving from a detailed and well-illustrated systematic study is Muir-Wood and Cooper's (1960, pp. 40–47) discussion of Productoidea. The relevance of taxonomic study to paleoecology can hardly be better exemplified than here.

If such taxonomic work is not undertaken, misunderstandings arise. An illustration of such difficulties is afforded by a paragraph from Lowenstam's discussion (1957) of the paleoecology of the Niagaran (Silurian) reefs of the Great Lakes area:

> An outstanding feature of the trilobites is the progression in population size of the bumastids from quiet- to rough-water conditions. They outstripped all other trilobites by a wide margin in this environment, and a reason for their success may be found in the shape of their carapace. Chiton-like, comparatively low lying, and above all well streamlined, the bumastids were ideally suited to withstand wave impact in a rough-water niche. They were thus morphologically pre-adapted to expand in a

habitat where other trilobites were unable to persist. (Lowenstam, 1957, p. 245.)

This is an intriguing suggestion regarding the habits of certain species of trilobites, for it is implied from the context that they were preadapted to the rough-water niche by the ability to cling to rock surfaces. It also appears that species of the genus *Bumastus*, of the family Illaenidae, are being referred to, since this genus is listed in the faunal assemblages and reference is made to local accumulations of glabellas and pygidia of *Bumastus* in faunas of the rough-water stage (Lowenstam, 1957, pp. 232, 233, 235). The suggestion of this particular habit is novel, and illaenid trilobites are abundant not only in these reef rocks but in other reef rocks such as the Upper Ordovician Boda and Kullsberg limestones of Dalarna, in Sweden. Many species of illaenids have a form like that of *Bumastus barriensis* (Figure 1*a*, *b*) from the Middle Silurian of Britain. In this species the depth of the cephalon was much greater than that of the thorax and pygidium, so that the trilobite could not cling to a rock surface with the edge of the exoskeleton everywhere in contact with this surface. *B. ioxus* and *B. decipiens* from the dolomites at Racine and Wauwatosa, Wisconsin, respectively, are like *B. barriensis* in form, and though streamlined, these species are not "chiton-like." Fenton and Fenton (1958, p. 230, figure) show a species of *Bumastus* of this type crawling on the sea bottom, and suggest that it may have ploughed into the sediments when feeding. In the dolomites at Wauwatosa occurs a second species, *Bumastus niagarensis* (Figure 1*c*–*e*), which has a chiton-like form. The margin of the exoskeleton is everywhere at about the same level so that it could be brought simultaneously close to a rock surface. Anteriorly on the cephalon the doublure is broad and gently convex, elsewhere the edge of the exoskeleton is flexed up and the margin narrow and rounded (Figure 1*d*). Is this the species, or one like it such as *B. cuniculus* or *B. dayi* (both said by Raymond, 1916, to be common at Wauwatosa), that Lowenstam had in mind? Yet a similar-appearing illaenid species has been portrayed by Seilacher (1959, p. 393, fig. 5f) as having a tunneling habit. These observations have been on collections from the Silurian of Wisconsin, described by Raymond (1916), made more than eighty years ago, poorly localized, and bearing no stratigraphical information. As Lowenstam (1957, pp. 216–217) points out, such material is difficult to relate to modern studies, and I have no idea whether or not *B. ioxus* and *B. niagarensis* occur together in the same facies at Wauwatosa, or whether or not this facies may be that interpreted by

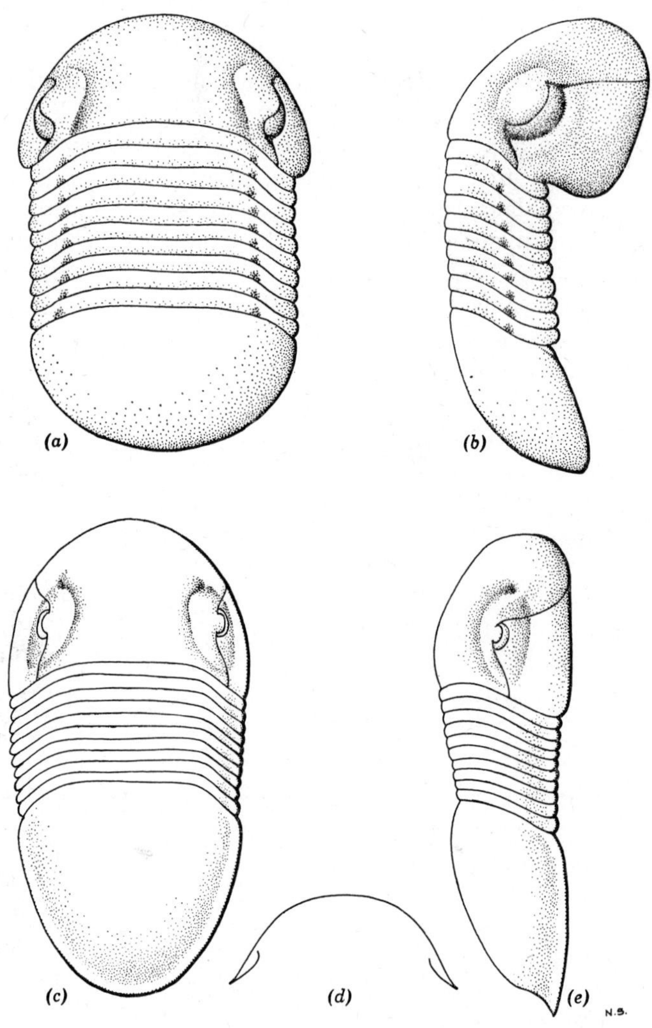

Fig. 1 (*a,b*) Bumastus barriensis *Murchison, 1839. Barr limestone, Wenlock Series, Middle Silurian, Great Britain. Dorsal, right lateral views based on type material in Geological Survey Museum, London,* × *0.8.* (*c,d,e*) "Bumastus" niagarensis (*Whitfield, 1880*). *Niagaran Series, Wauwatosa, Wisconsin. Dorsal view, transverse section through anterior portion of pygidium, right lateral view,* × *2. Museum of Comparative Zoology, Harvard, n. 643, original of Raymond, 1916, plate, 1, fig. 3. Drawings by N. Strekalovsky.*

Lowenstam as the rough-water niche. It is quite evident that these uncertainties will not be clarified without thorough taxonomic study of the illaenids in these rocks, and observations on where and how they occur. When form and occurrence are better known we shall have a sounder basis on which to speculate on possible function, taxonomic value of characters, and habit.

The problem of what is a species in paleontology has been much discussed (e.g., Sylvester-Bradley, 1956; Imbrie, 1957), and no doubt will continue to provoke comment. Despite the arguments, the discrimination of species in paleontology is necessary and valuable, and may lead to paleoecological deductions. For example, Imbrie (1959), in a study of brachiopods from the Devonian Traverse Group of Michigan, discriminated eight species of *Strophodonta* from the Alpena limestone. The populations appear to have been small and localized. "Now the Alpena limestone is also remarkable for the presence in it of biohermal masses apparently representing ancient reefs. The coincidence of reefy lithology with maximum strophodont speciation involving small populations suggests strongly that the taxonomic diversity is a reflection of an environment marked by a diversity of ecological niches" (Imbrie, 1959, p. 375). Had the taxonomic work not been undertaken this adaptive radiation would have remained undetected and the diversity of ecological niches thereby unsuspected. A parallel example comes from recent work on trilobites from Newfoundland (Whittington, 1963). In an unbedded, pure white limestone that may be part of a reef core occur several genera, each represented by three to six species. These species are found together in patches of drifted, disarticulated exoskeletons, probably not far from their original habitat, and so were contemporaneous. The inference is the same as Imbrie's, that these species inhabited a diversity of ecological niches in a probable reef environment. Lowenstam (1957, pp. 234–235) refers to the great numbers of species characterizing the wave-resistant stage of reef development. We may tentatively conclude that sympatric species of certain genera appear to characterize ancient reef environments—an inference in paleoecology again based on taxonomic considerations.

No further examples seem necessary to elucidate the conviction that thorough morphological study of fossils is essential both in taxonomy and in the approach to paleoecological problems—the two are inseparable facets of paleontology. That there are other facets that cannot be neglected is demonstrated in this book—and, for example, by discussions of the probable environment in which early Paleozoic chordates lived (White, 1958, Westoll, 1958, and references). In this paleoecological problem the fossils have been studied with great care, but there remains a sharp division of opinion as to whether these animals inhabited fresh or salt water. In seeking to shed new light on the problem it will be necessary to investigate more precisely the way in which the fossils occur and to make more intensive studies of the enclosing sediments.

The taxonomic basis is not the sole basis upon which paleoecological inferences may rest, but its importance stems from the fact that paleoecology is concerned with fossils. We need to know the specific identity of the fossils we are dealing with and, as far as possible, what each species was like in life, if interpretations of value are to be made and expressed in a manner intelligible to others. It is poor practice to ignore Elton's words.

REFERENCES

Bandy, O. L., and R. E. Arnal, 1960, Concepts of foraminiferal paleoecology: *Am. Assoc. Petrol. Geol.*, v. 44, n. 12, pp. 1921–1932.

Batten, R. L., 1958, Permian Gastropoda of the southwestern United States, 2: *Bull. Am. Mus. Nat. Hist.*, v. 114, pp. 157–246.

Coope, G. R., F. W. Shotton, I. Strachan, 1961, A late Pleistocene fauna and flora from Upton Warren, Worcestershire: *Phil. Trans. Roy. Soc. London*, Ser. B, n. 714, v. 244, pp. 379–421.

Elton, C., 1927, *Animal Ecology*: New York, Macmillan Co., xvii + 207 pp.

Fenton, C. L., and M. A. Fenton, 1958, *The Fossil Book, A Record of Prehistoric Life*: Garden City, N. Y., Doubleday and Co., xiii + 482 pp.

Finks, Robert M., 1960, Late Paleozoic sponge faunas of the Texas region: *Bull. Am. Mus. Nat. Hist.*, v. 120, pp. 1–160.

Holm, G., 1898, Über die organization von *Eurypterus fischeri* Eichw.: *Acad. Sci. St. Petersbourg, Mem.*, ser. 8, v. 8, n. 2, pp. 1–57.

Imbrie, J., 1955, Quantitative lithofacies and biofacies study of Florena shale (Permian) of Kansas: *Am. Assoc. Petrol. Geol.*, v. 39, n. 5, pp. 649–670.

_______ 1957, The species problem with fossil animals, in *The Species Problem* (ed. by E. Mayr), pp. 125–153: Am. Assoc. Advan. Sci., Pub. 50, ix + 395 pp.

_______ 1959, Brachiopods of the Traverse Group (Devonian) of Michigan, Part 1: *Bull. Am. Mus. Nat. Hist.*, v. 116, pp. 349–409.

Kermack, K. A., 1954, A biometrical study of *Micraster coranguinum* and *M.* (*Isomicraster*) *senonensis: Phil. Trans. Roy. Soc. London*, Ser. B, v. 237, pp. 375–428.

Kozlowski, R., 1949, *Les Graptolithes et quelques nouveaux groupes d'animaux du Tremadoc de la Pologne:* Palaeont. Polonica, v. 3, xii + 235 pp.

Ladd, H. S., (ed.), 1957, Treatise on marine ecology and paleoecology, v. 2, Paleoecology: *Geol. Soc. Am.*, Mem. 67, x + 1077 pp.

Lowenstam, H., 1957, Niagaran reefs in the Great Lakes area: *Geol. Soc. Am.*, Mem. 67, pp. 215–248.

Muir-Wood, H., and G. A. Cooper, 1960, Morphology, classification and life habits of the Productoidea (Brachiopoda): *Geol. Soc. Am.*, Mem. 81, xi + 447 pp.

Newell, N. D., 1957, Paleoecology of Permian reefs in the Guadalupe Mountains area: *Geol. Soc. Am.*, Mem. 67, pp. 407–436.

Newell, N. D., J. K. Rigby, A. G. Fischer, A. J. Whiteman, J. E. Hickox, and J. S. Bradley, 1953, *The Permian Reef Complex of the Guadalupe Mountains Region, Texas and New Mexico:* San Francisco, W. H. Freeman and Co., xiv + 236 pp.

Nichols, D., 1959*a*, Changes in the Chalk heart-urchin *Micraster* interpreted in relation to living forms: *Phil. Trans. Roy. Soc. London*, Ser. B, v. 242, n. 693, pp. 347–437.

——— 1959*b*, Mode of life and taxonomy in irregular sea urchins: *Systematics Assoc.*, London, Pub. n. 3, pp. 61–80.

Raymond, P. E., 1916, New and old Silurian trilobites from southeastern Wisconsin, with notes on the genera of the Illaenidae: *Bull. Mus. Comp. Zool.*, Harvard, v. 60, pp. 1–41.

Teichert, C., 1956, How many fossil species?: *J. Paleont.*, v. 30, pp. 967–969.

Rowe, A. W., 1899, An analysis of the genus *Micraster*, as determined by rigid zonal collecting from the zone of *Rhynchonella cuvieri* to that of *Micraster coranguinum: Quart. J. Geol. Soc.*, London, v. 55, pp. 494–547.

Seilacher, A., 1959, Vom leben der Trilobiten: *Die Naturwissenschaften,* v. 12, pp. 389–393.

Simpson, G. G., 1960, The history of life, *Evolution after Darwin* (S. Tax, ed.), v. 1, *The evolution of life*: University of Chicago Press, pp. 117–180.

Sylvester-Bradley, P. C., (ed.), 1956, The species concept in palaeontology: *Systematics Assoc.*, London, Pub. n. 2, vi + 145 pp.

Westoll, T. S., 1958, The origin of continental vertebrate faunas: *Geol. Soc. Glasgow, Trans.*, v. 23, pp. 79–105.

White, E. I., 1958, Original environment of the craniates, pp. 212–234, *Studies on fossil vertebrates:* (T. S. Westoll, ed.), University of London, Athlone Press, xii + 263 pp.

Whittington, H. B., 1963, Middle Ordovician Trilobites from Lower Head, Western Newfoundland: *Bull. Mus. Comp. Zool., Harvard,* v. 129, pp. 1-118.

Wills, L. J., 1959, The external anatomy of some Carboniferous "scorpions," part 1: *Palaeontology,* v. 1, pp. 261–282.

——— 1960, The external anatomy of some Carboniferous "scorpions," part 2: *Palaeontology,* v. 3, pp. 276–332.

Yochelson, E. L., 1956, Permian Gastropoda of the southeastern United States, part 1: *Bull. Am. Mus. Nat. Hist.*, v. 110, pp. 177–275.

——— 1960, Permian Gastropoda of the southwestern United States, part 3: *Bull. Am. Mus. Nat. Hist.*, v. 119, pp. 209–293.

The Biogeographic Basis of Paleoecology

by J. Wyatt Durham *University of California, Berkeley*

Biogeography may be defined as the scientific study of the distribution of organisms on a world-wide basis. Paleoecology has been defined as "ecology which deals with fossil organisms" (*Webster's New International Dictionary*). In turn ecology has been defined (*idem*) as "the branch of biology which deals with the mutual relations among organisms and between them and their environment." In paleoecology however it is usually necessary to detour from the direct observational methods of ecology and attempt to infer past environments by the study of the fossil content and the physical characters of sedimentary rocks. The organic aspect of paleoecology is dependent on the principle of uniformitarianism and our knowledge of organisms. Within the "organic realm" one of the basic pillars on which paleoecology rests is geographic distribution and the factors which control it, or biogeography. Without data from biogeography it is impossible to evaluate the significance of the presence or absence of particular organisms in fossil biotas. Paleoecologic interpretations based on specific organisms, either directly or indirectly, can be made only if biogeography indicates that it was possible for these organisms to have been present in the region being studied.

The broad geographic distribution of organisms is controlled by numerous factors, many of them closely interrelated. However, these may be reduced to two basic types: first, those factors concerned with the dispersional ability of organisms; and second, the factors related to the distribution of barriers and suitable habitats.

The dispersal of organisms is effected by various means and may be either active or passive. Active dispersal is almost entirely limited to the animal kingdom and usually occurs during the adult stages. Typical examples of actively dispersed animals are highly mobile terrestrial mammals, such as the horse and cougar; powerful swimmers, such as fish and squid in the sea; and flying animals, such as birds and insects in the air. Some birds have remarkable powers of flight and may rapidly cover great distances. For instance the Arctic tern breeds in the Arctic and "winters" in the Antarctic.

Less striking, but much more important because it involves by far the greater number of organisms, is passive dispersal. Here the individual does not move from one region to another under its own power, but is transported (see Allee and Schmidt, 1951, pp. 68–88; Darlington, 1957, pp. 14–20) at some stage in its life history by an external agent. These external agents not only include such things as currents in the oceans and winds in the atmosphere, but other organisms and rafts of various types (see Guppy, 1917). Passive transport by currents regularly affects the plankton (including not only larval stages and various smaller organisms but occasional large animals) in the sea. Occasionally larger organisms are transported across water bodies by the various types of rafting, and in the air winds may lift and carry numerous small animals and plants as well as seeds and spores over varying distances.

The effectiveness of these various means of passive dispersal is limited by the distribution of suitable habitats, food, dispersal routes, and barriers. The larva of stenotopic marine organisms may be carried long distances by currents (Thorson, 1961), but unless the proper substrate, appropriate food, and necessary physical conditions are present at the end of the voyage, they cannot survive and establish themselves. Different combinations of factors affect the dispersal of stenotopic terrestrial organisms but the net result is the same.

Barriers to dispersal are of many types. Such land bodies as Central America bar modern marine thermophilic organisms from moving from one ocean to another, but the same body of land serves as a dispersal route for actively vagile terrestrial animals. However a knowledge of the geologic history of such areas is necessary in order to fully evaluate their significance. For instance geological evidence demonstrates that the Central American land area was largely submerged during the middle and late Mesozoic and that, although it was much more emergent during the Cenozoic, it was only during the earliest Tertiary and in the Pliocene to Recent epochs that it was continuous enough to make a pathway between North and South America for terrestrial mammals. In contrast, during the Jurassic and Early Cretaceous the broad seaway through the area permitted the development of numerous tropicopolitan marine organisms.

The Bering land bridge is another highly significant feature that has acted both as a barrier and a dispersal route. Evidence now available (Hopkins, 1959; Durham and Allison, 1960, pp. 68–69) indicates that during the latest Mesozoic and throughout the Tertiary until about the end of the Pliocene it was in existence, and during much if not all of this time it served as a migration route between Eurasia and North America for terrestrial vertebrates. At the same time it acted as a barrier between the marine faunas of the North Atlantic-Arctic region and the North Pacific. With the development of Bering Straits at the end of the Pliocene, numerous marine organisms previously endemic to the North Pacific migrated into Arctic and North Atlantic regions (Durham and Allison, 1960, pp. 68–69, 79), and a few moved in the opposite direction.

Barriers of other types may be less apparent but are no less significant to biogeography. A wide expanse of the offshore Eastern Pacific is characterized by deep water and a lack of islands. Because of these characters it acts as a barrier (*East Pacific Barrier*, Ekman, 1953, pp. 21, 72–74; Durham and Allison, 1960, p. 69) and few species of shallow water stenotopic organisms are able to cross it.

Temperature exercises much control over distribution. There is much more biotic diversity in the tropics than in polar regions (Fischer, 1960; Thorson in Ladd, 1957, pp. 461–534). The shelled marine molluscan fauna of the tropical Panamic region has been estimated to number over 2500 species whereas the fauna of the frigid region around Point Barrow, Alaska, includes less than 200 species. An analysis (unpublished) of the distribution of 964 marine gastropod genera (based on nearly 12,000 records) showed that only 108 genera were recorded from regions where the surface temperatures were below 5°C, whereas 671 genera were known from areas where the surface temperature was above 20°. In contrast, individuals of a given species may be exceedingly abundant in the colder zones and rare in the tropics.

The effects of temperature likewise may control the usefulness of organisms for other ecologic inferences. Most hermatypic corals are present in a region only if the minimum water temperature is above 18°C. Within the region their local distribution is primarily controlled by the depth of water, salinity, and the presence of a suitable substrate. Thus unless the regional temperature is above the necessary minimum, this highly sensitive group of organisms is not available for use in determining other facets of the ecology.

The preceding examples illustrate some of the ramifications of biogeography that control the significance of any paleoecologic inferences that may be attempted. They likewise emphasize the mutual interdependence of the two fields. For instance, the peculiar solitary coral, *Dasmia*, has long been recorded only from the early Eocene of

England. It is now known (Durham and Allison, 1960, p. 74) from the late Eocene of Oregon. It would appear, therefore, that this coral can now be expected in the Eocene of any part of the world where the appropriate ecologic environment existed.

REFERENCES

Allee, W. C., A. E. Emerson, O. Park, T. Park, and K. P. Schmidt, 1949, *Principles of Animal Ecology:* Philadelphia and London. W. B. Saunders, 837 pp.

________ and Karl P. Schmidt, 1951, *Ecological Animal Geography,* Second Edition: New York, John Wiley and Sons, 715 pp.

Beaufort, L. F. de, 1951, *Zoogeography of the Land and Inland Waters:* London, Sidgwick and Jackson Ltd., 208 pp.

Cloud, Preston E., Jr., 1959, Paleoecology—retrospect and prospect: *J. Paleont.,* v. 33, pp. 926–962.

________ 1961, Paleobiogeography of the marine realm, *Oceanography,* (Mary Sears, ed.): Amer. Assoc. Adv. Sci., publ. 67, pp. 151–200.

Darlington, Philip J., Jr., 1957, *Zoogeography: the Geographical Distribution of Animals:* New York, John Wiley and Sons, 675 pp.

Durham, J. Wyatt, and Edwin C. Allison, 1960, The biogeography of Baja California and adjacent seas, Part 1: The geologic history of Baja California and its marine faunas. *Syst. Zool.,* v. 9, pp. 47–91.

Ekman, Sven, 1953, *Zoogeography of the Sea:* London, Sidgwick and Jackson Ltd., translated by Elizabeth Palmer, 417 pp.

Elton, Charles S., 1958, *The Ecology of Invasions by Animals and Plants:* London, Methuen and Co., Ltd., 181 pp.

Fischer, Alfred G., 1960, Latitudinal variations in organic diversity: *Evolution,* v. 14, pp. 64–81.

Glover, R. S., 1961, Biogeographical boundaries: the shapes of distributions, *Oceanography,* (Mary Sears, ed.), Amer. Assoc. Adv. Sci., publ. 67, pp. 201–228.

Guppy, H. B., 1917, Plants, Seeds, and Currents in the West Indies and Azores: the Results of Investigations Carried Out . . . between 1906 and 1914, London, Williams and Norgate, 531 pp., 1 pl.

Hedgepeth, J. W., (ed.), 1957, Treatise on marine ecology and paleoecology, v. 1: *Ecology,* Geol. Soc. Am., Mem. 67, v. 1, 1296 pp.

Hopkins, David M., 1959, Cenozoic history of the Bering land bridge: *Science,* v. 129, n. 3362, pp. 1519–1528.

Ladd, Harry S., (ed.), 1957, Treatise on marine ecology and paleocology, v. 2: *Paleoecology.* Geol. Soc. Amer., Mem. 67, v. 2, 1077 pp.

Moore, Hilary B., 1958, *Marine Ecology:* New York, John Wiley and Sons, 493 pp.

Thorson, Gunnar, 1961, Length of pelagic life in marine bottom invertebrates as related to larval transport by ocean currents, *Oceanography,* (Mary Sears, ed.), Amer. Assoc. Adv. Sci., publ. 67, pp. 455–474.

Zenkavitch, L. A., 1961, Certain quantitative characteristics of the pelagic and bottom life of the ocean, *Oceanography,* (Mary Sears, ed.), Amer. Assoc. Adv. Sci., publ. 67, pp. 323–335.

Stratigraphic Basis of Paleoecology

by Alfred G. Fischer *Princeton University*

Earth History

At any one moment the earth is a complex three-dimensional mass of matter and energy. In the fourth dimension—time—the patterns of mass and energy distribution are being continually rearranged and modified. The kinds of rearrangements which take place are termed *processes,* and the finite steps in which they occur are called *events.* Earth history may thus be thought of as dealing with a four-dimensional fabric of events and their causative processes in the space-time matrix in which the earth has developed, and in which we exist.

The Stratofabric

Earth history is concerned with all parts of our planet, but not with equal success: We have learned much more about the history of the surface of the lithosphere than about any other parts of the earth, and thus our classification of earth history into periods, eras, etc., is based on the history of this surface. This is due mainly to two causes: (1) We are more familiar with the lithospheric surface than with other parts of our planet. (2) This surface is essentially two-dimensional. Many events which happen on it are recorded in successively superimposed layers of sediment which come to form a concrete, three-dimensional *stratofabric,* in which the spatial dimension normal to bedding is essentially representative of the time-dimension in the conceptual space-time fabric of history. Thus the sequence of surficial events is comparatively simple to unravel.

The term stratofabric, here proposed, is designed to apply to the nature and arrangement of the sedimentary layers, prior to tectonic deformation. It is akin to Sander's (1930) term *Anlagerungsgefüge* (translated by E. B. Knopf, Sander, 1951, as *depositional fabric*), but is more restricted. *Anlagerungsgefüge* deals with the full range of fabrics from crystals, grains, and pores to beds and larger stratigraphic units, whereas *stratofabric* refers only to strata and larger stratigraphic units and excludes consideration of the fabric within a given stratum. It can be applied at various scales; for example, the laminations in a single bed constitute its stratofabric; formations of flysch type show a striking stratofabric of alternating shales and graded planar sandstones; the stratofabrics of the Mid-Continent Pennsylvanian are characterized by cyclic repetition of larger sedimentary units, holding the stratigraphic rank of members and formations. One may even speak of the stratofabric of an entire sedimentary basin or a geosyncline. The study of stratofabrics—their physical description, correlation, dating, etc.,—is the realm of *stratigraphy*.

Paleoecology

The stratofabric records a vast number of events—erosion and deposition of particles and particle aggregates (sediments), or the life and death of individual organisms and the appearance and disappearance of organic assemblages (biotas). At any given place in the stratofabric these events reflect processes which operated at some pinpoint in the space-time matrix of earth history. So long as we focus only on the sedimentary or the organic events and processes we are practicing sedimentology or paleontology. But when we attempt to view this local setting in a more comprehensive way, as a landscape with certain physical and chemical attributes, populated by organisms living in a delicate balance with the physical environment with each other, then we are practicing *paleoecology* in a widely used (though not comprehensive) sense of the term.

In actual practice, most investigators begin by asking paleoecological questions from the very start. The first question upon stepping up to an outcrop, or examining a hand specimen, may be: What kind of rock is this, and what kind of fossils does it contain? But the second one is: How did this rock form? What kind of a setting in the earth's past does it represent? What was the landscape—physically, chemically, and organically? The answers to these questions are derived mainly from the events recorded locally, that is, from *intrinsic clues*, derived directly from the realm of sedimentology or of paleontology. The thin section, the hand specimen, and the outcrop are replete with such clues. The limitations of this first approach to paleoecology lie in our ability to decipher them, to interpret them in terms of processes, and to understand their relationships.

Fig. 1 Relations of paleoecology, paleogeography, and earth history.

Paleoecologic Synthesis into Paleogeography and History

The local landscapes of the past, which emerge from paleoecologic studies at the local level, may be combined into larger pictures. Their "lateral" extension, parallel to time planes in the stratofabric, yields regional landscapes, or *paleogeography*. Their "vertical" extension through the stratofabric, parallel to the time dimension, yields *history*—local or regional. These relationships are shown in Figure 1.

The purpose of the investigators may differ widely: Some are chiefly interested in the physical history of the globe, and they may use organic criteria of past conditions only as a means toward this end. Others are primarily concerned with the history and development of life on earth, and view the physical side only as a stage on which this has occurred. These viewpoints are shown on different sides of the cube (Figure 1). But no matter what the ultimate aim, the tools and methods of paleoecological work are essentially the same.

Micro-, Meso-, and Mega-stratigraphy

Stratigraphy is thus basic to all paleoecological, paleogeographical, and geohistorical work. However, many stratigraphers have not been aware of the scope of demands which are made upon their subject.

Since the days of D'Orbigny stratigraphers have been concerned with the recognition and tracing of rather large units—periods and stages—over the face of the globe, thus dealing with rather coarse aspects of the historical fabric, with tools which are amenable to far-flung application but have a resolving power measured in millions of year. To Schindewolf (1957, 1960) this is the sum total of stratigraphy. At the other extreme, the paleoecologist may be concerned with the environmental setting, growth, and demise of a small oyster bar which existed for a few hundred years, or with a sequence reflecting seasonal climatic changes (varves). He is called upon to reconstruct a local but extremely fine-textured historical fabric with tools which will resolve time to an accuracy of years or seasons. We may accordingly speak of a *microstratigraphy* applied mainly to local paleoecologic studies, of a *mesostratigraphy* applied on the scale of a sedimentary basin, and of a *megastratigraphy* applied on the regional and intercontinental scale. At all these levels, the tracing of time planes through the stratofabric is important, but the tools of microstratigraphy are not those of megastratigraphy, and vice versa. Figure 2 is an attempt to assess the temporal resolving power of various tools in relation to distance of correlation on a log-log scale. It demonstrates the dependence of the microstratigrapher on the tracing of bedding planes or of distinctive beds, and the dependence of the megastratigrapher on biotic zones.

The Feedback to Paleoecology

When local bits of ecologic information or interpretation are combined with paleogeographies and histories, the whole becomes greater than the sum of its parts. Each ecologic bit may now be re-examined for its fit in the larger setting, and acquires new meaning and significance. The deciphering of primary intrinsic clues will remain the chief element of paleoecologic work, but the feedback of information from paleogeographical, historical, and tectonic considerations (Figure 3) is an important supplement and may be decisive in some settings.

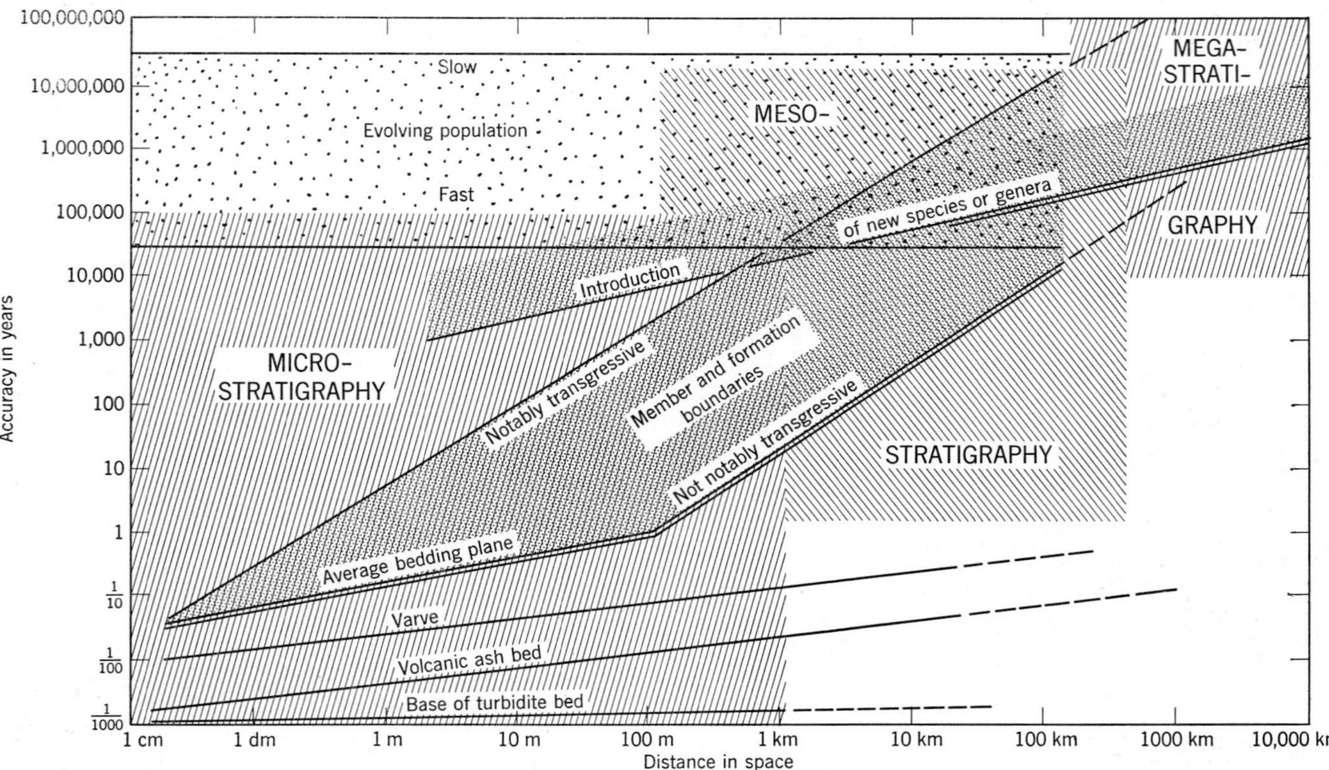

Fig. 2 Accuracy versus distance of stratigraphic time-correlation, and domains of stratigraphy.

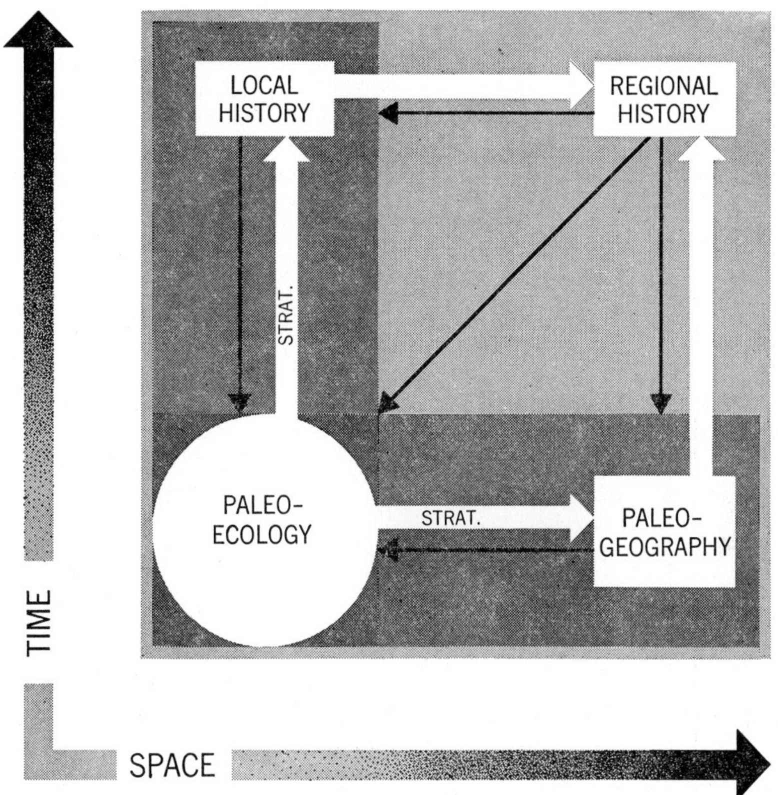

Fig. 3 The feedback of information to paleoecology.

The literature contains many examples in which the vertical sequence of beds has been used to supplement the intrinsic clues of each bed in providing an ecologic interpretation. Sequence of beds has played an important role in the interpretation of cyclic sediments, such as those of the Mid-Continent Pennsylvanian (Wanless, 1955; Weller, 1956, 1957), and has been emphasized by the writer (Fischer, 1961) in an attempt to interpret the Illinois-type and the Cherokee cyclothems (Figures 4 and 5).

One of the best examples of an integrated approach to paleoecology is the picture of the Permian Capitan reef complex in Texas and New Mexico (Figure 6), which has developed from the work of King (1948), Adams and Frenzel (1950), Newell et al. (1951), and others. Through these papers and summaries (Newell, 1957) this facies com-

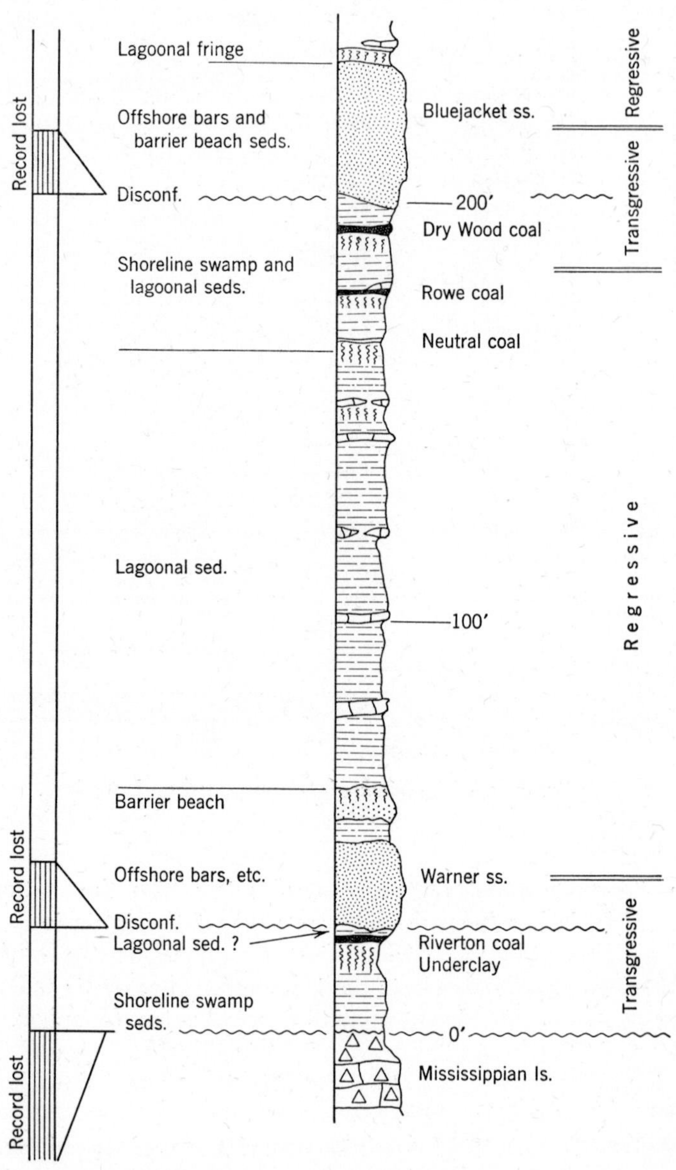

Fig. 4 Lower part of Cherokee group (Pennsylvanian) in southeastern Kansas. From Fischer (1961), partly after Howe (1956).

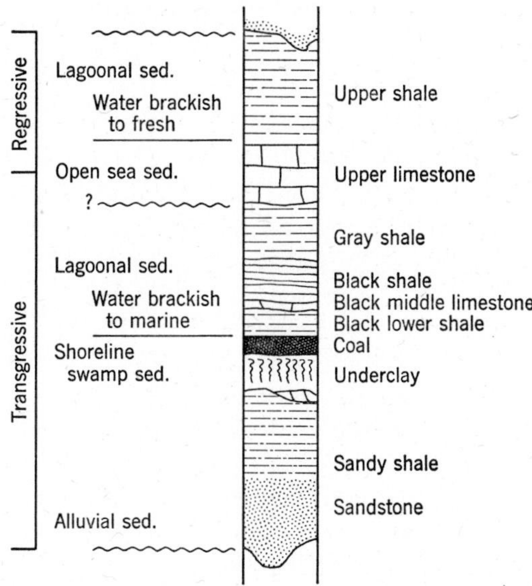

Fig. 5 Idealized Pennsylvanian cyclothem of the Illinois type. From Fischer (1961) partly after Weller (1956).

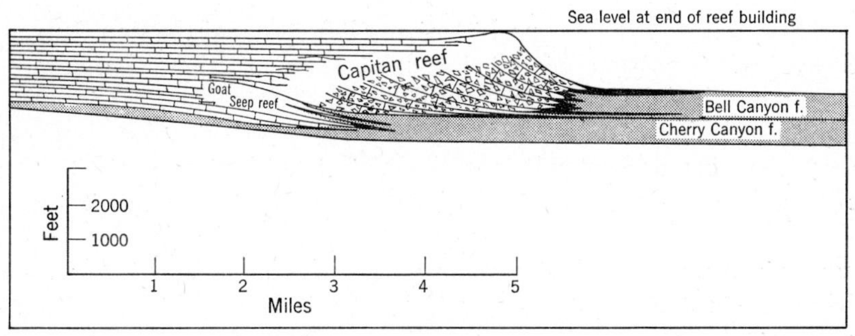

Fig. 6 Diagrammatic cross section of Capitan reef, West Texas, at end of Guadalupian epoch. Modified from Dunbar & Rodgers (1957), after King (1948).

plex has become so well known that its review here seems superfluous. Each facies—the Capitan reef rock proper, the backreef (Carlsbad) facies, the foreslope or talus facies (included in the Capitan formation), and the basin facies (Bell Canyon formation—contains intrinsic clues to the environment, yet its ecology becomes very much clearer when it is seen as a part of the whole stratofabric of the reef complex. A few examples will suffice to illustrate this point.

Consider first the massive "reef core" proper (which remains the least-well known part of the complex and which contains a variety of undescribed subfacies). Its fabric, its diversity of biota, and its abundance of algae show much of it to have been organic reef developed in shallow water of normal salinity. Its lateral relationships —the observations that it forms, at any one time-horizon, a narrow band passing (in the Guadalupe Mountains) northwestward into bedded rocks with very poor faunas and southeastward into steeply dipping talus—shows that it was a barrier reef.

The poverty of the lagoonal (Carlsbad) faunas is not immediately explicable on the basis of internal clues, but the stratofabric shows northwestward interfingering of lagoonal limestones and sandstones with evaporite-bearing redbeds, suggesting that the lagoon was largely hypersaline. To the southeast the reef rock grades into sedimentary breccias, which suggest reef talus. These breccias show dips of up to 35°—dips which were once considered to be tectonic, but which are shown to be largely primary by the observation that the overlying and the underlying beds are nearly flat-lying. The reef talus interpretation is thus confirmed.

Toward the southeast this reef talus interfingers with the sandstones and fine-grained argillaceous, bituminous limestones of the Bell Canyon formation. The fine bituminous lamination of these limestones, coupled with the abundance of pelagic fossils (ammonites) in some of the beds, suggests deposition below wave base, in possibly deep water, but our understanding of the intrinsic ecologic clues is still far removed from a more precise depth assignment. Such an assignment can, however, be made by considering the stratofabric geometry of the complex as a whole. The youngest parts of the reef now tower some 550 to 600 meters above the equivalent basin beds (the Lamar limestone, youngest member of the Bell Canyon formation), to which they are linked by steeply dipping reef talus. King (1948) conservatively assumed that part of the talus dip and part of this difference in elevation are the result of subsequent deformation, and estimated water depth in front of the reef at 300 meters. Adams and Frenzel (1950) saw no need for such a correction, and considered the ancient relief to have been about the same as the present elevation difference. Newell et al. concluded that the area had been affected by a slight eastward tilt and that relief at the reef front, in Lamar time, was on the order of 500 meters.

Conclusion

Stratigraphy, the study of stratofabrics, builds local ecologic observations into geologically meaningful paleogeographies and histories, and feeds information back from these to the local setting. In order to accomplish this task it must work at all levels of the stratofabric—from the local (microstratigraphic) unraveling of the finest stratofabric textures to the world-wide (megastratigraphic) correlation of systems, series, and stages.

REFERENCES

Adams, J. E., and H. N. Frenzel, 1950, Capitan barrier reef: Texas and New Mexico, *Jour. of Geol.,* v. 58, p. 289–312.

Fischer, A. G., 1961, Stratigraphic record of transgressing seas in light of sedimentation on Atlantic coast of New Jersey: *Amer. Assoc. Petrol. Geol., Bull.,* v. 45, pp. 1656–1666.

King, P. B., 1948, Geology of the southern Guadalupe Mountains: Texas, *U.S. Geol. Survey Prof. Paper* 215, 183 pp.

Newell, N. D. *et al.,* 1953, *The Permian Reef Complex of the Guadalupe Mountain Region:* Texas and New Mexico, Freeman and Co., 236 pp.

Newell, N. D., 1957, Paleoecology of Permian reefs in the Guadalupe Mountains area, *Treatise on Marine Ecology and Paleoecology* (H. Ladd, ed.): Geol., Soc. Amer. Memoir 67, v. 2, pp. 407–436.

Sander, B., 1930, *Gefügekunde der Gesteine:* Springer, Vienna.

——— 1936 Beiträge zur Kenntnis der Anlagerungsgefüge: *Mineral. u. Petrogr. Mitt.,* v. 48, pp. 27–139.

——— 1951 (same paper, translated by E. B. Knopf), Study of depositional fabrics; *Amer. Assoc. Petrol. Geol.,* special pub., 207 pp.

Schindewolf, O. H., 1957, Comments on some stratigraphic terms: *Amer. Jour. Sci.,* v. 255, pp. 394–399.

——— 1960, Stratigraphische Methodik und Terminologie: *Geol. Rundschau,* v. 49, pp. 1–35.

Wanless, H. R., 1955, Pennsylvanian rocks of the Eastern Interior Basin: *Amer. Assoc. Petrol. Geol., Bull.,* v. 39, pp. 1730–1820.

Weller, J. M., 1957, Paleoecology of the Pennsylvanian period in Illinois and adjacent States, *Treatise on Marine Ecology and Paleoecology* (H. Ladd, ed.): Geol. Soc. Amer. Mem. 67, v. 2, pp. 325–364.

Biologic Approaches to Paleoecology

Adaptive Morphology in Paleoecological Interpretation

by E. R. Trueman *University of Hull, England*

Introduction

The principle that the structures of an animal are adapted to their function emerged early in the study of comparative anatomy, for instance, by John Ray in the seventeenth century (Raven, 1942). It has been long appreciated even in everyday speech. We commonly think of adaptations as being those structural features of an organism which seem peculiarly fitted to its mode of life or to the function of its parts, for example, carnassial dentition in a carnivore in contrast to the grinding molars of a herbivorous mammal. Such anatomical modifications may be assessed by a study of functional morphology. Although less obviously apparent, there are also physiological adaptations of organisms to their environment which appear more clearly from a study of comparative physiology. In many instances the two fields overlap and an understanding of both functional morphology and comparative physiology are essential before adaptive morphology may be utilized as a tool in paleoecological interpretation.

The process of adaptation of an animal to a particular environment may involve its structure, form, behavior, metabolism, or any combination of these factors, so that the animal is better fitted for survival. Evolutionary adaptation is an inevitable consequence of the process of natural selection on organisms exhibiting inherited variations. (Natural selection takes place from a number of possible forms, and in competition the variety best adapted for the particular environment has the best chance of survival.) Accordingly an animal living in a particular habitat usually exhibits functional adaptations which may be related to successful life therein, as, for example, the adaptations of the mammalian body for an aquatic life in the Cetacea or for flight in the Chiroptera. Animals of widely different evolutionary origin living in the same general habitat often show similarity of structure.

Thus the effect of the forces of environmental selection may give rise to the phenomenon of convergence. This is exemplified both by the strong superficial resemblance between whales and fossil ichthyosaurs and by the similarity of the ciliary feeding mechanism in the Mollusks, Polychaetes, Protochordates, and Brachiopods, while the greater part of the structure of these animals is quite different.

Another important principle of comparative anatomy is the existence of a limited number of patterns of architecture: the vertebrate, the molluscan, the arthropodan, and so on. Not every sort of organization is found that the mind could conceive. In recent physiological and biochemical research much attention has been focused on the structure and function of the cell. Data have been used from a wide variety of organisms to interpret the functional anatomy of a living cell (e.g., Brachet, 1961). The cell is the fundamental unit of which all living organisms are made, and in comparison to the evolutionary divergence of plants and animals there is remarkable similarity of structure and biochemical operation in the living cell. It would appear that the number of kinds of molecules available to organisms for the construction of adaptive systems must be limited. This is exemplified by the limitation of molecules which are used for the development of respiratory pigments. Hemoglobins are repeatedly and independently developed by unrelated animals in which there is a functional need for increasing the power of the blood to carry oxygen. Most organisms already contain the iron porphyrin compound needed for the construction of hemoglobin in the intracellular respiratory system of cytochromes. The organism is limited in choice of molecule (with which to construct an adaptive system) to iron porphyrin and copper protein compounds, because of their peculiar properties; both are widely used as oxidizing catalysts.

Thus we are presented with a picture of adaptation not as a graded series but as a finite number of solutions of functional problems with a kit of more or less standard parts. The methods of strengthening long molecules of fibrous proteins shows the effect of this restriction. In vertebrates this process of stabilization of proteins is carried out by the cross-linkage of adjacent long chains by sulfur linkages similar to the vulcanization of rubber. It gives rise to the keratin of the skin and its derivatives, such as hair, nails, and feathers. In most invertebrate groups, the echinoderms being a major exception, the alternative of aromatic tanning is utilized, most notably in the exoskeleton of insects and in the byssus and ligament of bivalves. All invertebrate occurrences of this form of bondage are found in extracellular proteins secreted by a glandular structure, whereas in the vertebrates the keratins are characteristically intracellular proteins (Brown, 1950). The extracellular nature of aromatic tanning and its dominance in the invertebrates implies an exoskeleton as an invertebrate characteristic. An exoskeleton in turn imposes on the invertebrate problems of growth which do not occur with an intracellular secretion, such as keratin. Growth takes place either by peripheral enlargement, as in the coelenterates and mollusks, or by molting, as in the arthropods. Thus the functional patterns at the disposal of these groups are restricted by their molecular design.

Types of Adaptive Reactions

The adaptations of animals to environmental stress fall into two broad categories. First are those responses in an individual which occur within the limits of genetic lability. Generally, these are physiological adaptations to a change in conditions of temperature, oxygen concentration, salinity, etc., which place the animal in a state of stress. Animals can either adjust themselves to correspond to the environment or regulate themselves by means of protective mechanisms, thus maintaining an internal constancy. For example, most animals (poikilotherms) are at the temperature of the external environment but some (homiotherms) exhibit temperature regulation. In both cases, adjustment must be made to the metabolism when subjected to environmental change. A morphological example of this type of response is the shell shape of the limpet *Patella vulgata.* Those found on the lower part of the beach have a more obtuse shell than those on the upper shore, the latter being subjected to a greater amount of desiccation, which causes a more contracted posture and the secretion of the shell into a more acute cone shape. Experimental movement of limpets from the lower shore to a position higher on the beach causes a change in the shell shape (Moore, 1934).

The second type of adaptive reaction involves selection of genetic mutations from a variable population, some of which, in different environmental conditions, may confer "advantage." Such modifications may be morphological or physiological, or both. It is this type of adaptation that is of interest to the paleoecologist.

Types of Paleoecological Inferences

The paleoecological conclusions which may be drawn from a study of adaptive or functional morphology fall into two broad categories: first, general assumptions of habitat conditions based on physiological or general morphological grounds; and second, detailed interpretation of a specific fauna which requires detailed knowledge of the nearest living representatives.

Any interpretation of fossils belonging to extinct groups must almost certainly be in the first category. The trilobites presumably held as prominent a position in the fauna of ancient seas as the Crustacea do today, and they occupied many diverse ecological niches. Some appear to be adaptively modified in comparison with such a generalized type as *Triarthrus* and indeed bear resemblance in form to living Crustacea whose habits are reasonably well known. For instance, *Cryptolithus* appears to be blind and may have been associated with tunneling in a soft substratum, while others, for example, *Cyclopyge* and young specimens of *Triarthrus* have large and laterally situated eyes similar to many planktonic crustaceans. But these conclusions must be tentative without direct recourse to living trilobites.

Similarly there has been much speculation regarding the mode of life of ammonites and nautiloids. Few externally shelled forms of cephalopods survive today and comparison between similar species can hardly be made. However, recent work on the cuttlebone of *Sepia* (Denton, 1961; Denton and Gilpin-Brown, 1961) has shown that its chambers contain liquid in addition to gas, and by variation of these amounts the density may be changed. Fluid tends to pass in by the hydrostatic pressure of the sea and to be withdrawn by the osmotic difference between the cuttlebone liquid and the blood (Figure 1). An osmotic difference between cuttlebone liquid and cuttlefish blood holds water out of the cuttlebone. Animals caught in 73 m of water had a maximum pressure pushing water into the cuttlebone of 8.2 atm. The gas pressure inside the cuttlebone was 0.8 atm, leaving 7.4 atm to be balanced by the difference in osmotic pressure. This requires the concentration of the cuttlebone fluid to be about 69% sea water, and determinations establish that this is approximately so. The osmotic difference does not, however, balance the crushing effect of the pressure of the sea on the cuttlebone, which is very strong, the plates being held apart by numerous pillars. The shell is strong enough to withstand external hydrostatic pressure, which in *Sepia* may reach 20 atm. The shells of *Nautilus* and *Spirula* are so closely related to *Sepia* both anatomically and histologically that it seems likely that they all work in the same way, but *Spirula* is found at depths down to 1750 m and here simple osmosis could not possibly be the only force holding liquid out of the shell. A. M. Bidder (1962) has recently discovered that the gas in the chambers of the shell

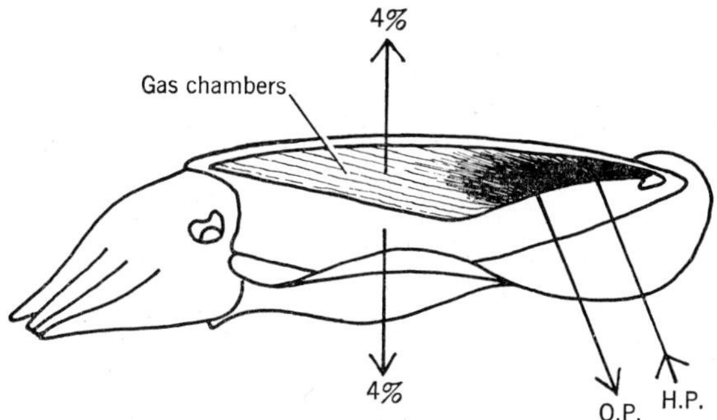

Fig. 1 Diagrammatic longitudinal section of Sepia *showing the liquid within the cuttlebone, marked black. The oldest and posterior chambers are almost full of liquid and the replacement of this by gas would tend to tip the posterior end of the* Sepia *upward. The newest chambers, situated centrally, are filled with gas and give buoyancy without disturbing the posture of the cuttlefish. The hydrostatic pressure (H. P.) of the sea is balanced by the osmotic pressure (O. P.) between the cuttlebone liquid and the blood. The cuttlebone is here represented with a density of about 0.6, giving a net lift of 4% of the animal's weight in air so balancing the excess weight of the remainder of the animal (after Denton and Gilpin-Brown, 1961).*

of *Nautilus* is not under pressure in specimens taken from a depth of 200 m, and she has been able to extract quantities of liquid from the gas chambers (Joysey, 1961). It is possible that fossil cephalopods resembled the modern *Sepia,* having both liquid and gas in their chambered shells, and thus the assumption in calculations of buoyancy and posture that these shells contained only gas is perhaps invalid. From a consideration of various straight shelled nautiloids it would appear extremely probable that the shell was tilted up like a church steeple by means of its buoyant early chambers so that its body was directed more or less downward (Trueman, 1941). With the buoyancy of the early chambers possibly reduced, either by contained fluid or by the precipitation of mineral material onto the apical shell from such a fluid as Joysey (1961) suggests, the shells could extend more or less horizontally—a view which agrees with that of Ruedemann (1921), based on the color markings of the shell. A detailed examination of the living *Nautilus* would appear to be the last chance of exploring this situation, and a knowledge of the functional morphology of its shell could have interesting general applications to the interpretation of fossil cephalopods.

Physiological Factors in Adaptation

General and sometimes tentative paleoecological assumptions may often be made from an examination of physiological features. The validity of these assumptions depends largely on the closeness of the relationship between living and fossil faunas, and although the comparative physiology of animals may form a useful guide to the paleoecologist, certainty is lacking even in the case of direct association. Important physiological factors involve feeding habits, osmoregulation, respiration, breeding habits, and behavior. These factors can be usefully surveyed in the interpretation of any fossil assemblages and accordingly are briefly reviewed.

Feeding Habits

The food of all animals in the sea is ultimately derived from marine plants which may be eaten by animals, or their dead bodies may provide a source of organic material utilized by bacteria. The bacteria in turn may form animal food, or the organic material may be transformed into substances which can be used as food (Zobell and Feltham, 1938). The feeding mechanisms utilized by animals exhibit diverse adaptations, but in general there is a close relationship between the means of obtaining food, the food available, and the type of habitat. Yonge (1928) has suggested a classification of feeding mechanisms of invertebrates with three main categories, (1) mechanisms for dealing with small particles, (2) mechanisms for dealing with larger particles or masses, and (3) mechanisms for dealing with fluid or soft tissues.

Mechanisms for dealing with small particles are usually only found in aquatic animals and many of these are sessile or sluggish. A viscous secretion of mucus is often produced in which the food may be trapped, prior to ingestion. Yonge further divides this category according to the structures used in feeding, namely, pseudopodia, tentacles, setae, cilia, and muscles for the pumping of water. Of these, the use of setae in the Crustacea and of ciliary mechanisms commonly occurring in the Porifera, tubicolous Polychaeta, Bryozoa, Brachiopoda, Bivalvia, some Gastropoda, and Protochordata are probably the most important. All filter feeders require an aquatic habit and a supply of minute zooplankton, phytoplankton, protozoa, bacteria, or organic detritus. The size of this food varies considerably, in particle size, from several hundred microns in certain algal cells to the (submicroscopic) colloidal dimensions of detrital matter. Selection of food is usually quantitative rather than qualitative, acceptance or rejection being made on a basis of particle size or density, notably in the bivalves (Yonge, 1928) and the polychaete, *Sabella* (Nicol, 1930). It is noteworthy that while many bivalves using ciliary feeding mechanisms are suspension feeders (e.g., *Cardium, Spisula, Venus, Ensis,* and *Mya*), drawing particles suspended in water into their mantle cavities, other bivalves (notably *Tellina, Gari,* or *Donax*) are deposit feeders feeding on organic debris from the surface of the sand (see Figure 4).

Within the category of mechanisms for dealing with large particles or masses (Yonge, 1928) are methods for dealing with inactive food, seizing prey, scraping, and boring. There are many benthic animals which swallow bottom deposits with little selection, from which they extract organic material for nourishment. In these animals, organs of mastication are absent. Many polychaetes fall into this group (e.g., *Arenicola*) as do the heart urchins. Animals that seize prey are characteristically carnivorous, showing, for example, the development of chelae in the decapod crustaceans or sucker-bearing arms, horny jaws, and radulae in the cephalopods. Animals which scrape off encrusting organisms or bore through the hard skeleton of living prey have well-developed rasping devices, such as the radula of gastropods or the Aristotle's lantern of regular echinoids.

Although it is not possible to make many generalizations regarding the feeding mechanisms of specific groups of invertebrate animals, each fossil assemblage should be examined in comparison with the most similar present-day faunas. Reference should be made to the summaries of work in this field made by Yonge (1928 and 1937) or Nicol (1960). In some groups certain nutritional trends may be usefully observed. Almost all members of Coelenterata, for example, are carnivores and, with the exception of some that make use of ciliary currents, they usually capture their prey by means of tentacles armed with penetrating or adhesive nematocysts. Experiments show that the presence of suitable food evokes an orderly series of feeding reactions. The most active chemical substances are proteins and their derivatives, while carbohydrates evoke little if any response (Pantin, 1943). This selective sensitivity is obviously correlated to the purely carnivorous habit of these animals. Further, Madreporaria cannot digest starch (Yonge, 1930), so that one may deduce that coral reef formation takes place only in conditions of an abundant supply of zooplankton, and that these conditions may have prevailed wherever these structures occur. Yonge (1940) has also shown that the presence of symbiotic zooxanthellae in madreporarian corals, as a means of rapid removal of metabolic by-products but not as a food material, is essential to the growth of reef-building corals. Zooxanthellae require the presence of light for photosynthesis. Accordingly, coral reef formation is limited to relatively shallow water.

Osmoregulation

Some interpretation of the conditions of salinity of past environments may be obtained from an examination of the distribution of the present fauna. Echinoderms, cephalopods, and corals appear to have been always characteristically marine animals; sponges and polyzoa are predominantly marine, while bivalves and gastropods are widely distributed in both marine and fresh water. Marine animals, except vertebrates, are generally in osmotic equilibrium with their environment but successful life in low salinities requires the presence of an osmoregulatory mechanism, whereby salts are retained in the body and excess water is removed. The manner in which this is carried out differs in the different animal groups. Krogh (1939), Brown and Prosser (1961), and Robertson (1957) have reviewed this subject. An example of the practical value of knowledge of salinity distribution of animals is illustrated by certain Carboniferous bivalves, for example, *Carbonicola, Anthracosia,* and *Naiadites.* These have long been described as nonmarine possibly because of their remarkable similarity in general character to present-day British fresh water mussels (Trueman, 1946). The distribution of the tubicolous polychaete, *Spirorbis,* on the valves of a number of genera (e.g., *Carbonicola, Anthracosia, Naiadites*) usually in the region of the inhalent siphon, is thought to indicate a commensal association (Figure 2) (Trueman, 1942). It certainly indicates that the posterior margin of these shells would have normally projected above the substrate into the surrounding water so as to allow attachment of the polychaete. Spirorbids today are exclusively marine and this would point to the marine nature of the fauna. However, the species of *Spirorbis* is not necessarily the same as present-day forms. Of living polychaetes some species of one genus are exclusively marine, for example, *Nereis pelagica,* while another *N. diversicolor* commonly inhabits estuaries, possessing limited powers of osmoregulation and tolerating waters with salinities as low as 0.5‰ (Nicol, 1960). The fossil spirorbids may have been similar in osmoregulatory ability and have been tolerant of brackish water. This view is supported by recent estimates of the boron content of associated sediments (Eagar, 1960) and confirms the prior suggestion of Weir (1945) that *Naiadites* was essen-

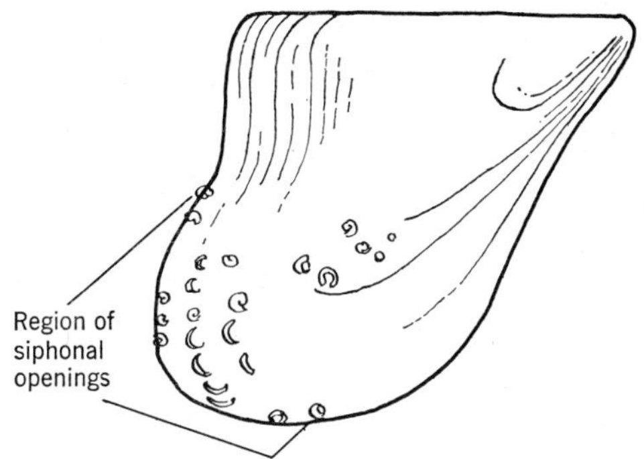

Fig. 2 Diagram showing the attachment of Spirorbis *to* Naiadites. *The probable region of siphonal openings is indicated (after Trueman, 1942).*

tially a brackish water genus with some tolerance of more or less saline conditions, and that *Carbonicola, Anthracosia,* and *Anthraconaia* ranged from fresh to brackish water.

Evidence from the field of osmoregulation has been used in discussion of the habitats of early vertebrates. The salt concentration of the plasma of all aquatic vertebrates, except the myxinoid cyclostomes and the elasmobranchs (Robertson, 1957), is much less than that of sea water. This requires osmotic regulation which could only have evolved in fresh-water environment and so implies that the ancestors of these animals were at some stage living in fresh-water conditions. Even when they returned to the sea, like many teleost fish, the low salt content of the blood was maintained. In fresh-water teleosts it is clear that a well-developed glomerular kidney is advantageous in maintaining osmotic equilibrium. The glomerular kidney is considered by Smith (1932) as having evolved in fresh-water protovertebrates as a device for excreting large quantities of water which enters in accordance with the osmotic gradient. In a discussion of the validity of this hypothesis Robertson (1957) points out that glomerular kidneys are found in such a typical marine group as the myxinoid cyclostomes, in which there is virtually no osmotic gradient between the internal and external medium, and that the kidneys of *Myxine* have a filtration surface almost equal to that of fresh-water teleosts. Organs analogous to the vertebrate kidney also occur in marine invertebrates where there is no osmotic gradient, for example, the decapod Crustacea. Robertson comments that there is no valid reason for invoking large osmotic differences as being a necessary stimulus for the development of a glomerular-type kidney. Glomerular kidneys may well have existed in marine protovertebrates and subsequently may have been a useful preadaptation for life in fresh water.

Respiration

In the field of respiration some general assumptions may be made regarding habitat on the basis of such physiological features as the oxygen affinity of the blood pigment. For example, the modern decapod cephalopods have blood pigments suitable for conditions of plenty of oxygen and little carbon dioxide, rather comparable to that of a mackerel, and usually live in conditions of well-oxygenated water (Florkin, 1949). In contrast to this, the pigment of *Limulus* or *Busycon* is suitable for life in conditions of oxygen deficiency and higher concentrations of carbon dioxide.

Breeding Habits

A knowledge of breeding habits and the behavior of larval and immediately postlarval marine invertebrates may also contribute to the paleoecological scene. In warm, shallow waters the larval stage of the bottom dweller is predominantly planktonic and this type becomes progressively less abundant in colder seas. In colder water and also in abyssal water, planktonic development rarely occurs, the parents being either viviparous or oviparous, producing a few large yolky eggs. Thorson (1950) associates the absence of planktonic larvae in shallow, cold water with the shortness of the season during which there is an insufficient production of phytoplankton to feed the larvae, and the shortage of suspended food in the water is correlated with the absence of abyssal, planktonic larvae. A necessary requirement of animals with pelagic larval stages is clearly an abundant supply of plankton, which in turn must depend on marine and climatic conditions. Larvae with a pelagic stage clearly insure both the wide distribution of the species and the possibility of colonizing any space available to them. Considerable wastage of larvae takes place through predation and because there is only a relatively small chance that a larva will find a suitable substratum upon which to settle. Many larvae have been shown to be highly specific in their requirements, for example, *Balanus* (Knight-Jones, 1954). Most larvae are, however, able to postpone metamorphosis for a time if they do not find suitable conditions, and water currents may thus offer a chance of sampling a much wider area than would be accessible with their own powers of locomotion. Wilson (1952) considers that the ability to delay metamorphosis is possessed by larvae of animals belonging to a number of phyla and may be fairly general, especially for those species restricted to specialized environments as adults. However, apart from a few polychaetes, for example, *Ophelia* (Wilson, 1954), little work has been done on the settling behavior of larvae of species living on or in sandy and muddy bottoms. Holme (1961), in discussing the bottom fauna of the English Channel, suggests that shelter from excessive disturbance is the survival factor for many forms. In an account of the spatfall of *Cardium edule,* Baggerman (1953) remarks that it is not known whether newly metamorphosed *Cardium* shows any preference for certain places to settle. Young cockles certainly occur in large numbers in certain localities and strong indications were obtained that these animals, whose rate of fall through the water can be compared with that of sand of the size 100 to 250 μ, are deposited especially in places where currents are weak. Clearly a more extensive knowledge of the settling behavior of bottom fauna would help to clarify the interpretation of fossil assemblages where certain bottom-living sedentary species are abundant.

The adaptations just considered suggest a few of the ways in which a knowledge of the physiology and distribution of living animals may be useful in paleoecological interpretation. Deductions from evidence of this kind are largely general in application and point out the environment only in wide terms. For the interpretation of the habitat of a species or genus the investigator must examine the nearest living representative. Since the fossil record is principally a record of the hard parts of animals, most attention must be paid to these in respect to their functional anatomy and to the deductions which can be made about the tissues from an examination of the skeleton. Apart from the Porifera and the Echinodermata, the invertebrates characteristically have an exoskeleton secreted by some part of the superficial epithelium. This is principally formed of calcium carbonate, chitin, and aromatically tanned protein in all metazoan invertebrates. Once secreted as a hard outer coat an exoskeleton imposes a shape and form upon an animal and raises a problem of further growth. This is solved in at least two ways: by peripheral enlargement, as in the coelenterates and mollusks; or by molting, as in the arthropods. In the mollusks increase in size of the shell is dependent on the secretion of the mantle margin, with consequent restrictions on the shape of the shell. The main patterns observed are a hinged bivalved shell, in the bivalves, or coiling, in the gastropods, where a helical spiral as in *Helix* is probably the most compact way of increasing in size. The chitons, with the shell divided into plates, have obtained a measure of freedom because the independent growth of each plate gives the net effect of an all-over increase in size rather than enlargement at the margins.

Adaptive Morphology of Living Bivalve Mollusks

Examples of adaptive changes in shell form occur among the Bivalvia. In this molluscan group four main features may be considered: shell shape, muscle scars, hinge ligament, and hinge teeth.

Hinge Teeth

Hinge teeth are certainly not pivotal structures about which the valves open and close. They should be considered as a mechanism for insuring the correct alignment of the valves when the shell is closed and open. However, little is known of their functional anatomy and until this is remedied evidence concerning hinge teeth is of small value to the paleoecologist.

Shell Shape and Muscle Scars

Adaptive changes in the shape of the shell may be conveniently observed in relation to the evolution of the monomyarian condition. The bodies of bilaterally symmetrical animals have an anteroposterior growth axis, and in the Mollusca a second growth axis has been acquired by the secretion of a shell, which increases peripherally by marginal increment. The external form of the bivalves is the result of the growth of the mantle and its secretion of the shell, but it is important when discussing this group to also consider the body, with its inherent, though often modified, anteroposterior axis. Yonge (1955) suggests that the most convenient way to consider problems of bivalve form is by reference to axes or projections from the curved surface of the mantle/shell in the sagittal plane, namely, the anteroposterior and median axes of the body and the demarcation line of the mantle/shell. The median axis (Figure 3*A*) is defined as a line running from the mid-dorsal point of the body through the middle of the base of the foot to the mid-point below the foot or byssus (Yonge 1953*a*). The demarcation line represents a projection onto the sagittal plane of the line of maximum inflation of each valve, commencing from the umbones. Considering a symmetrical equi-

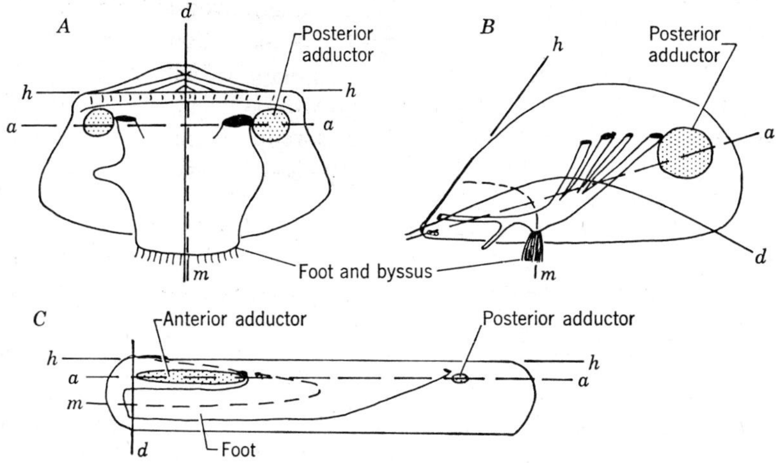

Fig. 3 Relation of axes of body and of mantle/shell in (A) Arca, *(B)* Mytilus, *and (C)* Ensis, *showing anteroposterior (a) and median (m) axes (broken lines) of the body together with hinge (h) and demarcation (d) lines of mantle/shell. The symmetry of body and mantle/shell, shown as an example in* Arca, *a byssally attached dimyarian, is altered in* Mytilus *by reduction of the anterior end of the body and secondarily reduction of mantle/shell. In* Ensis *the posterior elongation of the mantle/shell has had major effects on the form of the body. Adductor muscles stippled, insertions of pedal retractor muscles solid black, right valve and sectioned tissues shown (after Yonge, 1955).*

valve such as *Glycymeris* or *Arca* (Figure 3*A*), the hinge line and anteroposterior axis are parallel, while at right angles to these the median axis and demarcation line effectively coincide.

Yonge (1955) points out that the symmetry of both body and mantle/shell may be altered either by changes in the form of mantle/shell affecting the body or by changes in the body affecting the mantle/shell. The former is exemplified in the Solenidae (Figure 3*C*), where in *Ensis* the elongation posteriorly of the mantle/shell by greater growth in that region has major effects on the form of the body. Where attachment by the byssus to a substratum has taken place, as in *Mytilus* or *Modiolus,* changes of form affect first the body and only second the mantle/shell. Under these conditions the ventral surface of the foot must be regarded as the fixed point about which the shell and body axes must move, because whatever else may be affected, the mid-ventral region of the body remains constant in relation to the environment (Yonge, 1953*a*). Thus, in *Modiolus,* the anterior part of the body is reduced, both foot and byssus, ventrally, and the ligament, dorsally, appearing to have moved anteriorly. The anteroposterior and median axes and the demarcation are affected as shown in Figure 3*B*, the curvature of the demarcation line being due to a tangential component of shell growth (Owen, 1953*a*, *b*). At the same time, the anterior adductor is reduced, and the posterior muscle together with the adjacent region is enlarged. Byssal attachment does not necessarily bring about the reduction of the anterior adductor, for example, in *Arca* (Figure 3*A*). This dimyarian genus is normally attached by a massive byssus to a hard substrate, and water with suspended food particles is drawn in both in front of and behind the byssus.

In the opinion of Yonge (1953*a*), the strength of attachment probably accounts for the success of the genus, but the danger of blocking the inhalent current prevents the individuals from growing in masses together. In *Modiolus* and *Mytilus*, the inhalent current enters posteriorly and these genera form beds with the animals living very close to each other. Reduction of the anterior end in such genera obviously has survival value. Consequent on byssal attachment in the heteromyaria, there is a reduction of the region of the body anterior to the median axis. This has a secondary effect on the mantle/shell with the complete loss of the anterior adductor. Because of continued reduction of the anterior part of the body, the influence of the anteroposterior axis of the body on the form of the shell disappears. The mantle/shell now tends to revert to a fundamental symmetry describing the almost perfect circle of many Pectinidae. From the initial attachment with the sagittal plane at right angles to the substratum, as in *Mytilus*, Yonge (1953*a*) considers that the monomyarian condition may have been attained in either of two ways. First, this may come about without change of symmetry, as in the Limidae and Tridacnidae, or, second, the change to the monomyarian condition is accompanied by the loss of bilateral symmetry with vertical shell valves and the substitution of an asymmetric shell with valves situated horizontally. Yonge divides the monomyaria into groups according to their habit. Those which are attached marginally by byssus (e.g., *Pinctada* or *Pteria*) are thought of as primitive in habit compared with those which have attained adult freedom (e.g., *Pecten*) or have become attached by cementation (e.g. *Ostrea*). The importance of byssal attachment to the anisomyarian condition cannot be over stressed. The presence of heteromyarian genera in any fossil assemblage would thus usually point to byssal attachment to some fairly hard substrate, although *Pinna* (Yonge, 1953*b*) is a noteworthy exception. Monomyarian forms would indicate a wider range of habitats but the majority, apart from those which have gained adult freedom, normally require suitable substrate conditions for attachment (see Yonge, 1953*a* for a full discussion of form and habit in the monomyarian bivalves).

Dimyarian bivalves are characteristic of soft substrata. In these, the hinge and anteroposterior axes are approximately parallel. The ventral part of the body may have been considerably affected by changes of the mantle/shell, for example, the anterior pedal opening in *Ensis* (Figure 3*C*). Their fundamental characteristics, such as the lateral flattening of the body and foot, enclosure between a hinged bivalved shell, and the great development of the gills, make them ideally suited for this environment. In burrowing forms some degree of ventral mantle fusion commonly takes place, but perhaps the most obvious adaptation to burrowing is the possession of siphons. The process of ventral mantle fusion and of siphonal formation is fully discussed by Yonge (1948, 1957). The most significant feature for the paleoecologist is probably the extent of the so-called pallial sinus or muscle scar of the pallial muscles which function as the retractor muscles of the siphons. In general, the deeper the infolding of the pallial muscle scar the deeper the animal lives below the surface of the substrate. Thus a genus with short siphons lives near the surface of the sand (e.g., *Cardium*) and has a much shallower "sinus" than does *Mya*, for example.

Bivalves that burrow may be divided into two broad groups according to the method of their food collection (Figure 4). Some (e.g., *Cardium* or *Mya*) are suspension feeders, while others are deposit feeders (e.g., *Tellina* or *Scrobicularia*). In the latter category the siphons are separate, the inhalent siphon being able to grope freely for food, independent of the exhalent siphon, and the foot is large and active. Deposit-feeding lamellibranchs are admirably fitted for rapid movement through sand, often having a very compressed, smooth shell. This allows deep retreat beneath the sand in intertidal forms and the possibility of horizontal movement to a new feeding ground. By contrast, *Cardium* (Figure 4*a*), a suspension feeder living near the surface of the sand, has a globular shell marked with conspicuous ribs which grip the sand. The foot is large and powerful, which it needs to be to move such a cumbersome shell beneath the sand. *Cardium* is able to burrow but only deep enough to cover the shell. Bivalves inhabiting exposed and therefore relatively unstable sand must be able to burrow rapidly by the aid of their foot. The most highly specialized in this respect are species of the Solenidae (Owen, 1959). Suspension-feeding lamellibranchs living in relatively

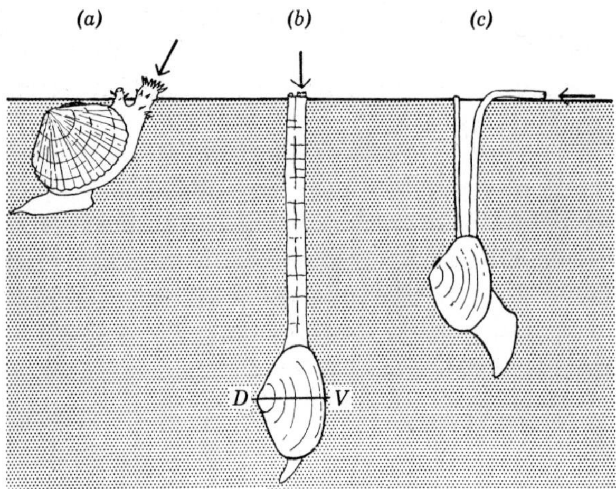

Fig. 4 Positions in situ of (a) Cardium edule, *a shallow burrowing suspension feeder, (b)* Mya arenaria, *a deep burrower with long fused siphons for suspension feeding, and (c)* Tellina tenuis *an actively burrowing deposit feeder. The arrows indicate the direction of the inhalent water current in the deposit feeder from the surface of the sand. The extent of the foot when protruded is shown. D-V indicates the dorsoventral axis of the shell of* Mya *(partly after Yonge, 1949).*

more stable muddy substrata tend to remain permanently embedded in one place after settlement. They burrow deeper with increasing age, the foot becoming of less importance as the siphons grow longer (e.g., *Mya, Panope, Lutraria*). These examples represent separate families, namely the Myidae, Hiatellidae, and Mactridae, respectively, and provide an interesting example of convergence in adaptation to a common habitat. In all three, the siphons are fused and have a strong covering of periostracum.

Owing to their basically simple structure, the Bivalvia represent excellent material for the study of evolutionary change. Changes in habitat have come about as a result of relatively simple variations in the form of the mantle/shell and body. How this may have occurred within a single group is well exemplified in a recent study of the functional morphology of British Veneracea (Ansell, 1961). The radiation of this group into a variety of habits such as shallow burrowing (*Venus*), deep burrowing (*Dosina*), nestling in rock crevices by byssal fixation (*Venerupis*), and rock boring (*Petricola*) is shown in relation to the adaptive morphology.

Hinge Ligament

To the paleoecologist a study of the functional anatomy of the hinge ligament may also prove fruitful, for the ligament shows certain adaptive features which can be recognized in fossil forms. It has been established for many years (see, e.g., Dall, 1889), that the principal function of the ligament in the bivalves is to open the shell when the adductor muscles relax. Unfortunately, in much of the earlier literature the mode of operation and the comparative anatomy of the ligament is confused. In addition to its principal function the ligament serves to hold the dorsal margins of the valves together and to exclude the entry of particles from the exterior, notably in burrowing forms. Before discussing the functioning of the ligament, its general anatomy should be outlined. The ligament is an integral part of the shell, which consists of two valves and ligament, and is secreted by the mantle tissues in the same manner as the valves. The outer and inner layers of the valves and of the ligament represent local modification of the same two layers of the shell. Both valves and ligament are covered by the periostracum and this together with the outer and inner layers forms the primary ligament (Figure 5*a*) (Owen, Trueman, and Yonge, 1953). Secondary extension may take place at either or both ends of the primary ligament as described by Yonge (1957).

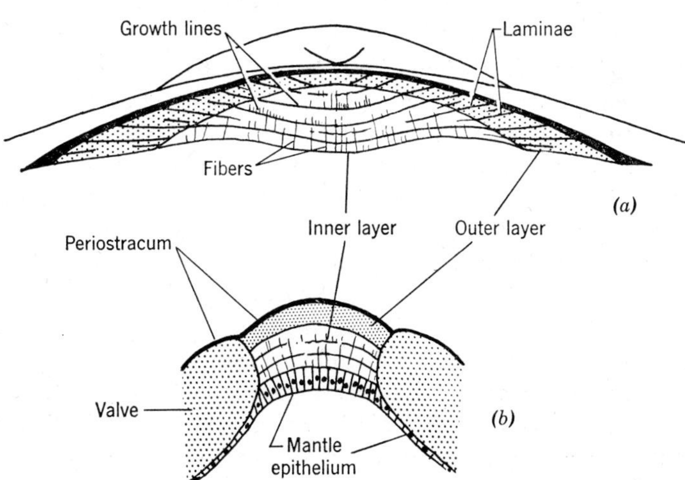

Fig. 5 Diagrams of primary ligament viewed (a) in sagittal section attached to the valve and (b) in transverse section through the umbo.

Fusion of the outer lobes of the mantle edge results in the addition of a fourth layer to the ligament—the fusion layer. Where the fusion layer forms a long extension to the primary ligament, as in *Pinna* (Yonge 1953*b*), it is of considerable importance in maintaining a long and flexible union of the valves but only plays a minor role in the mechanical operation of the ligament. Where the fusion layer is situated above the primary ligament it functions in precisely the same way as the outer layer, and in the following discussion of the function of the ligament no attempt will be made to differentiate these two layers.

The outer layer of the ligament, sometimes called the lamellar layer (Newell, 1937), is composed of nearly parallel lamellae of fibrous protein. It is characteristically dark brown in color and has undergone hardening by aromatic tanning, giving molecular cross linkage of adjacent polypeptide chains (Trueman, 1950; Beedham, 1958) and contains no calcium carbonate. The inner layer, termed cartilage or resilium (Dall, 1889; Jackson, 1890) or fibrous ligament (Newell, 1937) is fibrous in structure and typically consists of relatively little tanned protein, and calcium carbonate. It exhibits growth lines which usually correspond to the laminations of the outer layer, and both may be considered to represent phases of secretory activity of the mantle (Figures 5 and 7). The interpretation of ligament structure in a fossil shell should be based on the anatomy of living bivalves, but unfortunately only the attachments of the ligament remain and it is not always easy to decipher the ligament structure.

In a shell in which the inner layer is compact enough to lie between resilifers (e.g., *Lutraria, Mya,* or even *Ostrea*), a clear impression of its form is usually seen on the valve when the ligament is removed. This often bears the impression of the growth lines (see Figure 9). Where the inner layer is elongate, as in *Mytilus, Anodonta,* or *Tellina,* it can only be recognized by the extent of the long flat ligament ridges or nymphae which support it on either valve. The location of the outer layer is usually marked by a narrow groove running near the edge of the valve, parallel to the nymphae in the ligaments of the last three genera, but it is less obvious in bivalves with restricted inner layers. Care should be exercised in the interpretation of the subumbonal region of opisthodetic ligaments, in which the oldest part near the umbo has been broken in some species by tangential growth of the valves (Owen, 1953*b*), and the damage repaired by a secretion, sometimes quite a massive one, of the outer layer at the anterior end of the ligament. The appearance of the subumbonal region of the valves of the Carboniferous mussels, *Carbonicola* and *Anthracosia*, for instance, would lead one to believe that there was an internal resilium of the inner layer were it not for the presence in some particularly well-preserved material of an opisthodetic parivincular ligament showing repair between the umbones.

Mechanically the ligament of *Mytilus* is one of the simplest structures. It is essentially a bar, approximately rectangular in cross section, attached between the dorsal margins of the valves, as shown diagrammatically in Figure 6. The main forces involved in the opening and closing of the valves are shown by the arrows adjacent to outer and inner layers and adductor muscle, the size of the arrows indicating the relative amplitude of the stresses in these parts. The valves never gape to their maximum extent during the life of the animal so that a small residual strain is indicated in the ligament (Figure 6*a*) to counteract this, a slight contraction of the adductor muscle is suggested, although in life, other factors, such as the substrate, are probably involved. In the closed position (Figure 6*b*),

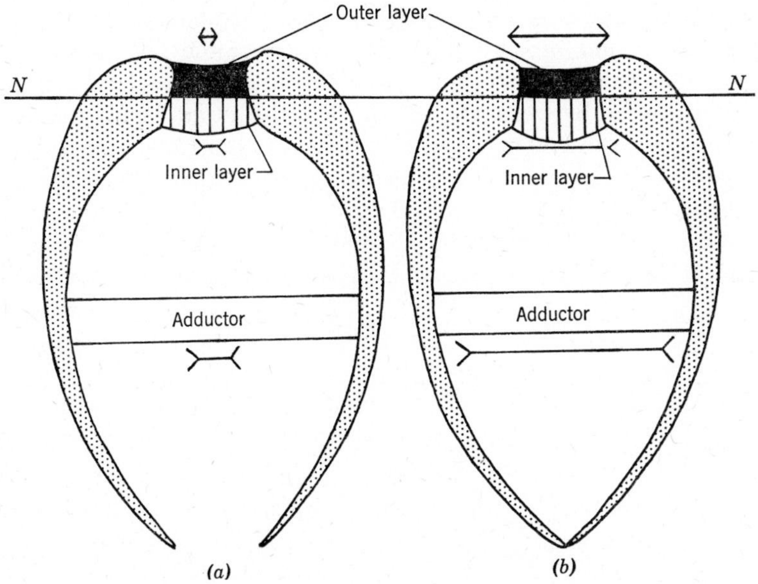

Fig. 6 Diagrammatic representation of the valves of Mytilus, *(a) gaping and (b) closed. The relative amounts of stress on the adductor muscles and outer and inner layers of the ligament are indicated by the size of the arrows. The valves shown in section are stippled and the approximate position of the neutral axis (N) of the ligament is indicated.*

the adductor muscle is contracted and the strain on the ligament is at a maximum. Closure of the valves causes the stretching of the outer layer and the compression of the inner. The force so derived tends to open the valves and has been measured in terms of a moment about the hinge or pivotal axis of the shell. It is referred to as the opening moment of the ligament (Trueman, 1953). The line *N* (Figure 6) situated approximately between the outer and inner layers indicates the approximate position of the neutral axis of the ligament where compression and tensile stress are at a minimum. The hinge or pivotal axis, about which the opening moment of the ligament may be determined, is considered to lie along the plane of the neutral axis equidistant from the valves.

The mechanical arrangement described for *Mytilus* applies to the ligament of many bivalves. In those with external parivincular ligaments (e.g., *Tellina, Anodonta*), the condition is similar, with the neutral axis lying between the curved outer layer and the inner. However in the alivincular ligament of, for example, *Ostrea,* the neutral axis does not correspond to the division between outer and inner layers, but the only part of the inner layer which is functional is situated below the axis (Figure 7), that part above is subjected to tensile stress and becomes fractured. Indeed, the fibrous structure of the inner layer appears unsuited to withstand lateral tension, and fractures occur between the fibers. On the other hand, the inner layer is elastic to compression, and determinations of its modulus of elasticity in compression give values of about 2200 g/mm^2 for that of *Ostrea edulis* or *Lutraria lutraria* (Trueman, 1953). The molecular arrangement of the scleroprotein of the outer layer, in which chemical bands unite adjacent polypeptide chains, appears to be

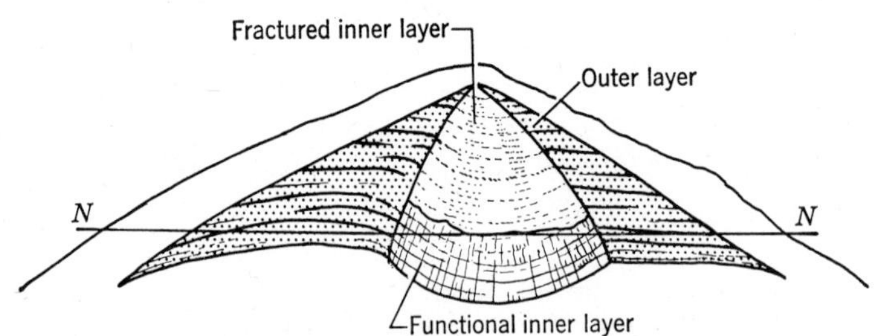

Fig. 7 Diagram of the ligament of Ostrea *in sagittal section attached to the right valve. The position of the neutral axis (N) is shown and the inner layer above this is fractured and not functional.*

TABLE 1. *Summary of the results of the determination of the opening and closing moments of the ligaments of certain bivalves**

Species	Number of Specimens	Closing Moment, $M_c/V \pm SE$ (g mm/ml)	Opening Moment, M_o/V (g mm/ml)
Arcacea: *Glycymeris glycymeris*	2	105	83
Mytilacea: *Mytilus edulis*	30	780 ± 48	660
Pectinacea: *Pecten maximus*	7	167 ± 16	160
Chlamys opercularis	29	148 ± 3.8	142
Ostreacea: *Ostrea edulis*	6	425 ± 24	370
Unionacea: *Anodonta cygnea*	15	115 ± 7.75	103
Isocardiacea: *Glossus humanus*	1	102	91
Cyprinacea: *Arctica islandica*	2	610	550
Cardiacea: *Laevicardium crassum*	6	90 ± 6.9	70
Cardium edule	35	140 ± 10	114
Veneracea: *Dosinia lupinus*	8	595 ± 71	535
Venus fasciata	7	156 ± 6.5	137
Mactracea: *Lutraria lutraria*	8	285 ± 5.3	265
Tellinacea: *Tellina crassa*	29	370 ± 13	320
Tellina tenuis	43	550 ± 18	480
Abra alba	12	100 ± 9	73
Gari tellinella	8	106 ± 5.2	90
Solenacea: *Ensis siliqua*	9	131 ± 9	120
Myacea: *Mya arenaria*	10	191 ± 11.3	174

* The mean closing moment (M_c) and the estimated mean opening moment (M_o) have been expressed in relation to the volume (V) of the shell

well suited to its mechanical role of withstanding tensile stress. The modulus of elasticity of the outer layer, determined by stretching small pieces suspended between small clamps so that the stress is applied in the same direction as in the intact ligament, ranges from 4500 g/mm^2 in *Cardium edule* to 21,000 g/mm^2 in *Arctica islandica.* In this last species it is noteworthy that the ligament is very powerful (Table 1).

When tissues are removed from a bivalve, the valves gape widely and may be gradually closed by the addition of known weights. Thus the resistance of the ligament to the closure of the shell may be determined as a moment about the hinge axis; this is termed the *closing moment* (for details of the method, see Trueman, 1953).

From the closed condition, removal of weight allows the valves just to open and this is expressed as the opening moment of the valves. To obtain some basis of comparison between different species the moments were related to the volume of the shell. A number of examples are listed in Table 1. The opening moment of the ligament is of importance in the opening of the valves of all bivalves, except where the ligament is reduced or absent, as in the Adesmacea. In some, the ligament is the only method for opening the valves, for example, *Mytilus, Pecten,* and *Ostrea,* these being free or attached bivalves with a reduced foot. The ligament of *Mytilus edulis* is particularly strong, probably because of its length in relation to the size of the shell, and the strength of the ligament may well be an advantage in a crowded community. By contrast, bivalves with chevron or duplivincular ligaments have little opening moment—for example, *Glycymeris* and several other species of the Arcacea which were observed. It is reasonable to suppose that any bivalve with the rather cumbersome chevron ligament must have used a powerful foot to assist in opening the valves, perhaps similar to that of living arcas. Although this does not necessarily mean byssal attachment, the absence of a strong ligament may have precluded life in crowded communities.

The functional adaptation of the ligament is best observed in members of the Pectinidae, most of which are free swimmers by habit (e.g., *Pecten maximus*). The closing and opening of the valves by means of the addition and subtraction of known weights may be represented as a load-extension curve, the load being the weight applied to the valve, expressed in terms of a moment about the pivotal axis of the ligament, and the extension being indicated by the angle of gape of the valves (Figure 8). The loading curve (*AB*) corresponds with the closure of the shell, and the unloading curve (*BCD*) to its opening. On such a curve the point *B* corresponds to the closing moment and point *C* to the opening moment. The difference between the opening and closing moments is some measure of the internal resistance of the ligament, and the smaller the area enclosed the lower is the work loss and the higher the efficiency of the ligament. The ligament of *P. maximus* (and also *Chlamys opercularis*) has loops of small area compared with a wide range of other bivalves (e.g., *Mytilus edulis, Arctica* (*Cyprina*) *islandica, Ostrea edulis,* or *Mya arenaria*). The ligament of the Pectinidae differs from that of most other lamellibranchs since the main part of the inner layer is not calcified. Its modulus of elasticity in compression is consequently somewhat lower (320 g/mm^2) and the resistance per unit cross-

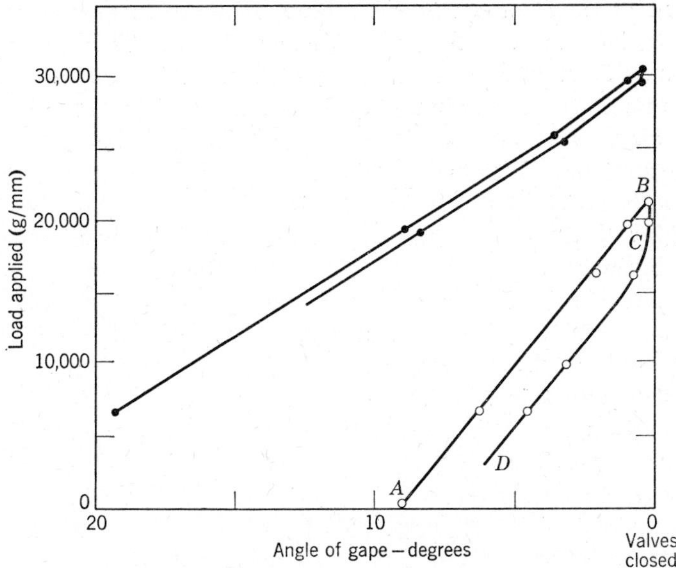

Fig. 8 Stress-strain curves for the loading of the ligament of Pecten maximus (●—●—) *and* Mytilus edulis (○—○—). *AB shows the loading of the ligament, BCD the unloading. See text for further description.*

sectional area of the ligament to the closure of the valves is less. Nevertheless, a noncalcified inner layer of the ligament may be considered to greatly increase the efficiency of the ligament (Trueman, 1953), and this is particularly important in an animal which flaps its valves open and shut as a means of locomotion. However, this could also be an adaptation for frequent cleansing of the mantle cavity and may have preceded free life. It does not necessarily mean that all pectinoids are similarly adapted, but that forms without this peculiar ligament must have had much less freedom of movement.

Examination of Table 1 shows that there is no definite relation between ligament strength and habitat. Although the ligament of certain burrowing species is powerful (e.g., *Arctica islandica, Dosina lupinus, Tellina tenuis*), no general relations may be observed, and each species must be separately examined. The ligaments of burrowing bivalves are in general no more powerful than those of attached forms, although the former may have to overcome the additional resistance of the substratum when opening their valves. In the case of *Mya arenaria,* a deeply burrowing bivalve, this resistance has been shown to vary between approximately 15 times the opening moment of the ligament in clean sand, 10 times in muddy sand, to about 3 times in offshore mud (Trueman, 1954). The opening moment may be supplemented by the foot in those in which the ventral mantle margins are mainly free (e.g., *Anodonta, Tellina, or Cardium*) or, where fusion of the mantle margins has closed the ventral gape, by fluctuations of the hydrostatic pressure of the water enclosed in the mantle cavity (e.g., *Mya* or *Lutraria*).

In *Mya,* the hydrostatic pressure together with the opening moment of the ligament is certainly sufficient to open the valves against muddy sand, but hardly enough to open the valves against clean sand (Trueman, 1954). Both *Mya* and *Lutraria* are bivalves which burrow deeply and have a long siphon. Chapman and Newell (1956) have shown that in *Mya* the siphon is protracted by means of the hydrostatic pressure in the mantle cavity, while in *Scrobicularia,* a member of the Tellinacea in which the ventral mantle margins are largely free, extension of the siphons is brought about by the action of the muscles of the siphonal wall and the blood contained therein. The mantle cavity of the clam *Mya* acts as a closed fluid-muscle system when the siphonal sphincters are closed, retraction of the siphons causing the valves to be forced apart and adduction of the valves causing protrusion of the siphon. With the large siphons of deeply burrowing forms divarication of the valves at their posterior end is commonly encountered subsequent to withdrawal of the siphon. Associated with this, adaptative changes in the ligament have taken place. Whereas in most bivalves the ligament only allows the gaping of the valves about a hinge axis running along the dorsal margins of the valves, in *Mya* and *Lutraria* the ligament also allows the rocking of the valves on a dorsoventral axis (see Figure 4).

Thus, in these genera, the ligament not only tends to open the valves but also acts as a flexible joint, which allows the rocking motion of the valves. This is possible since the ligament, which is basically an opisthodetic structure, is considerably reduced in anteroposterior length even though the mantle/shell has elongated on either side of the demarcation line. In *Lutraria* (Figure 9), the outer layer is very short and only a small region of the inner layer functions in compression and as a pivot in the rocking of the valves. A flexible sheet of periostracum unites the dorsal margin of the valves (Owen, 1958). Thus the adaptation of the ligament in *Lutraria,* and a similar modification in the unrelated *Mya* allows posterior divarication of the valves and the withdrawal of long siphons. The condensation of the ligament in this manner, together with elongate siphons as shown

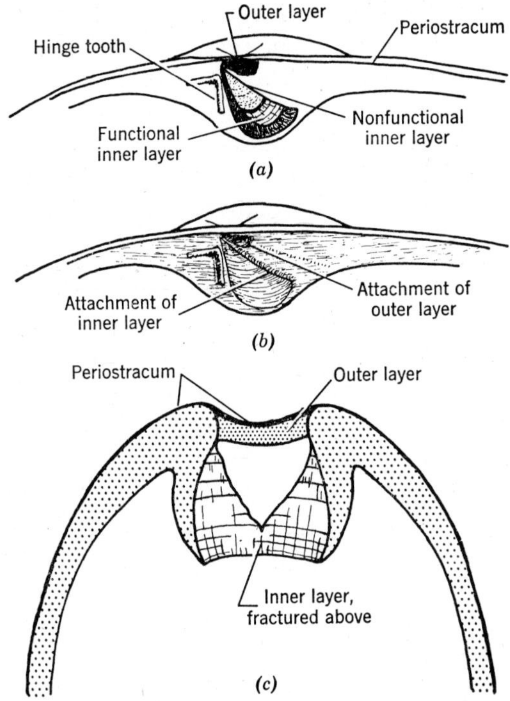

Fig. 9 The ligament of Lutraria lutraria *shown (a) in sagittal section with right valve, (b) right valve with ligament removed leaving impression on valve, (c) transverse section of ligament. The very reduced outer layer and the inner layer functioning only over a small region at the ventral margins are adaptations related to deep burrowing and the rocking of the valves.*

by the depth of the "pallial sinus," is thus clearly an adaptation to a deeply burrowing habit.

The rock-boring habit has evolved in the Bivalvia by at least two routes. Boring in *Platyodon* and in the pholads represents further modification of the deep burrowing habit. In the pholads, boring proceeds by the rocking of the valves about the dorsoventral axis, and the ligament is either lost or remains as a functionless vestige. In other bivalves (e.g., species of *Petricola, Hiatella,* and *Botula*), the habit of boring was probably preceded by that of nestling in rock crevices while attached by the byssus. In these, the ligament is retained. Indeed, the long ligament of the Mytilidae, and consequent powerful opening moment, represents a preadaptive factor which made boring in *Botula* possible (Yonge, 1955, 1958).

In this survey of the bivalves it has been possible to indicate some of the ways in which a group of relatively simple animals has become adapted for different habits. Although many recent investigations have been made in this field, it should be stressed that the interpretation of fossil forms requires detailed knowledge of the most similar living species and that this may require investigation before adequate information is available to the paleoecologist.

Adaptive Morphology in an Extinct Echinoid (Micraster)

An excellent example of the use of this procedure in paleoecology is a recent investigation of changes in the chalk heart urchin, *Micraster,* in which paleontological interpretation is related directly to living forms (Nichols, 1959). The genus *Micraster* gives an excellent example of continuous evolution of individual characters, which appear, however, to be independent of environmental conditions, for example, depth, particle size, and temperature. Nichols considered that the changes in the fossils must either represent gradual improvement in organization of the animal's structure or change in ecological niche with an effectively unchanged habitat. To discover the significance of the changes, the functional morphology of seven living species of British irregular echinoids was studied in detail. The normal burrowing activity of three species was observed and particular attention was given to *Echinocardium cordatum,* which burrows to a maximum depth of about 18 cm. It is shown in Figure 10 in its normal attitude. It maintains contact with sea water by a respiratory funnel built by the tube feet of the anterior ambulacrum and by a single sanitary tube originating at the shield-shaped subanal fasciole. The course of the respiratory currents is indicated in this diagram.

An important result of this work is the hypothesis that the low zonal *Micraster* (e.g., *M. corbovis*) burrowed less deeply than the high zonal series (e.g., *M. cortestudinarium* and *M. coranguinum*). One of the factors influencing the depth of burrowing in living forms is the degree of development of heavily ciliated regions for the purpose of respiration. There is no reason to doubt that the epidermis of *Micraster,* as in all living urchins, was heavily ciliated; thus, while the low zonal forms with "smooth" ambulacra relied on the normal ciliation of the body, the high zonal ones increased the number of cilia in the region of the test where they were most needed to maintain a respiratory current. It is suggested by Nichols that the increase in ciliation results from an increase in ornamentation of the test. If this is correct, then it may be concluded that the low zonal

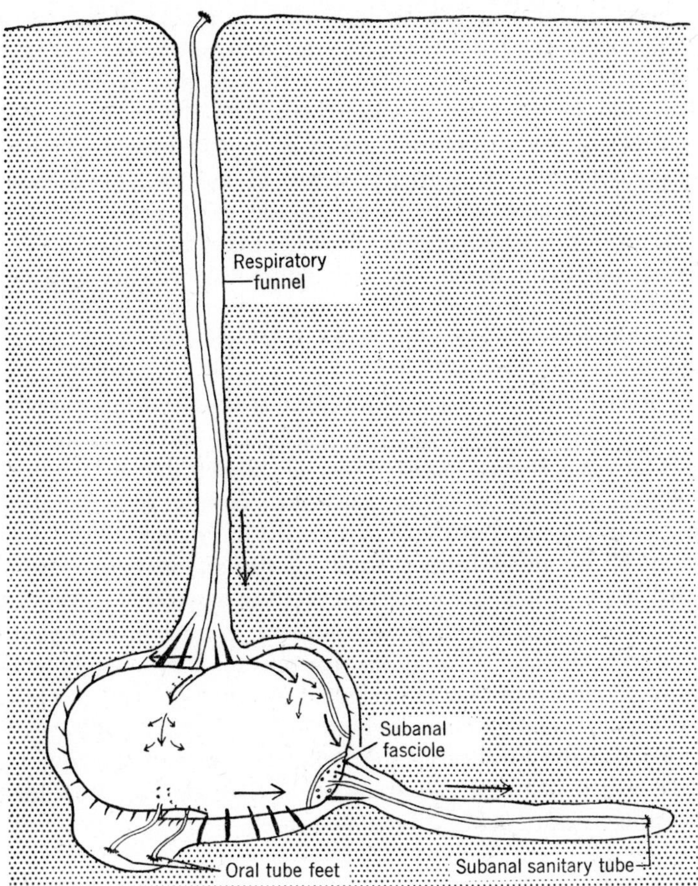

Fig. 10 Diagram showing Echinocardium cordatum *in its burrow from the side. The respiratory funnel to the surface of the substrate is normally maintained by the tube feet of the dorsal region of the anterior ambulacrum, one of which is drawn. Two oral feeding and one subanal burrowing tube feet are also included. Arrows indicate the course of respiratory currents, which are brought down the respiratory funnel by ciliation of the body, down the ambulacra and between the respiratory tube feet to the subanal fasciole from which they pass along the sanitary tube (after Nichols, 1959).*

forms required less ciliation for some reason, and since the coherence of the substrate apparently remained unaltered, the most likely reason is that the low zonal forms burrowed less deeply and in consequence required less motive power to pass the same amount of water over the respiratory surfaces. It is fairly certain that the micrasters, like living heart urchins, built a sanitary tube to receive the waste products, since they are provided with similar structures in the posterior region. In the high zonal micrasters the subanal fasciole becomes broader, and in the light of observations on the fascioles of living forms, this suggests the production of stronger currents which would be required to achieve a greater depth of burrowing. Nichols also makes an assessment of conditions of the chalk sea based both on knowledge of the mode of life of present-day heart urchins and on the associated fossil fauna. He concludes that *Micraster* lived in a calm sea with little current action and that there was a rain of detrital material adequate to provide large quantities of food for microphagous feeders.

This investigation of *Micraster* indicates how the interpretation of a specific fauna requires detailed knowledge of the nearest living representatives. It has been pointed out above that a knowledge of physiology, including behavior, may give certain general results regarding paleoecology but that for precise information all the evidence that may be obtained from a study of the adaptive morphology of the hard parts of animals must be carefully assessed. Unfortunately for the paleoecologist, in many groups of marine invertebrates, our knowledge of functional anatomy is concerned principally with the tissues of the body so that the relevant information may not be available without investigation. A realization of this should stimulate the paleoecologist to observe the living animal and the invertebrate zoologist to attend to the requirements of the paleoecologist, for these should prove fruitful fields of future research.

REFERENCES

Ansell, A. D., 1961, Function morphology of British Veneracea: *J. Mar. Biol. Ass. U.K.*, v. 41, pp. 489–518.

Baggerman, B., 1953, Spatfall and transport of *Cardium edule: Arch. Neerl. Zool.*, v. 10, pp. 315–341.

Beedham, G. E., 1958, Observations on the non-calcareous component of the shell of the Lamellibranchia: *Quart. J. Microscop. Sci.*, v. 99, pp. 341–357.

Bidder, A. M., 1962, Use of tentacles, swimming and buoyancy control in the pearly *Nautilus: Nature,* v. 196, pp. 451–454.

Brachet, J., 1961, The living cell: *Sci. Am.*, v. 205, pp. 51–61.

Brown, C. H., 1950, A review of the methods available for the determination of the types of forces stabilizing structural proteins in animals: *Quart J. Micr. Sci.* v. 91, pp. 331–339.

Brown, F. A., Jr., and C. L. Prosser, 1961, *Comparative Animal Physiology,* Second Edition: Philadelphia, Saunders, 668 pp.

Chapman, G. and G. E. Newell, 1956, The role of the body fluid in relation to movement in soft-bodied invertebrates; II. The extension of the siphons of

Mya arenaria (L.) and *Scrobicularia plana* (da Costa): *Proc. Roy. Soc.*, B, v. 145, pp. 564–580.

Dall, W. H., 1889, On the hinge of pelecypods and its development: *Am. J. Sci.*, 3rd series, v. 38, pp. 445–462.

Denton, E. J., 1961, The Buoyancy of Fish and Cephalopods: *Progress in Biophysics,* New York, Pergamon Press, v. 11, pp. 177–234.

Denton, E. J. and J. B. Gilpin-Brown, 1961, Papers on aspects of the buoyancy of the cuttlefish, *Sepia officinalis* (L.): *J. Mar. Biol. Ass. U.K.*, v. 41, pp. 319–381.

Eagar, R. M. C., 1960, A summary of the results of recent work on the palaeoecology of Carboniferous non-marine lamellibranchs: *C. R. 4me Congres de Strat. et de Geol. du Carbonifere,* Heerlen, v. 1, pp. 137–149.

Florkin, M., *Biochemical Evolution:* New York, Academic Press, 157 pp.

Holme, N. A., 1961, The Bottom fauna of the English Channel: *J. Mar. Biol. Ass. U.K.*, v. 41, pp. 397–462.

Knight-Jones, E. W., 1954, Laboratory experiments on the gregariousness during settlement of *Balanus balanoides* and other barnacles: *J. Exp. Biol.*, v. 30, pp. 584–598.

Jackson, R. T., 1890, Phylogeny of the Pelecypoda: the Aviculidae and their allies: *Mem. Boston Soc. Nat. Hist.*, v. 4, pp. 277–400.

Joysey, K. A., 1961, Life and its environment in ancient seas: London, *Nature,* v. 192, pp. 925–926.

Krogh, A., 1939, *Osmotic Regulation in Aquatic Animals:* Cambridge Univ. Press, 242 pp.

Moore, H. B., 1934, The relation of shell growth to environment in *Patella vulgata: Proc. Malacol. Soc. Lond.*, v. 29, pp. 217–222.

Newell, N. D., 1937, Late Paleozoic pelecypods: Pectinacea: *State Geol. Surv. Kans. Publs.*, v. 10, pp. 1–123.

Nichols, D., 1959, Changes in the chalk heart urchin *Micraster* interpreted in relation to living forms: *Phil. Trans. Roy. Soc. Lond., B,* v. 242, pp. 347–437.

Nicol, E. A. T., 1930, The feeding mechanism, formation of the tube, and physiology of digestion in *Sabella pavonina: Trans. Roy. Soc. Edin.*, v. 56, pp. 537–598.

Nicol, J. A. C., 1960, *The Biology of Marine Animals:* London, Pitman, 707 pp.

Owen, G., 1953*a*, The shell in the Lamellibranchia: *Quart. J. Micr. Sci.*, v. 94, pp. 57–70.

——— 1953*b*, On the biology of *Glossus humanus* (L.) (*Isocardia cor* Lam): *J. Mar. Biol. Ass. U.K.*, v. 32, pp. 85–106.

——— 1958, Shell form, pallial attachment and the ligament in the Bivalvia: *Proc. Zool. Soc. Lond.*, v. 131, pp. 637–648.

——— 1959, Observations on the Solenacea: *Phil. Trans. Roy. Soc. Lond.*, B, v. 242, pp. 59–97.

——— E. R. Trueman, and C. M. Yonge, The ligament in the Lamellibranchia: London, *Nature,* v. 171, pp. 73–75.

Pantin, C. F. A. and A. M. P. Pantin, 1943, The stimulus to feeding in *Anemonia sulcata: J. Exp. Biol.*, v. 20, pp. 6–13.

Raven, C. E., 1942, *John Ray, Naturalist, His Life and Works:* Cambridge University Press, 502 pp.

Robertson, J. D., 1957, The habitat of early vertebrates: *Biol. Rev.*, v. 32, pp. 156–187.

Ruedemann, R., 1921, Observations on the mode of life of primitive Cephalopoda: *Geol. Soc. Am. Bull.*, v. 33, pp. 315.

Smith, H. W., 1932, Water regulation and its evolution in the fishes: *Quart. Rev. Biol.*, v. 7, pp. 1–26.

Thorson, G., 1950, Reproductive and larval ecology of marine bottom invertebrates: *Biol. Rev.*, v. 25, pp. 1–45.

Trueman, A. E., 1941, The ammonite body-chamber with special reference to the buoyancy and mode of life of the living ammonite: *Quart. J. Geol. Soc. Lond.*, v. 96, pp. 339–383.

_______ 1942, Supposed commensalism of Carboniferous spirorbids and certain nonmarine lamellibranchs: *Geol. Mag.*, v. 79, pp. 312–320.

_______ 1946, Stratigraphical problems in the coal measures of Europe and North America: *Quart. J. Geol. Soc. Lond.*, v. 102, pp. xlix–xcii.

Trueman, E. R., 1950, Quinone-tanning in the Mollusca: London, *Nature,* v. 165, p. 397.

_______ 1953, Observations on certain mechanical properties of the ligament of *Pecten: J. Exp. Biol.*, v. 30, pp. 453–467.

_______ 1954, The mechanism of the opening of valves of a burrowing lamellibranch, *Mya arenaria: J. Exp. Biol.*, v. 31, pp. 291–305.

Weir, J., 1945, A review of recent work on the Permian nonmarine lamellibranchs and its bearing on the affinities of certain nonmarine genera of the upper Palaeozoic: *Trans. Glasgow Geol. Soc.*, v. 20, pp. 291–340.

Wilson, D. P., 1952, The influence of the nature of the substratum on the metamorphosis of the larvae of marine animals: *Ann. Inst. Oceanog. Monaco,* v. 27, pp. 49–156.

_______ 1954, The attractive factor in the settlement of *Ophelia bicornis: J. Mar. Biol. Ass. U. K.*, v. 33, pp. 361–380.

Yonge, C. M., 1928, Feeding mechanisms in the invertebrates: *Biol. Rev.*, v. 3, pp. 21–76.

Yonge, C. M., 1930, Studies on the physiology of corals; II. Digestive enzymes: *Sci. Rept. Great Barrier Reef Exped.*, Brit. Mus., v. 1, pp. 13–37.

_______ 1937, A review of digestion in the Metazoa: *Biol. Rev.*, v. 12, pp. 87–115.

_______ 1940, The biology of reef-building corals: *Sci. Rept. Great Barrier Reef Exped.*, Brit. Mus., v. 1, No. 13, pp. 353–391.

_______ 1948, Formation of siphons in Lamellibranchia: London, *Nature,* v. 161, p. 198.

_______ 1949, On the structure and adaptations of the Tellinacea, deposit feeding Eulamellibranchia: *Phil. Trans. Roy. Soc. Lond.*, B, v. 234, pp. 29–76.

_______ 1953*a*, The monomyarian condition in the Lamellibranchia: *Trans. Roy. Soc. Edin.*, v. 62, pp. 443–478.

_______ 1953*b*, Form and habit in *Pinna carnea* Gmelin: *Phil. Trans. Roy. Soc. Lond.*, B, v. 237, pp. 335–374.

_______ 1955, Adaptation to rock boring in *Botula* and *Lithophaga* (Lamellibranchia, Mytilidae) with a discussion on the evolution of this habit: *Quart. J. Micr. Sci.*, v. 96, pp. 383–410.

_______ 1957, Mantle fusion in the Lamellibranchia: *Publ. Staz. Zool. Napoli,* v. 29, pp. 151–171.

_______ 1958, Observations on *Petricola carditoides* (Conrad): *Proc. Malacol. Soc. Lond.*, v. 33, pp. 25–30.

Zobell, C. E., and C. B. Feltham, 1938, Bacteria as food for certain marine invertebrates: *J. Mar. Res.*, v. 1, p. 312.

General Correlation of Foraminiferal Structure With Environment

by Orville L. Bandy *University of Southern California, Los Angeles*

ABSTRACT

A study of foraminiferal assemblages of modern seas has disclosed striking correlations between form, structure, and environment. Among hyaline genera, species of *Virgulina* in shallow waters have opaque walls and closely appressed chambers. A few species have delicate striae. Bathyal species are smaller; some are nodose, others are cylindrical with partly or completely translucent and iridescent walls, with or without spines. Among species of *Bolivina, Bulimina,* and *Uvigerina,* small, less ornamented types occur on the continental shelf and there is a progressive increase and differentiation of surface sculpture with increasing depth of water.

Most porcelaneous Foraminifera are abundant in inshore waters; however, biloculine types display diverse adaptations. Those on shelf areas are simple and mostly less than 1 mm in diameter. Deep bathyal species are differentiated into those with cylindrical necks, serrated edges, and sizes up to 5 mm. Arenaceous genera also exhibit important trends. For example, specimens of *Cyclammina* show a marked size increase from about 1 mm in upper bathyal waters to a diameter of about 5 mm in deeper basin waters.

Evolutionary convergence may be the principal reason for correlation of form and structure with environment. General trends of this type are important corroborative criteria in paleoenvironment studies.

Introduction

Investigation of the relationships between environment and the composition, structure, and form of Foraminifera shows striking cor-

Reprinted by permission from the Report of the International Geological Congress, XXI Session, Norden, 1960, Part XXII., International Paleontological Union, Copenhagen, 1960.

relations in all of the major groups of Foraminifera. This study is designed to direct attention to convergent evolutionary trends of this nature as a step in developing and testing the validity of resulting general criteria in the reconstruction of paleoenvironments. Among the numerous descriptive taxonomic, evolutionary, and ecologic studies of Foraminifera, there is none that is primarily concerned with the development of convergent evolutionary trends and the environmental significance thereof. A brief preliminary report was given on this subject recently (Bandy, 1956*a*); since then, additional findings illustrate abundant evidence in support of convergent adaptation as a primary tool for the paleoecologist.

Most major general trends are those that correlate with changes in bathymetry and temperature. Benthic marine environments include the following categories: (1) bays and estuaries; (2) the inner shelf (0–50 meters); (3) the central and outer shelf (50–150 meters); (4) the upper bathyal zone (150–610 meters); (5) the middle bathyal zone (610–2438 meters); the lower bathyal zone (2438–4000 meters); and the abyssal zone (below 4000 meters). Generally, the lower bathyal zone includes about the same type of foraminiferal assemblage as the abyssal zone.

Bathymetric ranges of some species vary somewhat from one area to another, most likely because of variation in temperature gradient and bottom character; however, within any given region, the trends discussed herein appear in sequence with increasing depth of water. Bathyal species of the tropics do not become shelf species of the cold temperature and polar regions; conversely, shelf species of polar regions have related forms in the shelf areas of the tropics. For example, *Elphidium,* an inner shelf genus characterized by a single row of sutural pores, occurs in both the Arctic and tropics in the same general type of environment. A related genus, *Elphidiella,* an inner shelf species characterized by a double row of sutural pores, is mostly restricted to the central and northern temperate regions and to the Arctic Ocean. Occurrence of these forms in the central and outer shelf areas is brought about by displacement or by expansion of brackish waters farther seaward than usual. Deep water forms such as *Virgulina nodosa* R. E. and K. C. Stewart occur in similar depths of the Arctic Ocean and in the temperate and tropical regions of the Pacific Ocean, always characteristic of the bathyal zone, but with somewhat different upper levels of occurrence.

It is convenient to discuss convergent trends with respect to three general groupings of the Foraminifera, viz., arenaceous or agglutinated types, calcareous imperforate or porcelaneous types, and the calcareous perforate or hyaline types.

Reference to wall structure is based largely upon the work of Wood (1949). Discovery of the aragonitic category was also reported (Bandy, 1954).

Correlation of Foraminiferal Structure and Environment

Arenaceous Trends

Arenaceous or agglutinating Foraminifera illustrate several important general trends (Figure 1). Simple genera predominate in inshore waters, bays, lagoons, and in estuaries. Occasionally, in estuaries and other brackish waters, a genus such as *Ammobaculites* will be the dominant foraminifer (Bandy, 1956*b*). Other genera include *Nouria, Saccammina, Trochammina, Eggerella,* and *Haplophragmoides.* Important arenaceous faunas of the inner shelf regions are also simple, being typified by *Trochammina, Eggerella* of small size, *Textularia,*

	Bays	Shelf			Bathyal Zone		
		Inner	Central	Outer	Upper	Middle	Lower
General							
Simple interior							
Labyrinthic interior				*Liebusella*		*Cyclammina*	
Rotaloid							
Compressed test							
Globular test							
Multiserial-Triserial	<1 mm Small coarse		*Eggerella*			Large smooth	>1 mm
Multiserial-Uniserial						*Martinottiella* Large smooth	
Triserial-Uniserial			*Clavulina*				
Biserial							
Triangular in side view		*Textularia candeiana*					
Lanceolate test							
Siphonate Chambers							

Fig. 1 Arenaceous morphology and bathymetry.

and *Reophax.* Locally, *Rhabdammina* and a few other related genera may dominate the arenaceous fauna.

Central and other shelf faunas begin to demonstrate marked increases in complexity and differentiation of arenaceous faunas. Members of the preceding types still persist, although they are rarely of major importance, excepting for *Rhabdammina.* Types with vesicular or labyrinthic filling of the chambers make their appearance in the form of genera such as *Liebusella, Cuneolina,* and *Textulariella,* with sizes of up to 5 mm or more. These genera are most significant on some of the shelf-edge prominences in the northeastern Gulf of Mexico (Ludwick and Walton, 1957). Some species of *Textularia* and *Spiroplectammina* develop siphonate chambers in this environment in many parts of the tropics.

Bathyal arenaceous faunas include additional complex and diverse types of Foraminifera. *Cyclammina* makes its appearance and it is identified with the bathyal zone throughout modern oceans (Akers, 1954). Most specimens are about 1 or 2 mm in diameter; however, recent studies reveal the development of gigantic specimens more than 5 mm in diameter in deeper basins off southern California. These basins, which have sills deeper than 1300 meters, are well aerated with temperatures of about 2 or 3°C. Curiously, this large form (*C. cancellata* [Brady]), is apparently absent in deep sea sediments of the abyssal zone off southern California. The basins also contain large specimens of *Martinottiella pallida* (Cushman) which may be as long as 5 or 6 mm. Bathyal forms of many oceanic areas include large, smoothly finished species of *Karreriella, Eggerella, Vulvulina,* and large coarse specimens of *Alveolophragmium.* A ubiquitous bathyal arenaceous foraminifer is *Glomospira,* which has been found in deeper sediments of most oceans.

Fossil representatives of the arenaceous genera include complex types such as *Loftusia* and *Choffatella.* The first is a Cretaceous arenaceous isomorph of the fusulinids and alveolinids, and it represents, most likely, a central or outer shelf environment. The second is a homeomorph of *Cyclammina* and may represent a bathyal genus of the Mesozoic.

Porcelaneous and Imperforate Calcareous Trends

Imperforate calcareous Foraminifera display important trends, some of which are of especial importance in the interpretation of paleoenvironments (Figure 2). As a general group, miliolids become exceptionally abundant in the inner shelf zone and in channels and open bays, amounting often to as much as 50 per cent and more of the total

	Bays	Shelf Inner	Shelf Central	Shelf Outer	Bathyal Zone Upper	Bathyal Zone Middle	Bathyal Zone Lower
Miliolids							
Quinqueloculina							
Triloculina							
Biloculines							
Broad aperture			<1 mm			1–5 mm	
with tooth							
with flap							
Round aperture						1–5 mm	
± serrate edge							
Discoidal types							
Simple interior							
With pillars							
With chamberlets							
Fusiform types							
With chamberlets							

Fig. 2 Porcelaneous foraminiferal morphology and bathymetry.

foraminiferal population. They are diverse, including quinqueloculine, triloculine, and biloculine forms. Quinqueloculine and triloculine forms include species that are more euryhaline than other members of the group, and are therefore particularly dominant in estuaries, channels, and bays.

Central and outer shelf miliolids do not generally dominate foraminiferal faunas. They consist of the same general types as in the inner shelf zone; however, *Biloculinella* appears here, characterized by a biloculine test and apertural flap. Bathyal miliolids are generally rare except for *Pyrgo,* which develops into a remarkably diverse group of species in deeper waters, some with serrate edges and others with smooth edges, some with round apertures and cylindrical necks and others with broad low apertures. Perhaps the most distinctive feature is the development of large size with great depth. Many specimens of *Pyrgo* and the related form *Pyrgoella* attain diameters of more than 5 mm in deep basins which are well ventilated. Diameters of 1 and 2 mm are usual for specimens of *Pyrgo* from the biloculine ooze between Iceland and Norway. Conversely, shelf types of *Pyrgo* are generally much less than 1 mm in diameter.

Adaptations among the larger discoidal imperforate calcareous

Foraminifera illustrate less diversification than occurs in the miliolids. Many of them live on anchored vegetation and may be rafted easily when this vegetation is broken loose. This group is stenohaline, tropical to subtropical in distribution, and largely restricted to the continental shelf habitat. Those with simple tests, such as *Peneroplis,* and also those with pillars, such as *Archaias,* occur in greatest abundance at depths of 0–30 meters whereas those with chamberlets, such as *Sorites, Heterostegina,* and *Cycloclypeus,* attain their greatest abundance between depths of about 20 and 80 meters. These live on the deeper anchored types of seaweed. A few variations are reported in deeper waters, as, for example, the more complex *Amphisorus hemprichii* Ehrenberg with hexagonal chamberlets, which occurs abundantly in the Red Sea at a depth of 941 meters (Said, 1949).

A unique modern isomorph of the fusulinid Foraminifera of the later Paleozoic is the genus *Alveolinella,* a spindle-shaped genus that abounds in depths of 20 to 80 meters in the region of the Sulu Sea. It is stenohaline, restricted to tropical waters, and generally associated with the larger discoidal forms which have chamberlets.

Hyaline or Calcareous Perforate Trends

Numerous important convergent trends occur within this large group of Foraminifera. Among those with granular as opposed to radial wall structure, *Pullenia* is represented by compressed species on the continental shelf and by mostly globose species in the bathyal zone (Figure 3). *Pullenia* is generally evolved from *Chilostomella* and this genus from *Allomorphina,* by many authors following the analysis by Cushman (1948). *Chilostomella* and *Allomorphina* are distinctly bathyal types in modern oceans. If *Chilostomella* gave rise to *Pullenia,* the deeper water globose types of *Pullenia* appeared first and the shallower water compressed species evolved later. It is also reasonable to assume that *Nonion* gave rise to some if not all of the members of *Pullenia,* as Galloway derives the genus (1933), and that the direction of adaptation has produced deeper water globose forms which are like members of the Chilostomellidae in apertural character, due to convergence not to direct relationship.

Hyaline rotaloid Foraminifera with radial wall structure show several interesting trends (Figure 3). Coarsely perforate genera such as *Cibicides* are represented by many variations on the central and outer continental shelf and in the upper bathyal zone, as, for example, the variations of *C. mckannai* Galloway and Wissler. In deeper water, this species tends to develop reflected sutures. In middle and lower bathyal zones of modern oceans, the most cosmopolitan species is

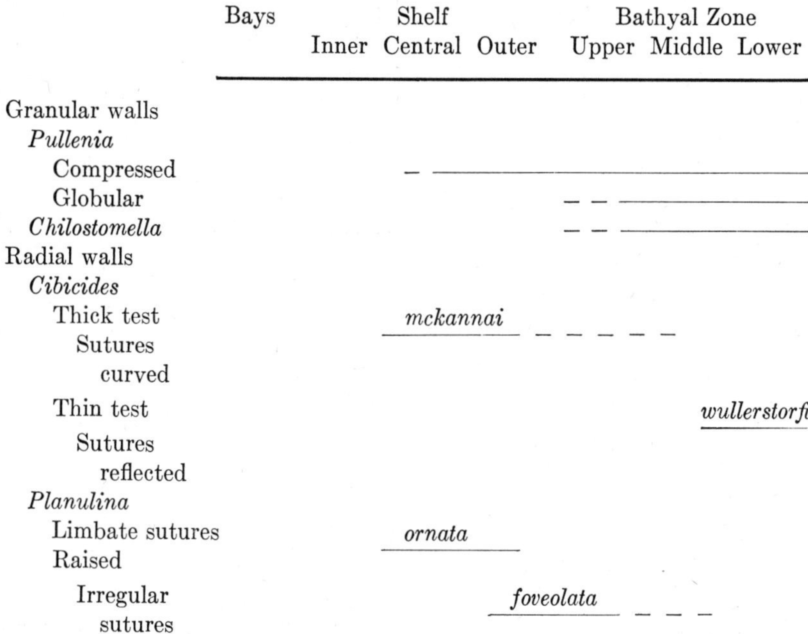

Fig. 3 Chilostomellid and coarsely perforate rotaloid morphology and bathymetry.

C. wullerstorfi (Schwager), a larger species, quite compressed, and with prominent reflected sutures in the type and all typical specimens. Coarsely perforate planispiral types are primarily dominant on the central and outer shelf, as represented by *Planulina ornata* (d'Orbigny). Forms with raised crenulate sutures, *P. foveolata* (Brady), occur on the outer part of the shelf and in the upper bathyal zone. Most deeper water species assigned to *Planulina* are not truly planispiral and belong in *Cibicides*. A few deep water species are known and have the pronounced reflected sutures that also characterize the deep water types of *Cibicides*.

Hyaline, finely perforate rotaloids, with radial wall structure, should be considered of major importance to the paleoecologist because of their domination of many environmental categories (Figure 4). The many species of *Eponides* include mostly large (0.5–1.5 mm) types on the central and outer parts of the continental shelf, as exemplified by *E. antillarum* (d'Orbigny) and *E. repandus* (Fichtel and Moll). Bathyal representatives are small, mostly less than 0.20 mm in diameter, as ably represented by *E. tumidulus* (Brady) and *E. turgidus* Phleger and Parker. The larger bathyal species known commonly as *E. tener* is here considered to belong in *Gyroidina*.

	Bays	Shelf Inner	Shelf Central	Shelf Outer	Bathyal Zone Upper	Bathyal Zone Middle	Bathyal Zone Lower
Eponides							
Large		*antillarum* 0.5 mm					
Small							*tumidulus* 0.3 mm
General							
Rounded with internal pillars	*Streblus*	– – –	– – –	– – –			
Sharp edge Simple interior		*Hanzawaia*					
Rounded edge Simple interior					*Gyroidina-Valvulineria*		
Epistominella							
Small, rounded edge		– – –	0.3–0.4 mm				
Globose				–	———	———	———
Medium size Sharp edge				–	———	0.5 mm	———

Fig. 4 General rotaloid morphology and bathymetry.

Other finely perforate rotaloids show general associations that are dominant in many benthic populations. Most rotaloids with pillars are inner shelf inhabitants, as represented by the cosmopolitan *Streblus* and by the tropical Pacific *Calcarina* and *Baculogypsina*. *Streblus* is euryhaline and eurythermal whereas the others mentioned are stenohaline and stenothermal. The central and outer part of the continental shelf is characterized by the dominance of sharp edged rotaloids in many parts of the world, well exemplified by the genera *Hanzawaia* and *Cancris*. Bathyal and abyssal rotaloids include many characteristic species of *Valvulineria, Baggina,* and *Gyroidina,* all types with mostly rounded edges and either globose chambers or tests.

Species of *Epistominella* are unique among the rotaloids in having an aperture oriented parallel to the plane of coiling. Small species with abruptly rounded to sharp edges occur as shallow as the central and outer self province, occasionally in the inner shelf zone. Prominent planoconvex species with a sharp edge and larger size (diameter greater than 0.5 mm) characterize the upper and middle bathyal zones. Some very small biconvex species are common and abundant in deeper basins of the eastern Pacific. Others, such as *E. exigua* (Brady), appear to be cosmopolitan abyssal and bathyal types, occurring in many oceans and nearly always in deeper waters. A more complicated aperture is seen in the middle and lower bathyal genus *Osangularia* that has one aperture along the base of the last septal face and a second that extends upward into the last septal face.

Common tropical and subtropical rotaloids characterized by finely perforate radial walls, and by complexities of accessory chambers are those such as *Eponidella, Asterigerina,* and *Amphistegina* (Figure 5). The first genus has supplementary ventral chamberlets which do not alternate with the chambers, the dorsal spire is visible, and the aperture is expanded into the apertural face. This genus characterizes brackish inner shelf, lagoonal, and bay environments (Akers, 1952). *Asterigerina* has chamberlets that alternate with the main chambers on the ventral side, and the dorsal spire is also visible; this genus is dominant in the inner shelf zone under conditions of stable salinity, especially in reef environments. The third genus, *Amphistegina,* has secondary chamberlets alternating with the chambers on the ventral side, but this genus is involute also on the dorsal side with no spire

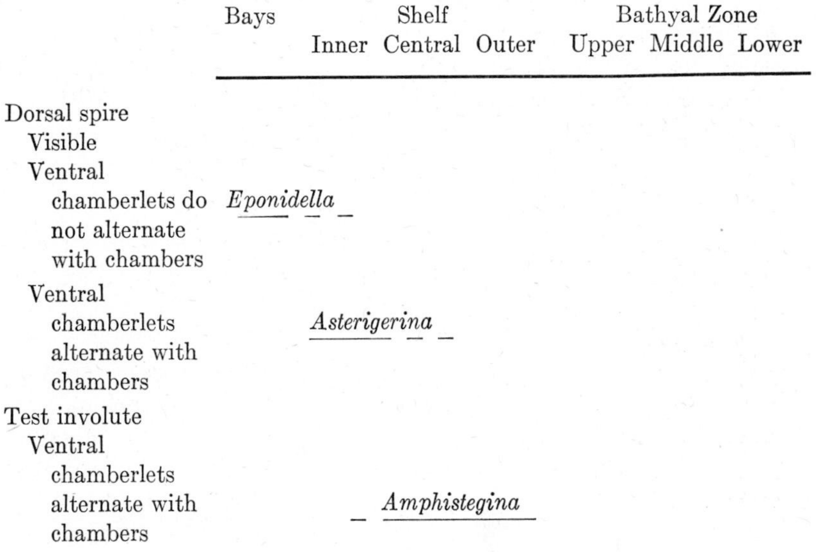

	Bays	Shelf			Bathyal Zone		
		Inner	Central	Outer	Upper	Middle	Lower
Dorsal spire							
Visible							
Ventral chamberlets do not alternate with chambers	*Eponidella*						
Ventral chamberlets alternate with chambers		*Asterigerina*					
Test involute							
Ventral chamberlets alternate with chambers			*Amphistegina*				

Fig. 5 Asterigerinid morphology and bathymetry.

showing. *Amphistegina* is mainly characteristic of depths greater than 20 meters extending beyond across the central and outer shelf zone (Bandy, 1956*b*).

Buliminids offer unusual trends in size and ornamentation or surface sculpture correlative with environmental categories (Figure 6). This group also has a radial wall structure. Small species of *Buliminella,* such as *B. elegantissima* (d'Orbigny), with 9 to 12 chambers per whorl and less than 0.40 mm in length, are abundant in inshore waters of many regions of the world. Somewhat larger species with fewer chambers per whorl occur in the central and outer shelf province and in the bathyal zone. Species of *Bulimina* with spines provide useful indices of bathymetry in modern oceans. Species which are about 0.50 mm long with few spines and also those with only marginal spines along the base of each chamber, as in *B. denudata* Cushman and Parker and *B. marginata* d'Orbigny, make their first appearance in depths of 20 meters on the continental shelf, and they are abundant over much of the central and outer parts of the shelf and in the upper bathyal zone. *B. denudata* is more typical of the temperate zone, whereas *B. marginata* is characteristic of the tropical and warm tem-

	Bays	Shelf			Bathyal Zone		
		Inner	Central	Outer	Upper	Middle	Lower
Buliminella							
Small, 8 to 10 chambers per whorl	*elegantissima* <0.4 mm						
Bulimina							
Few small spines (temperate zone)			*denudata* 0.5 mm				
Spinose fringe along base of each chamber (tropics)			*marginata* 0.5 mm				
Large heavy spinose test						*striata mexicana* 1.0 mm	
Small costate							*rostrata* <0.4 mm
Large smooth				0.75 mm	*affinis*	1.5 mm	

Fig. 6 Buliminid morphology and bathymetry.

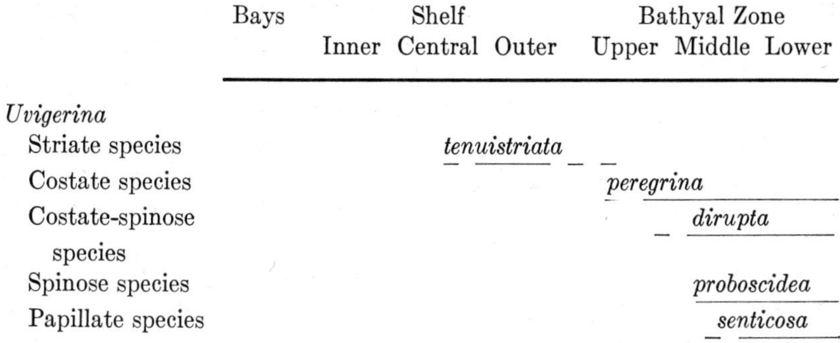

Fig. 7. Uvigerinid morphology and bathymetry.

perate regions. In deep bathyal waters, large spinose species develop with a maximum length of more than 1 mm, as represented by the common bathyal species *B. striata* var. *mexicana* Cushman. In deeper bathyal waters, the principal species is *B. rostrata* Brady, which is small (about 0.3 mm long), costate, and rather widely distributed in modern lower bathyal and abyssal waters. In some areas this species grades into slightly spinose types that occur in shallower waters of the middle bathyal zone. Smooth or unornamented species of *Bulimina,* typified by *B. affinis* d'Orbigny, range from the outer shelf to deeper bathyal waters. Even here there is a distinct size trend in maximum length, for the shallow depth range the maximum size is about 0.75 mm in the middle bathyal zone, and in well aerated basins the maximum size is often 1.5 mm or more.

Uvigerinid morphology and bathymetry is analogous somewhat to the trends of the buliminids (Figure 7) (Bandy, 1953). This group has a radial wall structure throughout. In the eastern Pacific there is a complete gradation of species, all of which are about 1 mm long but variable in other respects. Species of the outer shelf and the upper bathyal zone are mostly striate and slender, typified by *U. tenuistriata* Reuss. Upper and middle bathyal species are about the same length, but they are thicker and more heavily costate, as represented by the species *U. peregrina* Cushman. Deeper bathyal species begin to develop spines, as in *Uvigerina proboscidea* Schwager, and the lower part of this zone is dominated by papillate species such as *U. senticosa* Cushman. In the Asiatic area, the common upper bathyal species, *U. schwageri* Brady, has sparse costae which tend to disappear on the last few chambers. This form is replaced by spinose forms in deeper bathyal waters in the Asiatic area, just as in the eastern Pacific. In poorly ventilated basins small or dwarfed variations develop that may be half or one third as long as the typical specimens. Many of the small species of *Uvigerina* that have spines are probably dwarfed forms of other larger species; however, some of these may have arisen independently as the result of convergence. Costate forms probably arose from more than one source at various times through iterative evolution. The same is true of striate forms of *Uvigerina.* Many examples of convergence should be recognized in this and similar groups of Foraminifera.

A major group of Foraminifera with a granulate wall structure and fine perforations is the Cassidulinidae. General trends among members of this group are apparent and very useful in paleoecology (Figure 8). Inner shelf members of this family are limbate, large (0.5–1.0 mm), and characterized by either a sharp edge or an abruptly rounded edge. Central and outer shelf populations include large (diameter of more than 1.0 mm), globose, and diversified types, especially on off-shore banks and prominences in the temperate regions. Bathyal cassidulinids are either small with sharp edges, as in *C. delicata* (Cushman), or large and more or less biumbonate, as *C. translucens* (Cushman and Hughes). It is in the bathyal zone that a marked uncoiling of cassidulinids occurs with the appearance of

	Bays	Shelf (Inner, Central, Outer)	Bathyal Zone (Upper, Middle, Lower)
Cassidulina			
Large with sharp or abruptly rounded edge		*limbata*	
Large globose		*subglobosa*	
Large biumbonate			*translucens*
Small with round edge		*minuta*	
Small with sharp edge			*delicata*, *laevigata*
Uncoiled cassidulinids			
Virgulina			
Appressed chambers		*schreibersiana*	
Nodose chambers			*nodosa*

Fig. 8 Cassidulinid and virgulinid morphology and bathymetry.

Ehrenbergina and *Cassidulinoides.* Often, these genera are more abundant and characteristic of deeper water than most species of *Cassidulina.* Few members of the Cassidulinidae have a radial wall structure (Wood, 1949).

Virgulinids represent another group of Foraminifera with the granulate wall structure that exhibit useful trends with bathymetric change (Figure 8). Species with rather closely appressed chambers occur in the inner shelf zone and also in the central and outer shelf province. A few also range into the bathyal zone where they diversify into some that have translucent walls in whole or in part and into those with opaque walls and nodose chambers, as in *V. nodosa* (R. E. and K. C. Stewart). This species is most characteristic of the middle and lower bathyal zone although this form is reported in upper bathyal depths in cold temperature regions. Species that occur in closed basins, even well ventilated basins, include small types with very delicate, translucent, and iridescent walls, as typified by *V. spinosa* (Heron-Allen and Earland). It is probable that not all of those specimens assigned to *V. nodosa* were derived from the same ancestral stock, but that convergent evolution may explain the general uniformity of ornamentation types and morphology with the environmental categories.

Trends in the genus *Bolivina,* a biserial hyaline genus with radial wall structure, are those involving size, the development of surface structures, size of perforations, and regularity (Figure 9). Lagoonal and brackish water species are rare, represented by a relatively small form, *B. striatula* Cushman. The later sutures in this species are somewhat irregular, and there are very faint longitudinal striae on the test. The inner shelf zone is inhabited by small smooth species which arcuate such as *B. quadrata* Cushman and McCulloch. In the central and outer shelf zone, regular striate species appear with arcuate sutures, as represented by *B. acutula* Bandy. In some tropical and subtropical areas a lanceolate smooth species with arcuate sutures is the dominant bolivine in the outer shelf zone, for example, *B. daggaria* Parker, and in other cases the dominant outer shelf form is *B. acuminata* Natland, with chambers that terminate in short spines. In the tropics, costate bolivines become dominant in the outer shelf and upper bathyal zones. Other characters exhibited by one or more bathyal species are features such as coarse perforations, sinuous sutures, heavy limbations, and by sizes of more than 0.50 mm, although some small species still persist in deeper waters. *Bolivinita,* a small bolivine with a truncated edge, is very common locally in the bathyal zone and its maximum size is rarely more than 0.30 mm.

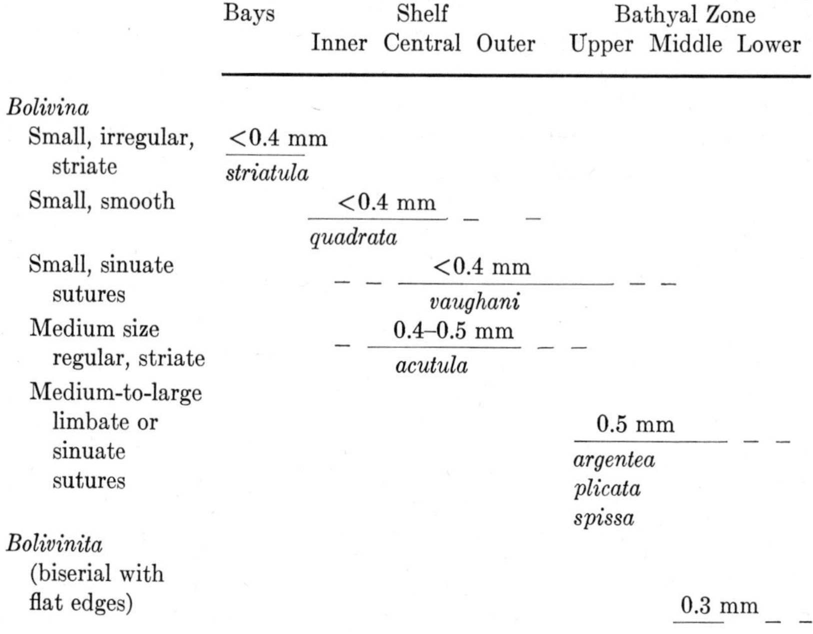

Fig. 9 Bolivinid morphology and bathymetry.

Species of larger bolivines illustrating bathyal characters discussed above include *B. spissa* Cushman, *B. plicata* d'Orbigny, and *B. argentea* Cushman.

Among additional interesting trends demonstrated by the Foraminifera, that of irregularity or abnormality in the formation of chambers is striking and has been investigated recently by Arnal (1955). Comparing his work with recent investigations of modern faunas, it is apparent that abnormal Foraminifera become developed not only in shallow brackish waters, but in deep closed basins as well. Dwarfism and irregularity are observed in several of the deep basins of southern California.

It was thought that aragonitic Foraminifera might show some type of trend that would be of value to the paleoecologists; however, it was found that aragonitic Foraminifera are common in the Arctic, Antarctic, and in temperate and tropical regions of the world. Members of the same species are found in both warm and cold waters, as well illustrated by the cosmopolitanism of species of *Ceratobulimina, Robertina,* and *Cushmanella.* An important member of the aragonitic foraminifers is *Höglundina elegans* (d'Orbigny). The largest specimens of this species apparently occur in deep basins off southern California where diameters of more than 2.5 mm have been observed. Smaller specimens of this species are known to occur on the outer part of the continental shelf, in the bathyal zone, and even in the abyssal zone. It occurs in both temparate and tropical regions, although the largest size is recorded in deep waters where the temperatures are 2 or 3°C. On the basis of present information, there is only one apparent trend, viz., that of size increase with increasing depth of water and decrease of temperature.

Conclusions

1. Among the arenaceous Foraminifera, only simple types occur in the lagoonal and bay environments. Under conditions of low pH and reduced salinities of some estuaries, members of this group may be the most abundant Foraminifera represented. Internal labyrinthic and vesicular tissues occur in types that make their appearance in the central and outer shelf zone and in the bathyal zone. Large specimens of *Liebusella* are characteristic of the calcareous prominences of the outer shelf and upper bathyal zone; large specimens of *Cyclammina* and *Martinottiella* are characteristic of the colder waters of the middle bathyal zone, especially in well ventilated basins.

2. Among the porcelaneous and calcareous imperforate Foraminifera, diverse miliolids are most characteristic of the bay and inner shelf environment. Large, diverse, biloculine types with variable characteristics are identified with middle and lower bathyal zones.

3. Large discoidal imperforate calcareous foraminifers with simple interiors or with internal pillars are identified with the inner shelf zone of tropical areas where the salinity is stable and generally between 34 and 36 parts per thousand; those with chamberlets are mostly abundant in the central and outer portions of the shelf in tropical regions and under stable conditions of salinity. They may occur as shallow as 20 meters and also in much deeper waters of the bathyal zone on occasion.

4. Fusiform calcareous imperforate foraminifers are mostly abundant between 20 and 80 meters in tropical areas, especially of the Indo-Pacific region.

5. Among the hyaline or calcareous perforate Foraminifera, those with internal pillars are mostly inner shelf types; in the bolivines, those with small external spines appear on the central and outer part of the shelf. Striae and costae are generally associated with types found in the outer shelf or bathyal zone. Size increase and the development

of coarser surface features is quite characteristic of many trends in deeper water assemblages.

6. Convergence provides one important explanation of many of the correlations between foraminiferal morphology and environment. Spindle-shaped types are characteristic of depths between 20 and 80 meters in modern tropical and subtropical oceans. This same association is suggested with respect to the fusulinids of the later Paleozoic and for the arenaceous spindle-shaped Cretaceous foraminifer, *Loftusia*.

Similarly, fossil orbitoidal foraminifers find their modern counterparts among the continental shelf types of large discoidal calcareous Foraminifera, some being characteristic of inner shelf conditions, others being representative of central or outer shelf conditions, or indicative of reef-like conditions in any of these zones.

Among the other types of Foraminifera, whether miliolids or small hyaline types, there is much to be gained by comparing morphological categories with environmental trends in any of the fossil groups.

REFERENCES

Akers, W. H., 1952, General ecology of the foraminiferal genus *Eponidella*, with description of a Recent species: *J. Paleontology*, v. 26, n. 4, pp. 645–649.

——— 1954, Ecologic aspects and stratigraphic significance of the foraminifer *Cyclammina cancellata* Brady: *J. Paleontology*, v. 28, n. 2, pp. 132–152.

Arnal, R. E., 1955, Some occurrences of abnormal Foraminifera: *The Compass of Sigma Gamma Epsilon*, v. 32, n. 3, pp. 185–194.

Bandy, O. L., 1953, Ecology and paleoecology of some California Foraminifera; Part I, The frequency distribution of Recent Foraminifera off California: *J. Paleontology*, v. 27, pp. 161–182.

——— 1954, Aragonite tests among the Foraminifera: *J. Sedimentary Petrology*, v. 24, pp. 60–61.

——— 1956*a*, General relationships between Foraminifera and bathymetry: *J. Paleontology*, v. 30, n. 6, p. 1384 (abstract).

——— 1956, Ecology of Foraminifera in northeastern Gulf of Mexico: *U. S. Geological Survey Prof. Paper* 274-G, pp. 179–204.

Cushman, J. A., 1948, *Foraminifera, Their Classification and Economic Use:* Cambridge, Harvard University Press, pp. 1–605.

Galloway, J. J., 1933, A Manual of Foraminifera: Bloomington, Indiana, Principia Press, pp. 1–450.

Ludwick, J. C., and W. R. Walton, 1957, Shelf-edge calcareous prominences in northeastern Gulf of Mexico: *Bull. Amer. Assoc. Petr. Geol.*, v. 41, n. 9, pp. 2054–2101.

Said, Rushdi, 1949, Foraminifera of the northern Red Sea: *Cushman Lab. Foram. Res.*, Spec. Publication, n. 26, pp. 1–44.

Wood, Alan, 1949, The structure of the wall of the test in the Foraminifera; its value in classification: *Quart. J. Geological Soc. of London*, v. 104, pt. 2, n. 414, pp. 229–255.

Population Structure in Paleoecology

by B. Kurtén *University of Helsingfors, Finland*

The structure of a population is always affected by its interaction with the environment, and thus reflects the ecological conditions in which the population lives. The distribution of age classes, for instance, shows the effect of mortality on the population. The distribution of morphological characters in different age classes may give more detailed information on the manner in which the interaction is realized.

Sampling Problems

In studying the population structure of fossil forms we are of course immediately beset by all the difficulties resulting from various factors of bias. They are treated from various points of view in other contributions in this symposium and need not be gone into in detail.

Although field sampling is under our control, gross inaccuracies may be introduced here. To illustrate this we may cite one instance in Central Europe in which a bear cave was excavated by a museum in cooperation with local amateurs (see Kurtén, 1958). The material was distributed between the museum and the private collectors, but the museum had first choice. Now, a century later, the private collections are gone, and only the museum sample remains for a study of this bear population. It contains 90% male individuals and only 10% females. Of course this fantastic disproportion is entirely spurious. The museum took the pick of the specimens, favoring the large and impressive ones. The sex dimorphism in this species is very pronounced, the males being much larger than the females.

While the field sampling in principle is under our own control, the factors of deposition and diagenesis that have sorted and reduced the universe of the death assemblage and given us the universe of preserved individuals are facts of nature. In general it may be assumed that the representation of the most immature stages tends to be most affected, so that the juvenile individuals will tend to be underrepresented in our material. As a result, as Olson (1957) has shown, the size-frequency distribution of our material will often tend to form a bell-shaped curve, even if a true representation of the death assemblage would give a highly skewed distribution (Figure 1). In fact we find that the mortality for the adult span of life may be readily studied in many cases, but that the juvenile mortality may, at most, be estimated from other data.

Finally we arrive at the events that are most distant from ourselves —the once-living population and the production of the death assemblage out of it—which is the main subject of this paper. It may initially be pointed out, with respect to size of an age-correlated character, that quite varied distributions may appear as a result of different combinations of growth and mortality patterns. Among the series of illustrative models developed by Olson (1957) may be mentioned the combination of relatively slow and gradually retarded growth throughout life, with a mortality pattern showing fairly high infant mortality, low mortality in middle life, and high mortality in senescence. This is probably a fairly common type of population. The resulting size distribution (Figure 2) will be bimodal. In the

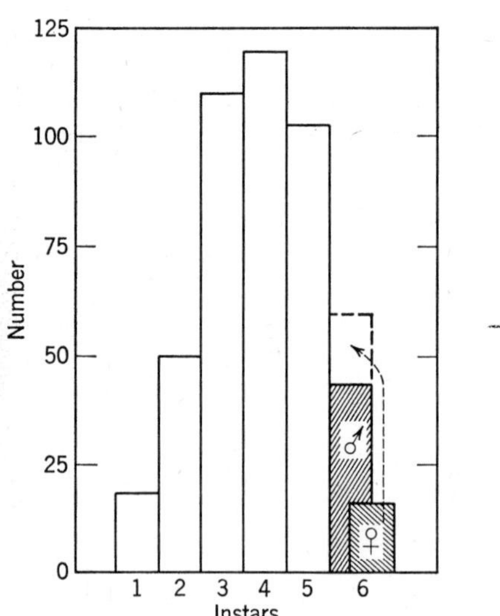

Fig. 1 Distribution of instars in a sample of the Wenlockian ostracod Primitiopsis planifrons, *to show the bell-shaped distribution often found in fossil samples. From Martinsson (1955, p. 4).*

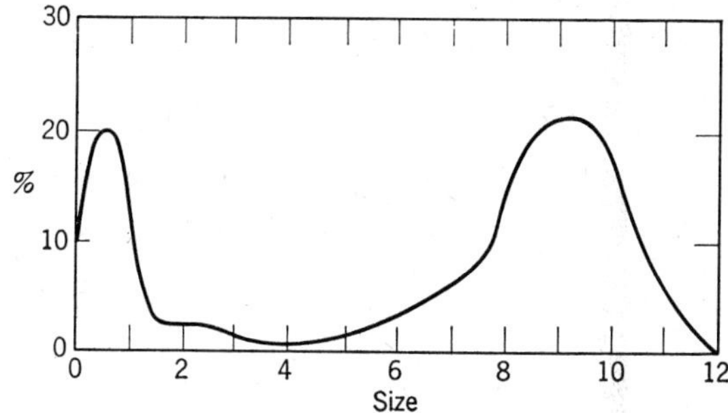

Fig. 2 A model developed by Olson (1957), showing size distribution among the dead resulting from a certain combination of mortality and growth patterns.

process of fossilization, the juvenile peak will generally be more or less obliterated, and we are left with a unimodal distribution of relatively old individuals.

Ageing

Fortunately, many samples give better material for population analysis than in this example, and we now face the problem of de-

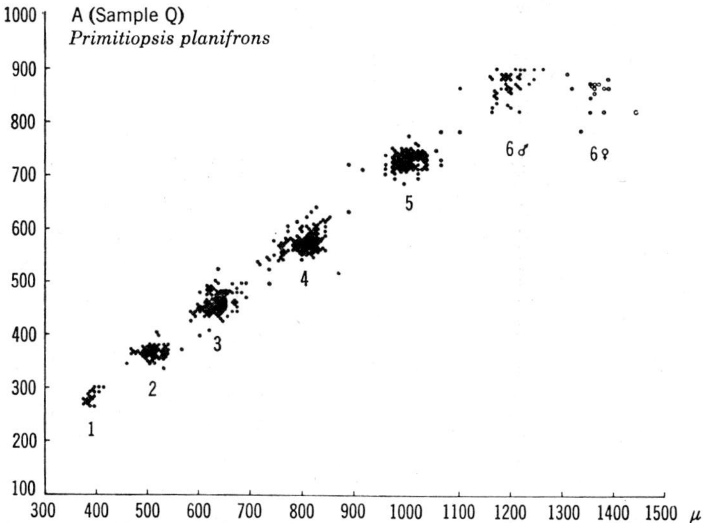

Fig. 3 Distribution of length (abscissa) and height (ordinate) in a sample of the ostracod Primitiopsis planifrons. *From Martinsson (1955).*

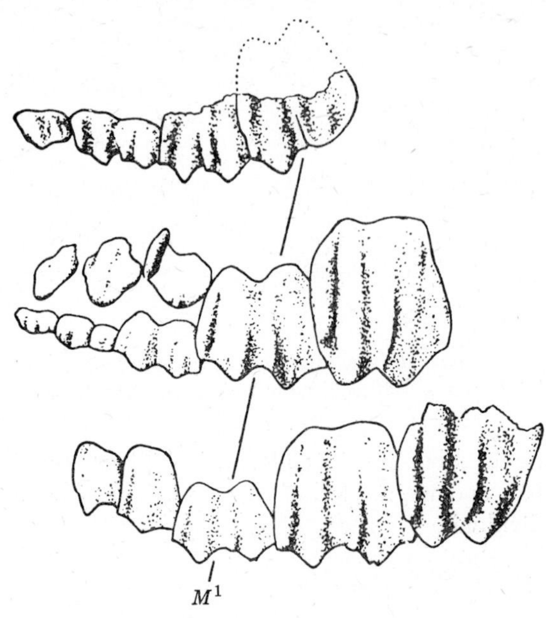

Fig. 4 Juvenile stages in the development of the upper cheek dentition of the Pliocene bovid ungulate Plesiaddax depereti *from China. Top, with milk teeth and unworn first molar; middle, with permanent premolars forming in jaw and second molar erupted; bottom, with entire permanent dentition (foremost premolar missing in this specimen). The stages are evidently one year apart in age. From Kurtén (1953).*

termining the individual age of the specimens at death. Often only relative estimates are possible, but these may sometimes be of great precision and permit further detailed analysis, such as the molting stages of various arthropods (Figure 3). On the whole, however, annual growth rings will probably remain the most useful index of age. Such rings are found, for instance, in many pelecypods, in fish scales and otoliths, and in the genital plates of sea urchins (Moore, 1935). They may vary in thickness, depending on the climatic factors of the period of growth. It would be a worthwhile project to study the relationship between individual growth and mortality in a clam population of this type. In mammals, annual growth rings appear in the deposition of dentine in the teeth, and this has turned out a particularly useful criterion for estimating the ontogenetic stage in some pinnipeds and ungulates (Scheffer, 1950; Laws, 1953). Growth rings are also found in the horny sheaths of some bovid horns, but these are rarely fossilized.

On the other hand, the age at death may be estimated if we have some reliable, recent standard with which to compare our fossil. As everybody knows, the age of a horse is shown by its teeth, and this should hold for a fossil horse as well (Lundholm, 1949). Anthropologists are able to determine the ontogenetic age of human skeletons with almost uncanny precision. Of course, in juvenile mammals, the replacement of the teeth may give very reliable data. In some mammals, the elephants for instance, replacement continues throughout life.

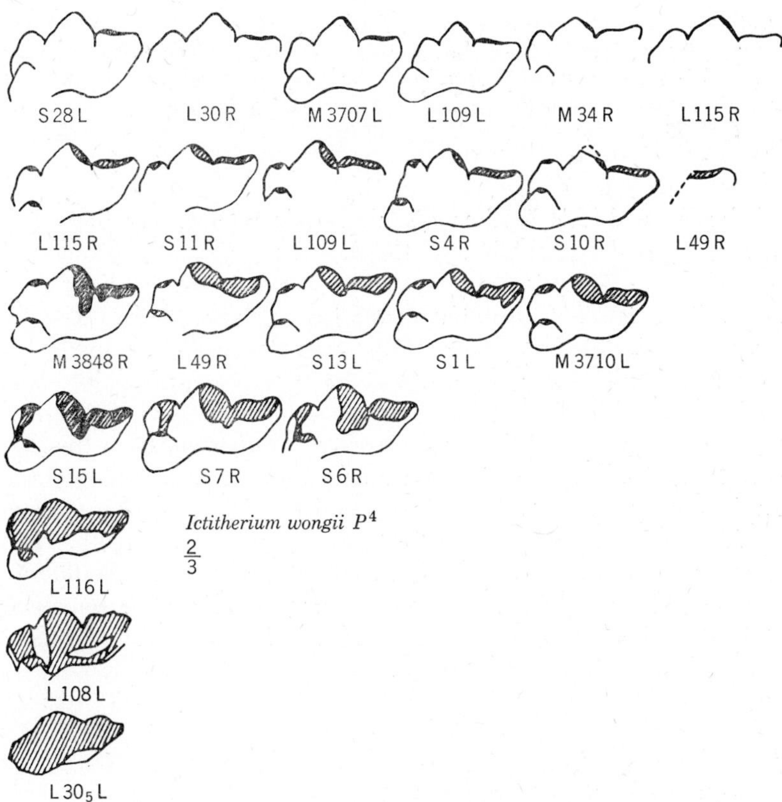

Fig. 5 Upper carnassials of the hyaenid carnivore Ictitherium, *from the Pliocene of China, seen from the inside to show progressive development of the wear facet. The groups are interpreted as annual age groups. From Kurtén (1953).*

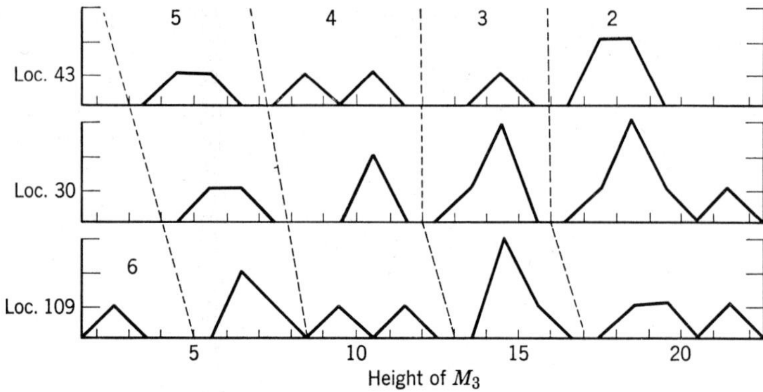

Fig. 6 Frequencies of crown heights of third lower molars in three local samples of the antelope Gazella dorcadoides *from the Pliocene of China. The groups numbered 2–6 are regarded as correlative age groups (in the youngest group, 1, the molar was not yet fully formed and so could not be measured). From Kurtén (1953).*

If the fossils do not by themselves give adequate ageing characters, there remains the possibility of seasonal deposition. In forms with seasonal parturition this will give a series of age groups one year apart in age. This is a not uncommon situation (Kurtén, 1953). The discreteness of the age groups, one year apart, is particularly evident in the juvenile individuals (Figure 4). In some mammals, adults may also be separated into annual age groups on the basis of the wear of the teeth. In the small hyaenid carnivore *Ictitherium* from the Pliocene of China, for instance, the dentitions are easily grouped on purely morphological criteria (Figure 5). In other cases, age determination may be based on the crown height of rapidly wearing teeth. In a gazelle from a single fauna, for instance, material from three different localities gave parallel series of age groups, based on the remaining height of the worn third molars (Figure 6). The values cluster at certain points with gaps in between.

Life Table Analysis

For the analysis of such relatively complete data as these the life table is an efficient tool. It summarizes information on survivorship, rates of mortality, and expectation of life within a population. These appear as functions of age, and the age may be relative (e.g., in terms of molt stages) or absolute (e.g., in years).

If we have an adequate and well-aged sample, we must at this juncture form an evaluation of the way in which the death assemblage was produced. Does the material represent the normal mortality in the population, or does it represent a census of the living population? The age structure of the living population is, of course, quite different from that of its dead, except when the rate of mortality is constant, irrespective of age.

Sometimes it is evident that what we have in hand is a sample of a

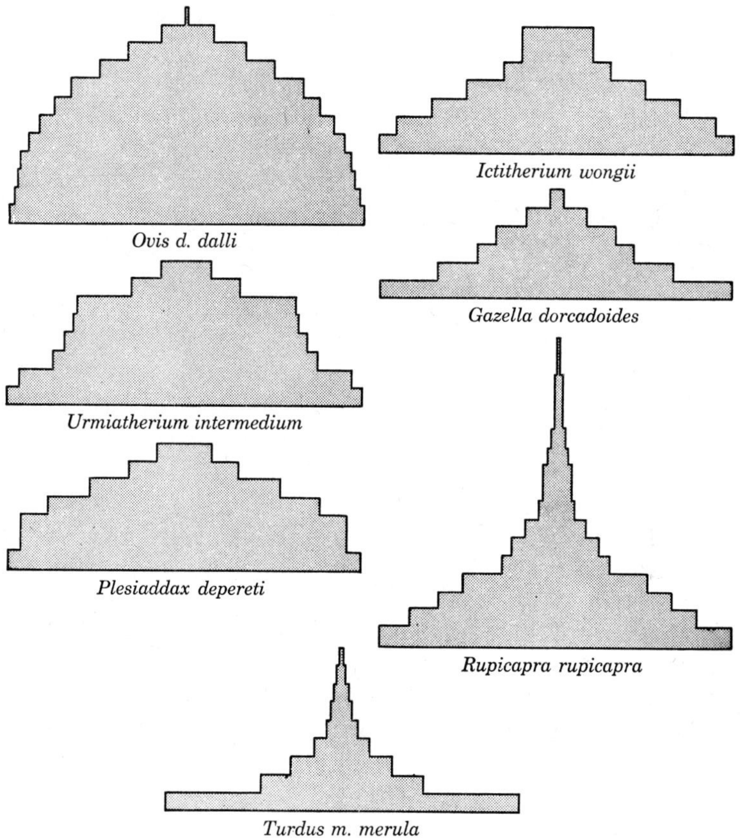

Fig. 7 Age pyramids for a number of populations, as labeled. The width of the bars is proportional to the number of living individuals at the corresponding age, beginning from bottom. Ovis dalli *(mountain sheep) and* Rupicapra rupicapra *(chamois) are recent mammals and* Turdus merula *(blackbird) a recent bird, whereas the remaining forms date from the Pliocene of China. From Kurtén (1953).*

minor population that has been destroyed wholesale by some violent agency. Fish dead in a dried-up lake or a herd of mammals drowned in a flood are obvious examples, and certainly not unusual ones. The data are then of the census type and might be pictured as population pyramids like those shown in Figure 7. Mortality is judged from the reduction in size of the age classes with increasing age. This is so-called time-specific analysis (Hickey, 1952). Actually, violent mass death is not the only way in which material for such analysis is produced. The exuviae of molting arthropods also give a sample of the census type.

On the other hand, the sample may represent the natural mortality of the species. One of the best examples is the European cave bear, *Ursus spelaeus*. This Pleistocene mammal habitually wintered in caves during the last glaciation. It was large and powerful, and the adult individuals must have been practically immune to the attacks of other carnivores. Judging from the teeth and their manner of wearing, the cave bear seems to have been almost exclusively vegetivorous, and so would not be likely to get involved in fights with the large ungulates. Probably its only dangerous enemy was man, and only at a relatively late stage of its geological history. The main mortality factor for this species is likely to have been undernourishment during winter sleep; according to the studies of Dr. P. Krott (personal communication), the natural mortality of the living brown bears is also concentrated in the time of hibernation. As a result, the bear caves contain immense numbers of bones of the cave bear, in some cases estimated to represent up to 30,000 individuals for a single cave. This does not mean that the standing population was very large, but it is a result of very intensive sampling, during the season of peak mortality, out of continuously quite small standing populations.

With material of this type the correct treatment is so-called dynamic analysis. The frequencies of the actual living age classes are computed by successive additions of the dead specimens, beginning with the oldest.

Table 1 shows two variants of the life table, dynamic and time-specific, for a fossil ostracod, *Beyrichia jonesi*, based on data by Spjeldnaes (1951). The age (x) is expressed in terms of molts, that is, a relative measure of age. The earliest age classes were underrepresented in the sample, and the analysis begins from the fourth class. The age is given (x') as per cent deviation from the mean length of life, a device making it easier to compare different populations with greatly different mean length of life. The number of deaths for each interval (d_x) is recorded, the number of survivors at

TABLE 1. *Life tables for the Silurian ostracod* Beyrichia jonesi

	x Age in terms of molt stages	x' Age as per cent deviation from mean longevity	d_x Number dying in age interval	s_x Number surviving at beginning of interval	$1000q_x$ Mortality rate per 1000 alive at beginning of interval	e_x Expectation of life or mean after lifetime (in molts)
Dynamic	4–5	−100	321	1000	321	2.38
	5–6	−58	218	679	321	2.3
	6–7	−16	152	461	330	2.1
	7–8	26	95	309	308	1.9
	8–9	68	78	214	365	1.5
	9–10	110	73	136	537	1.1
	10–11	152	43	63	682	0.8
	11–12	194	20	20	1000	0.5
Time-specific	4–5	−100	321	1000	321	2.62
	5–6	−62	207	679	305	2.6
	6–7	−24	174	472	369	2.5
	7–8	15	55	298	185	2.7
	8–9	53	16	243	66	2.2
	9–10	91	91	227	401	1.4
	10–11	129	75	136	552	1.0
	11–12	167	61	61	1000	0.5

Two alternative variants of the Life table, based on data by Spjeldnaes, analyzed dynamically and time-specifically, respectively. Time in terms of molt stages, with beginning at fourth instar. Original sample size 963 specimens.

the beginning of the interval (s_x) is given. The rate of mortality is indicated by q_x, and e_x gives the expectation of life, or the mean after lifetime remaining at the beginning of the interval. The initial value of e_x is identical with the mean longevity of the population.

If the values of s_x are entered against age (Figure 8), we get a survivorship curve. If s_x is plotted on a logarithmic scale, the rate of mortality will be expressed by the slope of the curve. The two interpretations of the *Beyrichia* data give roughly the same average slope of the curve; in fact the mean rate of mortality per age class is the same—32% for both interpretations. In other instances the dynamic and time-specific interpretations will diverge more strongly, and the correct choice will be more important.

The survivorship curve gives a clear and succinct picture of the dynamics of the population, and there are a number of characteristic types. In one type, exemplified by civilized man (see Figure 9), the mortality is quite low well up to middle life, then gradually increases and becomes very high only very late in life. The curve is convex, and the oldest individuals only reach ages about 50% higher than the mean longevity. In another type, exemplified by many birds, the mortality remains constant irrespective of age, and the oldest individuals reach ages greatly in excess of the mean longevity. The curve is a straight diagonal, and the difference between the two patterns depends on how large a fraction of the population survives up to the end of the potential longevity of the species. It follows that various types intermediate between the concave and diagonal curves will be found. Actually, some of them have been found among fossil populations (Figure 9).

A third basic pattern would be the concave curve, initially with very high mortality, which is later reduced. This is difficult to observe in nature, though it may be postulated theoretically that juvenile mortality, as a rule, should be higher than mortality in middle life. However, it may be directly demonstrated on the basis of samples in hand (e.g., in the cave bear; see Kurtén, 1958). Alternatively, it may be possible to estimate the productivity of young, which will lead to an estimate of the juvenile mortality. Figure 10 shows a sur-

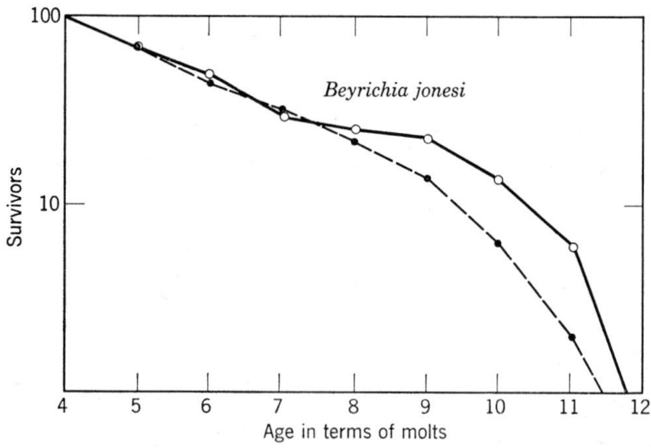

Fig. 8 Survivorship curves for the ostracod Beyrichia jonesi, *based on dynamic (dashed line) and time-specific analysis, respectively. Time in terms of molts. From Kurtén (1953).*

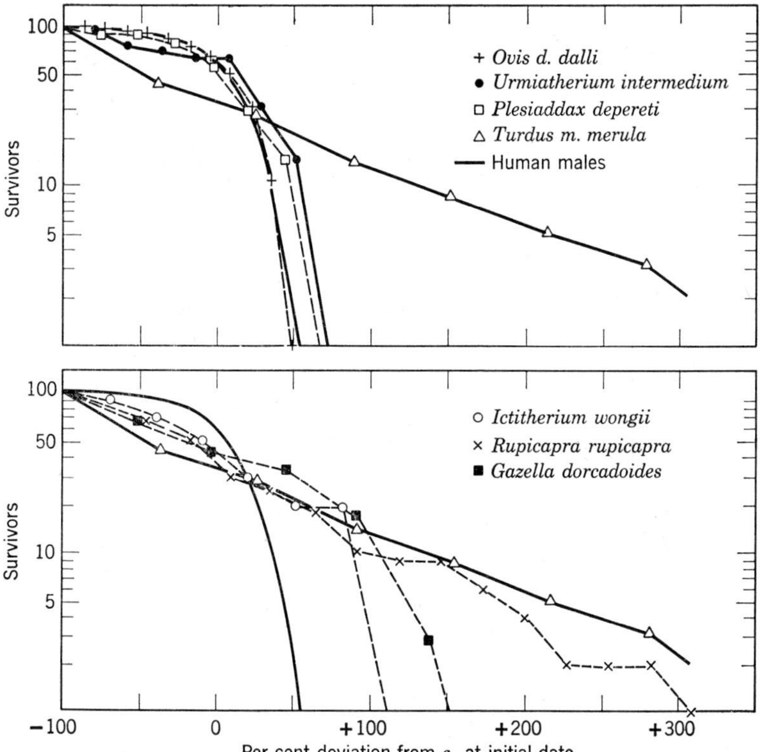

Fig. 9 Survivorship curves for the same species as the age pyramids in Fig. 8, with man (human males) added; only the adult span of life is included. The curves are brought to a common scale based on the mean longevity (at the zero point on the abscissa). The upper diagram shows curves of the convex type, the lower curves of the diagonal or intermediate type. Standards of comparison in both are the human (convex) and blackbird (diagonal) curves. From Kurtén (1953).

vivorship curve for a prawn, in which the juvenile mortality was estimated in this way. The adult curve is based on catch for two years, split up into age classes by means of size-frequency curves, a method also used in paleontology. There is evidently a tremendous first-year mortality in this population, amounting to no less than 99.8%, whereas the mortality in later life is stabilized at about 90% annually.

We can probably conclude that the general pattern of the survivorship curve, if we are able to follow a cohort of individuals from birth to the death of the last survivor, will be sigmoid: concave in early

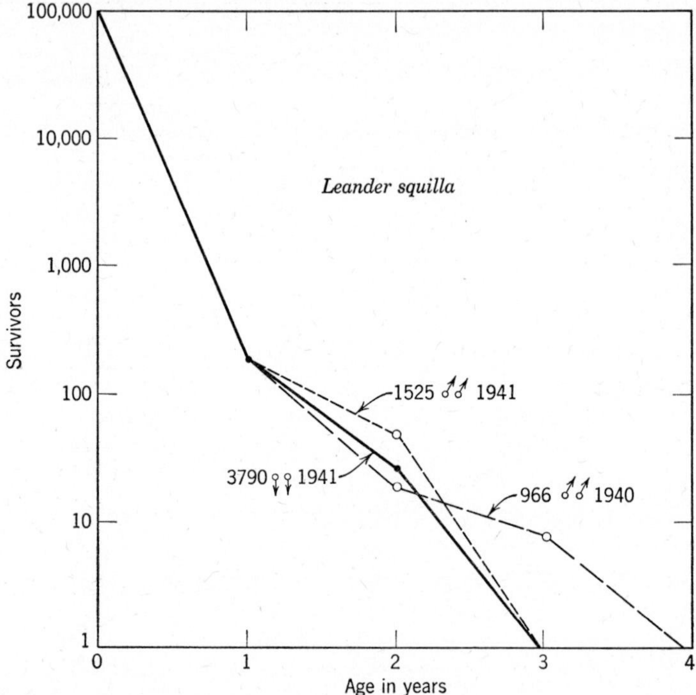

Fig. 10 Survival of the prawn Leander squilla, *based on data from Höglund (1943). From Kurtén (1953).*

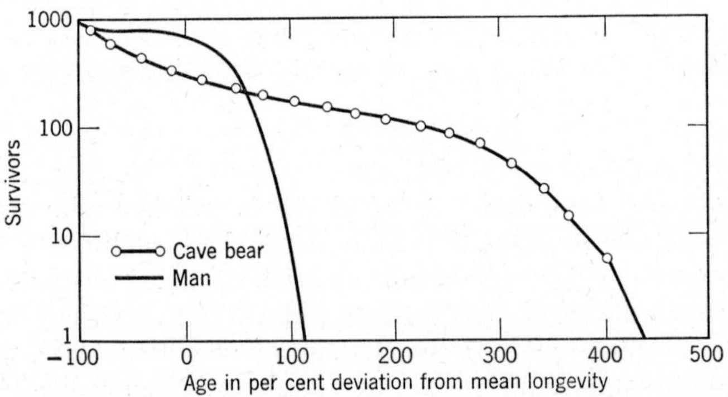

Fig. 11 Survivorship curves (from birth) for the cave bear, Ursus spelaeus, *and for human males, superimposed by the same method as that used in Fig. 10. From Kurtén (1958).*

life, reflecting high but gradually diminishing juvenile mortality; approaching the straight diagonal in middle life; and convex when senescence sets in and mortality rates again build up (Figure 11; see also Kurtén 1954*a*, *b*). However, such a complete record must be very unusual; mostly we will only be able to study a part of this sequence, usually the adult one.

Selection

The analysis may be further developed by coupling age data with morphology, sex distribution, localization, etc. The different sex distributions of cave bears at different localities have already been mentioned, but we should further point out that the disproportion is found in the adults only. The juvenile individuals show the normal 50/50 sex ratio, even in caves with great disproportions between adult males and females. This indicates that the disparity is a matter of ecological preference among the adults, and not of differential birth rates.

The correlation of age and morphology is another way of studying the interaction of the population and its environment. It gives us an insight into the process of selection by differential mortality, or so-called Darwinian selection. In such studies the problem is to find characters not affected by individual age. Qualitative characters may be useful when grouped numerically (see Simpson, Roe, and Lewontin, 1960), and meristic characters or other discontinuous quantitative variables seem to be particularly promising (Hecht, 1952). Among continuous quantitative variables, one of the most useful is tooth size in mammals, which is not affected by age (except for wear and, in special cases, lifelong growth, both of which should of course be recognized).

It can often be shown that there is a significant reduction in variation in the older age classes, resulting from the distal variants having higher rates of mortality than the proximal ones. Sometimes, for instance in the case of the cave bear, these data may be completely tied in with the life table analysis to demonstrate the annual amount of selection in the life history of the population. In other instances, only a rough distinction between young and old may be possible, but even so a study of this type may be of great interest. Again, comparison between populations of the same species in different environments or between nearly related species in similar environments will be of particular importance. A series of comparisons of this kind for a single dental character (relative width of a molar) in nine different

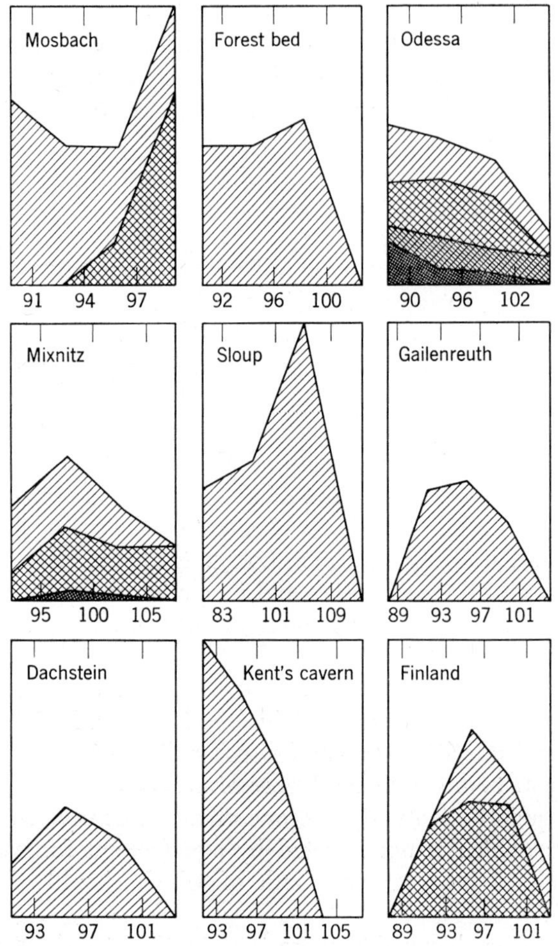

*Fig. 12 Selection patterns for the relationship between anterior and posterior width of the second lower molar in nine bear populations. Numbers on the abscissa give index values. The shaded fields represent survival, with differences in shading to indicate more detailed analysis into age groups. The samples are brown bear (*Ursus arctos*) from the middle Pleistocene of Mosbach, the Forest Bed, from the late Pleistocene of Kent's Cavern, and the Recent in Finland; and cave bear from the late Pleistocene of Odessa, Mixnitz, Sloup, Gailenreuth, and Dachstein. It may be noted that individuals with a low index tend to have higher survival rates in, for instance, the Odessa and Kent's Cavern samples, whereas a more central tendency is apparent in the Mixnitz, Sloup, Gailenreuth, Dachstein, and Recent Finnish samples. From Kurtén (1958).*

bear populations of the two species *Ursus arctos* and *Ursus spelaeus* indicated some apparent differences in the direction and strength of selection (Figure 12). Unfortunately the data at hand are not yet very complete and much remains to be done in this field. It seems, however, that differential survival does not always favor the central or modal type found in the population.

An extreme example was found in the cave bear from Odessa (Kurtén, 1957; 1958). The characters affected were the sizes of the paracone (or outer anterior cusp) of the second upper molar, its receptacle in occlusion, and the valley between the two outer cusps (protoconid and hypoconid) of the second lower molar (Figure 13). The possession of a paracone of smaller than mean size, or of a protoconid-hypoconid notch of larger than mean size, greatly increased the potential longevity. In fact all the individuals with a paracone larger than the initial mean (in per cent of total crown length) appear to have died before seven or eight years of age.

It appears very odd that selection of such intensity could have been going on for thousands of years without taking effect, but there are possible explanations for this. First, there may have been no available genetic variation; the population was a marginal one and may

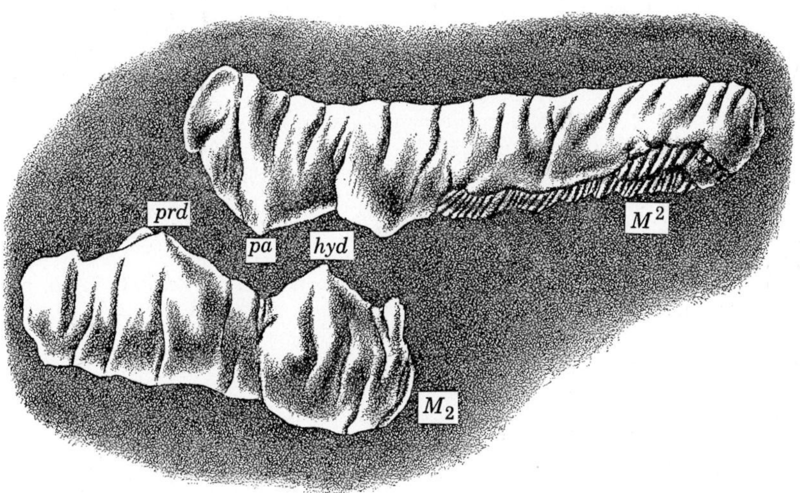

Fig. 13 Left second upper and lower molars of the cave bear, Ursus spelaeus, *external view, to show the occlusion of the paracone (pa) of the upper molar and the notch between the protoconid (prd) and hypoconid (hyd) of the lower.*

well have been isolated from the main body of the species. Or, perhaps more probable, there may have been a system of balanced polymorphism. However this may be, it is of considerable interest from the paleoecological point of view to find that in this population a slight malocclusion seems to have been the normal or modal condition.

REFERENCES

Hecht, Max K., 1952, Natural selection in the lizard genus *Aristelliger: Evolution,* v. 6, pp. 112–124.

Hickey, J. J., 1952, Survival studies of banded birds: Special Sci. Rept. *Wildlife,* n. 15, pp. 1–177.

Kurtén, Björn, 1953, On the variation and population dynamics of fossil and recent mammal populations: *Acta Zool. Fennica,* n. 76, pp. 1–122.

——— 1954*a*, Population dynamics and evolution: *Evolution,* v. 8, pp. 75–81.

——— 1954*b*, Population dynamics—a new method in paleontology: *J. Paleont.,* v. 28, pp. 286–292.

——— 1957, A case of Darwinian selection in bears: *Evolution,* v. 11, pp. 412–416.

——— 1958, Life and death of the Pleistocene cave bear, a study in paleoecology: *Acta Zool. Fennica,* n. 95, pp. 1–59.

Laws, R. M., 1953, A new method of age determination in mammals with special reference to the elephant seal (*Mirounga leonina,* Linn.): Falkland Islands Dep. Surv., *Sci. Rept.,* n. 2, pp. 1–11.

Lundholm, Bengt, 1949, Abstammung und Domestikation des Hauspferdes: *Zool. Bidr. Upsala,* v. 27, pp. 1–287.

Moore, H. B., 1935, A comparison of the biology of *Echinus esculentus* in different habitats, pt. II: *J. Mar. Biol. Ass.,* n.s., v. 20, pp. 109–128.

Martinsson, Anders, 1955, Studies on the ostracode family Primitiopsidae: *Bull. Geol. Inst.* Uppsala, v. 36, pp. 1–33.

Olson, Everett C., 1957, Size-frequency distributions in samples of extinct organisms: *J. Geology,* v. 65, pp. 309–333.

Scheffer, V. B., 1950, Growth layers on the teeth of Pinnipedia as an indication of age: *Science,* v. 112, n. 2907, pp. 309–311.

Simpson, G. G., A. Roe, and R. C. Lewontin, 1960, *Quantitative Zoology:* New York, Harcourt, Brace & Co., 440 pp.

Spjeldnaes, N., 1951, Ontogeny of *Beyrichia jonesi* Boll: *Jr. Paleont.,* v. 25, pp. 745–755.

The Community Approach to Paleoecology

by Ralph Gordon Johnson *Department of the Geophysical Sciences, University of Chicago, Chicago, Illinois*

ABSTRACT

The application of the principles of community ecology to studies of ancient benthic marine communities should yield information of both geological and biological significance. The potential value of this approach is offset by imposing practical and theoretical difficulties. The community approach is evaluated by reviewing the reproduction, composition, spatial relations, and changes in modern marine communities as these features relate to paleoecological problems.

Features of larval ecology bear upon interspecific correlation, shifts in habitat, local extinctions, and substrate relations. Shallow water communities can comprise several or several hundred species. About 30% of the species and individuals in modern shallow-water communities are preservable by virtue of possessing resistant hard parts. Sediments that are most favorable for the preservation of animals *in situ* usually contain the least number of preservable animals. Almost all of the fluctuations in animal numbers in benthic communities that have been studied are associated with changes in the physical rather than the biological environment. In the context of geologic time, recovery from anomalous fluctuations of the environment and invasions of new areas is virtually instantaneous. Evidence is cited in support of the view that benthic communities are associations of largely independent species that occur together because of similar responses to the physical environment.

The author is indebted to J. W. Hedgpeth and E. C. Olson for stimulating discussions on the problems considered here. Data from Tomales Bay, California were obtained with the aid of a grant from the National Science Foundation.

Introduction

The application of the principles of community ecology to studies of ancient benthic marine communities should yield information of both geological and biological significance. Such studies may reveal features of the distribution and organization of ancient communities that can be used in the interpretation of evolutionary events. The stratigraphic and environmental implications of a natural assemblage of species should be far more specific than those of a single species or taxonomic group. The potential value of this approach is offset by imposing practical and theoretical difficulties. Chief among these difficulties are the inherent limitations of the fossil record, problems of the recognition of life associations, data gathering and analysis, and inadequate knowledge of modern benthic communities.

Statistical methods for recognizing and analyzing life assemblages in the fossil record have been developed by several workers. The labor involved in obtaining appropriate data for statistical analysis raises the question of whether or not the community approach can be used to solve real problems. Only a few paleontologists have actually stressed the community approach in their work (e.g., E. C. Olson, D. I. Axelrod, J. A. Shotwell, J. R. Beerbower, R. G. Johnson). Since the literature is sparse, we should explore the subject by reviewing major aspects of the structure of modern benthic communities, since these features bear upon paleoecological problems. This review is based mainly on the literature since Thorson's 1957 summary and on the author's studies of modern marine communities.

The Community Concept

While most biologists regard communities as real units of biological integration, a few have denied the reality of communities (e.g., Muller, 1958). Critics of the community concept have observed that the species composition of associations belonging to a single recognized community type may vary considerably from place to place. Biologists have not been able to define a community in such a way as to encompass the varied viewpoints of all ecologists, partially because communities do not exhibit a fixed composition and because a community may broadly intergrade with neighboring communities. One of the striking features of the biosphere, however, is that all species living today do not occur in all possible combinations in natural assemblages. Rather, we observe around us a finite number of recurring associations of species. The high recurrence of species combinations would appear to be a phenomenon of considerable biological significance. Our failure to arrive at a rigorous description of this phenomenon is not proof against its reality but is probably a reflection of our ignorance and propensity for preconceived notions.

Both concrete and abstract definitions have been proposed for the term "community." The concrete definitions specify a particular assemblage of organisms at a particular place. The abstract definitions are based on some assumed general attribute of communities such as the recurrence of suites of species, the degree of interspecific interaction, or economic independence. For this discussion, a concrete definition will be used for the term "community": the assemblage of organisms inhabiting a specified space. The recurrence concept will be used for a definition of community type: an assemblage of organisms which often occur together. These definitions seem useful inasmuch as they involve attributes that can be demonstrated from field observations.

In order to apply the concepts of community ecology to the fossil record we must be able to recognize the components of particular communities in fossil assemblages. Paleontologists have used three kinds of evidence for recognizing ancient communities: (1) field evidence of burial *in situ,* (2) taxonomic analogy with a modern community, and (3) recognition of recurring suites of species analogous to the recurrence observed among modern communities.

Rarely is there unequivocal field evidence that the fossil assemblage has been buried in place without the introduction of foreign elements. Taxonomic analogues are particularly useful in studies of late Cenozoic assemblages but their utility diminishes with greater geologic age. The recognition of community types seems to be the most generally useful approach and has been employed, at least subconsciously, by most paleontologists. The field paleontologist, after some experience in an area and stratigraphic section, comes to recognize recurring assemblages of species and hence occasional irregular associations. Recently, several workers have attempted to quantify this experience and thereby introduce objectivity (Beerbower and McDowell, 1960; Johnson, 1962). Measures of interspecific association are used to recognize pairs of species which frequently occur together. These pairs are assembled into groups of highly associated species. The ecologic aspect, stratigraphic, and lithologic distribution of the groups may then be studied for evidence that the groups are composed of members of the same community type. These techniques appear to offer considerable promise but represent a great effort in acquiring suitable collections, data reduction, and analysis. This approach cannot be evaluated until we have tried it a number of times. Meanwhile we can judge whether or not all the effort is justified by examining modern benthic communities to find features that could illuminate paleontological problems. The following discussion is limited to level bottom communities as these are the most commonly encountered types in the marine fossil record.[1] It is one of the theses of this paper that the level bottom community types differ in certain important ways from rocky intertidal, coral reef, and terrestrial community types.

Modern Marine Communities of the Level Bottom

Reproduction and Larval Ecology

The mode of reproduction or recruitment of benthic marine communities is one of their most singular features. As Thorson has emphasized in several papers, 70 to 90% of modern bottom dwelling invertebrates possess pelagic larval stages in their life histories. Curiously enough, the presence or absence of pelagic larvae in the ontogeny of a marine organism cannot be directly correlated with the extent of geographic range or any other obvious single feature. A number of cosmopolitan and circumpolar species exhibit direct development.

Pelagic larvae of benthic animals may spend from a few hours to several months in the overlying water mass. A benthic species really represents two kinds of animals inhabiting grossly different kinds of environments, possessing separate sets of adaptions, and presumably undergoing more-or-less separate evolutionary histories. In recent years, evidence has been accumulated indicating that the larvae of many species actively select a suitable environment for settlement.

In Table 1, the environmental factors associated with the settlement of pelagic larvae are shown for 39 species. Experimental evidence indicates that the larvae of many species actively search for a suitable environment and are able to put off metamorphosis considerably beyond the normal period if necessary (e.g., see Wilson, 1952). As the larval period is so extended, discrimination diminishes, and eventually the larva settles regardless of the suitability of the environment.

Marine biologists have long recognized a high degree of association between the distribution of species and substrate (e.g., see Pratt,

[1] The term "level bottom communities" is used in the sense of Thorson (1957) to apply to the benthic communities developed on or in essentially flat deposits and to exclude most intertidal and all coral reef communities.

1953; Sanders, 1958; Jones, 1952; Stickney and Stringer, 1957; Southward, 1957). Most of the species for which the larval ecology has been studied appear to respond actively to some feature of the substrate (Table 1). Settlement may be associated with particle size, particle shape, organic content, surface roughness or with some cryptic substance that can be isolated from preferred substrates. The fact that the nature of the substrate is involved in the settling response of many species in several phyla is of considerable interest to the paleontologist. The deposit type and many of its properties are environmental features that can be studied in the fossil record. Thorson and others have pointed out that while the substrate may act as the key factor in inducing larval settlement, this does not necessarily mean that the properties of the substrate are themselves the significant factors of the effective environment of the adult organism. The sediment at a particular site is related to many other features of the environment, such as distance from land, depth, and water movement. Properties of the sediment are often important ecological factors affecting the growth and mortality of a benthic species (see, e.g., Loosanoff and Tommers, 1948; Pratt, 1935). As size, sorting, and mineralogy are readily measured, these properties have received the most attention from paleontologists. Evidence is accumulating, however, indicating that other properties of the sediment, such as organic content, porosity, proportion of clay, surface roughness, and the firmness or cohesiveness of the deposit, may be even more directly related to the mode of life of many benthic animals.

Larvae exhibiting selective behavior must still possess tolerance for conditions grading away from those for optimal development. Larvae must react to substrata possessing the minimal conditions for settlement, as they cannot have the forsight to refuse a substrate in anticipation of a more favorable site downcurrent. Thus chance will be an important factor in the distribution of a species even though the animal may exhibit considerable selectivity.

Most of the species whose larval development has been studied in detail have restricted environmental distributions. Animals that are able to flourish in a variety of environments probably settle at random to survive in favorable circumstances or die if they chance upon an unfavorable environment. A high degree of selectivity could be expected among deposit feeders and forms that must attach themselves to stable surfaces. Lower selectivity could be expected in predators, scavengers, or filter feeders. Only a few observations have been made, in this regard, on species having broad environmental tolerances. Kristensen (1957) suggests that the larvae of the filter feeder,

TABLE 1. *Environmental factors found to be associated with the settlement of pelagic larvae in 39 modern species*

Species	Factors Associated with Settlement	Author
Annelida		
Polychaeta		
Hydroides norvegica	Temperature, light, orientation of substrate	Wisely, 1959
Notomastus latericeus	Sediment size	Wilson, 1937
Ophelia bicornis	Sediment size, shape, organic content, Microbenthos	Wilson; 1948, 1953, 1954, 1955
Owenia fusiformis	Sediment size	Wilson, 1932
Pygospia elegans	Unknown feature of substratum	Smidt, 1951
Scolecolepis fuliginosa	Sediment size	Day & Wilson, 1934
Spirorbis borealis	Algal filmed surfaces, presence of own species	Knight-Jones, 1951; 1953 Wisely, 1960
Spirorbis pagenstecheri	" "	Crisp & Ayland, 1960
Archiannelida		
Protodrilus rubropharyngeus	Sediment size, water soluble inorganic substance in substrate	Jägersten, 1940
Bryozoa		
Alcyonidium hirsutum	Species of macro-algae, surface texture, mucous-free surfaces	Ryland, 1959
Alcyonidium plyoum	" "	
Celleporella hyalina	" "	
Flustrellidra hispida	" "	
Bugula avicularia	Temperature	Wisely, 1959
Bugula neritina	"	
Bugula flagellata	Clean surfaces	Crisp & Ryland, 1960
Watersipora cucullata	Light, temperature	Wisely, 1959
Acanthodesia tenuis	Horizontal surfaces " "	Pomerat & Reiner, 1942
Electra hastingseae	" "	
Phoronida		
Phoronis mulleri	Sediment size, clay content	Silen, 1954
Phoronis pallida	" " " "	

TABLE 1. *Environmental factors found to be associated with the settlement of pelagic larvae in 39 modern species (Continued)*

Species	Factors Associated with Settlement	Author
Mollusca		
Pelecypoda		
Cardium edule	Sediment size, water movement	Orton, 1937
Crassostrea commercialis	Temperature	Wisely, 1959
Mytilus edulis	Depth, orientation of substrate	Chippenfield, 1953
Ostrea edulis	Water movement, orientation of substrate, surface texture	Cole & Knight-Jones, 1939; Erdmann, 1934; Korringa, 1940
Ostrea gigas	Surface orientation	Schaefer, 1937
Ostrea lurida	" "	Hopkins, 1935
Ostrea virginica	Copper concentration in water, salinity, temperature, surface texture	Prytherch, 1934
Teredo norvegica	Organic extract of wood	Harrington, 1921
Venerupis pullastra	Surface orientation	Quayle, 1952
Gastropoda		
Nassarius obsoletus	Water soluble substance in substratum	Scheltema, 1961
Arthropoda		
Cirripedia		
Balanus, 6 species	Presence of adults, temperature, surface texture, light, algal film	Pomerat & Reiner, 1942; Gregg, 1945; Weiss, 1947; Crisp & Barnes, 1954; Knight-Jones, 1955; Wisely, 1959; Connell, 1961
Eliminius modestus	Presence of adults, surface texture	Knight-Jones, 1950; 1955; Crisp & Barnes, 1954
Crustacea, Cumacea		
Cumella vulgaris	Sediment size, organic content	Wieser, 1956

Cardium edule, show little or no selective behavior. Holme (1961) argues that widely distributed species probably do not exhibit selective behavior in settling. The experiments of Scheltema (1956, 1961) indicate an interesting difference in the larval behavior of two species of the gastropod genus *Nassarius.* Scheltema demonstrated that *Nassarius obsoletus* exhibits a complex behavior pattern leading to preferential settling on a particular substratum. He obtained from the preferred substratum a water soluble substance capable of inducing settlement in sea water not in contact with a favorable substratum. *Nassarius vibex,* which lives in the same region as *Nassarius obsoletus,* does not metamorphose in response to bottom sediment. Since *Nassarius obsoletus* is a deposit feeder, its selective behavior would seem to have considerable adaptive value. *Nassarius vibex,* on the other hand, is a scavenger and not as directly dependent on sediment properties.

In his 1957 review Thorson stated, "we have evidence enough to abandon the 'raining down at random' theory hitherto accepted by most marine biologists" (Thorson, 1957, p. 482). It now seems more probable, however, that benthic invertebrates exhibit a spectrum of selectivity, some species showing highly specific behavior while others approach random fallout.

Thorson has discussed the possible influence of adult populations on the settlement of larvae. There is evidence that the larvae of *Ostrea, Balanus,* and *Spirorbis* are attracted to sites occupied by adults of the same species (Thorson, 1957; Table 1). It also seems possible that the effect of the adult population on the substratum, through fecal accumulation, for example, may render a particular site unattractive to larvae. Some field observations tend to support this possibility, but no direct evidence is yet available. Certainly the presence of a dense population of adults may directly affect settlement by mechanical obstruction or other means. Kristensen describes experiments in which larvae were inhaled by adult clams and subsequently smothered by the coating of mucus they received in the process (Kristensen, 1957). Such deterring effects by the adult population could be responsible for the populations of animals of nearly the same size that are occasionally encountered.

If the presence of adults at a certain density does repel larvae of the same species, certain important results are theoretically possible. Since the life span of most benthic species is seldom more than a few years, the species composition at some site might change over a relatively short period of time. The composition of the entire community might remain the same, while the spatial distribution of species within the community continually changes. Such a model as this might explain the lack of correlation between the numbers of individuals of different species and the high incidence of sympatric species in these kinds of communities. There would be insufficient time for subtle interactions between neighboring sedentary individuals to affect the natural regulation of numbers. As the carrying capacity of the environment is approached, interaction might become quite important. The wide fluctuations in animal numbers observed in some level bottom communities and the variation from place to place suggests, however, that the full potential of most environments is seldom utilized in nature. If neutral relations between species are common in level bottom communities, this fact would have important implications bearing on the evolution of benthic organisms.

The reproductive ecology of benthic invertebrates is important to paleoecology in several ways. The dual nature of most benthic species makes the task of interpreting change in the fossil record more difficult. It has often been pointed out that the continuity of any species at a particular site is dependent on the weakest link in its life cycle, which almost invariably involves reproductive phases. Since pelagic larvae are often instrumental in selecting the bottom environment of the adults, shifts in adult habitat may partly be due to changes in larval response. Failure of a species to maintain itself at some locale may be caused either by these changes in larval response or by the failure of larvae to reach the site due to some chance combination of current, temperature, biological activity, etc. Offsite conditions could thus influence the permanency of a population irrespective of the stability of local environmental conditions. The disappearance of a species in a local stratigraphic sequence does not always, therefore, imply a change in the local benthic environment.

While the larva represents a complex of adaptions to an environment quite different from that of the adult, the evolutionary history of both phases must be closely linked. Failure of an appreciable number of larvae to reach an environment suitable for adult growth and reproduction will ultimately result in the local extermination of the species. Changes in pelagic ecosystems in geological time might lead to the world-wide extinction of many species without leaving the paleontologist any trace of the causal factors. The duality of benthic species may have other evolutionary implications. It is conceivable, for example, that genes having selective value for larval life could exert influence on adult morphology by pleiotropy in a fashion analagous to the mechanism of the theory of senescence proposed by Williams (1957).

Not all of the sediment attributes involved in settling behavior of different species may be preserved in the fossil record. For this reason we cannot consistently hope to obtain a high association between the occurrence of a fossil and lithology even when the species may be highly responsive to some property of the substratum in life. Undoubtedly there are sediment properties of ecological significance that are preserved but are not yet recognized. The lithologic distribution of a fossil assemblage derived from a single community type may reveal such properties to us. As imperfectly preserved as it may be in the fossil record, the substrate is one complex of environmental factors for which we can have direct evidence. It is important to note here that a variety of processes may produce very similar sedimentary rocks. Diagenetic changes can further mask subtle differences between products of different processes. The fossils can provide another criterion for selecting a unique set of processes but only after we are able to demonstrate that the fossils were derived from a single community type.

Composition

The composition of a benthic community can be described in terms of species, numbers of individuals, biomass, and the proportion of various ecologic roles represented.

The number of species at any station within a community may vary from a few to several hundred per square meter. The entire community can comprise several species or hundreds of species. These ranges are comparable to those encountered within stratigraphic units in the fossil record. Evidence from several extensive surveys (e.g., see Barnard, Hartman, and Jones; 1959) suggests that on the level sea bottom (in shallow waters to 200 meters) there is no marked trend in the number of species present in a community with respect only to depth or distance from shore. The finer silts and coarser sands support fewer species than intermediate-sized sediments, but this is not invariably the case. In very shallow water the presence of plants is often associated with a larger number of species than the same substrate without plants. In modern seas to 200 meters depth, there appears to be no regular relation between the proportion of various taxonomic groups and depth. Frequently mollusks are more abundant and varied in waters from 1 to 50 meters than in deeper water, but not invariably. Paleontological speculation on the depth distribution of organisms probably has been unduely influenced by the results of

TABLE 2. *Number of animals/m² reported in several recent shallow water investigations. Various sampling methods and mesh sizes employed*

Number of Animals/m^2	Place	Author
10–292	English Channel	Holme, 1953
266–1290	Japanese Bays	Miyadi, 1940, 1941
2356	English Channel	Mare, 1942
3500 (average)	Southern California Shelf	Barnard, Hartman, Jones, 1959
1064–12,576	Buzzard's Bay, Mass.	Sanders, 1958
4554–23,014	Scottish Loch	Raymont, 1949
5556–46,404	Long Island Sound	Sanders, 1956
40–63,600	Dutch Waddensea	Smidt, 1951

the major oceanographic expeditions which encompass great ranges in depth.

Table 2 contains tabulated data on numbers of individuals per square meter as obtained in eight recent ecological surveys. These data are for organisms larger than 1 or 1.5 mm. Such data are difficult to compare since different collecting gear and screen sizes were used. At any rate, as few as 10 and as many as 63,000 individuals per square meter have been reported. Only a few studies have been made of the microbenthos (e.g., see Mare, 1942). The numbers of individuals reported range from 10^5 to 10^9 individuals per square meter. All environments in shallow seas, studied to date, support life, and usually abundant life. In the fossil record, if we identify a particular sediment as being of marine origin, we may safely assume it supported life.

Table 3 shows some of the preliminary results of Barnard, Hartman, and Jones (1959) from an intensive survey of the communities on the continental shelf off southern California. In this area the gray sands and muds support greater numbers of individuals than the coarser red sands and rock and rubble. There are a greater number of species on the gray sands but not much greater than on the other substrates. The lower biomass together with the large numbers of individuals on the gray sands reflect the fact that this substrate supports large numbers of small species. The nature of the bottom deposits in this area is not independent of distance from shore, as the coarser sediments occur nearer shore. When the numbers of species and individuals are arranged by depth, no consistent differences can be rec-

TABLE 3. *Number of specimens, species, and biomass reported in an extensive survey of the continental shelf area of Southern California (Barnard, Hartman, Jones, 1959). Number of stations shown in parentheses*

Bottom Deposit	Average Number of Specimens/m^2	Average Number of Species/0.25 m^2	Average Weight in gm/m^2
Black mud	3711 (10)	79 (10)	252 (28)
Green mud	4540 (61)	87 (61)	294 (193)
Gray sand	5047 (18)	96 (18)	157 (53)
Red sand	2536 (11)	67 (11)	200 (14)
Rock or rubble	3210 (4)	73 (4)	291 (16)

ognized from 4 to 300 meters. The biomass does drop off, implying smaller species with depth. If the sediments were uniform on the shelf, we would probably observe a decrease in biomass and numbers with distance from shore as related to the transportation of food materials.

A striking characteristic of shallow water benthic communities is the marked dominance of one or a few species. Almost invariably one to a dozen species account for 95% of the individuals and biomass of the community. This feature can be illustrated from the data of Sanders (1960). In a soft-bottom community in Buzzards Bay, Massachusetts, he found that one species made up 59% of the individuals and another species accounted for 29% of the biomass of a community consisting of 79 species. Eleven species accounted for 95% of the individuals and 8 species for 95% of the biomass. A similar circumstance is found in many fossil assemblages but does not necessarily reflect the species abundance relations of a living community. The fossil assemblage, as an accumulation, more closely approaches the total production of preservable individuals of the community rather than a standing crop. Interpretation of species abundance is further complicated by the fact that the number of individual fossils present per unit space is influenced by the rates of mortality and deposition. Since the dominant species in the community may not be preserved, we may obtain a false impression of the importance of a species in an ancient community. It also follows that the number of individuals does not necessarily reflect the suitability of an environment for a particular species or group of species. Thus, a high fossil density may not indicate near optimum conditions for settlement or growth but high mortality and/or low rates of deposition. Conversely, a relatively low fossil density may actually represent near optimum conditions for survival and growth but a high rate of deposition. Reworking can further modify density. For these reasons, it is difficult to biologically interpret differences in fossil density from place to place. Further, it is difficult to interpret measures of association based on the numbers of specimens as related to lithology or the numbers of other species.

The composition of modern benthic communities provides some insight into the preservability of these kinds of life assemblages. We have reviewed data from modern communities of the level sea bottom and determined the percentage of the macrobenthos possessing resistant hard parts. These are animals which we have guessed to be preservable under the ordinary circumstances of the preservation of death assemblages; they are chiefly mollusks and some echinoderms. No attempt was made to evaluate other factors affecting preservation (e.g., rate of deposition, permanency of deposit, selective solution, etc.). In Table 4, data from 9 modern quantitative surveys, involving 534 samples, are shown. As before, different collecting methods were employed. If an average value could be computed for these data, it would probably fall around 30% for both the percentage of species and percentage of individuals. Such a value is as high as it is due to the abundance of mollusks today and is as low as it is primarily because of the predominance of polychaetes in recent shallow seas. The higher values were obtained in communities dominated by one or a few

TABLE 4. *Range of percentage of animals possessing resistant hard parts, in shallow water benthic communities*

Bottom Deposit	Number of Samples	Species, %	Individuals, %
Mud	142	10–55	8–70
Muddy sand	319	7–35	1–72
Clean sand	47	21–50	18–79
Gravel	26	7–67	4–87
	534		

Data based upon 9 modern surveys and 534 samples. Data from Smith, 1932; Thorson, 1933; Jones, 1952, 1956; Holme, 1953; Sanders, 1956, 1960; Southward, 1957; Jones, 1961.

TABLE 5. *Average percentage of animals possessing resistant hard parts in some benthic communities in the Irish Sea. Depths between 9 and 26 meters (based on data from Jones, 1952)*

Bottom Deposit	Number of Samples	Species, %	Individuals, %
Mud	7	10	8
Muddy sand	93	30	68
Fine sand	37	35	79
	137		

preservable species. Thus, while 87% of the individuals of the community may be preservable by virtue of possessing resistant skeletons, the preservable component of the community may be extremely biased with regard to the total species present. Nevertheless, these figures seem encouraging although we cannot apply them directly to ancient faunas. Certainly, the benthic marine community today is the most preservable community on earth from the viewpoint of preservable hard parts and environments favoring rapid burial.

As shown in Table 4, the number of preservable forms relative to the type of bottom deposit is quite variable. However, there is some evidence of a relationship to deposit type when a single geographic region is considered, as shown in Tables 5 and 6. Table 5 shows the percentage of the macrobenthos possessing resistant hard parts in some communities in the Irish Sea. Low percentages are found associated with muds. In Table 6 similar data are shown for fewer stations in the English Channel. Here again, the finest sediment is associated with the least number of preservable animals. This result is confirmed in other surveys. The sediments that in some respects are the most favorable for the preservation of animals *in situ* usually contain the least number of preservable animals. This circumstance probably reflects the dominance of polychaetes in the finer sediments and the feature that organisms inhabiting high energy environments (strong waves and/or currents) generally possess more substantial supporting structures.

Data from modern communities can also be used to examine the degree of correspondence between life and death assemblages. In the summer of 1959, an ecological survey of Tomales Bay, California was conducted by the author. Eighty-two stations were occupied throughout the bay.[2] Mollusks are the only common group that possess resistant hard parts in these waters. At ten stations, on various substrates, no preservable species were found either alive or dead. At the remaining stations an average of 20% of the living species of mollusks was also represented in the local death assemblage. At 31 stations the living molluscan assemblage was totally different from the dead molluscan assemblage. A clear relationship was observed between the correspondence of life and death assemblages and the type of bottom deposit. Muds and sands were about equally represented at the 82 stations. One third of the stations in mud showed no correspondence between life and death assemblages, while two thirds of the stations in coarser sediments lacked correspondence. The ten samples showing the highest agreement between life and death assemblages were all in clays, silts, and the finer muddy sands. These results agree with the expectation for the relation of correspondence and water movement. The proportion (39%) of stations showing completely dissimilar life and death assemblages seems high but probably is representative of the upper limits in shallow seas, since Tomales Bay is quite shallow and is subjected to considerable current and wave action. In deeper and hence quieter waters (below 15 or 20 meters) correspondence between life and death assemblages is probably considerably higher.

It was also noted in the Tomales Bay study that the areal distribution of the remains of a particular species was nearly always greater than its living representatives. If was found, for example, that the small pelecypod, *Transenella tantilla,* found at 37 stations, occurred

[2] Analysis of these data was made possible by a grant from the Atomic Energy Commission, supporting several projects pertaining to the marine geology and biology of Tomales Bay.

TABLE 6. *Average percentage of animals possessing resistant hard parts in some benthic communities in the English Channel. Depths between 40 and 70 meters (data from Holme, 1953)*

Bottom Deposit	Number of Samples	Species, %	Individuals, %
Muddy sand	3	11	9
Clean sand	10	32	33
Gravel	2	25	23
	15		

both alive and dead at 16 stations, dead only at 16 stations, and alive only at 5 stations. Such results are also to be expected under shallow bay conditions. The zones of gradation or intermingling between these death assemblages are generally broader than the zones of gradation or the ecotones between neighboring communities. This would suggest that abrupt lateral changes in the composition of fossil assemblages may be indicative of quiet waters and little or no transportation of remains.

Another important aspect of the composition of level bottom benthic communities in shallow water is the dominance of detritus feeders. About 70 to 80% of benthic invertebrates feed upon detritus (Sanders, 1956, 1960; Smith, 1932; Mare, 1942). In the fine sediments, the majority of the species are deposit feeders subsisting upon the detritus either on or in the sediment. In coarser sediments, suspension feeders may dominate. Under most circumstances, there is little difference between the kinds of organic matter being utilized by these feeding types (Holme, 1961). The important feature is that the food web and hence the biologic organization of these communities is simpler than that of the rocky intertidal, coral, and terrestrial communities. The overwhelming predominance of detritus feeders would seem to imply that many species may have more or less neutral relations with one another. This circumstance has important implications for the evolution of benthic invertebrates and will be discussed later.

Spatial Relations

Most living benthic communities exhibit vertical stratification as recognized in the distinction between epifauna and infauna (Thorson, 1957). Horizontal stratification is often pronounced in the intertidal zone, but in the absence of plants it is seldom evident below the low tide mark.

Most species and individuals of the infauna occur in the upper 15 cm of the sediment (Holme, 1953, reviews the literature on vertical distribution). The few individuals found below 15 cm tend to be large and may contribute most of the biomass of the infauna. Large pelecypods may occur as deep as a meter below the surface of the substrate (e.g., *Schizothaerus* of the western coast of North America). Bacteria are found in appreciable numbers well below 1 meter (ZoBell, 1957). Thus, while the highest concentration of organisms is near the surface of the substrate, biological activity may extend considerably below and still affect the alteration of organic remains buried quite deeply in the sediment.

One consequence of the vertical stratification of benthic communities is that a few animals will be found living amidst the relics of the preceding population. If a site is continually occupied for an appreciable length of time, a resulting fossil record will consist of mixtures of succeeding populations and overlapping life spans. Low rates of deposition and reworking may greatly exaggerate the disparity in age of remains within the same stratum. While mixing of this type limits our temporal resolution, it can be neglected as trivial in the context of geologic time for the purposes of most paleontological studies. Perhaps it is just as well that seasonal and annual variations will tend to be obscured, since they might distract our attention from the long term variations. This type of temporal mixing has long been recognized by paleontologists. The important implication of these circumstances is that abrupt vertical changes in the fossil record must, more often than not, indicate a major ecological event.

In the presence of plants, a diverse epifauna, itself strongly stratified, may be developed as on *Macrocystis*. In the absence of plants, the epifauna on a soft bottom may be virtually absent or limited to solid objects on the surface of the deposit such as stones or shells. A diverse epifauna in a fossil assemblage would strongly suggest the presence of plants or a firm substrate. The predominance of such epifaunal forms as the articulate brachiopods and crinoids in many pure, fine-grained limestones may mean that the ancient substrate was firm either as bare rock or stiff mud. The presence of a diverse gastropod assemblage, on the other hand, would suggest the presence of plants.

Thorson has pointed out that there is considerable difference in the environment of the epifauna and the infauna (Thorson, 1957). The infaunal environment of a particular deposit type tends to be more uniform in conditions for life from place to place and less subject to the effects of variations in the hydroclimate. In association with the uniformity of the infaunal environment, Thorson has argued that similar substrates throughout the world are inhabited by ecologically similar and phylogenetically related organisms. Thorson has termed such similar assemblages in similar substrates as parallel communities. As a generalization the concept suffers, as do all ecological generalizations, from the fact that deviations are common. Nevertheless, there remains a remarkable similarity between the infaunas of similar deposits throughout the world in sharp contrast to the distinctiveness of epifaunas. This circumstance has several paleoecological implications. We might expect infaunal and epifaunal organisms to differ in their rates of evolution. Since the composition of infaunas is less subject to local hydroclimates than the epifauna, infaunal organisms should make better index fossils, except for the fact that they may evolve more slowly and have greater stratigraphic ranges. These inferences might be tested with the fossil record.

Within the photic zone, the horizontal stratification of plants may confer horizontal stratification upon the animal populations. This is evident on hard substrates at least (Aleem, 1956). In the absence of plants and below the low tide mark there is little evidence of horizontal stratification in benthic communities. Environmental heterogeneity or interactions between organisms may result in distinct patterns of dispersion. Commonly individuals of a species are found to occur in clumps or colonies presumably brought about by the patchiness of the environment, the settlement of larvae in swarms, or the development of clones. Such patchiness is also a feature of the distribution of small algae and protozoa (Lackey, 1961). Within clumps, the individuals may occur clumped, evenly or randomly distributed (Holme, 1950; Connell, 1956; Johnson, 1959). Jones (1961) studied the pattern of dispersion of 19 species in shallow water. Fifteen of these species were found to be randomly dispersed in the study areas. Also, many sedentary organisms are quite capable of moving about. Some infaunal pelecypods (e.g., *Macoma, Solen, Cardium*) move about actively but gradually lose their ability with age.

The pattern of dispersion of fossils in an outcrop can be studied readily but is very difficult to interpret because of the strong likelihood that any pattern in life will be lost (Johnson, 1960). Positive evidence of patchiness in the distribution of fossils in a single stratum can perhaps be interpreted ecologically.

Changes in Abundance and Composition

Most of the studies of change in benthic marine communities involve periods of only a few years. Much of the information is from comparisons of recent and earlier surveys of the same region in connection with some disastrous event. Nearly always the compared surveys were made by different workers using different collecting methods at different times of the year. Data on fluctuations in benthic communities over a period of years are scarce.

Seasonal fluctuations appear to be far more pronounced in very shallow waters (e.g., Allee, 1919; Blegvad, 1951). Below the low tide mark there are tremendous regional differences in the extent of fluctuations in numbers. In some areas there appears to be considerable fluctuation (Poulsen, 1951; Segerstråle, 1960; Jones, 1961), while elsewhere variation seems slight (Sanders, 1956; Holme, 1953). Most of the communities that are characterized by marked fluctuations in numbers are found in very shallow waters and are exposed to frequent and considerable fluctuations in salinity or temperature. As discussed earlier, the normal temporal mixing in the fossil record would obliterate any trace of short term fluctuations in abundance under ordinary circumstances of preservation.

Occasionally a drastic environmental fluctuation has been observed to cause major changes in the local fauna. In northern regions, particularly hard winters may produce profound changes in the shallow water fauna. Kristensen (1957) found that the severe winter of 1946–1947 killed nearly all the shallow water cockles in the Dutch Wadden Sea. Allee (1919) described the effects of a hard winter on the benthic communities in the vicinity of Woods Hole, Massachusetts. He found that species in very shallow water and species at the northern extent of their ranges were the most affected. Raymont (1949) has observed the deleterious effects of lowered oxygen tensions in a sea loch. Hoese (1960) and Goodbody (1961) have recently described the biotic changes associated with salinity fluctuations. The detrimental effects of domestic and industrial wastes have been studied by numerous authors.

One of the major biological disasters of recent times was that associated with the eel grass epidemic of the early 1930's. Eel grass (*Zostera marina*) is a flowering plant of major importance in the cool, shallow (0–10 feet) waters of the northern hemisphere. In 1931–1932 vast beds of eel grass disappeared along the Atlantic Coast of North America and it declined markedly along the European Coast. There is still no agreement among plant pathologists as to the cause of the disease. The fungus-like mycetozoan *Labyrinthula* has been shown to be associated with the disease but it is not yet clear why the pathogen suddenly became active or why only particular strains of eel grass were affected (Cottam and Munro, 1954). At any rate, the biotic consequences of the disappearance of the eel grass were followed by many workers and reported in over 50 papers.

The early consequences of the disappearance of the eel grass were similar everywhere. The first animals to become rare were those whose habitat was the leaves of the plant (Wilson, 1949; Dexter, 1944; Poulsen, 1951). Some species managed to survive locally on algae (Dexter, 1944). Another common result of the epidemic was drastic changes in the bottom deposits previously covered by beds of eel grass. The plant effectively anchors organic muds and diminishes current and wave action. In many places the loss of the plant resulted in the fine sediments being swept away, leaving the coarser fractions behind

(Wilson, 1949; Cottam and Munro, 1954). An infauna more characteristic of a coarser deposit commonly invaded the area. Local changes in depth and current patterns also resulted.

The secondary, biological effects of the disappearance of eel grass were by no means general but instead were controlled by local circumstances. On the eastern coast of North America the Eastern Brant declined rapidly in numbers. Eel grass had constituted 80% of the bird's winter diet. In several years the Brant population had partially recovered, switched to a new diet of *Ulva, Enteromorpha,* and other algae, and had altered its migration routes.

Another species which appeared to undergo a rapid decline associated with the eel grass epidemic was the bay scallop, *Aequipecten irradians.* At the time it was thought that the decline of the scallop was due to its dependence on eel grass as a substrate for the attachment of spat. In contrast to the general decline of this species, in most places, Marshall (1947) observed that the scallop increased in such proportions in the Niantic estuary as to constitute a new fishery. Subsequent investigations (Marshall, 1960) indicate that the loss of the eel grass so improved circulation adjacent to the bottom that more nutrients were available in the area than before. Adequate sites for attachment of young were available on algae and other surfaces. It now seems likely that the decline of the scallop elsewhere was due to the changes in the substrate resulting from the loss of the eel grass. Conditions in the Niantic estuary apparently led to a neat balance between circulation of nutrients and bottom stability.

The loss of eel grass as a source of detritus was thought by some observers to be responsible for the observed decline of several important infaunal species. *Mya* and *Ensis* declined on the eastern coast of North America. These changes may have been due, however, to the alteration of the substrate or the fact that spat formerly held in place by eel grass were now being washed into less favorable environments. The observations made by the Danish Biological Station in the Limfjord of Jutland, which connects the North Sea with the Kattegat, are particularly pertinent to the ecological role of eel grass (Blegvad, 1951; Poulsen, 1951). Annual quantitative surveys, involving over 100 samples per survey, have been made in this area since the work of C. G. J. Petersen in 1909. In his classical studies of benthic communities Petersen had placed great emphasis on eel grass as a primary source of food for benthic organisms. The data accumulated by the Danish Biological Station over a long period, however, indicated no reduction in animal numbers that could be associated with the disappearance of eel grass, except for 3 or 4 species that lived directly upon or among the plants (Poulsen, 1951). A major species in these waters had been destroyed by a general epidemic with only very minor changes in the local biota! The fluctuations in numbers over the years since 1909 in the Limfjord appears to be more directly associated with the effects of severe winters (Blegvad, 1951).

The biological effects of the eel grass epidemic have interesting implications bearing on the effects of a major disaster and the organization of benthic communities. Except for a few instances, the general effect of this disaster on animal populations was an indirect one. The primary consequence of the disappearance of the eel grass appears to have been the freeing of the soil and the improvement of bottom circulation. The biological consequences of these changes were largely controlled by very local conditions. In some places the fauna associated with the eel grass was replaced by another; in other places, nothing happened. Frequently the animals directly involved with the plants switched to new substrates for attachment or new sources of food. In the Limfjord a dominant plant species disappeared without greatly affecting the fauna. This seems quite contrary to our expectations for a community as a biocoenosis in the original context of that term. Almost all of the fluctuations in animal numbers in benthic communities studied to date appear to be associated with changes in the physical rather than the biological environment. Even the artificial introduction of new species in a marine community is not accompanied by such drastic changes in the communities involved as have been observed with the introduction of species in terrestrial communities (see Elton, 1958). Paleontologists often ascribe sudden faunal changes to local disasters. The evidence cited here shows how complex and as yet unpredictable the biological consequences of such events are. The reactions of the population may be due to factors far removed from the primary environmental fluctuation.

Data on the recovery of populations following anomalous environmental fluctuations in the environment, and on succession, demonstrate the enormous colonizing capacity of marine invertebrates. The animals of Lagos Harbor, a lagoon system 160 miles long, are annually destroyed by the seasonal influx of fresh water (Sandison and Hill, 1959). The area is repopulated from very small populations surviving in protected places. A large population of cockles in shallow water of the Waddensee was destroyed by a particularly severe winter, but replenished in one year (Kristensen, 1957). Many other similar cases could be cited. Reish (1961) and many others have studied succession on newly available surfaces. It has been found that usually the first stage in colonization is the development of an algal film. Thereafter the course of events is swift, and a stable biota is achieved very rapidly. In the context of geologic time, recovery from anomalous fluctuations of the environment and the invasion of newly available and suitable areas would be instantaneous.

We conclude from these considerations that the widespread disappearance of a species or a fauna at some horizon in the fossil record cannot commonly be ascribed to anomalous fluctuations of some environmental factor. Instead, some major environmental change must be involved in most cases. The evidence available suggests that biological factors alone probably could not produce such an effect.

Discussion

Individuals of two or more species might live together because they interact with one another and/or have a similar response to features of the local environment. They may occur together by chance. Organisms may interact with one another in several ways (see Burkholder, 1952, for some possible kinds of relations). Our present knowledge of level bottom communities suggests that direct interactions between individuals is of less importance in determining the character of level bottom communities than in others. Many, if not most, of the species in level bottom communities appear to be quite independent of one another. These communities are dominated by detritus feeding organisms and hence are characterized by a comparatively simple food web. Fluctuations of numbers of individuals of different species are commonly associated with fluctuations of the physical environment and show little or no interspecific correlation. The loss of a numerically important species, such as eel grass, may have little or no effect on the remaining species. It is common to find two or more closely related members of the same genus living in the same area. All of these features suggest interspecific neutralism. The importance of predation, parasitism, and competition for space as ecological factors in level bottom communities cannot be denied, but these factors appear to be less important in such communities than in intertidal, coral reef, and terrestrial communities.

Species may occur in a particular community by chance. The distribution of species with broad environmental tolerances could be partially determined by the vagaries of currents. Transient species are often found in level bottom communities. A population of such species may persist locally for only one or two generations, disappear for a few years, and reappear again. The high recurrence of particular suites of species observed in modern environments, however, suggests that communities are not largely chance associations.

High recurrence of particular combinations of species could occur if such species had similar environmental responses and suitable environments were common. It seems likely that most of the species in level bottom communities occur together because of similar responses to the physical features of their environments. This seems evident from settling reactions of larvae, from the effects of environmental fluctuations, and from the modes of life represented in level bottom communities.

The independence of benthic species and their direct dependence on the physical environment suggests a simple organization. Such independence would seem highly adaptive from the standpoint of individual species. It is conceivable that this degree of independence and hence the relatively low order of organization of level bottom communities is the product of a long evolutionary history that might even have proceeded from a higher level of complexity.

The viewpoint that is developed here, and perhaps overstated, is that benthic communities are commonly associations of largely independent species occurring together because of similar responses to the physical environment. Such a concept is far removed from that of a community as a biocoenosis as originally defined by Möbius (Möbius, 1877, quoted in Allee et al., 1949, p. 35). If this is the case, then the biological organization of a level bottom community may not be an important influence on the evolutionary history of the members of the community. Rather, we should expect that the complexes of environmental factors represented by the hydroclimate and the sediment are of more direct influence.

Probably most adaptations to the substrate and to the hydroclimate involve physiological changes. We cannot directly observe such features but physiological adaptations to environment frequently, if not always, alter the spatial distribution of a species. Change in environmental distribution must commonly be associated with physiological changes affecting the settling behavior of pelagic larvae. By utilizing all species as a complex analyzer of environment—the community approach—we should be able to detect the results of adaptations we cannot directly perceive. Permanent changes in the association between species and between species and deposit type, with or without morphological change, must constitute the first signs of such adaptive shifts. Subtle shifts in association should, theoretically, be evident first in marginal environments, the ecotone in space, and its gradational equivalent in time.

To recognize such shifts in the fossil record we must utilize the evidence of high recurrence of the event at many localities. This means that large amounts of data must be collected in appropriate ways, reduced to some manageable form, and analyzed using the conceptual framework of marine biology. Statistical methods, such as the several measures of interspecific association that are now available, can facilitate data reduction and analysis. Concurrently, study of modern marine communities from the viewpoint of the paleontologist will provide more accurate analogues and the context for the interpretation of results.

Studies of shifts in interspecific association may guide us to other features of the environment of ancient communities that have left traces in the physical record. New insights into the evolution of species and communities may result from the combination of the quantitative studies of morphologic and community integration. These possibilities do seem to be worth the effort involved in the application of the community approach to paleoecology.

Invertebrate paleontology, by necessity, has been and is now largely a descriptive science. This work must continue, but at the same time we are moving into stages of synthesis and generalization. We have lauded the objectives of the paleoecological approach in what seems to be an endless chain of symposia, presidential addresses, and papers. Now the time has come to utilize the quantitative methods and the biological concepts that are available to exploit our tremendous accumulation of stratigraphic and systematic data.

REFERENCES

Aleem, A. B., 1956, Quantitative underwater study of benthic communities inhabiting kelp beds off California: *Science,* v. 123, p. 183.

Allee, W. C., 1919, Note on animal distribution following a hard winter: *Biol. Bull.,* v. 36, pp. 96–104.

Allee, W. C., O. Park, A. E. Emerson, T. Park, and K. P. Schmidt, 1949, *Principles of Animal Ecology:* Philadelphia, W. B. Saunders, 837 pp.

Axelrod, D. I., 1950, Evolution of desert vegetation in Western North America: *Pub. Carnegie Inst. Wash.,* n. 590, pp. 217–306.

Barnard, J. L., O. Hartman, and G. F. Jones, 1959, Oceanographic survey of the continental shelf area of Southern California; Benthic biology of the mainland shelf of Southern California: *Calif. State Water Pollution Control Board,* pub. n. 20, pp. 265–429.

Beerbower, J. R., and F. W. McDowell, 1960, The Centerfield biostrome; an approach to a paleoecological problem: *Proc. Penn. Acad. Sci.,* v. 34, pp. 84–91.

Blegvad, H., 1951, Fluctuations in the amounts of food animals of the bottom of the Limfjord in 1928–1950: *Rept. Danish Biol. Station,* n. 53, pp. 3–16.

Burkholder, P. R., 1952, Cooperation and conflict among primitive organisms: *Am. Scientist,* v. 40, pp. 601–631.

Chipperfield, P. N. J., 1953, Observations of the breeding and settlement of *Mytilus edulis* (L.) in British waters: *J. Marine Biol. Assoc. U. K.,* v. 32, pp. 449–476.

Cole, H. A., and E. W. Knight-Jones, 1939, Some observations and experiments on the settling behavior of larvae of *Ostrea edulis: Journal du Conseil,* v. 14, pp. 85–105.

Connell, J. H., 1956, Spatial distribution of two species of clams *Mya arenaria* L. and *Petricola pholadiformis* Lamarck in an intertidal area: *Invest. Shellfisheries Mass.,* rept. n. 8, pp. 15–28.

________ 1961, Effects of competition, predation by *Thais lapillus,* and other factors on natural populations of the barnacle *Balanus balanoides: Ecol. Monog.,* v. 31, pp. 61–104.

Cottam, C., and D. A. Munro, 1954, Eel grass status and environmental relations: *J. Wildlife Management,* v. 18, pp. 449–460.

Crisp, D. J., and H. Barnes, 1954, The orientation and distribution of barnacles at settlement with particular reference to surface contour: *J. Animal Ecol.,* v. 23, pp. 142–162.

________ and J. S. Ryland, 1960, Influence of filming and of surface texture on the settlement of marine organisms: *Nature,* v. 185, p. 119.

Day, J. H., and D. P. Wilson, 1934, On the relation of the substratum to the metamorphosis of *Scolecolepis fuliginosa* (Claparide): *J. Marine Biol. Assoc. U. K.,* v. 19, pp. 655–662.

Dexter, R. W., 1944, Ecological significance of the disappearance of eel-grass at Cape Ann, Mass.: *J. Wildlife Management,* v. 8, pp. 173–176.

Elton, C. S., 1958, *The Ecology of Invasions by Animals and Plants:* New York, John Wiley and Sons, 181 pp.

Erdman, W., 1934, Untersuchungen uber die Lebensgeschicte der Auster, n. 5, Uber die Entwicklung und die Anatomie der "ansatzreifer" Larven von *Ostrea edulis* mit Bemerkungen uber die Lebensgeschichte der Auster: *Wiss. Meeres. Abt. Helgoland,* v. 19, pp. 1–25.

Goodbody, I., 1961, Mass mortality of a marine fauna following tropical rains: *Ecology,* v. 42, pp. 150–155.

Gregg, J. H., 1945, Background illumination as a factor in the attachment of barnacle cyprids: *Biol. Bull.,* v. 88, pp. 44–49.

Harrington, C. R., 1921, A note on the physiology of the ship-worm (*Teredo norvegica*): *Biochem. J.,* v. 15, pp. 736–741.

Hoese, H. D., 1960, Biotic changes in a bay associated with the end of a drought: *Limnol. and Ocean.,* v. 5, pp. 326–336.

Holme, N. A., 1950, Population dispersion in *Tellina tenuis* da Costa: *J. Marine Biol. Assoc. U. K.,* v. 29, pp. 267–280.

________ 1953, The biomass of the bottom fauna in the English Channel off Plymouth: *J. Marine Biol. Assoc. U. K.,* v. 32, pp. 1–49.

________ 1961, The bottom fauna of the English Channel: *J. Marine Biol. Assoc. U. K.,* v. 41, pp. 397–461.

Hopkins, A. E., 1931, Factors influencing the spawning and settling of oysters in Galveston Bay, Texas: *Bull. U. S. Bureau Fish.,* v. 47, pp. 57–83.

Jagersten, G., 1940, Die Abhangigkeit der Metamorphose vom Substrat des Biotopes bei *Protodrilus: Arkiv. F. Zool.,* v. 32 A, pp. 1–12.

Johnson, R. G., 1959, Spatial distribution of *Phoronopsis viridis* Hilton: *Science,* v. 129, p. 1221.

________ 1960, Models and methods for the analysis of the mode of formation of fossil assemblages: *Bull. Geol. Soc. America,* v. 71, pp. 1075–1086.

________ 1962, Interspecific association in Pennsylvanian fossil assemblages: *J. Geology,* v. 70, pp. 32–55.

Jones, N. S., 1952, The bottom fauna and the food of flatfish off the Cumberland Coast: *J. Animal Ecol.,* v. 21, pp. 182–205.

——— 1956, The fauna and biomass of a muddy sand deposit off Port Erin, Isle of Man with an appendix on methods used for the analysis of deposits: *J. Animal Ecol.,* v. 25, pp. 217–252.

Jones, M. I., 1961, A quantitative evaluation of the benthic fauna off Point Richmond, California: *Univ. Calif. Pub. Zool.,* v. 67, pp. 219–320.

Knight-Jones, E. W., 1951, Gregariousness and some other aspects of the settling behavior of a *Spirorbis: J. Marine Biol. Assoc. U. K.,* v. 30, pp. 201–222.

——— 1953, Decreased discrimination during settling after prolonged planktonic life in larvae of *Spirorbis borealis* (Serpulidae): *J. Marine Biol. Assoc. U. K.,* v. 32, pp. 337–345.

——— 1955, The gregarious setting reaction of barnacles as a measure of systematic affinity: *Nature,* v. 173, p. 266.

——— and J. P. Stevenson, 1950, Gregariousness during settlement in the barnacle *Eliminius modestus* Darwin: *J. Marine Biol. Assoc. U. K.,* v. 29, pp. 281–287.

Korringa, P., 1940, Experiments and observations on swarming pelagic life and setting in the European flat oyster, *Ostrea edulis* L.: *Arch. Neerland. Zool.,* v. 5, pp. 1–249.

Kristensen, I., 1957, Differences in density and growth in a cockle population in the Dutch Wadden Sea: *Arch. Neerland Zool.,* v. 12, pp. 351–454.

Lackey, J. B., 1961, Bottom sampling and environmental niches: *Limnol. and Ocean.,* v. 6, pp. 271–279.

Loosanoff, V. L., and F. D. Tommers, 1948, Effect of suspended silt and other substances on rate of feeding of oysters: *Science,* v. 107, pp. 69–70.

Mare, M. F., 1942, A study of a marine benthic community with special reference to the microorganisms: *J. Marine Biol. Assoc. U. K.,* v. 25, pp. 517–554.

Marshall, N., 1947, An abundance of bay scallops in the absence of eelgrass: *Ecology,* v. 28, pp. 321–322.

———, 1960, Studies of the Niantic River, Connecticut, with special reference to the bay scallop, *Aequipecten irradians: Limnol. and Ocean.,* v. 5, pp. 86–105.

Miyadi, D., 1940, Marine benthic communities of the Tanabe-wan: *Annot. Zool. Japon.,* v. 19, pp. 136–148.

——— 1941, Ecological survey of the benthos of the Ago-wan: *Annot. Zool. Japon.,* v. 20, pp. 169–180.

Muller, C. H., 1958, Science and philosophy of the community concept: *Am. Scientist,* v. 46, pp. 294–308.

Olson, E. C., 1952, The evolution of a Permian vertebrate chronofauna: *Evolution,* v. 6, pp. 181–196.

Orton, J. H., 1937, Some interrelations between bivalve spatfalls, hydrography, and fisheries: *Nature,* v. 140, p. 505.

Pomerat, C. M., and E. R. Reiner, 1942, The influence of surface angle and light on the attachment of barnacles and other sedentary organisms: *Biol. Bull.,* v. 82, pp. 14–25.

Poulsen, E. M., 1951, Changes in the frequency of larger bottom invertebrates in the Limfjord in 1927–1950: *Rept. Danish Biol. Station,* n. 53, pp. 17–34.

Pratt, D. M., 1953, Abundance and growth of *Venus mercenaria* and *Callocardia morrhuana* in relation to the character of the bottom sediments: *J. Marine Res.,* v. 12, pp. 60–74.

Prytherch, H. F., 1934, The role of copper in the setting, metamorphosis and distribution of the American oyster, *Ostrea virginica: Ecol. Monographs,* v. 4, pp. 49–101.

Quayle, D. B., 1952, Structure and biology of the larvae and spat of *Venerupis pullastra* (Montagu): *Trans. Roy. Soc. Edinburgh,* v. 62, pp. 255–297.

Raymont, J. E. G., 1949, Further observations on changes in the bottom fauna of a fertilized sea loch: *J. Marine Biol. Assoc. U. K.,* v. 28, pp. 9–19.

Reish, D. J., 1961, A study of the benthic fauna in a recently constructed boat harbor in Southern California: *Ecology,* v. 42, pp. 84–91.

Ryland, J. S., 1959, Experiments on the selection of algal substrates by polyzoan larvae: *J. Exp. Biol.,* v. 36, pp. 613–631.

Sanders, H. L., 1956, Oceanography of Long Island Sound 1952–1954, X; the biology of marine bottom communities: *Bull. Bingham Ocean. Coll.,* v. 15, pp. 345–414.

——— 1958, Benthic studies in Buzzards Bay, I; Animal-sediment relationships: *Limnol. and Ocean.,* v. 3, pp. 245–258.

——— 1960, Benthic studies in Buzzards Bay, III; The structure of the soft bottom community: *Limnol. and Ocean.,* v. 5, pp. 138–153.

Sandison, E. E., and M. B. Hill, 1959. The annual repopulation of Lagos Harbor by sedentary marine animals: *Intern. Ocean. Congress Preprints,* pp. 584–585.

Schaefer, M. B., 1937, Attachment of the larvae of *Ostrea gigas,* the Japanese oyster, to plane surfaces: *Ecology,* v. 18, pp. 523–527.

Scheltema, R. S., 1956, The effect of the substrate on the length of planktonic existence in *Nassarius obsoletus: Biol. Bull.,* v. 111, p. 312.

——— 1961, Metamorphosis of the veliger larvae of *Nassarius obsoletus* (Gastropoda) in response to bottom sediment: *Biol. Bull.,* v. 120, pp. 92–109.

Segerstråle, S. G., 1960, Fluctuations in the abundance of benthic animals in the Baltic area: *Soc. Sci. Fennica Commentationes Biol.,* v. 23, pp. 1–19.

Shotwell, J. A., 1958, Intercommunity relationships in Hemphillian (Mid-Pliocene) mammals: *Ecology,* v. 39, pp. 271–382.

Silen, L., 1954, Developmental biology of Phoronidae of the Bullmar Fiord area (west coast of Sweden): *Acta Zoologica,* v. 35, pp. 215–257.

Smidt, E. L. B., 1951, Animal production in the Danish Waddensea: *Medd. Komm. Danmarks Fisk Havinders Ser. Fiskeri:* v. 11, pp. 1–151.

Smith, J. E., 1932, The shell gravel deposits and the infauna of the Eddystone grounds: *J. Marine Biol. Assoc. U. K.,* v. 18, pp. 243–278.

Southward, E. C., 1957, The distribution of Polychaeta in offshore deposits in the Irish sea: *J. Marine Biol. Assoc. U. K.,* v. 36, pp. 49–75.

Stickney, A. P., and L. D. Stringer, 1957, A study of the invertebrate bottom fauna of Greenwich Bay, Rhode Island: *Ecology,* v. 38, pp. 11–122.

Thorson, G., 1933, Investigations on shallow water animal communities in the Franz Joseph Fjord (East Greenland) and adjacent waters: *Medd. om Grønland,* v. 100, pp. 1–68.

——— 1957, Bottom communities, pp. 461–534, *in Treatise on Marine Ecology and Paleoecology* (J. W. Hedgpeth, ed.), v. 1, Ecology: Geol. Soc. Am. Mem. 67, 1296 pages.

Weiss, C. M., 1947, The effect of illumination and stage of tide on the attachment of barnacle cyprids: *Biol. Bull.,* v. 93, pp. 240–249.

Wieser, W., 1956, Factors influencing the choice of substratum in *Cuenella vulgaris* Hart (Crustacea Cumacea): *Limnol. and Ocean.,* v. 1, pp. 274–285.

Williams, G. C., 1957, Pleiotropy, natural selection, and the evolution of senescence: *Evolution,* v. 11, pp. 398–411.

Wilson, D. P., 1932, On the Mitraria larvae of *Owenis fusiformis* Delle Chiaje: *Phil. Trans. Roy. Soc. Lond.,* ser. B, v. 221, pp. 231–334.

——— 1937, The influence of the substratum on the metamorphosis of *Notomastus*-larvae: *J. Marine Biol. Assoc. U. K.,* v. 22, pp. 227–243.

——— 1948, The larval development of *Ophelia bicornis* Savigny: *J. Marine Biol. Assoc. U. K.,* v. 27, pp. 540–553.

——— 1949, The decline of *Zostera marina* L. at Salcombe and its effects on the shore: *J. Marine Biol. Assoc. U. K.,* v. 28, pp. 395–412.

——— 1952, The influence of the nature of the substratum on the metamorphosis of the larvae of marine animals, especially the larvae of *Ophelia bicornis* Savigny: *Ann. Inst. Oceanog.,* v. 27, pp. 49–156.

——— 1953, The settlement of *Ophelia bicornis* Savigny larvae: *J. Marine Biol. Assoc. U. K.,* v. 33, pp. 361–380.

——— 1954, The attractive factor in the settlement of *Ophelia bicornis: J. Marine Biol. Assoc. U. K.,* v. 33, pp. 361–380.

——— 1955, The role of microorganisms in the settlement of *Ophelia bicornis: J. Marine Biol. Assoc. U. K.,* v. 34, pp. 531–543.

Wisely, B., 1959, Factors influencing the settling of the principal marine fouling organisms in Sydney Harbour: *Australian J. Marine Freshwater Res.,* v. 10, pp. 30–44.

——— 1960, Observations on the settling behavior of larvae of the tubeworm *Spirorbis borealis* (Daudin Polychaeta): *Australian J. Marine Freshwater Res.,* v. 11, pp. 55–73.

ZoBell, C. E., 1957, Marine bacteria, pp. 1035–1040, in *Treatise on Marine Ecology and Paleoecology* (J. W. Hedgpeth, ed.), v. 1, Ecology: Geol. Soc. America, Mem. 67, 1296 pp.

Community Succession in Mammals of the Late Tertiary

by J. Arnold Shotwell *Museum of Natural History, University of Oregon, Eugene*

Nature of Paleocommunities

The members of a community are part of each others' environment. They have in common a particular habitat. They are more directly interrelated in their food-getting habits. It is not considered here that this relationship is of the nature of a supra-organism but that the interrelationship of the various members with each other and the habitat is close enough that changes in one require adjustments in the others, either in relative abundance or morphology. Although the animals and plants may alter the nature of their habitat it is likely that in sequences involving geologic time the changes in habitat initiate adjustments in the occupants. The nature of the adjustments in the animals of a community is determined by the rate and degree of change of the habitat with the extreme condition resulting in the development of a new community type or the loss of communities. Examination of these adjustments should result in empirical data reflecting the environment of evolution, the conditions of extinction, and the nature of environmental change which allows the successful invasion of migrants.

In the study of a *paleocommunity* we are not only interested in the membership or composition of the *community*. Other characteristics are of importance also and knowledge of them is necessary in order to make the fullest use of the community as a unit in the study of the environment of evolution. The relative abundance of each of the members is important if changes in the structure of the community are to be recognized. The role of various animals in the community and nature of the habitat of the community are of prime interest. A community is then not just a faunal list. The broadest definitions would

Studies described in this paper were supported by the American Philosophical Society and the National Science Foundation.

include plants, invertebrates, in fact, all of the organisms and their habitat. The nature of the occurrence of paleocommunities demands a somewhat more limited scope in that the plant materials, vertebrates, and invertebrates seldom occur together in the same sample. The methods of studying sediments are different from those applied to the study of the fossil organisms present, although they may parallel each other. The paleocommunity in practice is thus a composite of the efforts of several disciplines. In this paper only the mammalian community will be discussed in any detail, but these communities might better be referred to as vertebrate communities since lower vertebrates are also important elements in the samples studied.

Recognition of the Community

Several techniques of analysis are now available for the recognition of communities from carefully made samples. Each has its advantages and disadvantages. Selection of a technique is determined primarily by the nature of the occurrence of the bones to be studied. Samples may include primarily articulated skeletons or disarticulated elements, or samples may be large or small. Concentrations may be present or material may be more homogeneously spread through the facies under study. Often at least two of the techniques are practical in a given situation, and in some all may be employed.

Lithologic or Facies Method

It is assumed in this technique that a particular facies or lithology represents a limited habitat and that most of the species present lived in mutual association. This method requires very careful stratigraphic and sedimentary studies. It is useful when concentrations are not present and bones occur as articulated skeletons. A sample from this type of occurrence will represent more time than one from a concentration. However, the fact that a given facies may have appreciable thickness may indicate that the environmental situation remained relatively stable over a considerable period of time. Vertical control within such a situation is, of course, highly desirable. The role of some members of the community may be determined exceptionally by stomach contents in association with articulated skeletons. The relative abundance of members of the community may be determined by suitable collecting methods.

Olson (1952) uses a lithologic technique in his study of chronofaunas. A chronofauna is ". . . a geographically restricted, natural assemblage of interacting animal populations that has maintained its basic structure over a geologically significant period of time" (Olson, 1952, p. 181). A chronofauna may often represent a community.

Recurrent Groups

When numerous small samples of about the same size are taken, membership in an association can be postulated on the basis of the frequency of appearance of species in samples or the frequency of joint occurrence of species (Fager, 1957). This is a technique often used in quantitative plant ecology (see Greig-Smith, 1947, Ch. 6). A difficulty in its application has been in the conclusion that frequency of occurrence in samples represents abundance of the member in a community. Abundance must be determined from the relative numbers of each species occurring within each sample. It is susceptible then to the limitations of small samples in determining relative abundance. In the determination of the composition of the community it provides the best type of sampling technique for statistical analysis. It should prove highly useful, if the samples are available, in conjunction with the previous technique.

Proximity Method

This technique assumes that those organisms which lived adjacent to or in the site of deposition of a facies will be best represented in the resultant deposit. They will be on the average more completely preserved than will those included forms which lived elsewhere. This is similar to the insurance statistics which indicate that most, but not all, people die near where they lived. This method requires large samples and suffers with small ones (Shotwell 1958*a*). It is used by paleobotanists (Chaney 1924, and numerous later papers of Chaney and Axelrod) and has been adapted for use with mammals (Shotwell 1955). In its application to mammals it has the advantage that an indication of the number of individuals can be made, whereas this is not possible with plant materials. This method is most advantageous when large samples are available and disarticulated elements are the primary mode of occurrence. The fact that the sample comes from a single large concentration within a single kind of lithology allows excavation to proceed prior to stratigraphic and sedimentation studies. It provides evidence independent to other aspects of a paleoecological study. Potentially it can supply the most information from a single occurrence; however, it is expensive.

Collection of Samples

The methods just outlined do not represent all possible methods, but are representative of those by which data may be accumulated that provide objective conclusions as to the composition and to some extent structure of communities. They are all techniques of analysis which are statistical in concept and may be applied successfully only when the samples are collected with certain precautions. They all assume that the samples taken are representative of the total material present (in the facies or large concentration, whichever represents the whole). In the lithology technique, then, care must be taken to collect in such a way that excessive bias is not involved. In the other techniques all the material in a volume of sediment must be retained. This often requires wet or dry screening of the matrix.

Habitat Requirements

Once the composition of a community is established other aspects such as relative abundance, habitat, role of individual members, and the structure of the community may be determined. Indications of relative abundance are derived from the samples. Other aspects must be determined less directly.

Study of the functional morphology of the members of the community is necessary to determine the nature of the habitat. Their teeth may indicate that they are browsers, grazers, or seed eaters. Their limb bones may be adapted for (high speed) running, burrowing, aquatic, or amphibious life. When applied to all the members of the community various requirements of the habitat become apparent. These are, of course, rather broad categories. Mammals, having undergone much of their evolution in the Tertiary, rarely allow the comparison of habitat requirements of living morphologic equivalent species, since in most instances the difference between the living and fossil members of a phyletic line are too great. However, living mammals provide a basis for understanding the functional morphology of some fossil forms. The lower vertebrates, fish, turtles, amphibians, etc., occurring in the sample are likely to be of great assistance in picturing some aspects of the original habitat in more exact terms. Pollen, of course, is also a very useful source of this information. Plant leaves do not often occur in vertebrate localities, but an understanding of the floral associations derived from nearby plant localities of the same age will indicate additional details of the environment.

Some of the mammals present may represent adaptive types not seen in living forms—for example, three-toed horses. Historical biogeographic studies can sometimes point out the nature of their habitat requirements which cannot be determined by morphology alone (Shotwell, 1961).

The sediments provide an important source of information on environments at the sites of deposition. Sedimentary studies are especially challenging in sequences that contain volcanic ash, since the character of such rocks may change considerably from the time of deposition.

Role of Members

Morphological evidence can provide the pertinent information needed to determine the roles of the various members of the community in the food chain. Since some members may have no living counterparts (for instance, sabre-tooth cats), their role must be determined by deduction. Morphological studies of the sabre-tooth cats have suggested quite different concepts of the use of the sabre mechanism in getting food. One study indicates this mechanism to be the tool of a carrion eater (Bohlin, 1940); the other indicates a carnivorous habit (Simpson, 1941). The nature of their occurrence at Rancho La Brea, in Los Angeles, may provide important evidence as to the function of this mechanism. Stock (1949) and Marcus (1960) have shown that in this trap site the dire wolf, apparently a carrion eater, and the sabre-tooth cat (*Smilodon*) are the most common large mammals in the various pits excavated. Of the pits referred to by Marcus, these two forms made up over three quarters of the total number of individuals present. In the *Smilodon* material from Rancho La Brea there is a "relatively high frequency of lesions in particular elements . . . they are particularly evident in the limb bones and in the lumbar region of the vertebral column. Moreover, while fractures which have healed during the life of the individual are to be found in a number of bones of mammals and birds from the asphalt, abnormalities in bone growth were apparently rather prevalent among sabretooth cats" (Stock, 1949, pp. 37–38). This high frequency of disabilities during life seems unlikely for a carnivore which habitually pursued and felled its prey. A carrion eater would not be so seriously handicapped. This high frequency of successful but disabled individuals may thus reflect a carrion food-getting habit. It may also indicate that the tar traps provided food for sabre-tooth cats which were injured and thus selected for this part of the population. If the trap acted as an infirmary for injured carnivores in its easy supply of food, the bone effects just noted should be more evenly distributed throughout the large carnivores present in the pits. The high frequency of carrion-eating birds at Rancho La Brea may also indicate the type of carnivore attracted to such a trap (see Bohlin, 1948). Samples of communities where selection was not an important part of the accumulation indicate that the number of sabre-tooth cats present in a fauna was rather small at any one time (Shotwell, 1958*a*). It is not the purpose of this discussion to prove or disprove that the sabre-tooth cat was a carrion eater but to demonstrate how examination of the nature of the occurrence may provide pertinent evidence in understanding the function of a mechanism not existing in living forms.

It has been emphasized that a knowledge of functional morphology of the members of a community can provide important information as to their habitat requirements and role in the community. Other lines of evidence may also be important. They include paleobotany, other vertebrates, nature of occurrences in the site and elsewhere, and historical biogeography. Care in their application can greatly increase the knowledge of the nature of a community and its habitat as represented in a sample or series of samples.

Community Structure

The quantitative data in the sample of a community indicate the relative abundance of the various members of the community. In the mammalian communities thus far studied in the Northern Great Basin there seems to be a correlation between the number of high abundance forms and the community type. For instance; open grassland communities have one high abundance form, savanna communities more than one, and even more confined communities a greater number. This appears to be irrespective of age or the species involved. Although this work has not progressed to a point of formal presentation, it suggests that a particular community type may also have a particular structure. If this proves to be the case then structure of communities, especially in sequencial studies, will be an important aspect in the study of their development.

Late Tertiary Faunas of the Northern Great Basin

The Northern Great Basin of western North America provides an excellent opportunity for the study of community evolution of the late Tertiary. In this province, mammalian communities may be studied over a significant period of time in which many changes of physical

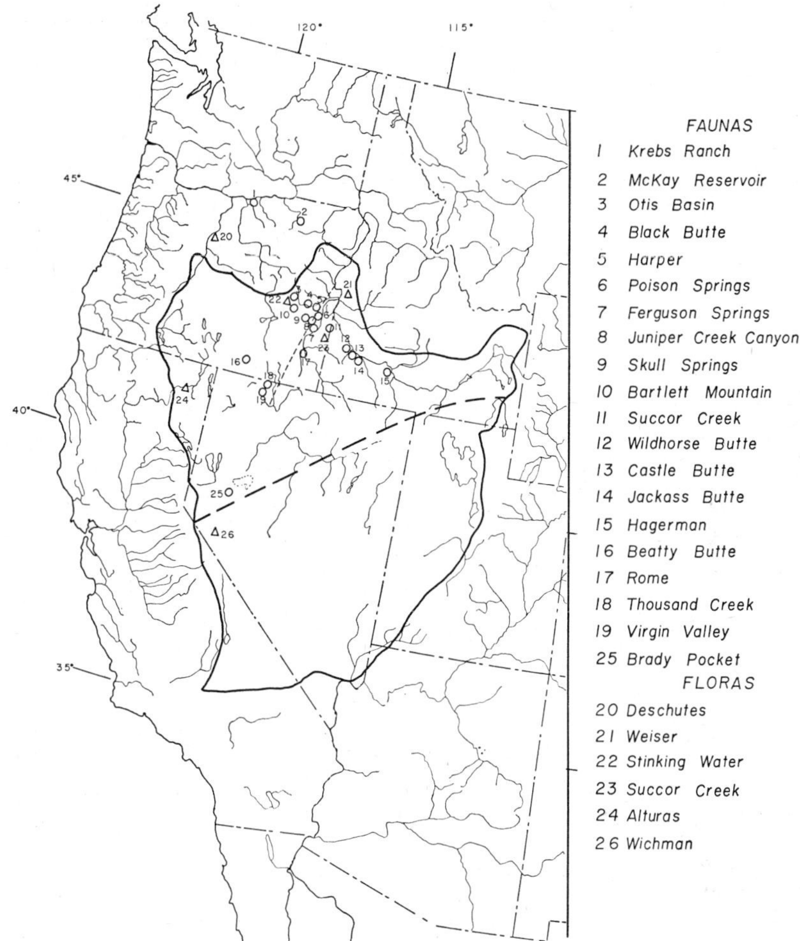

Fig. 1 Northern Great Basin. Heavy dashed line separates Northern and Central Great Basin.

and plant environment are known to occur—a time in which evolutionary changes are evident in the mammals. Figure 1 illustrates the limits of the Northern Great Basin of the late Tertiary and the location of faunas and floras used in this study. Many minor localities are not shown. Localities 1–14 of Figure 1 have been sampled for the purpose of paleocommunity studies. Each of the sites indicated represents a number of separate excavations. In order to maintain adequate controls, geologic mapping has been an important aspect of the work thus far completed. The chief aim has been to insure superpositional controls, so that the relative ages of the sites studied might be evident independent of the faunas. It is for this reason that the sites sampled are grouped together.

A diversity of communities has been recognized and studied from each of the steps in a late Tertiary sequence in the Northern Great Basin. These include (1) Barstovian (late Miocene), (2) Clarendonian (early Pliocene), (3) Hemphillian (mid-Pliocene), and (4) Blancan (late Pliocene) age faunas. The results from the mass of accumulated data, some of which have not yet been completely analyzed, allow a preliminary framework of the history of mammalian communities to be developed. Even at this preliminary stage some interesting aspects of the history of these communities are evident.

The changes of the fauna of the Northern Great Basin are illustrated in Figure 2. The modern fauna is included to show its origins in the Tertiary. The Pleistocene step is omitted, and the changes from Blancan to modern therefore appear disproportionately large. The chart consists of a vertical bar graph for each of the succeeding faunas; the unit of measurement is the genus. Genera are grouped in their next larger supergeneric category, family, or subfamily, depending on current classification of those taxa. Orders are indicated on the graph by alternating stipple pattern to emphasize their limits. The supergeneric categories are connected by lines from one fauna to the next, much in the way comparable stratigraphic sections would be, to point out loss and first appearances of categories. These groupings essentially represent phyletic lines. Where these groups are lost in the course of the faunal sequence studied, the resulting wedge on the chart is blacked in. Migrants are indicated by cross-hatching.

Losses from the fauna are high from Barstovian to Clarendonian and Hemphillian to Blancan. Migrants are an important part of the Hemphillian and Blancan faunas and insignificant in the Clarendonian fauna. The Hemphillian and Blancan faunas are thus quite different from each other and the preceding faunas, whereas the Clarendonian fauna appears as an impoverished Barstovian fauna. By the Clarendonian, 33% of the phyletic lines of the Barstovian have no representation in the known fauna, and only 23% of the Barstovian phyletic lines are represented in the modern fauna. Although some migrants are lost from subsequent faunas the major losses of the late Tertiary sequence are from the original Barstovian fauna. These losses appear to be greatest in the Clarendonian, least in the Hemphillian, and moderate in the Blancan fauna. These major changes in the late Tertiary

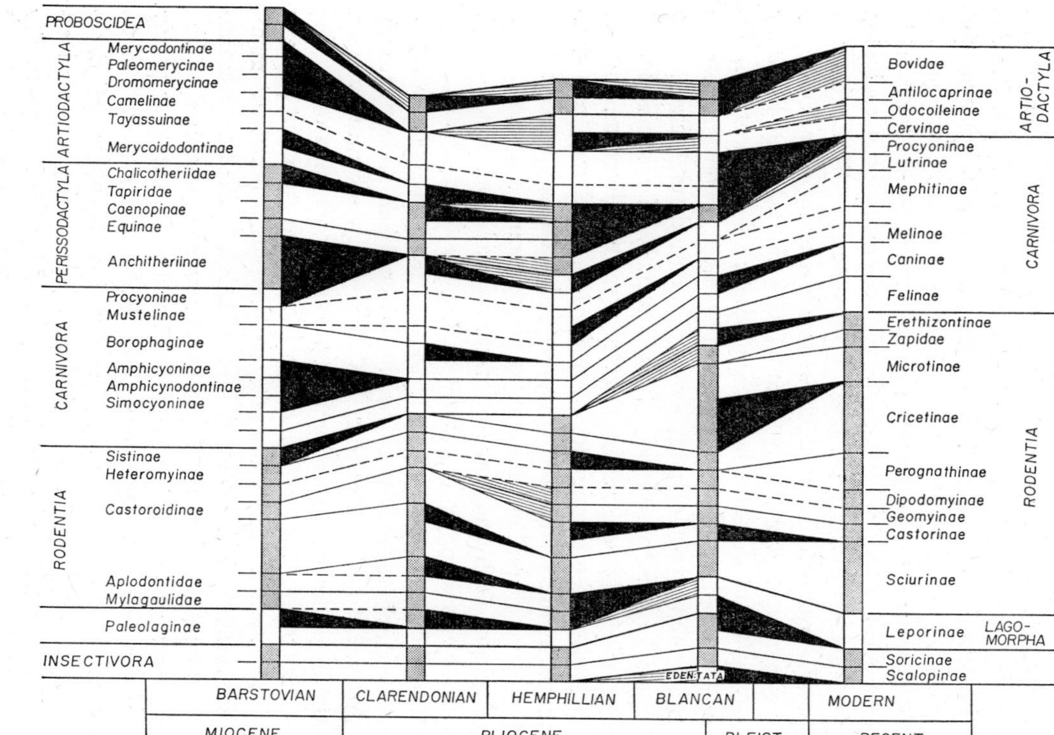

Fig. 2 Bulk fauna changes of the late Cenozoic in the Northern Great Basin. Blacked-in areas indicate losses; ruled areas indicate migrants.

fauna of the Northern Great Basin must be reflected in the history of the communities.

Mammalian Communities of the Northern Great Basin

The composition of communities has been determined using the proximity method described earlier (Shotwell, 1955; 1958*a*). Although the quantitative aspects of the analysis of the samples are not yet completed, community assignments can be made from the present status of the work. About 20,000 mammal specimens are involved in the samples used. The composition of the communities at each step in the sequence is shown schematically in Figure 3. The horizontal lines represent phyletic lines which in turn represent a series of descendant genera assigned to the community. The blacked in circles indicate the point of loss of a line. The open circles indicate the appearance of new members of communities whose origin is uncertain at this time. Open circles with a line through them indicate new migrant members of communities. The diversity of communities at any one step in the sequence is apparent from the diagram, and the history of each of the communities is indicated. Although two grazing communities are recognized (savanna and grassland, see Shotwell, 1961) they have a number of members in common. The most abundant members of each are, however, mutually exclusive.

The savanna community is present in the Barstovian fauna but is restricted to the northwest portion of the Northern Great Basin (west of the dashed line on Figure 1) by the Hemphillian and apparently lost by the end of the Hemphillian. A very similar community again appears in the Blancan. Its abundant members are migrants. The only members of the new savanna community which represent phyletic lines of the former savanna community are those which are also members of the grassland community, which makes its first appearance in the Hemphillian. Its abundant members are migrants to the Northern Great Basin at this time. The border community is poorly known but includes several relatively common mammals which do not occur as members of any other community. Samples of it indicate that it is at various times spatially related to the grassland savanna and woodland communities. More than one border community is probably involved. The woodland community is greatly reduced after the Barstovian and is not represented in the Hemphillian. Several mammals of the Blancan suggest by their morphology that they have woodland affinities; however, no samples are available of their community as yet. The stream-bank community occurs throughout the sequence.

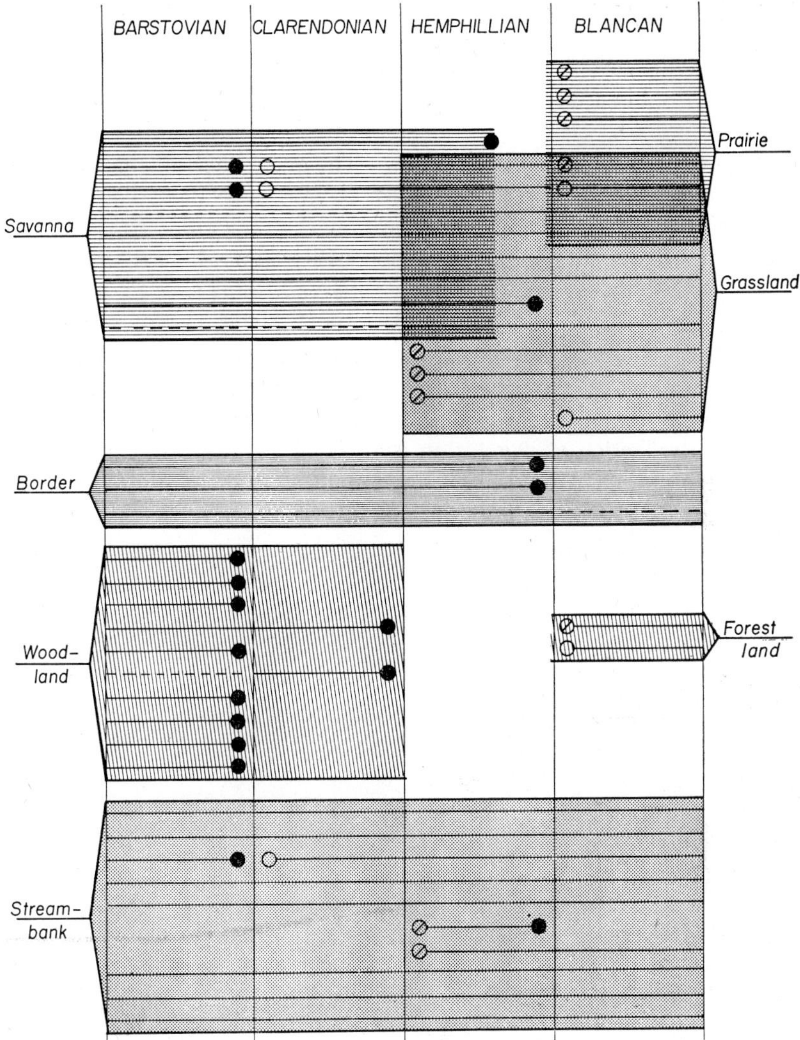

Fig. 3 History of Mammalian communities of the Northern Great Basin of the late Tertiary. See explanation in text.

The losses and gains of the faunas are reflected in the communities. The significant losses of the Barstovian are concentrated in the woodland community. However, some faunal changes occur in all the communities. Migrants are concentrated in the new communities and are important members of these communities.

Changes in Habitats

The vegetational history of the late Tertiary of the Northern Great Basin is shown in Figure 4. The data for the chart are from Axelrod (1950, Figure 4). The savanna, envisioned as woodland-savanna, is an extrapolation from Axelrod's data. The woodland-savanna is considered to be a habitat resulting from the withdrawal and reduction of woodland vegetation and the extension of grassland. Until woodland is greatly reduced, savanna is considered to be an important habitat (see Shotwell, 1961). Its extent is shown as a function of the amount of woodland and grassland at each point in the sequence. The vertical dashed lines of the chart indicate the position of the mammalian steps relative to the vegetational history. Figures 2, 3, and 4 show faunal changes to be a result of community history, which in turn is a reflection of vegetation change. The trends of the Barstovian to Hemphillian are temporarily reversed in the Blancan.

Although extinction and migration appear as major factors in the faunal change illustrated, evolution also plays a significant role. Its

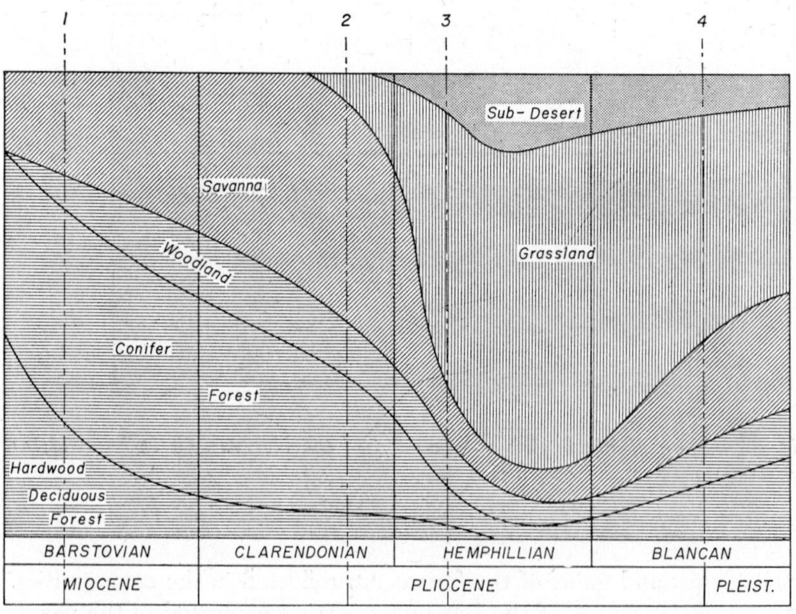

Fig. 4 Changing vegetation of Northern Great Basin in the late Tertiary. (From Axelrod (1950) with modifications.)

role in this example is within the communities and not in the origin of the new community types that appear. In Figure 3 phyletic lines are shown as continuous lines and do not indicate the nature of changes in these lines or at what points these changes occur. There are significant evolutionary changes in the phyletic lines of the savanna community in the Barstovian-Clarendonian step. There are no significant changes in the Clarendonian-Hemphillian step in the savanna. The phyletic lines of the grassland community exhibit significant changes from Hemphillian to Blancan time. Morphologic changes are noted from the Barstovian to the Hemphillian in the border community. No changes are recognized in woodland phyletic lines. The various phyletic lines of the stream-bank community show evolutionary changes throughout the sequence. Evolution as noted in the sequence is of the nature of changes of size or changes of characteristics. The castoroid beavers in the Blancan, for example, are nearly five times larger than their Barstovian ancestors, and they have ever-growing teeth, whereas their ancestors had rooted teeth. The changes in dental characteristics occur by the Hemphillian but the size increase is most evident after the Hemphillian. Other less spectacular series are present such as those of the mastodon of the savanna community and aplodontid and mylagaulid rodents of the border community (Shotwell, 1958*b*). The community members show changes but they still indicate adaptations for the same type of habitat.

Discussion

The climatic trends reflected in the vegetational changes of the Northern Great Basin involve reduction of rainfall and increase in extremes of temperature. Alterations of the distribution of rainfall throughout the year are also recognized. These climatic trends have affected all the vegetation but at different times and sometimes in opposite ways. For instance, in the early part of the sequence considered here, hardwood deciduous forest and conifer forest are reduced, while woodland and savanna increase, and open grassland makes its appearance. In the Hemphillian, woodland and savanna are greatly reduced as grassland becomes more prominent. In the Blancan, woodland and savanna again increase.

The various habitats of the mammalian communities have thus been affected at different times and to different degrees of intensity. These changes have been reflected in the communities we have studied in two general ways: (1) loss of the entire community or appearance of new community types, (2) retention of the community with adjustments. Some communities have shown both. The savanna community apparently adjusts in the Clarendonian—when evolution is seen in its phyletic lines—but is lost in the Hemphillian. The woodland community is lost in the Clarendonian and shows no adjustments. The stream-bank community adjusts to the changes of habitat throughout the sequence. Community development is most prominent in the stream-bank community and to a lesser extent in the savanna.

New community types appear as combinations of migrants and members which are common to the new community and a formerly established community which is contemporaneous. The new community must be considered to appear as a whole in the new area and not a result simply of the immigration of those members not formerly present in the area. It represents an extension of a new habitat into an area accompanied by a new community. The fact that the migrants of the open grassland community are all from the same geographic area further strengthens this view.

All of the recognized migrants represent adaptive types new to the Northern Great Basin or adaptive types previously present but lost in the early part of the sequence. Those migrants which occur not as members of new communities but in established communities appear as ecological uniques (namely porcupine, sloth, amphibious rhino, etc.). A lack of the basic morphological type necessary to produce the new adaptive type is apparently the primary reason these new forms are not derived from resident lines.

The rather sudden appearance of new community types and new adaptive types through migration tends to mask the development of resident communities and the evolution within phyletic lines of those communities. Although the communities are considered to represent the same system throughout their history, considerable changes have occurred in them and in their habitat. For example, the stream-bank community of the Blancan is very different from that of the Barstovian. Many of the same phyletic lines are present and their representatives occur in similar relative abundances throughout. However the mammals themselves have changed and so has the habitat. If we were comparing the two ends of the sequence, and were not aware of their intervening history, we might consider them as separate but related communities. In other words, the community has developed new characteristics both in the adaptive morphology of its members and the habitat it occupied, although we still recognize its general stream-bank assignment. The community has evolved. As we continue to study its members and the associated materials which can tell more of the nature and degree of habitat change (fish, amphibians, birds, and pollen), then we will better understand the nature of the environment of evolution, for this is the situation in which evolution has occurred.

Summary

The changing climate and its effects on vegetation appear as a major aspect of the history of mammalian communities in the Northern Great Basin. In the most general terms these changes tend toward aridity, reaching an extreme in the Hemphillian, then apparently reversing toward moister conditions in the Blancan. In the course of the trend toward aridity various habitats nearly or completely disappear. Woodland as a habitat is lost first, but some of its elements continue to make up the woodland-savanna. This habitat is in turn lost as the trend reaches its extreme in the Hemphillian. Before this point is reached a more arid habitat—grassland—makes its appearance. When the trend is reversed former habitats again appear. Savanna and possibly woodland habitats are thus again available; however, the former phyletic lines of the savanna had long since become extinct, except for those which also had representatives in the grassland communities. New habitats have thus appeared in the Hemphillian and Blancan in the Northern Great Basin. These habitats were not developed gradually from local ones but overlap local habitats in time and were more like those developed earlier in adjacent provinces. They might, in fact, be considered as extensions of biomes from adjacent areas into the Northern Great Basin. With them came communities already developed in these biomes. These in effect are migrant communities. Competition between communities or members of communities is not involved since their success or failure was determined by the effect of the climatic changes on their habitat. When the habitat was eliminated, those phyletic lines of mammals found only in that community became extinct.

The extremes of climatic change altered some habitats without eliminating them. The stream-bank community occupied such a habitat and is seen throughout the sequence. Evolution is an important factor in the adjustments made by this community. This study suggests that evolution is an important factor in community development but operates within limits. These limits are set by the nature and degree of environmental change to which a community and its habitat are subjected. Beyond these limits other factors (extinction and migration) determine the membership and nature of the communities present.

REFERENCES

Axelrod, D. I., 1950, Evolution of desert vegetation in Western North America: *Carn. Inst. Wash. Contr. Paleo.*, 590, pp. 215–306, 4 figs., 3 plates.

Bohlin, B., 1940, Food habits of the machaerodonts, with special regard to *Smilodon: Bull. Geol. Instn. Univ. Upsala,* v. 28, pp. 156–174, 4 figs.

——— 1948, The sabre-toothed tigers once more: *Bull. Geol. Instn. Univ. Upsala,* v. 32, pp. 11–20, 1 fig.

Chaney, R. W., 1924, Quantitative studies of the Bridge Creek flora: *Amer. Jour. Sci.,* ser. 5, v. 8, pp. 127–144.

Fager, E. W., 1957, Determination and analysis of recurrent groups: *Ecology,* v. 38, n. 4, pp. 586–595, 1 fig., 4 tables.

Greig-Smith, P., 1957, *Quantitative Plant Ecology:* New York, Academic Press, Inc. Chapter 6, pp. 117–162.

Marcus, L. F., 1960, A census of the abundant large Pleistocene mammals from Rancho La Brea: *Los Angeles Co. Mus. Contr. Sci.,* n. 348, pp. 1–11, 2 figs., 1 table.

Olson, E. C., 1952, The Evolution of a Permian vertebrate chronofauna: *Evolution,* v. 6, pp. 181–196, 5 figs.

Simpson, G. G., 1941, The function of sabre-like canines in carnivorous mammals: *Amer. Mus. Novit.,* n. 1130, pp. 1–12, 4 figs.

Shotwell, J. A., 1955, An approach to the paleoecology of mammals: *Ecology,* v. 36, n. 2, pp. 327–337, 4 figs., 3 tables.

——— 1958*a*, Intercommunity relationships in Hemphillian (mid-Pliocene) mammals: *Ecology,* v. 39, n. 2, pp. 271–282, 13 figs., 3 tables.

——— 1958*b*, Evolution and biogeography of the aplodontid and mylagaulid rodents: *Evolution,* v. 12, n. 4, pp. 451–484, 24 figs., 3 tables.

——— 1961, Late Tertiary biogeography of horses in the Northern Great Basin: J. Paleo., v. 35, n. 1, pp. 203–217, 10 figs.

Stock, C., 1949, Rancho La Brea, a record of Pleistocene life in California: *Los Angeles Co. Mus. Sci. Series,* n. 13, 4th ed., pp. 1–80, 33 figs.

Recent Foraminiferal Ecology and Paleoecology

by William R. Walton *Pan American Petroleum Corporation, Tulsa, Oklahoma*

Introduction

Much work has been done and many fine studies of modern foraminiferal distributions have been published in recent years. The usefulness of modern Foraminifera in delineating environments has been well established. Distributions of many species of Foraminifera, both in local areas and regionally, could be shown to illustrate discrete distributions.

In addition to these published studies, several thousand sediment samples were collected, during the period 1952–1956, in the northeastern Gulf of Mexico for faunal analyses as a part of a more comprehensive sedimentological study conducted by Gulf Research and Development Company. The regional aspect of the study required reconnaissance sampling over large areas, and local studies have been made from intensive sampling in smaller areas associated with specific sedimentary forms. These studies, in addition to previously published studies in the area, have resulted in the accumulation of considerable amounts of faunal data.

The purposes of Part I are to combine and summarize these data in terms of significant biofacies and faunal distributions, and to investigate those characters of recent faunas, exclusive of generic and specific differences, that may be useful in paleoecologic interpretations.

Recent sediment samples were collected by W. H. Glezen unless otherwise noted. William T. Smith made many of the faunal analyses. Illustrations were drafted by W. P. Fiehler. Grateful acknowledgment is made to Gulf Research and Development Company for permission to publish Part I of this paper and to Pan American Petroleum Corporation for permission to publish the subsurface paleontological data in Part II. Paleontological data were collected by Pan American's Paleontological Laboratory under the direction of Julius B, Garrett, Chief Paleontologist.

The principal motive in the many studies of modern faunas was to apply environmental criteria to the interpretation of fossil faunas and sediments. The purposes of Part II of this paper are to make analogies between modern and Tertiary Foraminifera, to determine which characteristics of modern faunas are most useful in interpreting Tertiary paleoecologies, and to make paleobathymetric maps based on these paleoecologies. The subsurface Anahuac Formation (Oligocene) has been used as an example of paleoecologic interpretation in the Tertiary since it is a widespread marine transgressive deposit with abundant, well-preserved faunas and is adequately described in the literature (Cushman and Ellisor, 1935; Ellisor, 1944.)

PART I: NORTHEASTERN GULF OF MEXICO FORAMINIFERA

Part I of this paper and the distribution maps are based on some 1393 faunal analyses from 950 sediment samples. These analyses include 649 new analyses, 16 off northern Florida (Lowman, 1949), 308 in the Mississippi Delta area (Phleger, 1955), 247 along profile A-A^{1}, profile G-G^{1}, and in the Mississippi coastal marshes (Phleger, unpublished data), and 173 in the northeastern Gulf of Mexico (Parker, 1954). The locations of samples and areas of concentrated sampling are indicated in Figure 1. As can be seen in Figure 1, the most complete sample coverage is in the area from the Mississippi River Delta eastward to Mobile Bay, Alabama, and extends from the shoreline to the edge of the continental shelf. To the east of this area four lines of samples are available: one off Pensacola Bay, Florida; two off Choctawhatchee Bay, Florida; and the other off Cape San Blas, Florida. Several lines of samples have been studied from off Florida (Bandy, O. L., 1956, "Ecology of Foraminifera in northeastern Gulf of Mexico," U. S. G. S. Prof. Paper 274-G, pp. 179–204). Two of these lines of samples occur in the area included in this report.

Four types of faunal analyses have been performed on the samples: dead benthonic population counts, living benthonic population counts, planktonic population counts, and faunal estimates. The faunal estimates consist of estimated total benthonic and planktonic populations and percentage occurrences of species and genera. The new analyses presented here have been made from two types of samples: (1) those collected by the small Phleger-type coring tube from which the surface was studied; and (2) those taken from the orange-peel dredge. All of the faunal counts have been made from the surface samples collected with the small coring-tube, and only the faunal estimates were made from the orange-peel dredge samples. Living counts were made from constant volume wet samples which had been preserved. Dead counts and faunal estimates have been made from dry samples washed over a sieve with an average opening of 0.062 mm (U. S. Standard Sieve Series, Mesh 230). Samples used by Lowman (1949) are anchor samples, and his faunal data were obtained by population counts. Phleger's samples (1954, 1955, and unpublished data) were collected with the small Phleger-type coring tube; Parker's samples were collected with the small coring tube, the orange-peel dredge, the Stetson-Iselin sampler, and an "underway" sampler (Parker, 1954). Species distribution tables are not presented for the sake of brevity.

Foraminiferal Distributions

The following faunal associations are presented under the headings of the most dominant genus within the fauna and defined in terms of the two or three next most common genera. The faunal boundaries, as may be expected, are not sharp but are gradational and must be considered in somewhat general terms. It would be far more satisfactory if foraminiferal faunas could be described in terms of species composition and classified as "estuarine," "bay," "sound," etc., faunas. This is not to imply that such classifications cannot be made as it is a simple task to define the "Mobile Bay fauna" or the "Mississippi Sound Fauna." It is the fact, however, that such faunal descriptions must be prefixed by place names that limit their usefulness for stratigraphic or paleoecologic purposes. At the present state of our knowledge it is not possible to adequately describe "bay" faunas or faunas of other commonly used coastal or physiographic features on the basis of species composition without prefixing the faunas with place names and limiting their descriptions to small areas under consideration. For example, the fauna of Tampa Bay, Florida (unpublished data) is essentially a calcareous fauna with the exception of small areas near the bay head. Mobile Bay, Alabama, on the other hand, is characterized by an arenaceous fauna with the exception of an area near its mouth. There are brackish water species in Mobile Bay that do not exist in Tampa Bay, yet Tampa Bay supports about twice as many indigenous species as does Mobile Bay. The warm, shallow, more saline bays of southern Texas and Florida apparently support an even more calcareous fauna than Tampa Bay and the shallow, brackish (almost fresh water) bays around the Mississippi

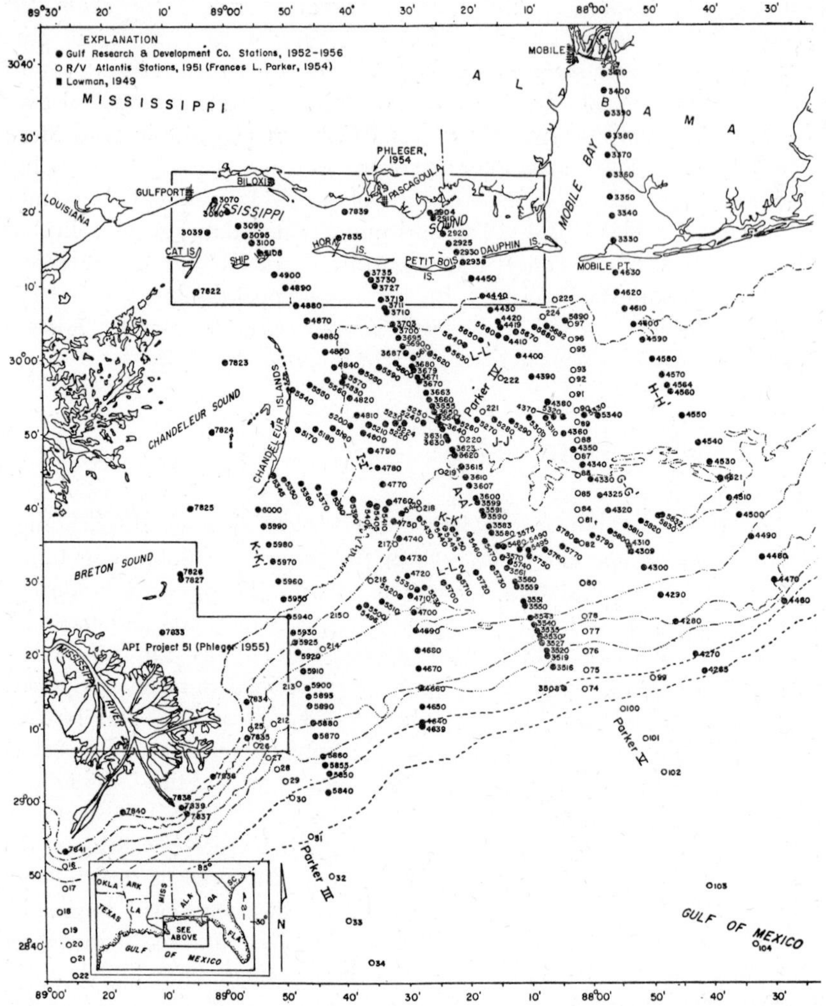

Fig. 1 Locations of

River Delta support an even more arenaceous fauna than Mobile Bay. The probability is low that an exact replica of a "Mobile Bay" fauna could be found in the subsurface strata of the Tertiary. This is not to belittle the significance or usefulness of species compositions and distributions, since it has been shown time and again that such distributions are good environmental indicators under limited con-

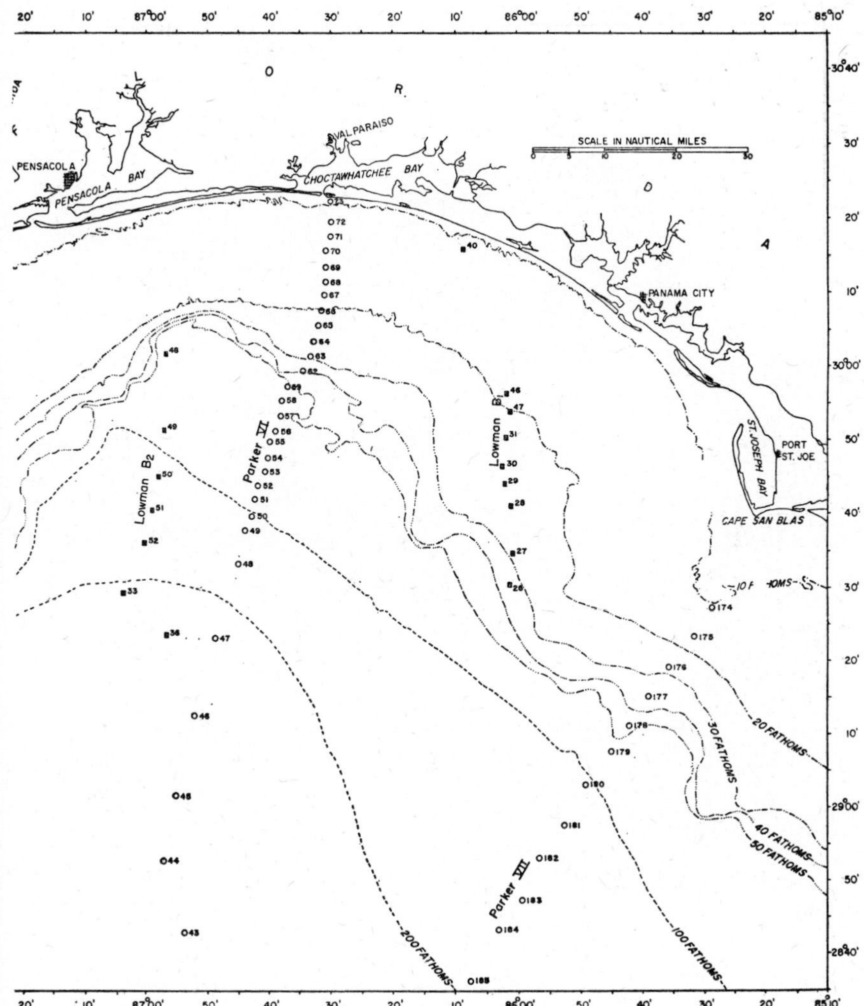

stations and sources of data.

ditions and within specific areas. The more specific and limited the criteria from recent distributions, however, the lower is the probability of finding analogous faunal criteria in ancient sediments.

The usefulness of recent faunal criteria to paleontologists working with faunas of various geological ages depends, to a large extent, on what observations can be made from ancient rocks and on the re-

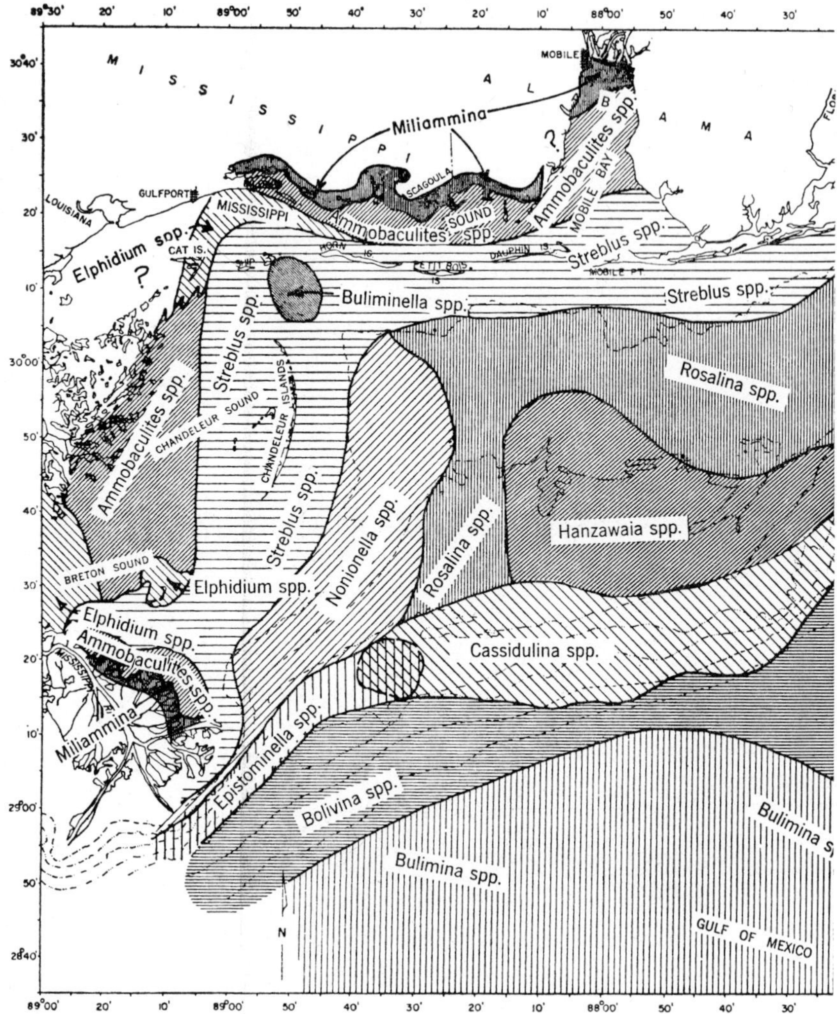

Fig. 2 Distribution

liability or persistence of the faunal characteristics in geologic history. With these things in mind, the following biofacies have been based on generic associations and characterized by the dominant faunal element. These faunal associations are specific enough to have environmental significance, but general enough to be applicable to Tertiary faunas.

Fourteen biofacies are recognized and are presented in Figure 2.

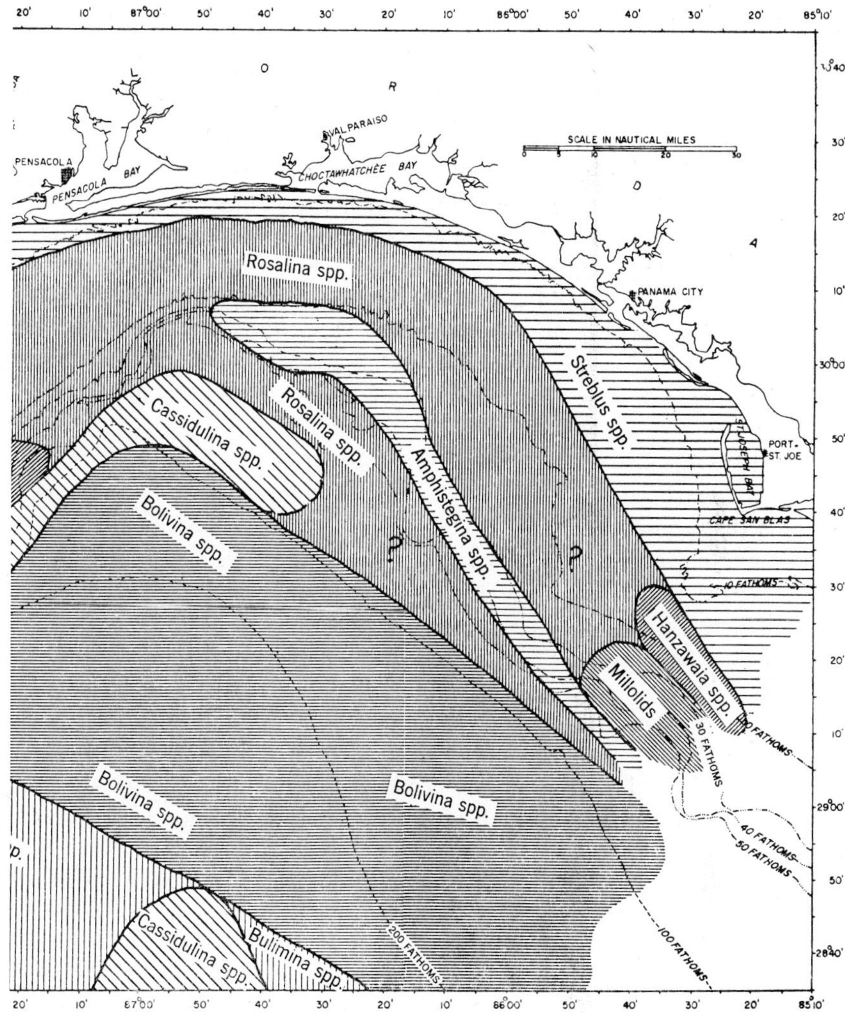

of generic dominance.

This figure shows the distributions of areas in which the named genus constitutes the largest portion of the fauna on a number percentage basis. Figure 2 and the following generic distribution maps are based on the sample coverage shown in Figure 1. As several different types of sediment samples and faunal analyses are represented, the resulting distributions are, to a certain extent, interpretive but believed to be essentially correct.

Marginal-Marine Faunas

The marginal-marine faunas are here described as those faunas that overlap and occur most abundantly in association with such nearshore marginal-marine features as bays, sounds, estuaries, and intertidal marshes and swamps. It is in these nearshore waters that the effects of dilution and concentration of the principal constituents of sea water occur and the area in which the relative concentrations of the principal constituents of sea water are not constant or predictable. These are also the areas in which: (1) the organic production is most profoundly affected by seasonal changes in river discharge and biologic activity; (2) the boundaries of the environmental zones are sharp; (3) the benthonic faunas are subjected to radical diurnal and seasonal changes in temperature; and (4) the most active transportation and deposition of detrital sediments occurs. It can be stated that the marginal-marine faunas occupy the most rigorous of all the environments that come under the marine influence. The limits of the marginal-marine faunas in the area under consideration are the terrestrial fresh-water environment on the shoreward side and the 10-fathom depth contour on the seaward side.

THECAMOEBINA FAUNA. The extreme shoreward edge of the marginal-marine fauna is characterized by specimens of small agglutinated forms no longer considered to be Foraminifera. These forms, previously reported as *Leptodermella* and *Urnulina* by Phleger (1954) in the Mississippi marshes and in the Mississippi River Delta (Phleger, 1955), have been shown to belong to the Thecamoebina, and assigned to the genera *Difflugia* and *Centropyxis.*

A pure Thecamoebina fauna apparently indicates fresh-water conditions. In the Mississippi Delta area, at the beginning of the marine influence, they are associated principally with the foraminiferal genera *Ammoastuta,* along with a few *Miliammina* and *Trochammina.* A pure Thecamoebina fauna is found in the Mississippi marshes, but it grades into associations with *Ammoastuta, Trochammina,* and *Haplophragmoides.*

This fauna is limited to the landward fringes of marine marshes, estuaries, and fresh-water swamps. Occasional specimens of the Thecamoebina are found in bays and sounds surrounding marshes.

MILIAMMINA FAUNA. The Thecamoebina fauna grades into the *Miliammina* fauna (Figure 2). The *Miliammina* dominant zone in the Mississippi Delta area is most commonly associated with *Ammoastuta, Trochammina,* and *Ammobaculites.* In the Mississippi marshes, other forms such as *Haplophragmoides, Ammoscalaria,* and *Arenoparrella* are common, whereas *Trochammina* rarely occurs.

In addition to the intertidal marsh areas just described, the *Miliammina* dominant fauna crosses the barrier between the periodically exposed marshes into the continuously inundated brackish water bays and estuaries. Here, however, the association changes and the second and third dominant forms become species of *Ammobaculites* and *Ammoscalaria.* The *Miliammina* dominant fauna at this point grades into an *Ammobaculites* dominant fauna. Good examples of the *Miliammina-Ammobaculites* fauna are found at the head of Mobile Bay, and in the Pascagoula River area in Mississippi.

AMMOBACULITES FAUNA. The distribution of the species of *Ammobaculites* is shown in Figure 3. The *Ammobaculites* dominant fauna occurs just seaward of the *Miliammina-Ammobaculites* fauna. It occurs over the central half of Mobile Bay, the landward half of Mississippi Sound and Chandeleur Sound, and in a narrow zone around the Mississippi River Delta (Figure 2). As may be expected, the *Ammobaculites* dominant zone varies in its associations from an *Ammobaculites-Miliammina* association near the *Miliammina* dominant zone to an *Ammobaculites-Streblus-Elphidium* association near the *Streblus* and *Elphidium* dominant zones.

ELPHIDIUM FAUNA. Although species of *Elphidium* are common over a large portion of the northeastern Gulf of Mexico, the zone of greatest abundance is usually shallower than 5 fathoms (Figure 4). Zones in which species of *Elphidium* dominate are small in area and fall between the *Ammobaculites* and *Streblus* dominant zones (Figure 2). Within the *Elphidium* dominant zone, the faunal association is *Elphidium-Ammobaculites-Streblus* on the shoreward side and *Elphidium-Streblus-Ammobaculites* (and occasionally miliolids) on the seaward side.

STREBLUS FAUNA. Distribution of the species of *Streblus* is shown in Figure 5. The *Streblus* dominant fauna is the most extensive of the marginal-marine faunas and is the transition fauna between the marginal-marine and open-marine major faunal groups. Species of *Streblus* dominate the foraminiferal faunas over the outer portions of the semi-enclosed sounds (Mississippi and Chandeleur Sounds) and the innermost portions of the open continental shelf over the entire study area (Figure 2). The *Streblus* dominant fauna is bounded on the shoreward side by the *Ammobaculites* and *Elphidium* dominant zones. The dominant faunal associations are *Streblus-Ammobaculites-Elphidium* or *Streblus-Elphidium-Ammobaculites.*

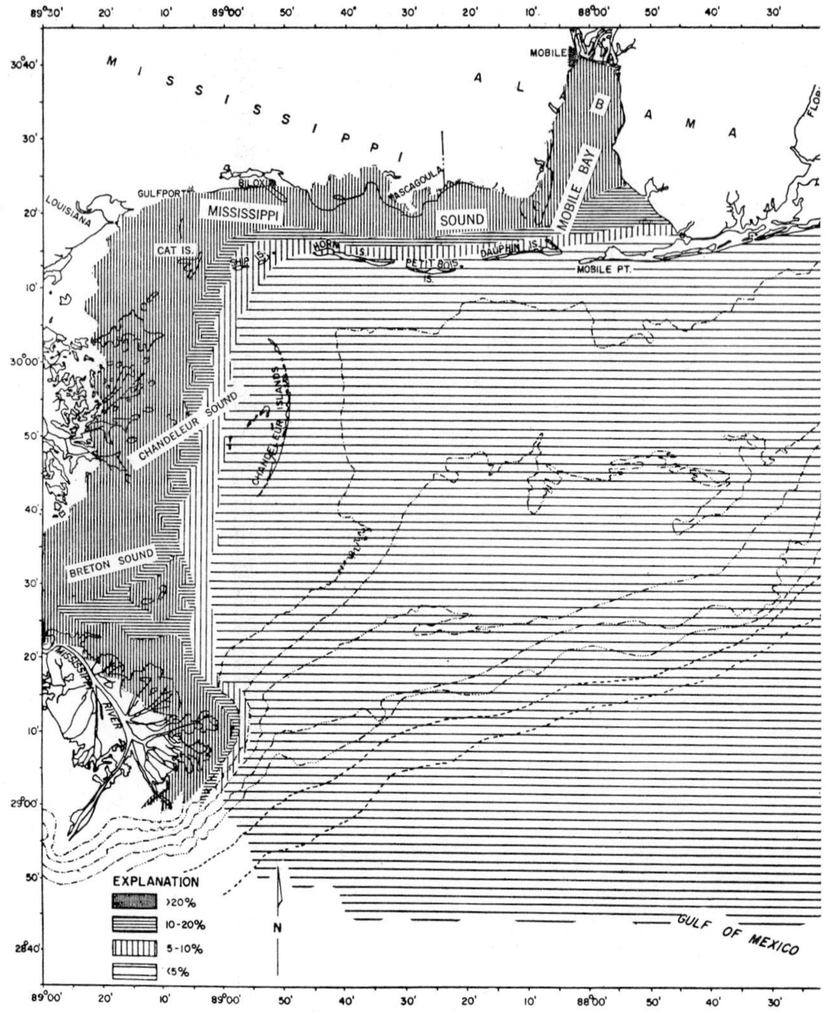

Fig. 3 Distribution of Ammobaculites *spp.*

The seaward edge of the *Streblus* dominant zone closely follows the 10-fathom depth contour in this area and is faunally bounded by the *Nonionella* dominant zone, along the eastern edge of the Mississippi Delta and Chandeleur Sound, and by the *Rosalina* dominant zone off the coasts of Mississippi, Alabama, and Florida (Figure 2). Close to the Mississippi Delta, the Chandeleur Islands, and Mississippi-Alabama barrier islands, the faunal association is *Streblus-Elphidium.*

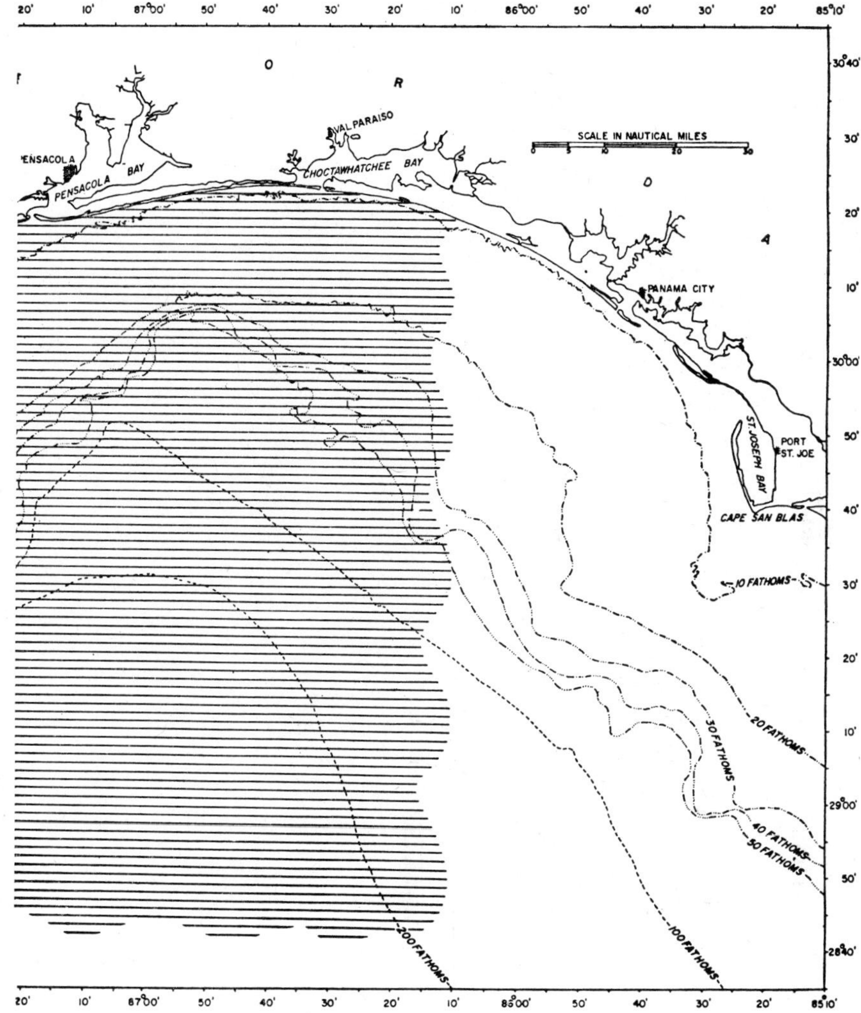

in per cent of total benthonic population.

Toward the outer edge of the *Streblus* dominant zone off Chandeleur Sound and the Chandeleur Islands, the faunal association is *Streblus-Bolivina lowmani-Buliminella-Nonionella,* which is unique to this area. This fauna grades into a *Nonionella* dominant fauna but still retains the subdominant *Buliminella* and *Bolivina lowmani* associations. In contrast, off the Mississippi-Alabama barrier islands, the *Streblus-Elphidium* fauna becomes associated with *Buliminella* and

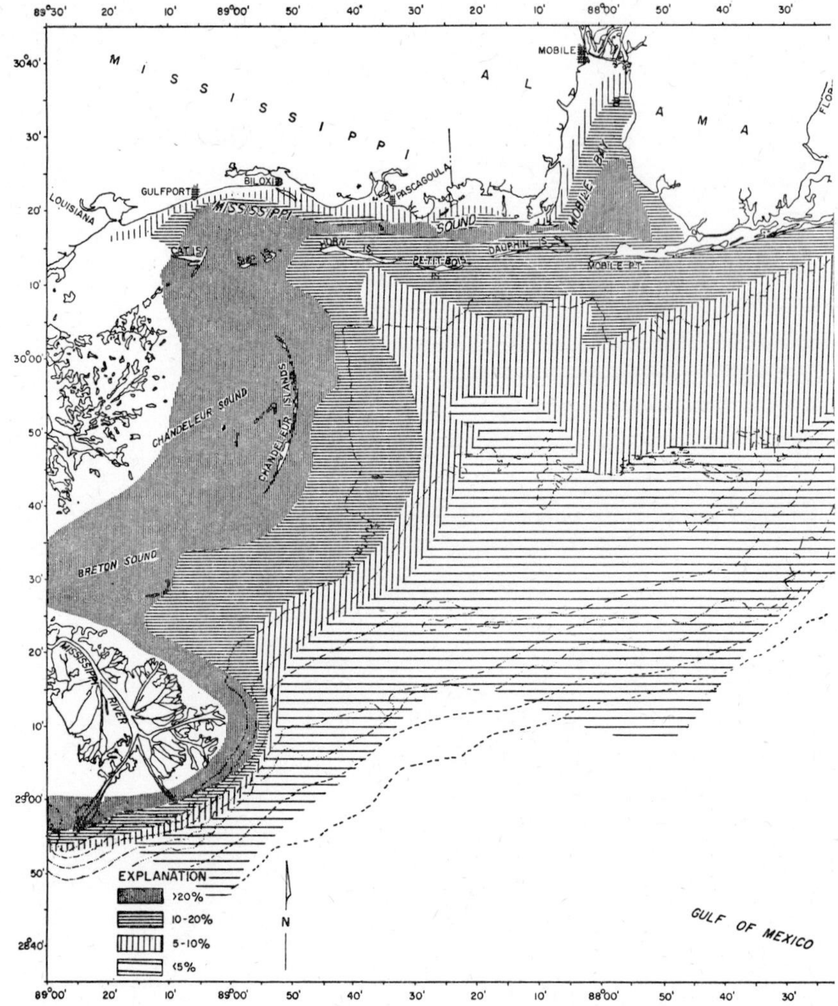

Fig. 4 Distribution of Elphidium *spp.*

Bolivina lowmani but grades into a *Streblus-Rosalina-Hanzawaia-Elphidium* association near the *Rosalina* dominant zone. Miliolids become subdominant in isolated areas. It is interesting to note that the *Nonionella* influence in the *Streblus* dominant zone becomes less significant to the east off the Petit Bois, the Dauphin Islands, and Mobile Bay, and insignificant off the coast of Florida.

Figure 6 is a schematic representation of the step-by-step progression of dominant microfaunal constituents of the marginal-marine faunas

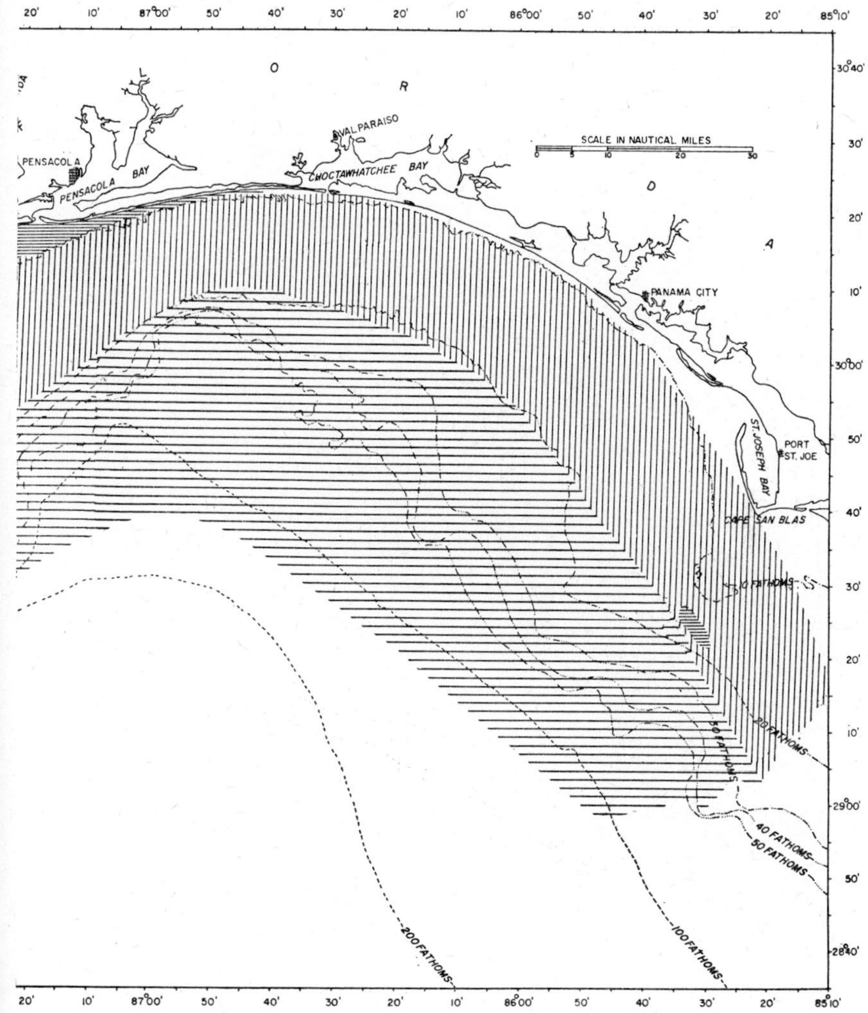

in per cent of total benthonic population.

from the fresh-water (Thecamoebina) environment to the open-marine (*Streblus*) environment.

Open-Marine Faunas

The open-marine faunas, in contrast to the marginal-marine faunas, are those that occur most abundantly on the open continental shelf outside of the influence of nearshore physiographic and hydrographic

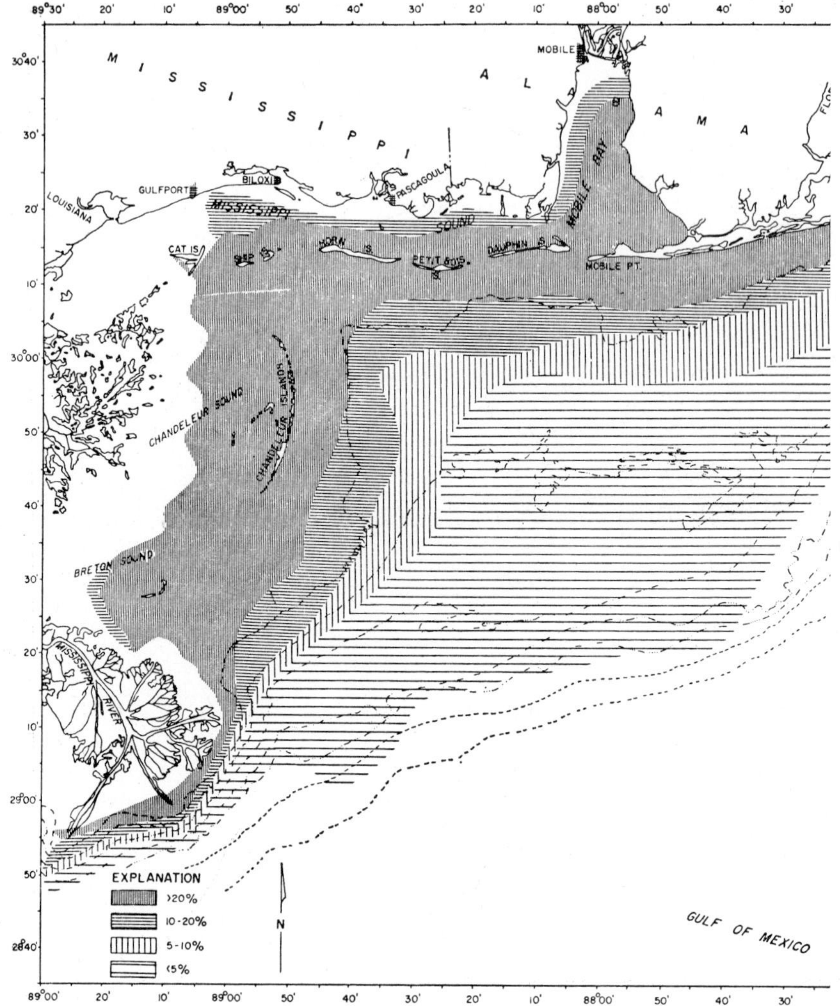

Fig. 5 Distribution of Streblus beccarii

barriers. This is not to imply that their distributions may not be affected, to some extent, by the presence of nearshore barriers and by the changes that take place in the composition of sea water in the nearshore environment.

As the marginal-marine faunas end with the *Streblus* dominant fauna, the open-marine faunas begin with the *Streblus* dominant fauna. As we noted, the *Streblus* fauna can be considered as a transition be-

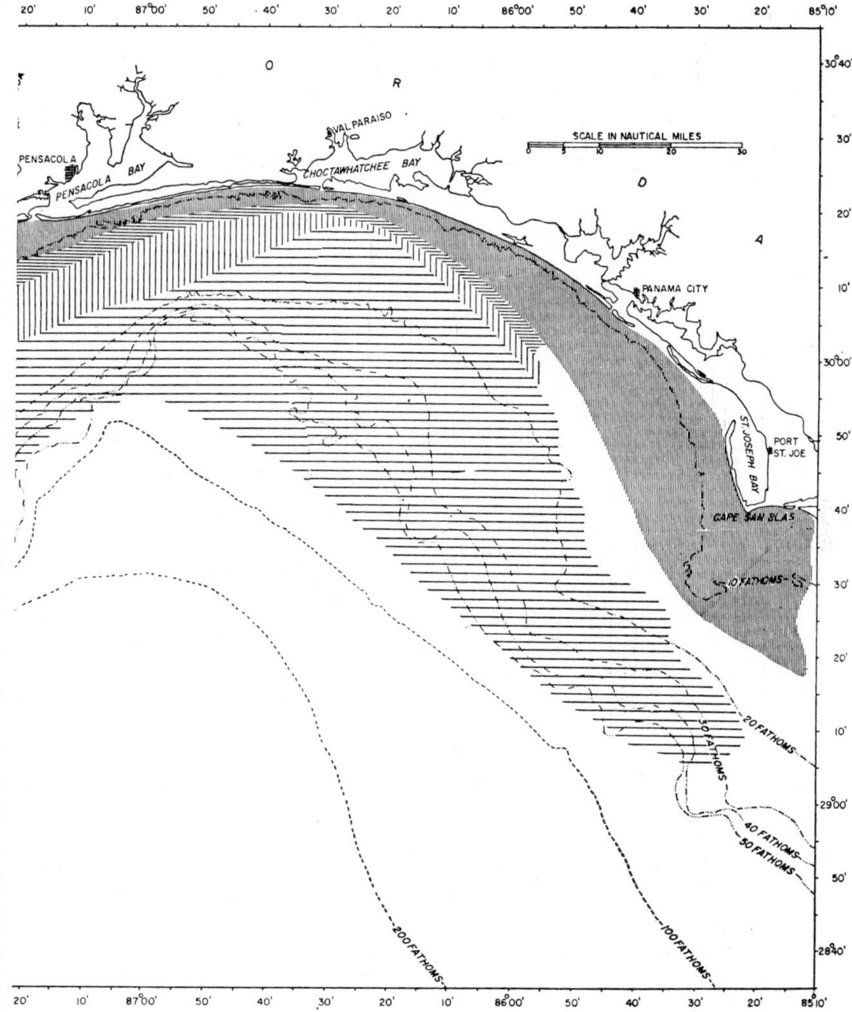

vars. in per cent of total benthonic population.

tween the marginal and open-marine faunas. Within the *Streblus* dominant zone, there occur local concentrations of two smaller faunas which are dominated by *Bolivina lowmani* and species of *Buliminella.*

BOLIVINA LOWMANI FAUNA. The distribution of *Bolivina lowmani* is shown in Figure 7. Because of its unique distribution, occurring abundantly within the *Streblus* dominant zone and the *Bolivina* dominant zone, it is presented here as a specific distribution instead of

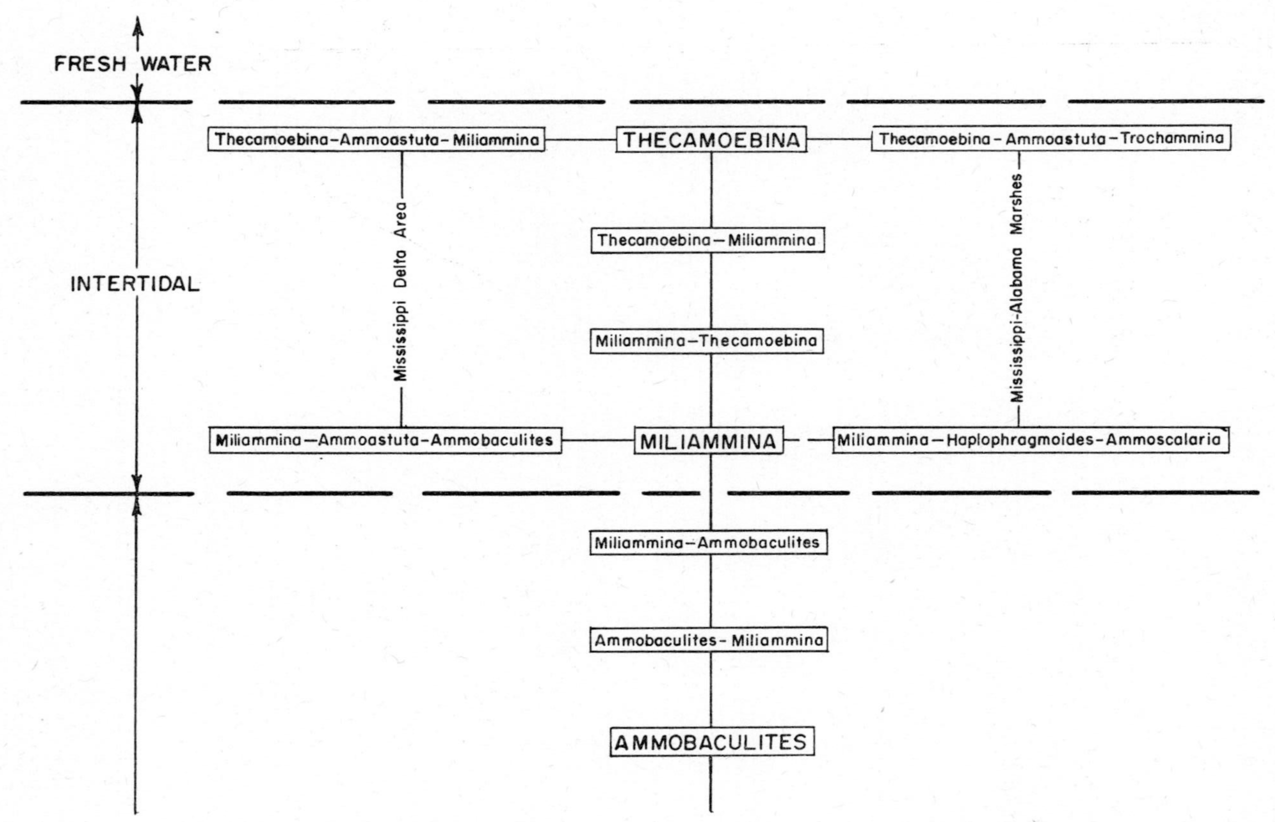

FRESH WATER
INTERTIDAL
Thecamoebina-Ammoastuta-Miliammina
THECAMOEBINA
Thecamoebina-Ammoastuta-Trochammina
Mississippi Delta Area
Mississippi-Alabama Marshes
Thecamoebina-Miliammina
Miliammina-Thecamoebina
Miliammina-Ammoastuta-Ammobaculites
MILIAMMINA
Miliammina-Haplophragmoides-Ammoscalaria
Miliammina-Ammobaculites
Ammobaculites-Miliammina
AMMOBACULITES

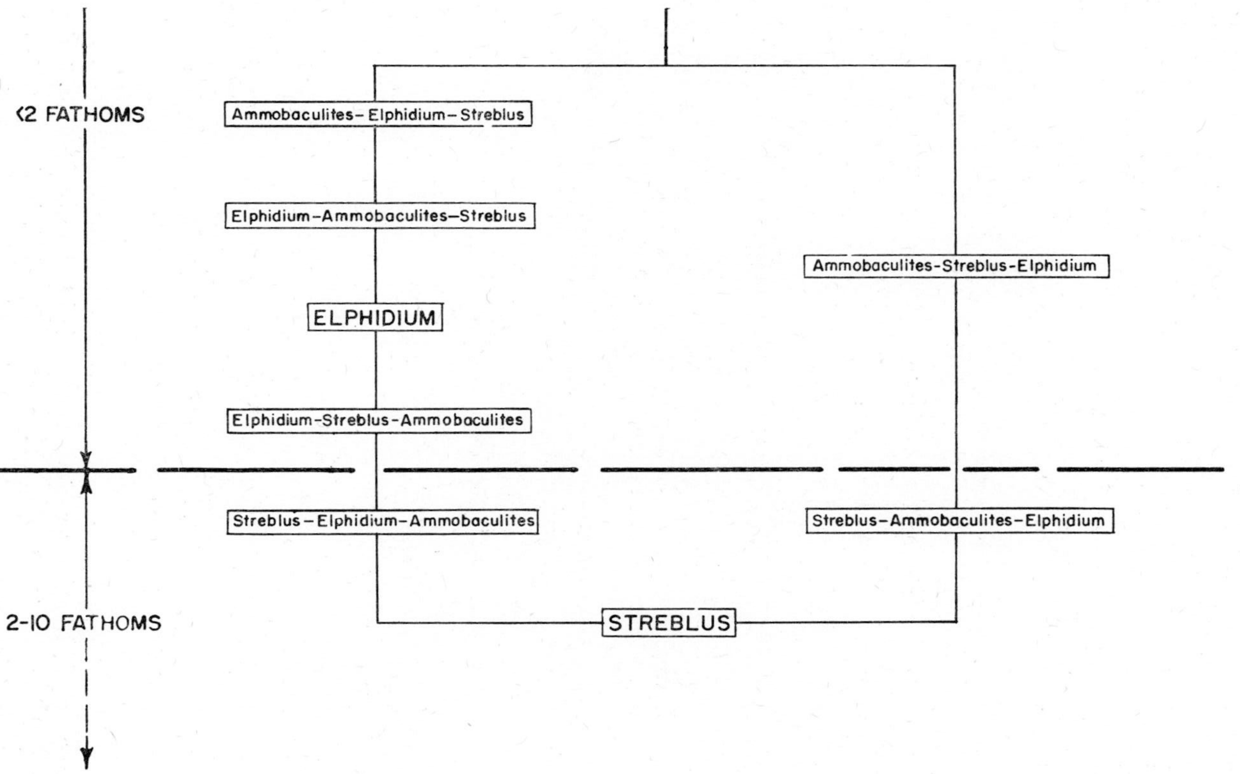

Fig. 6 Generic associations of dominant marginal marine faunas.

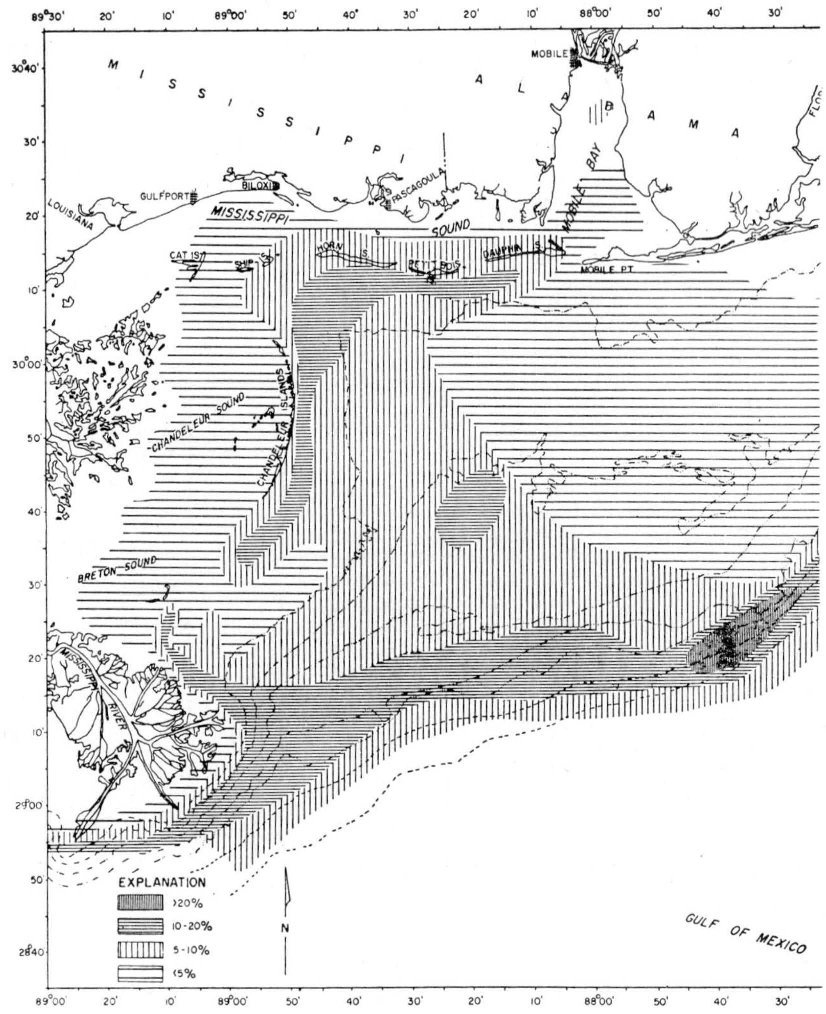

Fig. 7 Distribution of Bolivina lowmani *in*

being included in the generic groups. Within the *Streblus* dominant zone, *B. lowmani* is most common off the Mississippi River Delta, the Chandeleur Islands, and the Mississippi-Alabama barrier islands. It is not common east of Mobile Bay within this zone. In the few cases where it is most dominant (off the Chandeleur Islands) the faunal association is *B. lowmani, Streblus-Buliminella-Elphidium.*

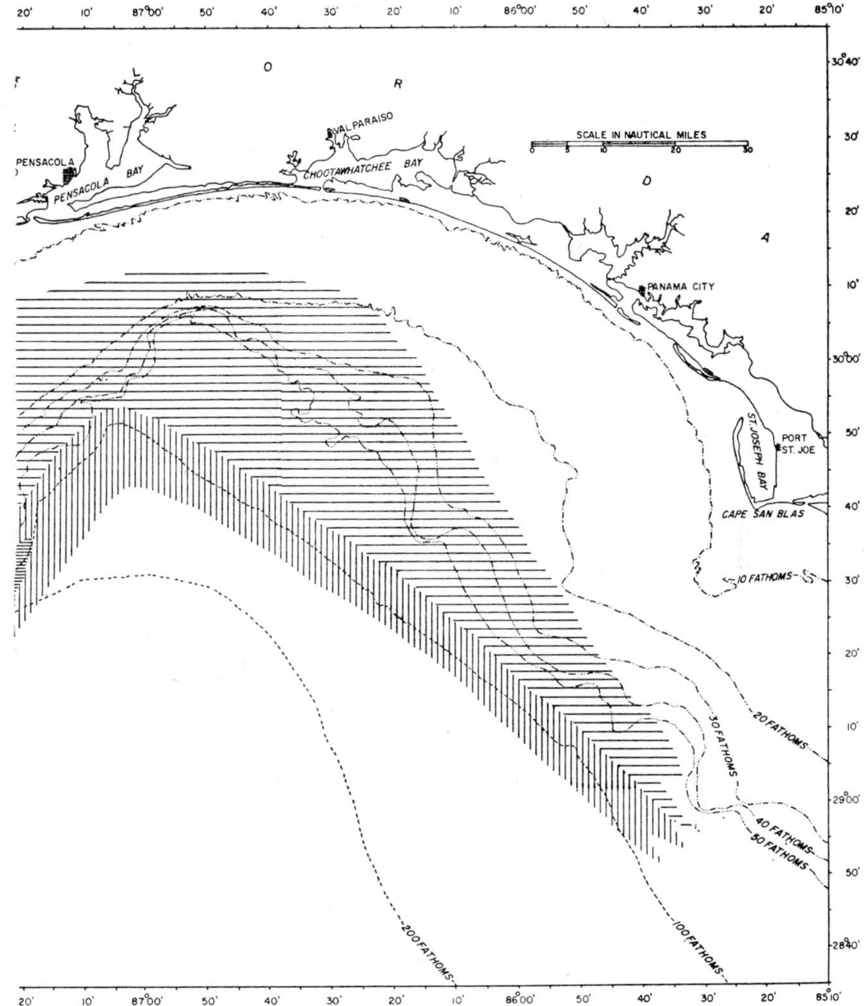

per cent of total benthonic population.

The distribution of *B. lowmani* outside of the *Streblus* dominant zone is discussed subsequently.

BULIMINELLA FAUNA. The distribution of the species of *Buliminella* is shown in Figure 8. Species of *Buliminella* are most dominant in a few small areas within the boundaries of the *Streblus* dominant zone and in one sample on the boundary of the *Epistominella* dominant

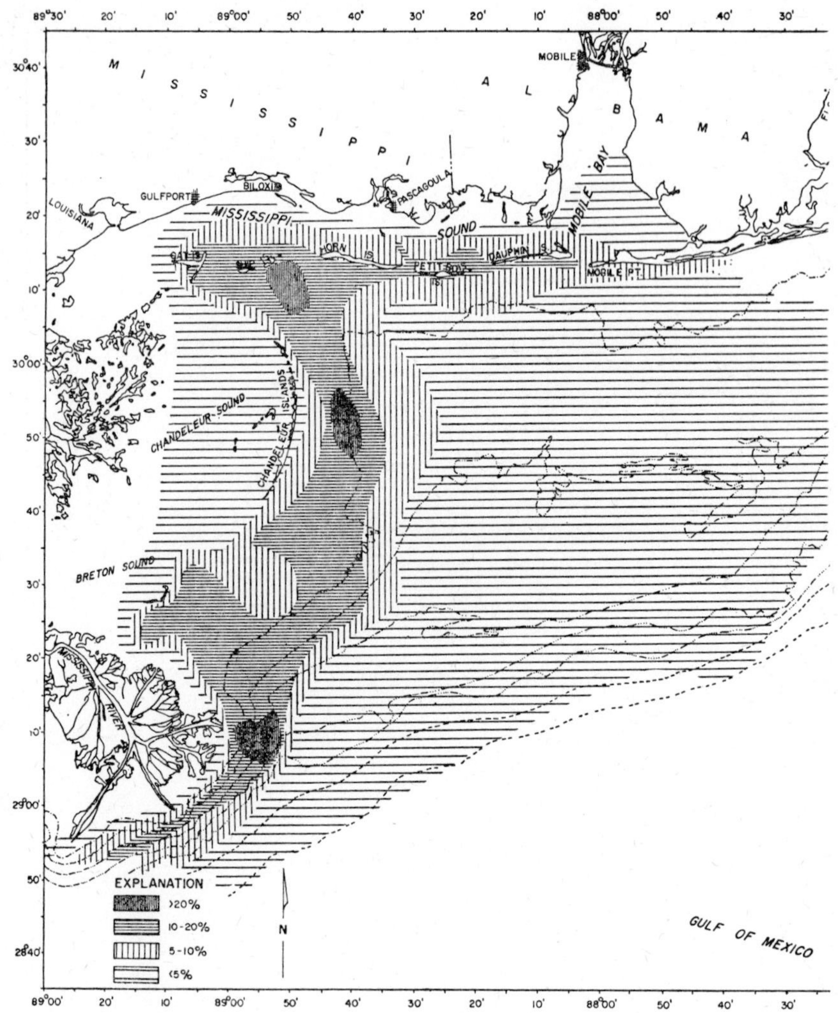

Fig. 8 Distribution of Buliminella *spp.*

zone (Figure 2). In the area between the northern tip of the Chandeleur Islands, Ship Island, and western tip of Horn Island, *Buliminella* is faunally associated with species of *Streblus* and *Elphidium* and *Bolivina lowmani.* Off the Mississippi Delta it is associated with *Nonionella* and *Epistominella.*

NONIONELLA FAUNA. The distribution of the species of *Nonionella* is shown in Figure 9. The zone in which they dominate the ben-

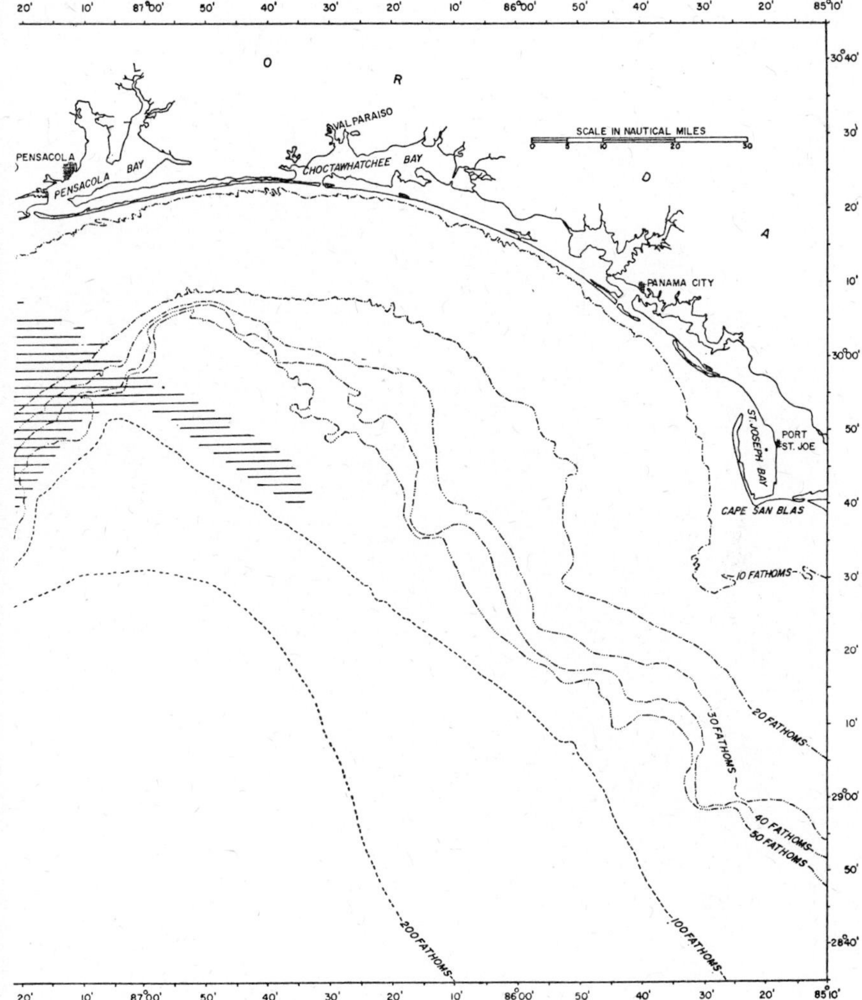

in per cent of total benthonic population.

thonic fauna is an arcuate zone that extends from off North Pass of the Mississippi Delta northward to the northern tip of the Chandeleur Islands (Figure 2). There is some indication that this zone continues around the Mississippi Delta but data are too few to confirm such a distribution.

The *Nonionella* zone is bounded by the *Streblus* dominant zone to the shoreward; the *Epistominella* dominant zone off the Mississippi

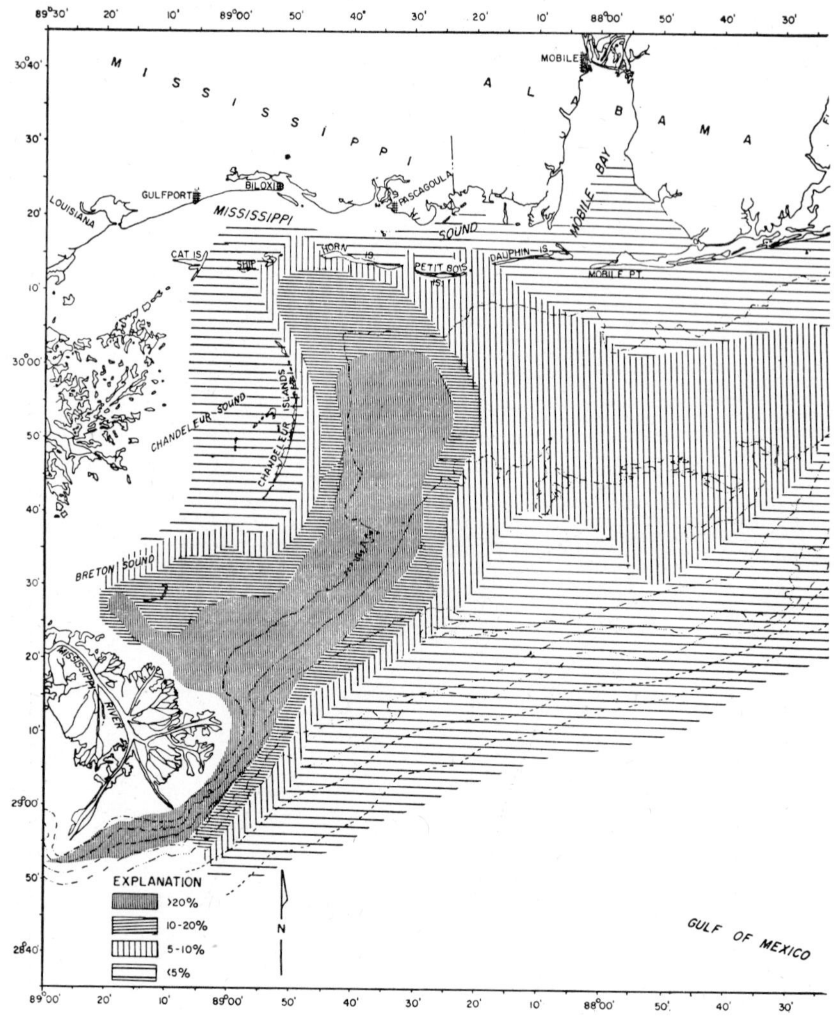

Fig. 9 Distribution of Nonionella *spp. in*

Delta, which grades into the *Cassidulina* dominant zone; and the *Rosalina* dominant zone off the Chandeleur Islands (Figure 2). The *Nonionella* dominant zone does not occur off the Mississippi-Alabama barrier islands or off the coast of northern Florida.

Near the Mississippi Delta on the shoreward edge of the *Nonionella* zone, the faunal association is *Nonionella-Streblus-Elphidium*. Offshore in this area, the association becomes *Nonionella-Epistominella-Buliminella*. Off the Chandeleur Islands on the nearshore edge of

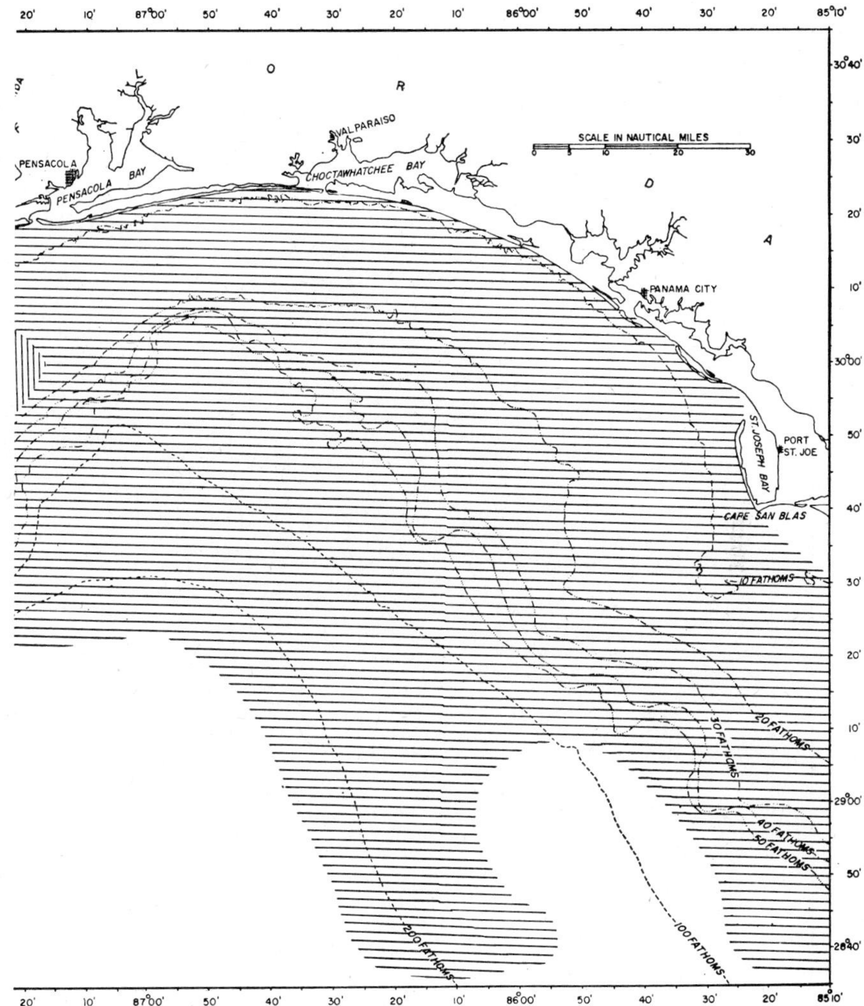

per cent of total benthonic population.

the *Nonionella* zone, species of *Nonionella-Streblus-Buliminella-Elphidium* dominate with *Bolivina lowmani,* and species of *Hanzawaia* are common. This fauna grades into a *Nonionella-Rosalina-Hanzawaia* fauna on the seaward edge of the zone with some *Streblus* and *Bolivina lowmani.*

EPISTOMINELLA FAUNA. The distribution of the species of *Epistominella* is shown in Figure 10. Comparison of Figure 9 (distribution of *Nonionella*) with Figure 10 shows a definite relationship be-

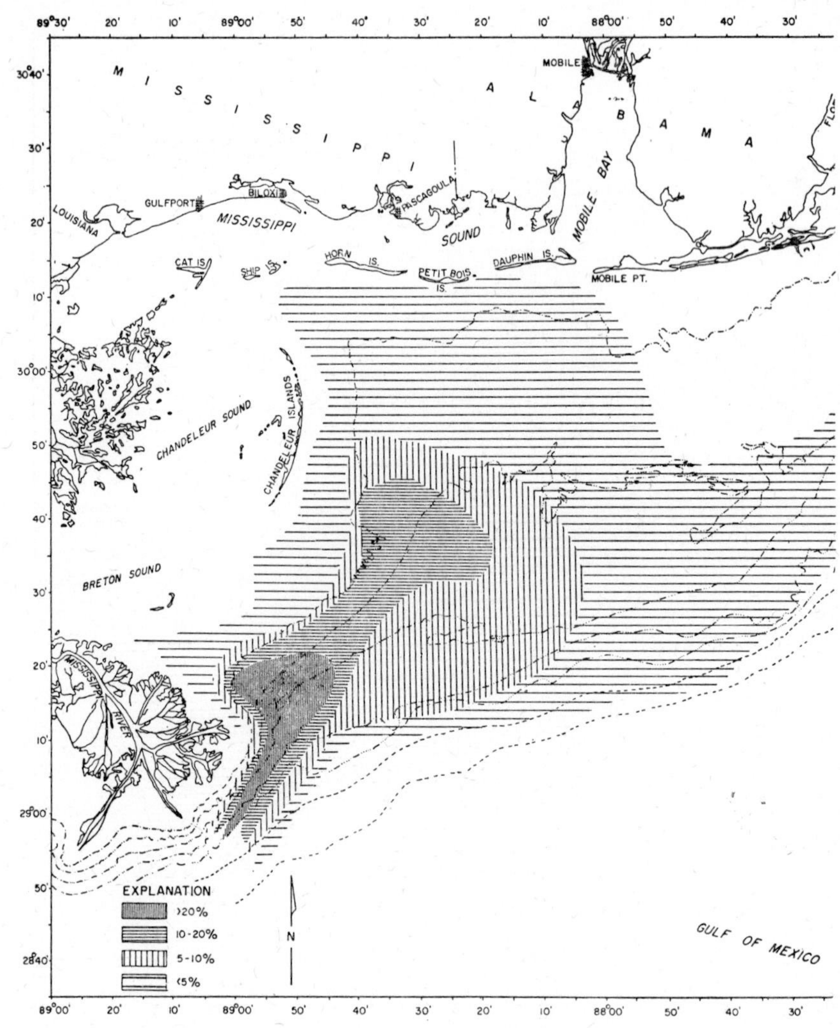

Fig. 10 Distribution of Epistominella vitrea

tween the two distributions. It is difficult, with the present sample coverage, to determine the relationship between the *Nonionella* and the *Epistominella* dominant zones around the Mississippi Delta proper. The *Epistominella* dominant zone, however, occurs seaward of the *Nonionella* dominant zone off North Pass of the Mississippi

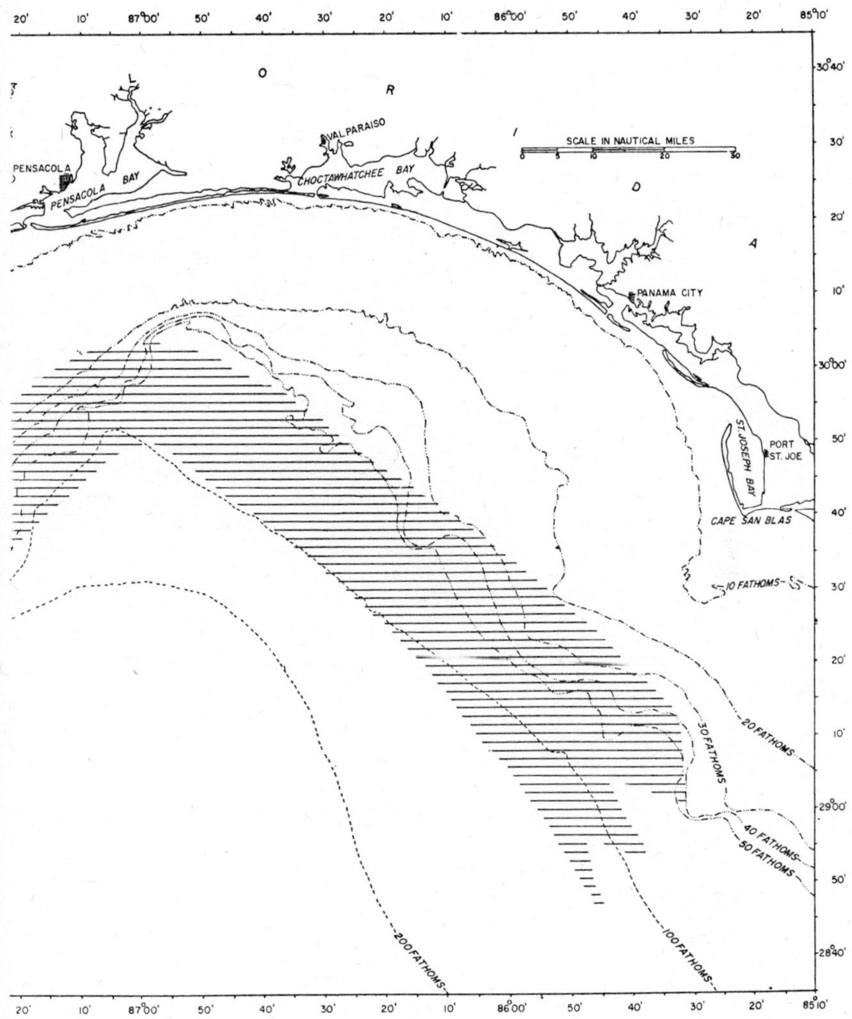

in per cent of total benthonic population.

Delta. This zone is bounded on its shoreward side all along its distribution by the *Nonionella* zone where the faunal association is principally *Epistominella-Nonionella-Buliminella.* The seaward edge of the *Epistominella* dominant zone is bordered by the *Bolivina* dominant zone. The faunal assemblage here is principally *Epistominella-*

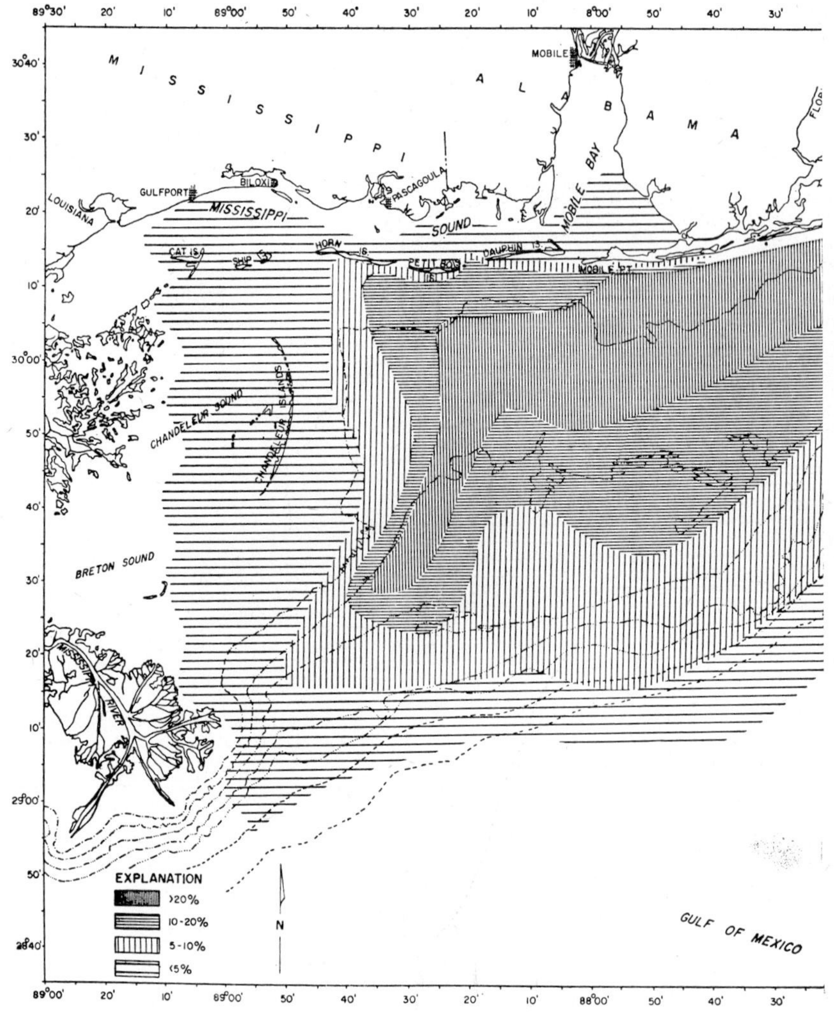

Fig. 11 Distribution of Rosalina *spp. in*

Bolivina-Cassidulina. Toward the northeast the *Epistominella* dominant zone grades into *Cassidulina-Nonionella* and *Rosalina-Hanzawaia-Nonionella* faunal assemblages.

ROSALINA-HANZAWAIA FAUNA. The distribution of the species of *Rosalina* is shown in Figure 11. The *Rosalina* dominant zone, along with the *Hanzawaia* dominant zone, occupies the greater portion of the continental shelf seaward of the 10-fathom depth contour. These

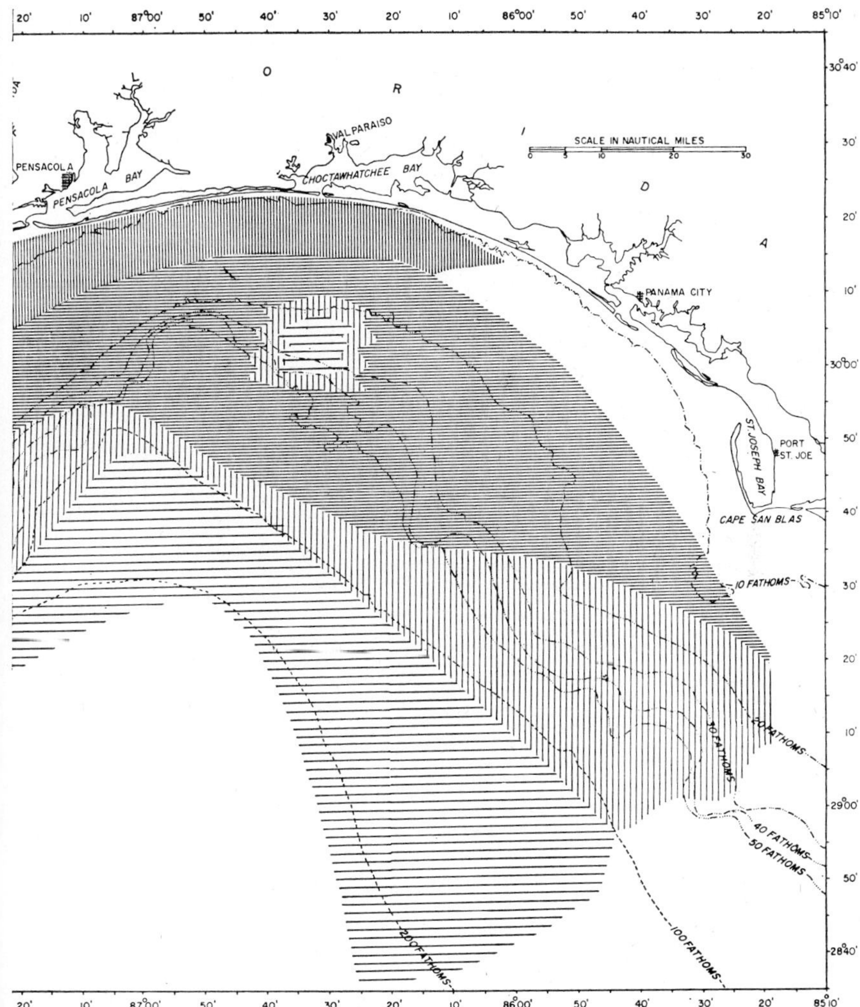

per cent of total benthonic population.

combined zones are bounded by the *Nonionella* zone on the west, the *Streblus* zone on the north, and the *Cassidulina* zone on the south.

For all practical purposes, these two zones can be considered a single biofacies in which faunal dominance varies between *Rosalina* and *Hanzawaia,* at least as far east as Mobile Bay, Alabama. The distribution of species of *Rosalina* (Figure 11) shows that they occur most abundantly shoreward of the zone of greatest abundance of

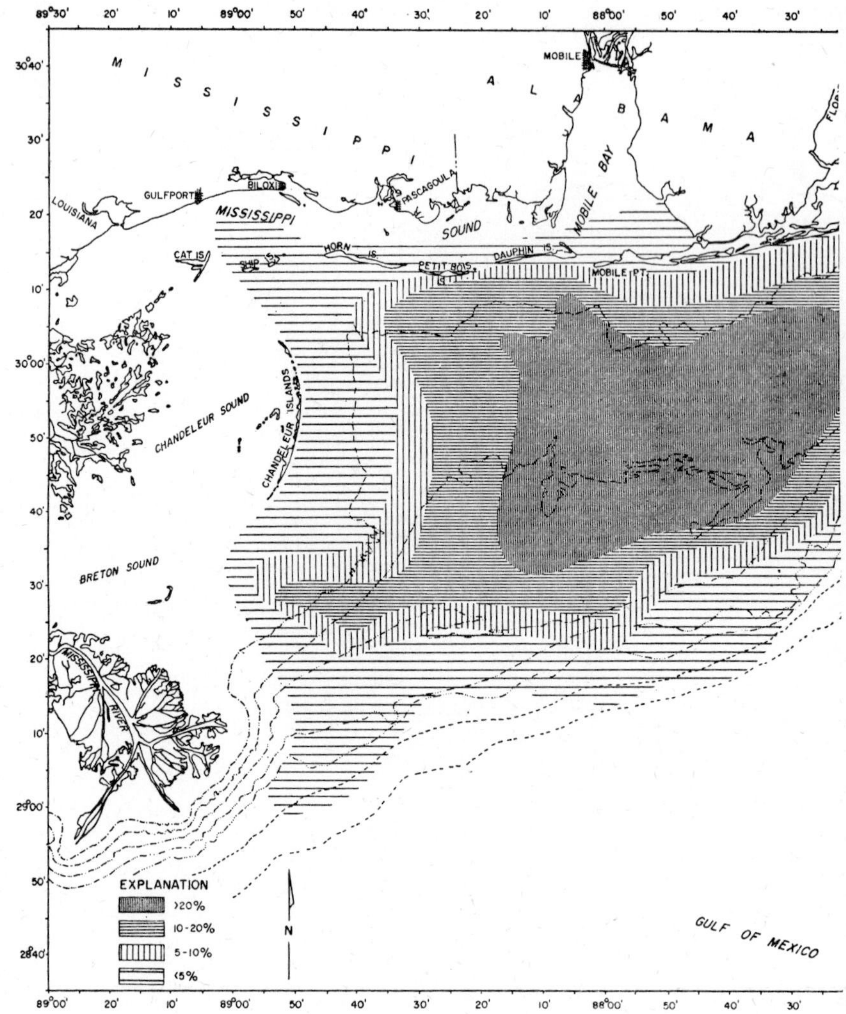

Fig. 12 Distribution of Hanzawaia *spp. in*

species of *Hanzawaia* (Figure 12). The generalization can be made, however, that species of *Rosalina* and *Hanzawaia* dominate the foraminiferal populations between the *Streblus, Nonionella,* and *Cassidulina* zones.

Near the Mississippi-Alabama barrier islands where the *Rosalina* zone is in contact with the *Streblus* zone, the principal faunal associa-

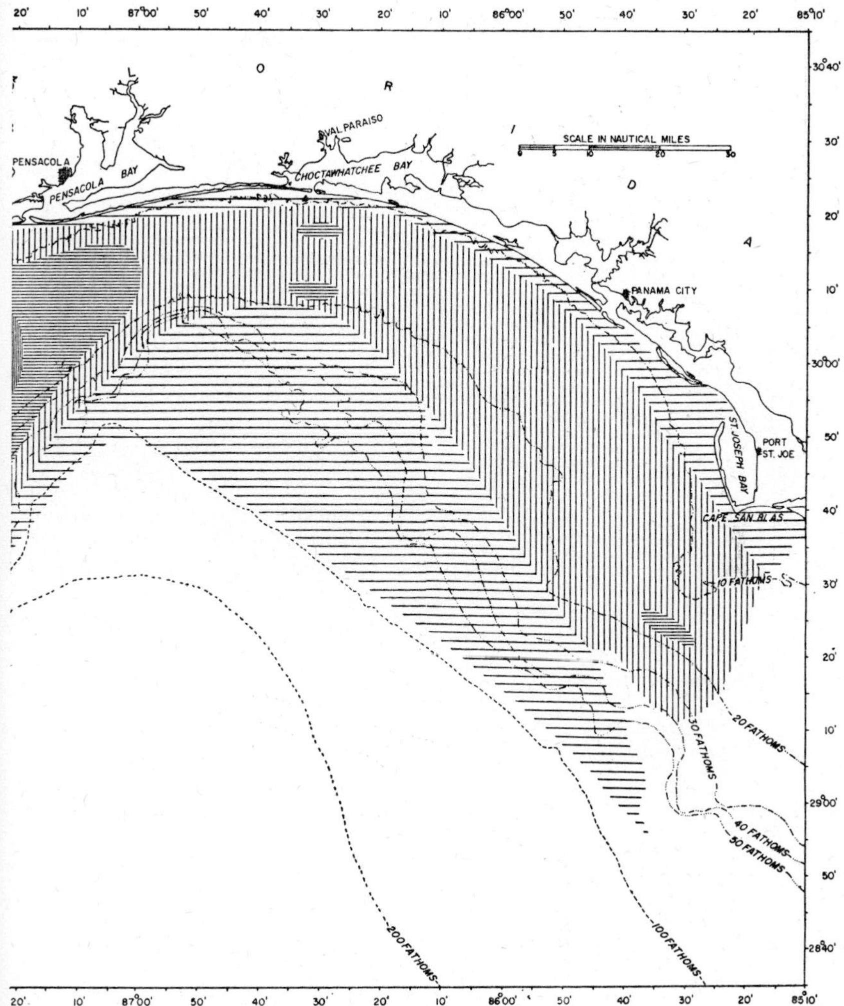

per cent of total benthonic population.

tion is *Rosalina-Hanzawaia-Streblus* with common-to-abundant miliolids and species of *Elphidium.*

On the western side where the *Rosalina* zone is in contact with the *Nonionella* zone the associations vary from a *Rosalina-Hanzawaia-Streblus-Nonionella* fauna in the north, through a *Rosalina-Nonionella-Hanzawaia* fauna to a *Rosalina-Nonionella-Epistominella-Cassidulina*

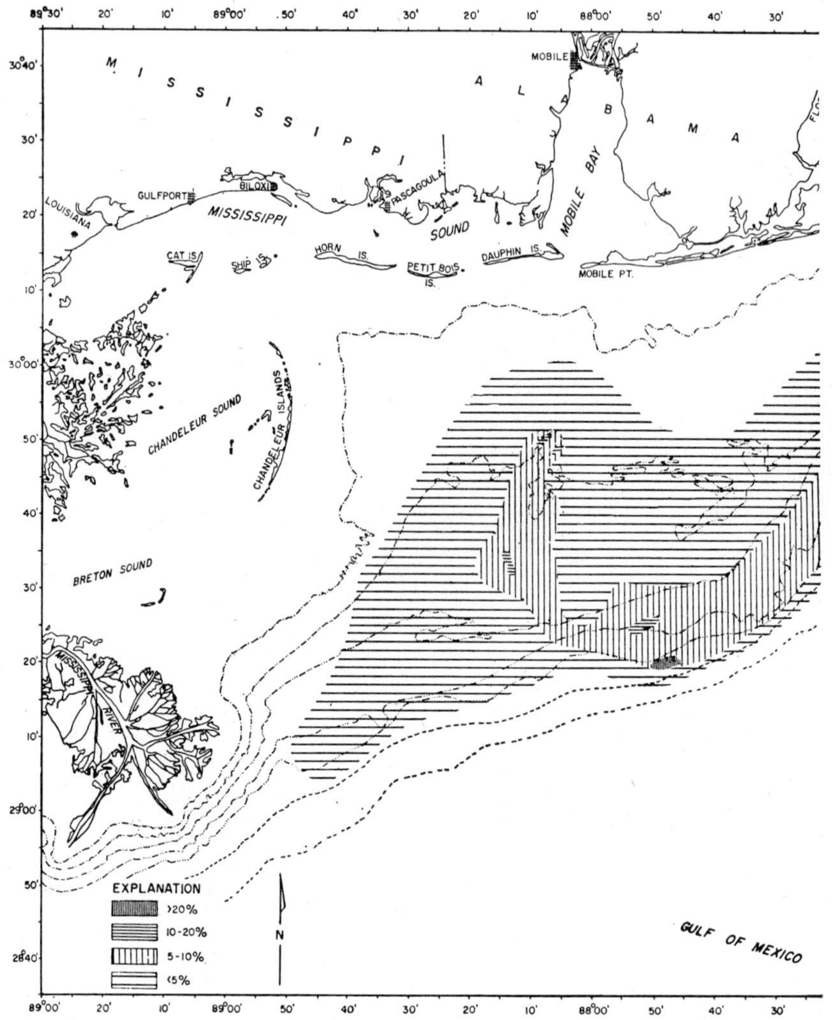

Fig. 13 Distribution of Amphistegina *spp.*

fauna near the junction of the *Nonionella, Cassidulina,* and *Epistominella* dominant zones. Where the *Hanzawaia* zone joins the *Cassidulina* zone, the principal faunal association is *Hanzawaia-Rosalina-Cassidulina.*

Within the *Rosalina-Hanzawaia* dominant zone, several species or groups of species become locally dominant. Only the larger zones,

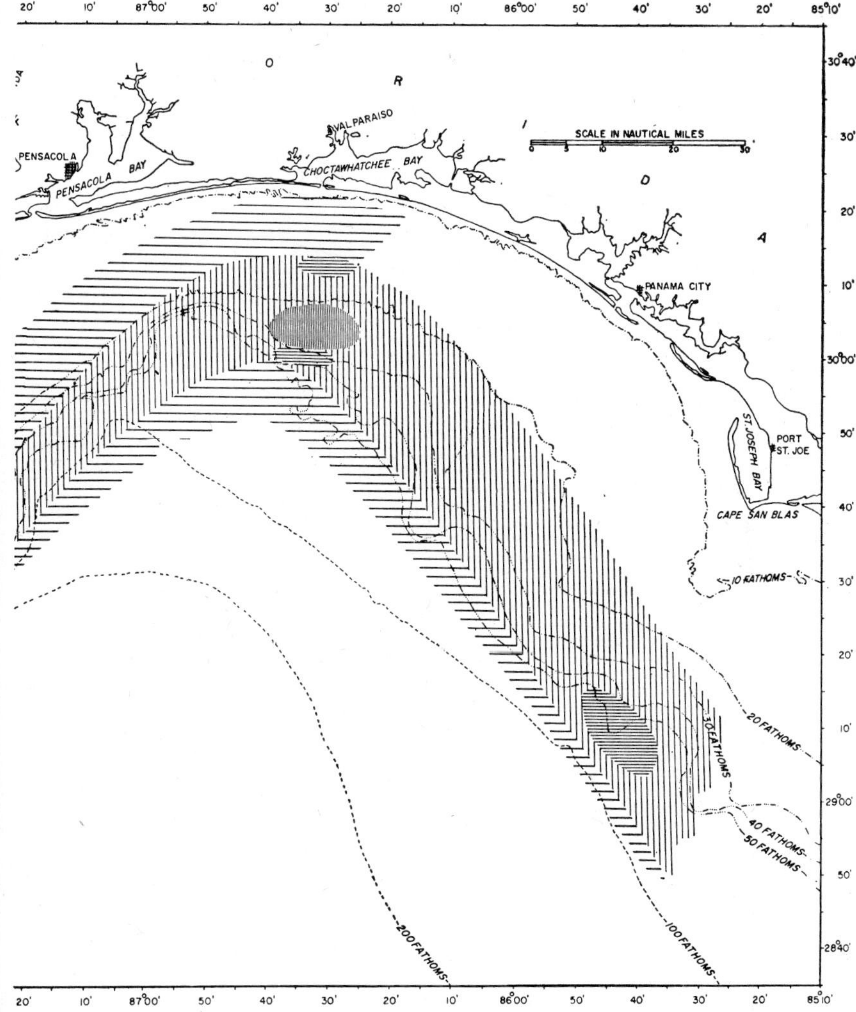

in per cent of total benthonic population.

the *Amphistegina* and miliolid zones off the coast of Florida, are shown in Figure 2. These Foraminifera are *Amphistegina* spp., *Asterigerina carinata*, *Planulina exorna*, and the miliolids.

The distribution of *Amphistegina* spp. is shown in Figure 13, and the zone in which they dominate the benthonic fauna lies between 20 and 50 fathoms off Choctawhatchee Bay, Florida and near 50 fathoms off

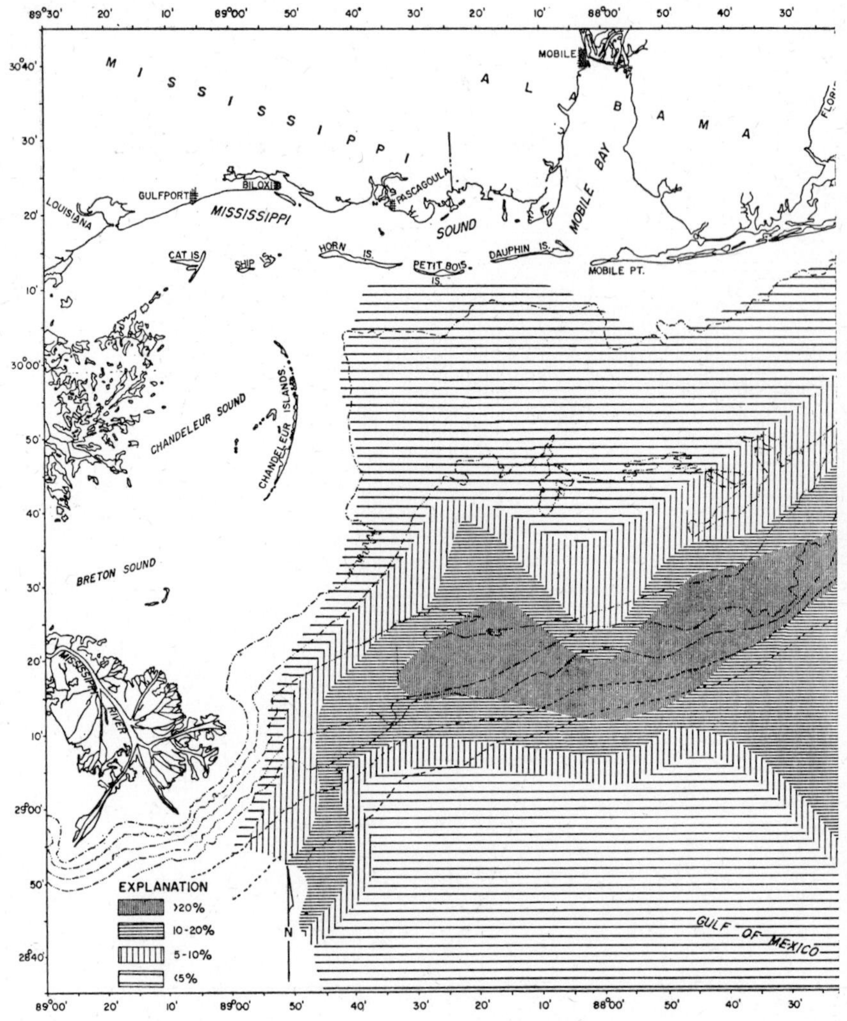

Fig. 14 Distribution of Cassidulina *spp.*

Mobile Bay, Alabama. *Amphistegina* spp. occur most abundantly between 20 and 50 fathoms in a zone that extends from Mobile Bay eastward at least as far as Cape San Blas, Florida. The occurrence of *Asterigerina* is similar to but a little shoreward of the *Amphistegina* abundant zone. It is most abundant off Choctawhatchee Bay, Florida betwen 10 and 20 fathoms and dominates the benthonic fauna at two stations in about 15 fathoms.

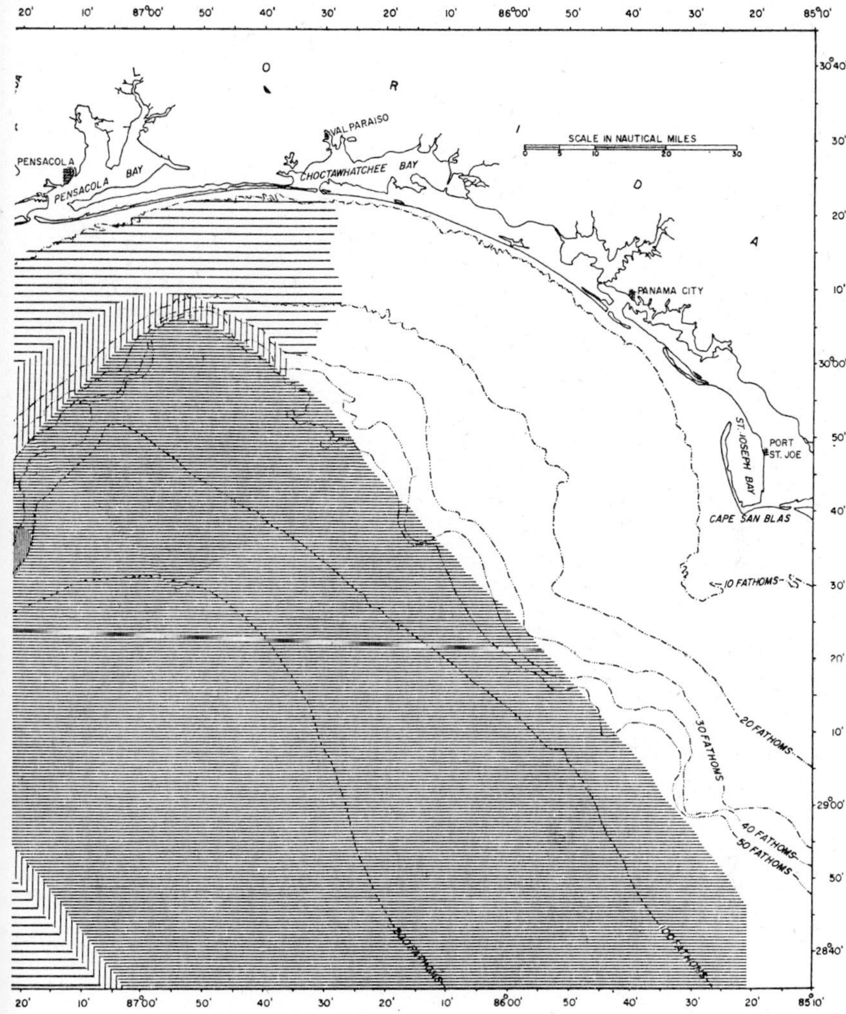

in per cent of total benthonic population.

Planulina exorna dominates the benthonic fauna in about 20 fathoms off Choctawhatchee Bay, Florida and between 20 and 30 fathoms off Mobile Bay, Alabama. It constitutes 10% to 20% of the benthonic fauna in a zone between 12 and 20 fathoms from Choctawhatchee Bay to Mobile Bay. The Miliolidae dominate the benthonic fauna principally off Cape San Blas, Florida, but isolated areas of dominance occur off Choctawhatchee Bay and in the central shelf areas off Mobile, Ala-

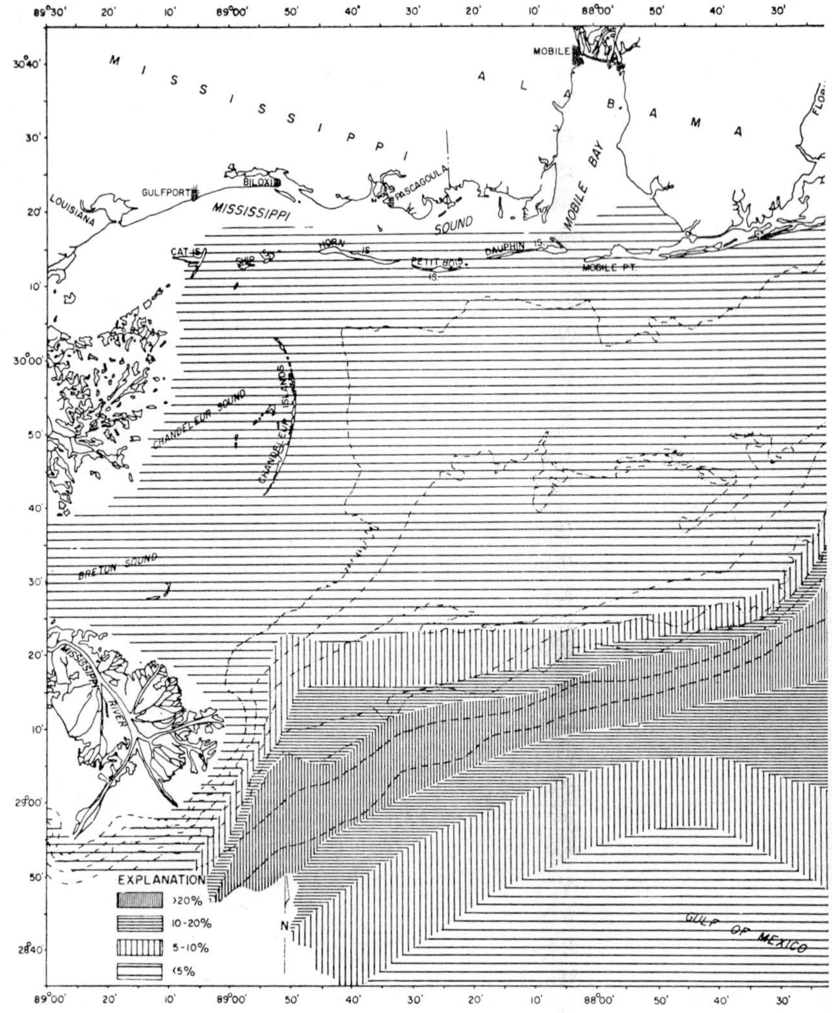

Fig. 15 Distribution of Bolivina *spp.*

bama. It constitutes 10% to 20% of the benthonic fauna in a wide band from 10 to 50 fathoms off Florida and Alabama.

CASSIDULINA FAUNA. The distribution of the species of *Cassidulina* is shown in Figure 14. The zone in which species of *Cassidulina* dominate the benthonic fauna (Figure 2) is bounded on the west by the *Epistominella* and *Nonionella* dominant zones, on the north by the *Rosalina-Hanzawaia* dominant zone and on the south, or seaward side,

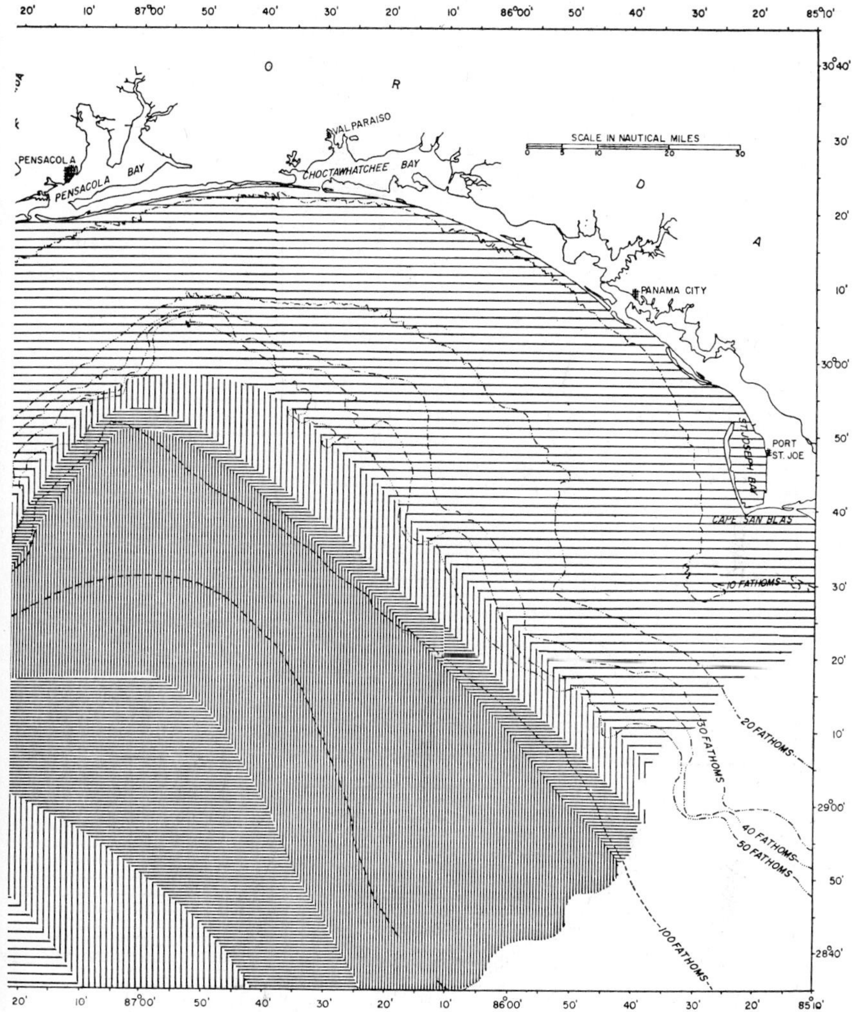

in per cent of total benthonic population.

by the *Bolivina* dominant zone. It extends from Pascagoula, Mississippi eastward as far as Choctawhatchee Bay, Florida and occurs between 30 and 100 fathoms. In the western part of its distribution the faunal association is *Cassidulina-Epistominella-Nonionella* or *Cassidulina-Nonionella-Epistominella* and *Cassidulina-Rosalina-Epistominella.* Along the shoreward side of its distribution, the faunas are principally *Cassidulina-Rosalina-Hanzawaia* and *Cassidulina-Hanza-*

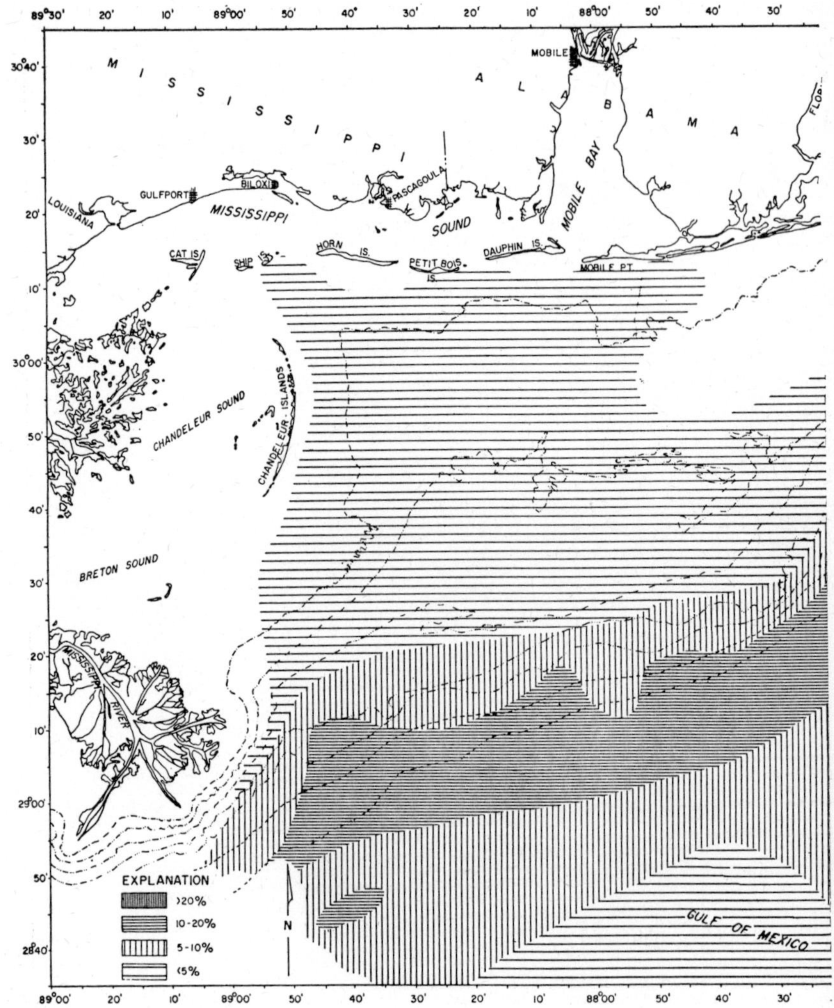

Fig. 16 Distribution of Uvigerina *spp.*

waia-Rosalina, with local abundance of *Amphistegina, Planulina,* and miliolids. To the seaward, where the *Cassidulina* dominant zone is in contact with the *Bolivina* zone, the faunal association is *Cassidulina-Bolivina-Bolivina lowmani.* In a few cases, specimens of *Bolivina lowmani* outnumber specimens of *Bolivina* spp.

BOLIVINA FAUNA. The distribution of species of *Bolivina* is shown in Figure 15. The *Bolivina* dominant zone occurs just seaward of the

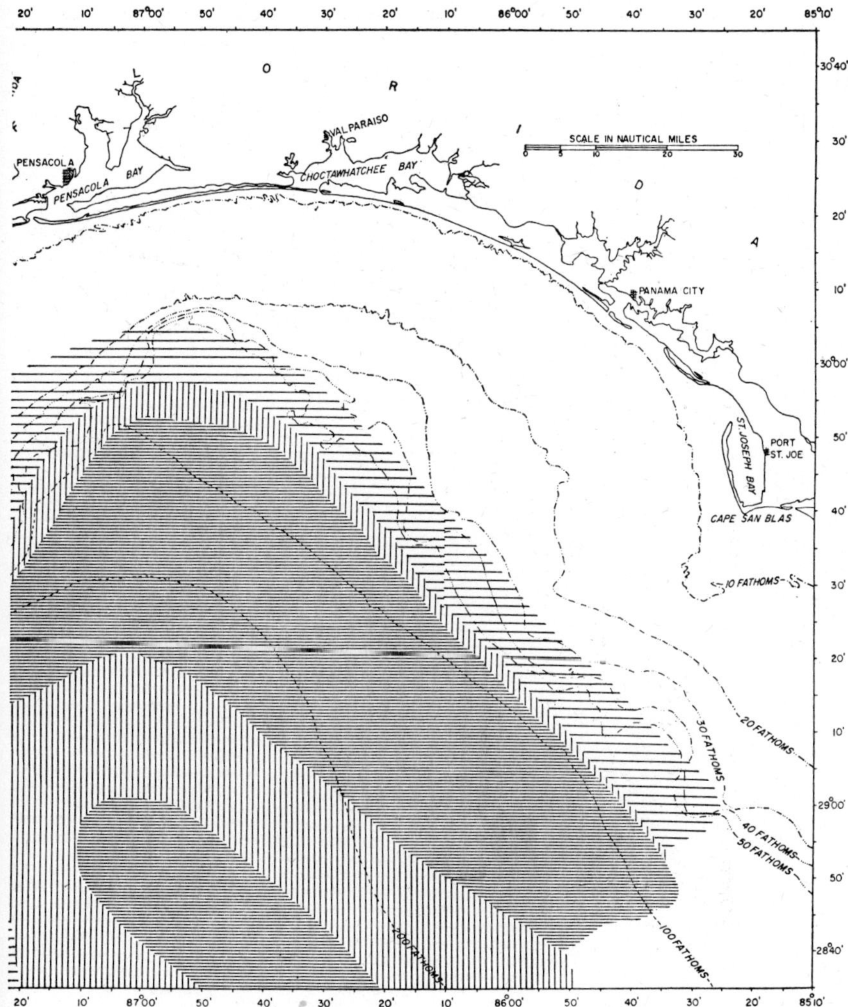

in per cent of total benthonic population.

Cassidulina zone and is in contact with the *Epistominella* zone off the Mississippi Delta and the *Amphistegina* zone off Cape San Blas, Florida (Figure 2); it is bounded by the *Bulimina* zone on its seaward side. The zone is narrow from the Mississippi Delta eastward to Mobile Bay, where it fans out and becomes about 50 miles wide off northern Florida. On the shoreward side of the zone the faunal assemblage varies from a *Bolivina-Epistominella-Bulimina* fauna near

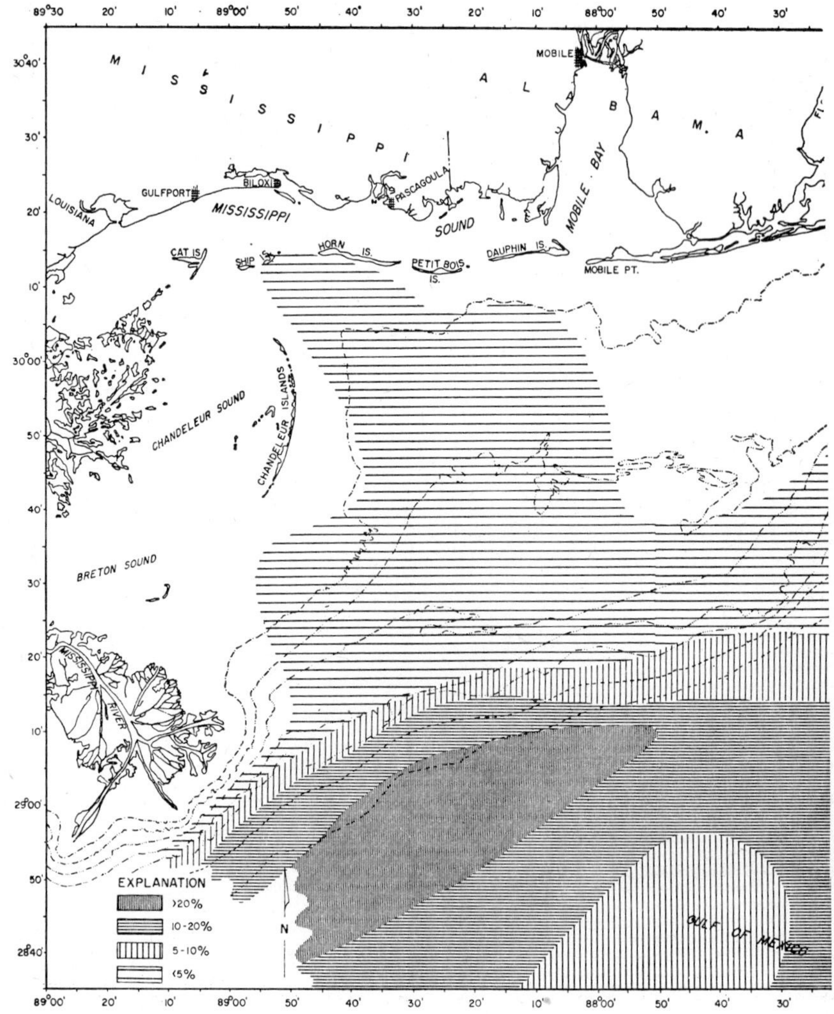

Fig. 17 Distribution of Bulimina *spp. in*

the Mississippi Delta to a *Bolivina-Cassidulina-Bulimina* or a *Bolivina-Cassidulina-Uvigerina* fauna off Alabama and Florida. These faunas grade into a *Bolivina-Bulimina-Cassidulina* or a *Bolivina-Bulimina-Uvigerina* fauna near the seaward edge of the *Bolivina* zone.

Throughout the *Bolivina* zone, at least as far east as Pensacola, Florida, specimens of *Bolivina lowmani* are common to abundant, and sometimes dominate the fauna. The significance of the bimodal distribution of this species is not obvious to the writer, but more than

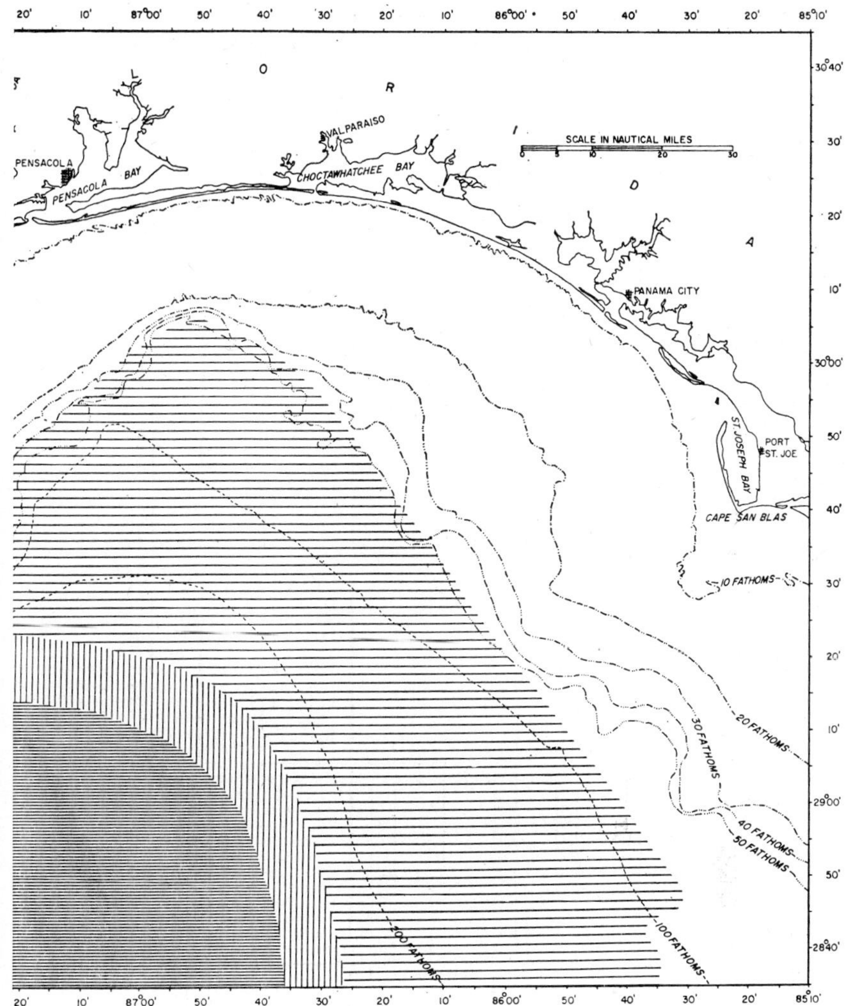

per cent of total benthonic population.

one closely related species may be included in the counts. It also is possible that this portion of the *B. lowmani* fauna is nonindigenous. There is, however, no difficulty in distinguishing the faunal associations in the *Bolivina* zone from those where *Bolivina lowmani* is abundant in shallow water.

BULIMINA FAUNA. The distribution of the species of *Bulimina* is shown in Figure 17. The *Bulimina* dominant zone is the deepest generic dominant group in the area under consideration. It lies to

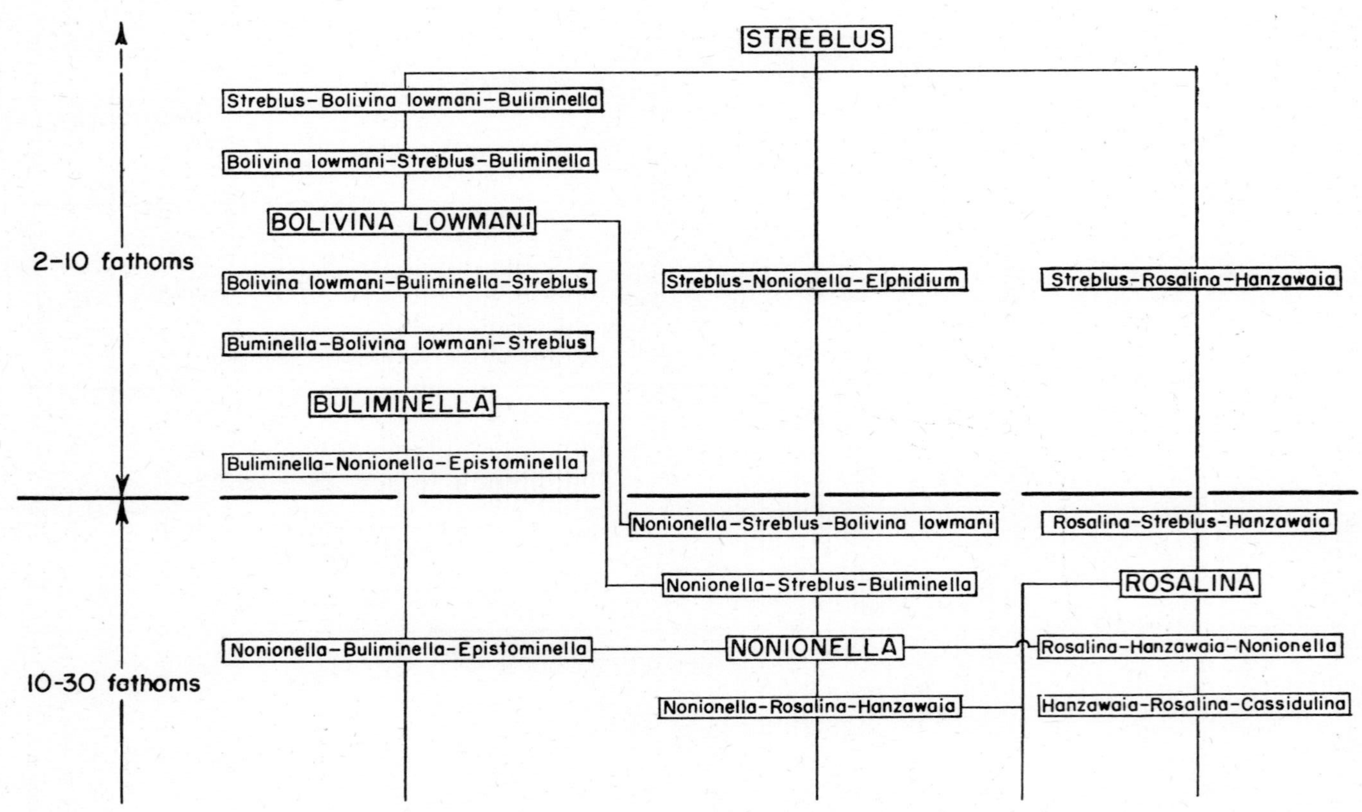

STREBLUS
2-10 fathoms
Streblus-Bolivina lowmani-Buliminella
Bolivina lowmani-Streblus-Buliminella
BOLIVINA LOWMANI
Bolivina lowmani-Buliminella-Streblus
Streblus-Nonionella-Elphidium
Streblus-Rosalina-Hanzawaia
Buminella-Bolivina lowmani-Streblus
BULIMINELLA
Buliminella-Nonionella-Epistominella
Nonionella-Streblus-Bolivina lowmani
Rosalina-Streblus-Hanzawaia
Nonionella-Streblus-Buliminella
ROSALINA
10-30 fathoms
Nonionella-Buliminella-Epistominella
NONIONELLA
Rosalina-Hanzawaia-Nonionella
Nonionella-Rosalina-Hanzawaia
Hanzawaia-Rosalina-Cassidulina

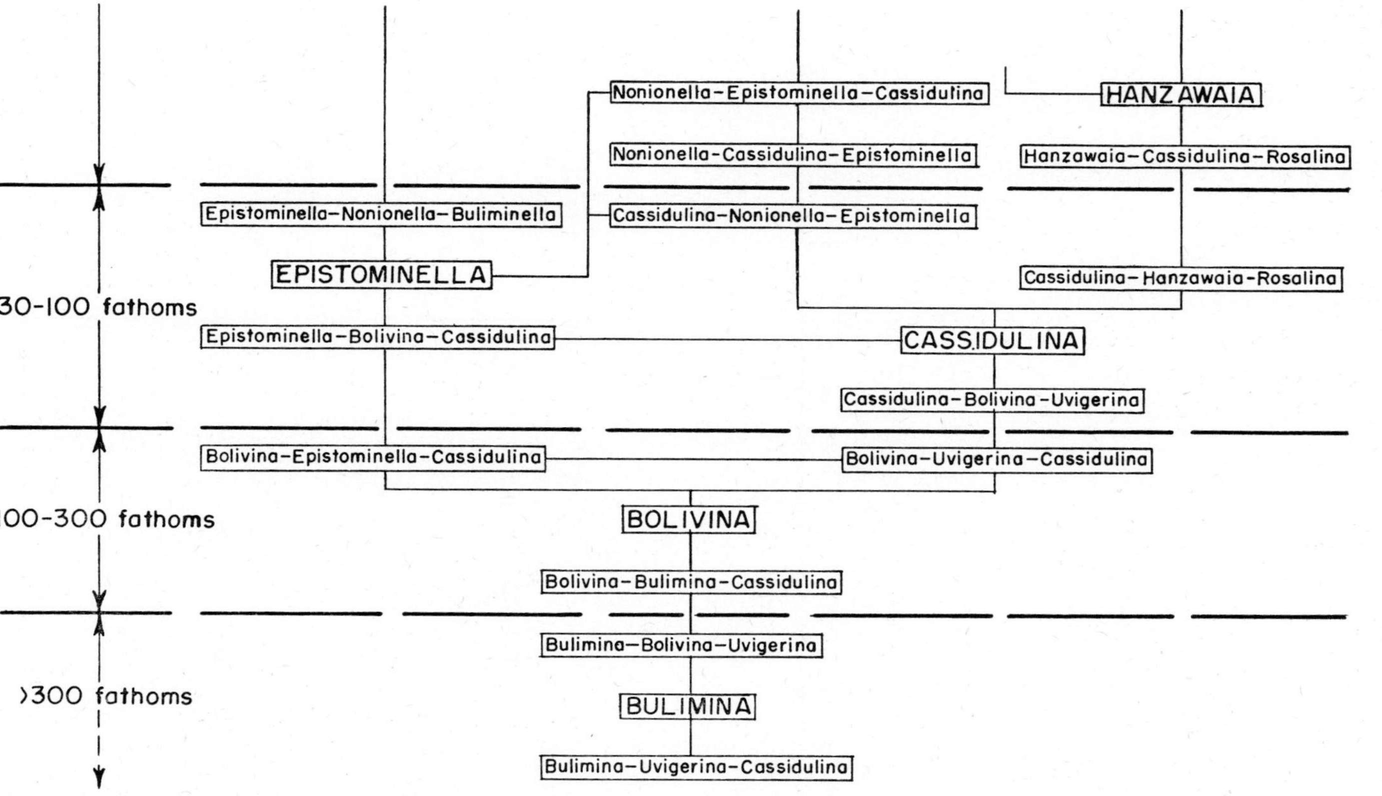

Fig. 18 Generic associations of dominant open-marine faunas.

the seaward of the *Bolivina* dominant zone. The secondary faunal associations within this zone vary between *Bolivina-Uvigerina* and *Cassidulina* with such species as "*Rotalia*" *translucens* Phleger and Parker, *Osangularia culter* (Parker and Jones), and *Epistominella decorata* (Phleger and Parker), constituting significant percentages of the faunas in some samples.

Figure 18 is a schematic representation of the offshore progression and the generic associations of the open-marine foraminiferal faunas. The depth ranges indicated are approximate and based on the distribution of the dominant genera (Figure 2).

Species Composition of Dominant Genera

The numbers of species which comprise the dominant genera just described vary from one to fifteen. As a general rule, however, two or three species occur far more abundantly than the others. We shall discuss these species since some have complementary distributions within their generic dominance distribution.

The specific identification of the forms listed is based on comparisons with holotype specimens available at the United States National Museum or with pleisotypes previously recorded from the northeastern Gulf of Mexico by Parker (1954). These species are illustrated by Parker (1954) and/or Phleger (1954).

THECAMOEBINA. The work done on these small Protozoa has been insufficient to list specific names, but it is known that at least two genera are present—*Difflugia* and *Centropyxis*.

MILIAMMINA. Two species of *Miliammina* are recorded from the area, the most dominant being *Miliammina fusca* (H. B. Brady). Another species, *Miliammina* sp. is reported from the Mississippi Delta and Mississippi-Alabama marshes, but it is not abundant. It is described as being more smoothly and finely arenaceous and narrower than *M. fusca*. Commonly associated with *Miliammina* are *Ammoastuta inepta* (Cushman and McCulloch), *Trochammina macrescens* H. B. Brady, *Haplophragmoides subinvolutum* Cushman and McCulloch, *Ammoscalaria fluvialis* Parker, and *Arenoparrella mexicana* (Kornfeld).

AMMOBACULITES. There are six species of *Ammobaculites* in the area. *A. salsus* Cushman and Bronnimann is by far the most common species and generally constitutes over 50% of the *Ammobaculites* fauna. In addition, specimens of *A. dilatatus* Cushman and Bronnimann, *A. diversus* Cushman and Bronnimann, *A. exiguus* Cushman and Bronnimann, and *A. exilis* Cushman and Bronnimann are common, and *A. salsus* var. *distinctus* Cushman occurs.

ELPHIDIUM. Nine species of Elphidium constitute the *Elphidium* fauna. Of these nine, *E. gunteri* Cole is the most abundant, but *E. incertum mexicanum* Kornfeld and *E. poeyanum* (d'Orbigny) are common. *E. discoidale* (d'Orbigny) is common in the offshore portion of the *Elphidium* distribution. Specimens of *E. advenum* (Cushman), *E. galvestonense* Kornfeld, *E. koeboeense* LeRoy, and *E. matagordanum* (Kornfeld) occur rarely.

STREBLUS. Two varieties of *Streblus beccarii* (Linné) constitute the bulk of the *Streblus* distributions. These varieties are *S. beccarii* (Linné) var. *tepidus* (Cushman) and *S. beccarii* (Linné) var. *sobrinus* (Shupack). They are synonymous with *S. beccarii* var. B and *S. beccarii* var. A of Phleger, Parker and Peirson (1953). They occur together over the *Streblus* distribution, but *S. beccarii* var. *sobrinus* is definitely more abundant in the more restricted areas behind barriers, while *S. beccarii* var. *tepidus* is more widespread in its distribution and occurs more abundantly in the offshore area.

BULIMINELLA. Two species, *B. elegantissima* (d'Orbigny) and *B. bassendorfensis* Cushman and Parker, constitute the *Buliminella* fauna. Of these two species, *B. elegantissima* has the shoalest distribution and is most abundant in the *Buliminella* dominant zone near Ship Island (Figure 2). *B. bassendorfensis* replaces *B. elegantissima* in the deeper portions of the *Buliminella* distribution off the Mississippi Delta.

NONIONELLA. The *Nonionella* fauna is composed of two species, *N. opima* Cushman and *N. atlantica* Cushman. The principal species within the *Nonionella* dominant zone (Figure 2) is *N. opima*. *N. atlantica* is present, but rare. East of Petit Bois Island off the coast of Mississippi, *N. opima* becomes subdominant to *N. atlantica*. This relationship holds in the central shelf area off Mobile Bay, Alabama where *Nonionella* occurs. *N. atlantica* continues to occur toward the east as far as Choctawhatchee Bay. Only rare and occasional specimens of *N. atlantica* are found east and south of Choctawhatchee Bay along the coast of Florida.

EPISTOMINELLA. For all practical purposes only one species, *E. vitrea* Parker, is included in this distribution.

ROSALINA. Six species constitute the *Rosalina* fauna: *R. bertheloti* d'Orbigny, *R. concinna* (H. B. Brady), *R. floridana* (Cushman), *R. floridensis* (Cushman), *R. parkerae* (Natland), and *R. suezensis* (Said). The two most widespread species are *R. concinna* and *R. floridana*, of which *R. concinna* is by far the most abundant.

HANZAWAIA. Two species, *H. strattoni* (Applin) and *H. concentrica* (Cushman), constitute the *Hanzawaia* dominant zone. *H. concentrica* is rare in the area and *H. strattoni* constitutes the bulk of the fauna.

AMPHISTEGINA. There appears to be more than one species in the *Amphistegina* dominant zone. What is thought to be *A. lessonii* d'Orbigny is the most common form. There is, however, considerable variation between specimens and many are replaced or glauconitized.

MILIOLIDAE. The miliolids constitute a large group of species (principally of the genera *Quinqueloculina, Triloculina, Spiroloculina,* and *Pyrgo*) that individually occur in small concentrations but which collectively constitute relatively high percentages of the benthonic population in certain areas. In terms of species, *Quinqueloculina compta* Cushman, *Q. lamarckiana* d'Orbigny, and *Q. bicostata* d'Orbigny are the most common, but they seldom constitute over 1 or 2% of the benthonic fauna.

CASSIDULINA. Six species of *Cassidulina* constitute the *Cassidulina* dominant zone: *C. carinata* Silvestri, *C.* aff. *crassa* d'Orbigny, *C. curvata* Phleger and Parker, *C. laevigata* d'Orbigny, *C. neocarinata* Thalmann, and *C. subglobosa.* The most common species in this group is *C. subglobosa.* It occurs widely in the study area but is most abundant near the shelf edge or deeper. In addition, *C. carinata, C. laevigata,* and *C. neocarinata* are rare on the continental shelf, but are common deeper than 100 fathoms.

BOLIVINA. *Bolivina* is the most variable genus (contains the largest number of species) of any of the dominant genera. Fifteen species have been recorded in the study area (Parker, 1954). The most common occurrence of most of these species is within or near the *Bolivina* dominant zone. The most dominant species is *B. subaenariensis mexicana* Cushman, which constitutes up to 20% of the benthonic populations. Deeper than about 100 fathoms, specimens of *B. albatrossi* Cushman, *B. barbata* Phleger and Parker, *B. fragilis* Phleger and Parker, *B. lanceolata* Parker, *B. minima* Phleger and Parker, *B. ordinaria* Phleger and Parker, *B. pusilla* Schwager, and *B. subspinescens* Cushman are common to abundant. What has been called *B. lowmani* Phleger and Parker is common to abundant in the *Bolivina* dominant zone as well as in shallower water in the *Streblus* zone. Specimens of *B. göesii* Cushman, *B. paula* Cushman and Cahill, *B. pulchella primitiva* Cushman, *B. striatula spinata* Cushman, and *B. translucens* Phleger and Parker are rare in the area.

BULIMINA. Five species constitute the *Bulimina* dominant zone. Of the three most common species, *B. marginata* d'Orbigny is most abundant around 100 fathoms, and *B. aculeata* d'Orbigny and *B.*

alazanensis Cushman are most abundant in water deeper than about 200 fathoms. *B. spicata* Phleger and Parker is also common deeper than 200 fathoms. *B. striata mexicana* Cushman occurs in low concentrations deeper than about 100 fathoms.

Total Benthonic Populations

The distribution of total benthonic populations (number of specimens per unit volume sample) in the study area is shown in Figure 19. The zone of greatest abundance of benthonic specimens (more than 10,000 specimens per 10 cc sample) occurs along the edge of the continental shelf off Florida and eastern Alabama and covers a large portion of the central shelf area off western Alabama and eastern Mississippi. Total benthonic populations decrease both landward and seaward of this zone. Isolated areas in the nearshore zone exceed 1000 specimens per sample (shown in Figure 19) but are not indicated due to their localized occurrences. The values given in Figure 19 are based largely on estimates and should be considered as representing orders of magnitude only.

Total Planktonic Populations

The distribution of the zones of relative abundance of planktonic foraminifera per unit volume sample is shown in Figure 20. As with the total benthonic population, these zones are based on estimates and should be taken to indicate orders of magnitude only.

The zone of greatest abundance of planktonic specimens (10,000 specimens per 10 cc sample) is wide off Florida and occurs deeper than 100 fathoms. Off Mobile Bay, Alabama, the maximum zone is constricted in a narrow belt along the outer edge of the continental shelf. The second most abundant zone (5000 to 10,000 specimens per unit volume sample) follows the same distribution but extends farther toward the west and terminates 10 to 15 miles east of the Mississippi River Delta. Off northern Florida there is a progressive increase in total planktonic populations in an offshore direction. Off Alabama and Mississippi, however, there is a sharp increase in planktonics at a depth of approximately 30 fathoms, reaching a maximum between 40 and 100 fathoms and decreasing deeper than 100 fathoms.

Living Foraminiferal Populations

A total of 423 analyses of living benthonic foraminiferal populations has been made in the study area. Approximately 150 of these sta-

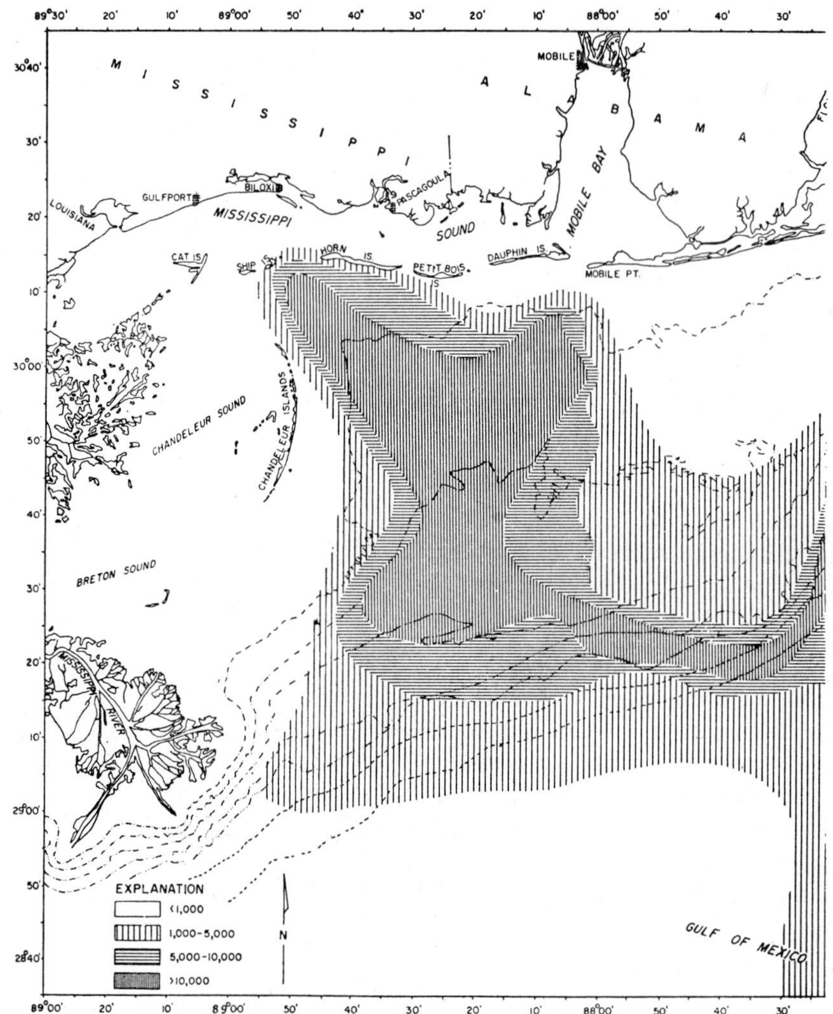

Fig. 19 Total benthonic populations

tions are located around the eastern Mississippi River Delta and Breton Island. The remainder is distributed over the continental shelf and slope along the profiles shown in Figure 1.

With regard to depth, the largest number of stations from which living populations were counted occurs in the 0 to 5 fathom depth range (136 stations). Forty samples occur in the 6 to 10 fathom range, 13 samples between 11 and 15 fathoms, 88 samples between 15 and 20

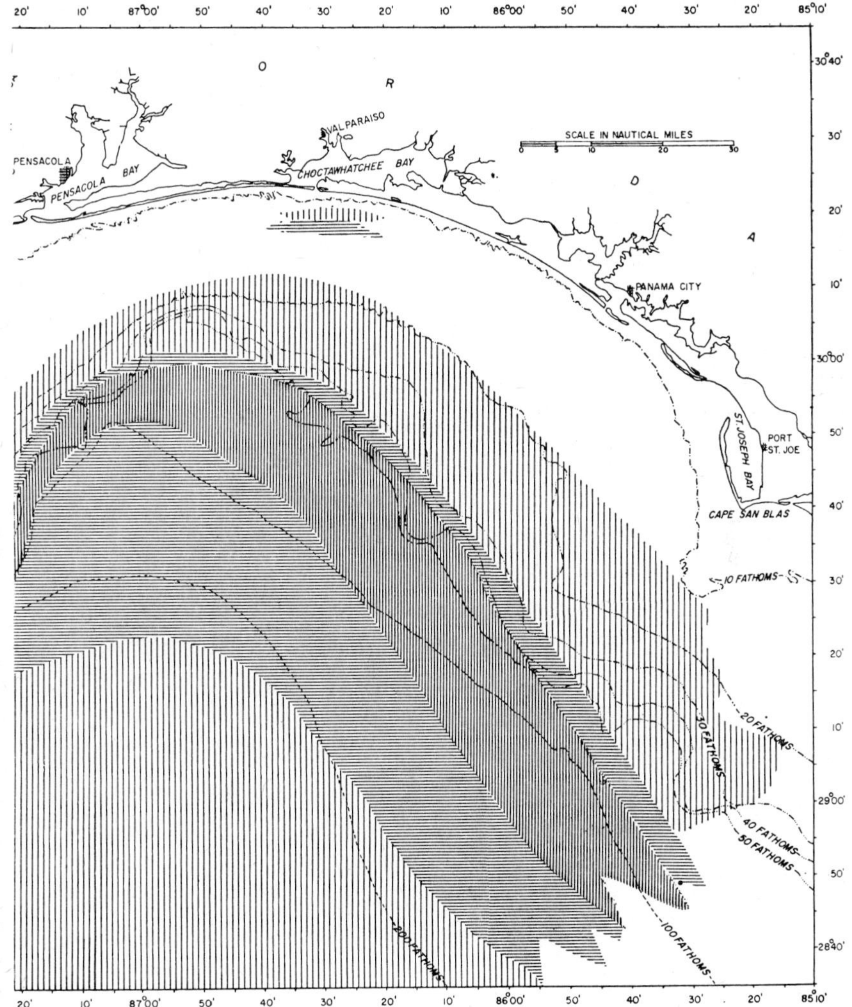

(*number of specimens per unit volume*).

fathoms, and 54 samples between 50 and 100 fathoms. The remainder of the samples occurs in various depths up to 1000 fathoms.

The largest concentration of living specimens occurs in the 6 to 10 fathom zone. Within this zone there is an average of over 180 specimens per unit volume sample (10 cc). This zone is characteristically the most productive depth zone in this area with living populations as high as 1000 specimens per unit volume sample. Living populations

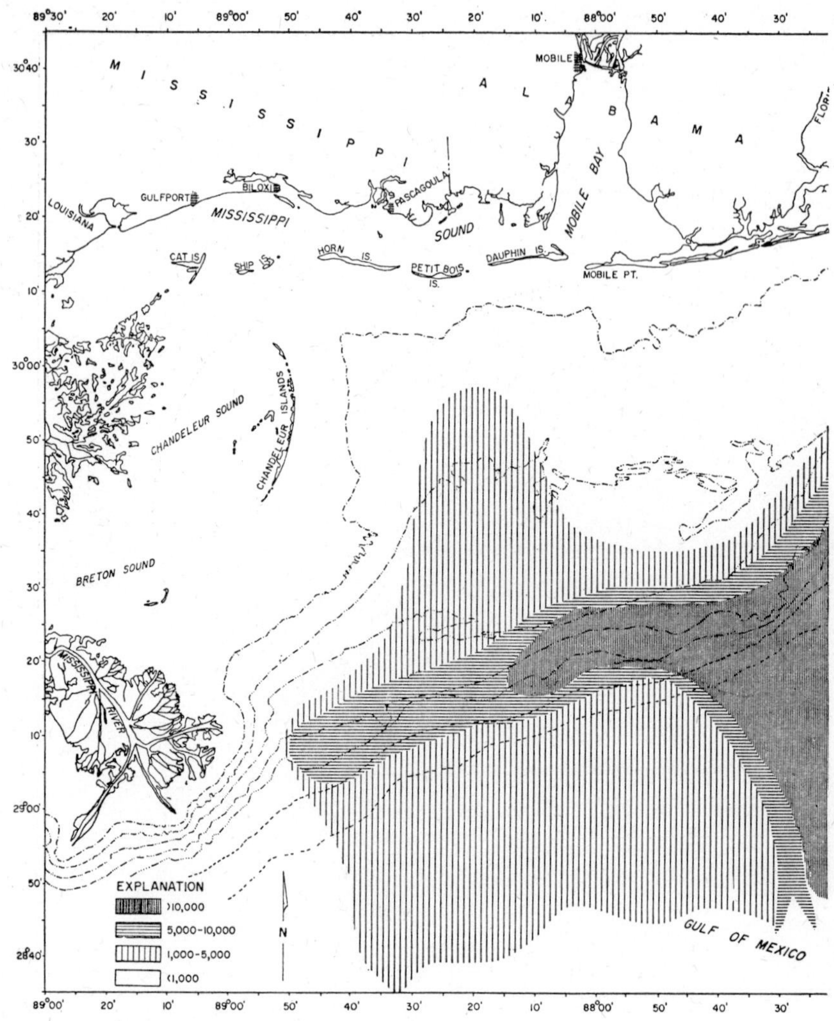

Fig. 20 Total planktonic populations

decrease with increasing depth to a minimum average of less than 10 specimens per sample deeper than 200 fathoms.

Geographically, the largest number of living benthonic specimens occurs off the active passes of the eastern Mississippi River Delta. The largest population recorded has 1152 living specimens and occurs in the *Nonionella* dominant zone. Total living benthonic specimens

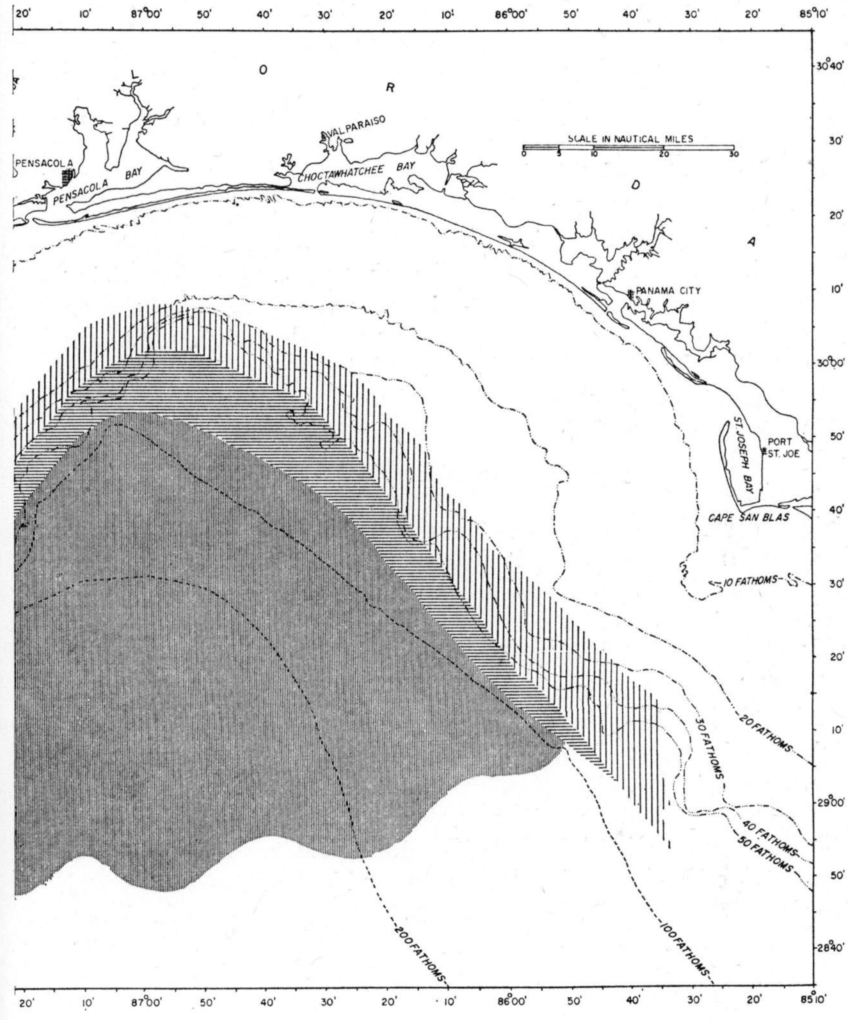

(*number of specimens per unit volume*).

are also abundant off Dauphin Island, Alabama, at the mouth of Mobile Bay.

The most common living species throughout the area is *Nonionella opima*. In the marginal-marine areas, *Ammobaculites salsus* and *Streblus beccarii* variants are locally abundant. The most common living species in the open-marine environment (deeper than 10 fathoms) are *Nonionella opima, Nouria polymorphinoides,* and *Hanzawaia strattoni.* Near the edge of the continental shelf, total living populations are low but living species of *Bolivina, Bulimina,* and *Uvigerina* are common. Living specimens of *Chilostomella* and *Globobulimina* are common deeper than 200 fathoms.

The distribution of the dominant generic groups discussed in a previous section is based on total populations of empty (dead) benthonic foraminiferal tests. The data are too few to construct similar distributions based on living species or genera. Sufficient living counts are available, however, to indicate that the major generic groups (Figure 2), with the exception of part of the *Rosalina* zone, are supported by the adequate production and deposition of foraminiferal tests at the present time.

The western part of the *Rosalina* zone and the *Cassidulina* zone appear to be relict zones in the sense that only isolated living specimens of the genera that dominate the dead populations are found. Living populations over the western part of the *Rosalina* zone are dominated by species of *Nonionella* or *Nouria.* To the east, off the coast of Florida, the *Rosalina* zone is adequately supported by living specimens of that genus. The most dominant living genera within the *Cassidulina* zone are *Nonionella* (in the western part), *Hanzawaia,* and *Bolivina.* Few living specimens of *Cassidulina subglobosa* were found, although it is the dominant species in the *Cassidulina* zone. Living specimens of *Cassidulina neocarinata* are common, however, near the shelf edge. The *Amphistegina* zone off Florida, as well as the zone of abundant *Amphistegina* along the shelf edge in association with the reefs (Ludwick and Walton, 1957) and in the central shelf area (Figure 1) are not adequately supported by living specimens, and dead specimens are principally glauconitized and/or replaced. These three zones, the *Rosalina, Cassidulina,* and *Amphistegina* zones, which are not adequately supported by living faunas, are discussed more fully in the following section.

There is a definite east-west variation in the living foraminiferal faunas. Living specimens of *Nonionella* become uncommon or rare east of Mobile Bay. Likewise, living specimens of *Streblus* decrease in abundance eastward in the open-marine environment. In contrast, living specimens of *Rosalina* become more abundant toward the east, and specimens of *Hanzawaia* continue to be common. The "West Indian" faunal influence appears off the coast of Florida where common living specimens of *Asterigerina, Nodobaculariella,* and *Peneroplis* occur. This influence is also obvious in the dead populations but not to the extent that either genus is dominant. In addition, the

Miliolidae become more common in the living populations toward the east and reflect the "West Indian" influence.

Nonindigenous Foraminiferal Populations

Four types of foraminiferal populations occur on the continental shelf in the northeastern Gulf of Mexico: (1) populations in which the dominant living species occur in large concentrations not reflected in the concentrations of empty tests of that species; (2) populations in which the dominant living species are the same as and occur in concentrations apparently in equilibrium with the dominant dead species; (3) populations in which the concentrations of empty tests are dominated by species that do not occur in significant numbers in the living fauna; and (4) populations that contain species in significant concentrations which have not been found living in the area (nonindigenous species).

The first type of foraminiferal fauna, a result of a very recent, regional environmental change, is seen in the central shelf and eastern part of the area. Species of *Nonionella, Nouria,* and *Cancris* are the most abundant living forms, yet they are not common in the associated population of empty tests. The second type of population includes the generic groups shown in Figure 2, with the exception of the western part of the *Rosalina* fauna, the *Cassidulina* fauna, and the *Amphistegina* fauna. The third type of population is represented by the western part of the *Rosalina* fauna, the *Cassidulina* fauna, and the *Amphistegina* fauna. Although living species of *Rosalina, Cassidulina,* and *Amphistegina* are present in the area, they are rare and could not support dominance in the dead faunas. As far as is known from meager data, living species of both *Rosalina* and *Amphistegina* are more abundant in the far eastern part of the area under consideration. Only rare occurrences of living *Cassidulina subglobosa,* which constitutes by far the largest percentage of the *Cassidulina* fauna, have been recorded. The ecological significance of this fauna is not known. It is aligned, however, along the shelf edge with the subregional reef trend and may be related to the associated residual reef fauna.

The fourth type of population contains a group of species—most specimens of which are brown in color, wholly or partially replaced with secondary calcite, or glauconitized—which have not been found living in the study area. They occur in the dead population over most of the continental shelf as far west as the Chandeleur Islands, and occasionally in large concentrations. Previously (Ludwick and Walton, 1957) this fauna has been referred to as the "brown fauna."

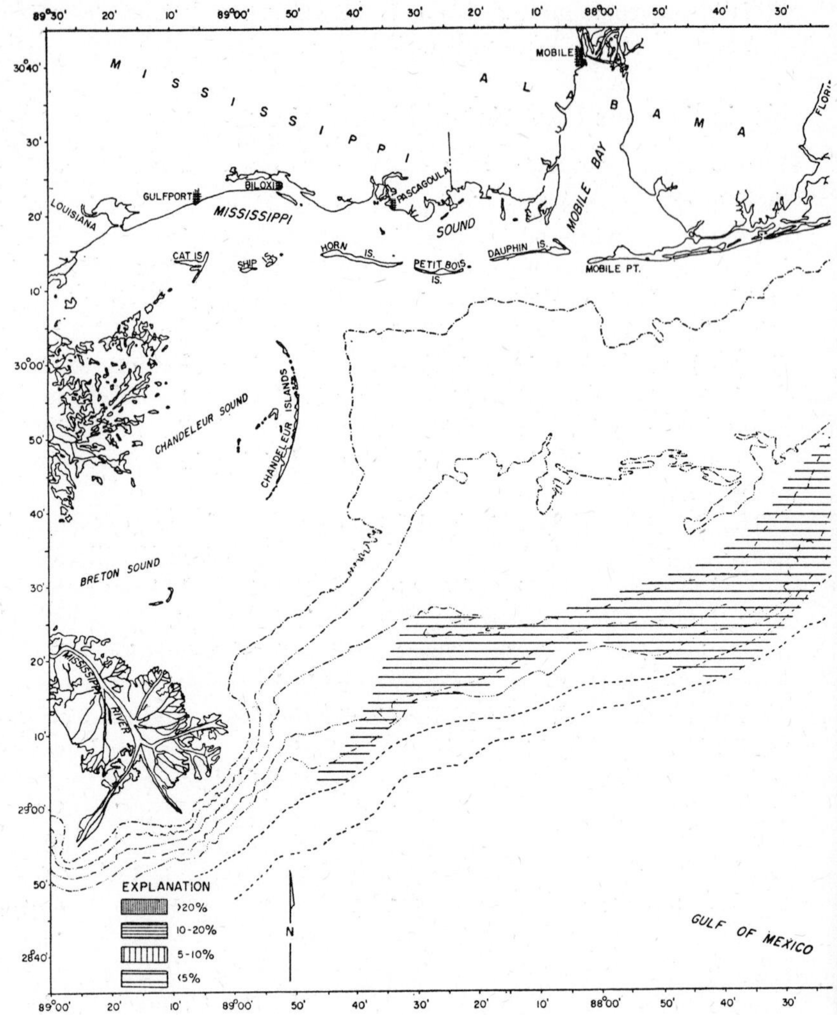

Fig. 21 Distribution of Liebusella *spp. in*

It consists of specimens of *Asterigerina carinata, Eponides repandus,* Miliolidae (large forms), *Nodobaculariella cassis,* and *Peneroplis proteus.* The distribution of these forms is spotty and possibly could be extended with additional samples. This fauna is a remnant of a previous, more extensive distribution of "West Indian" Foraminifera which now is confined to the shallow continental shelf area off Florida.

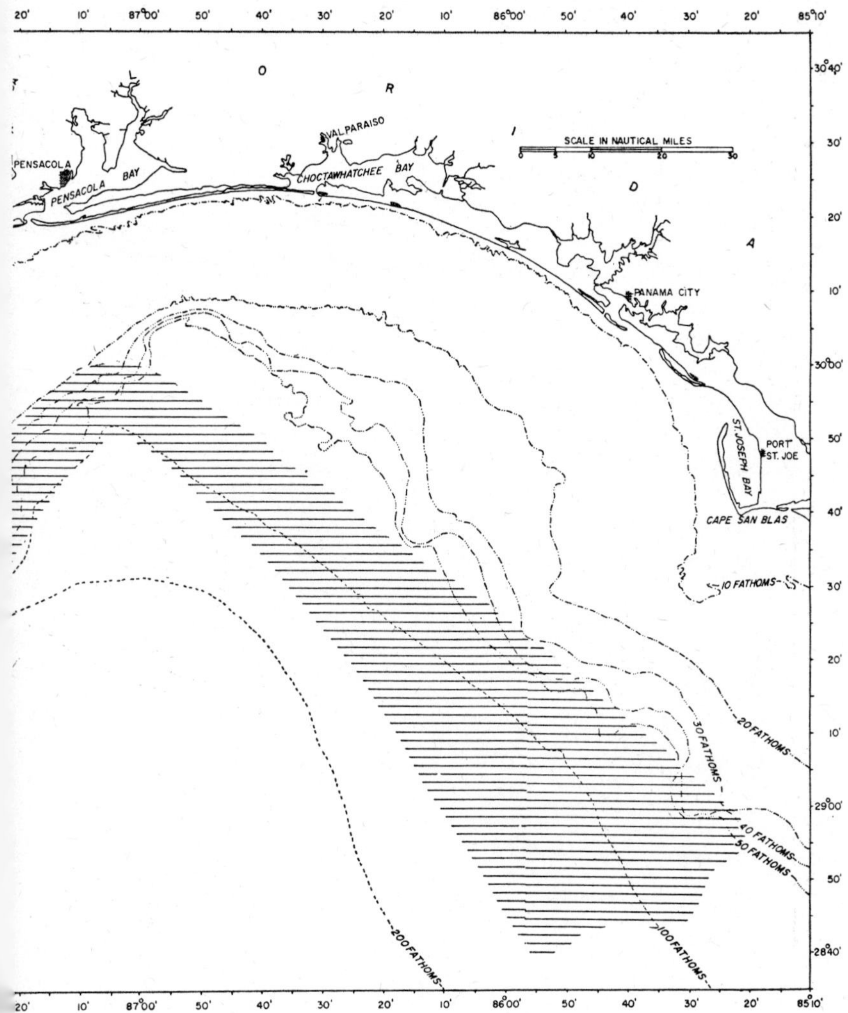

per cent of total benthonic population.

In addition to the above species, a second group of nonindigenous species occurs along the outer continental shelf: *Archais compressus*, *Liebusella* spp. (*L. soldanii* var. *intermedia* and *L. soldanii*), *Textulariella barrettii*, and *Cuneolina angusta*. The distribution of *Liebusella* spp. are shown in Figure 21. This latter group of species is associated with the reef trend along the outer edge of the continental

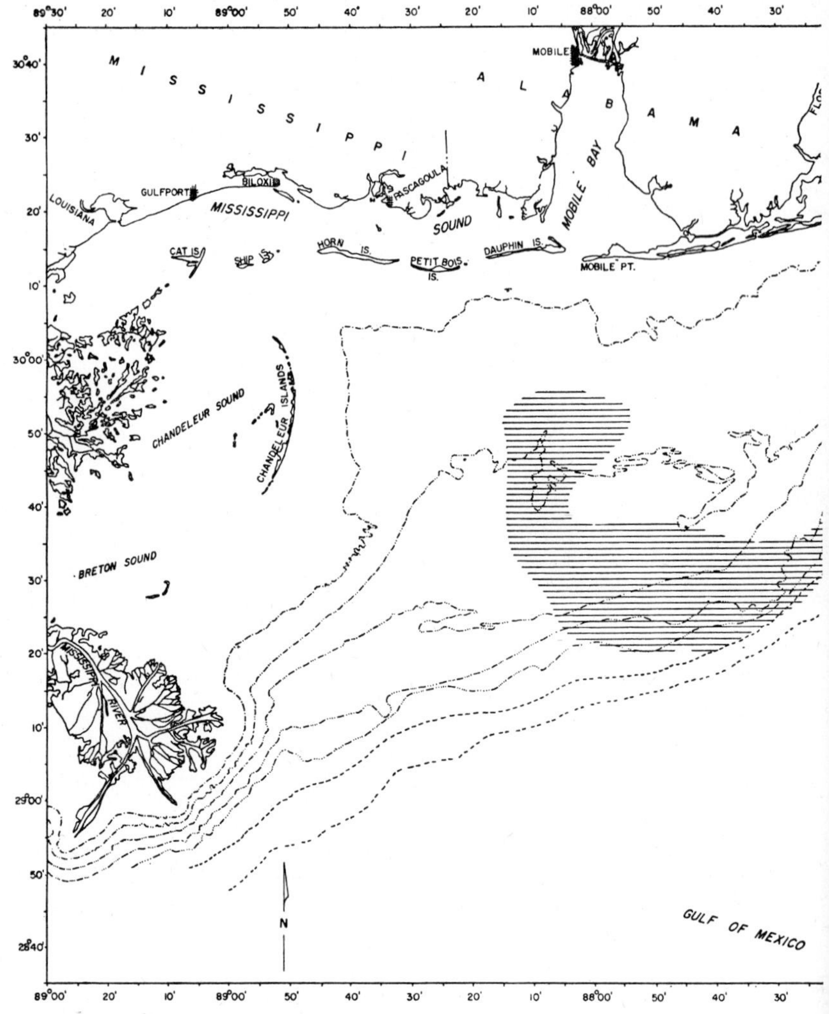

Fig. 22 Area of occurrence of

shelf. Where it occurs, this unusually large fauna (in size of specimens) is associated with abundant biogenic, calcareous debris in the form of algae, pieces of carbonate rock, and mollusk shells.

These two nonindigenous foraminiferal faunas appear to have different relative ages in the development of the continental shelf even though they have certain species in common. Figure 22 indicates the area in which the nonindigenous faunas occur. Their actual occur-

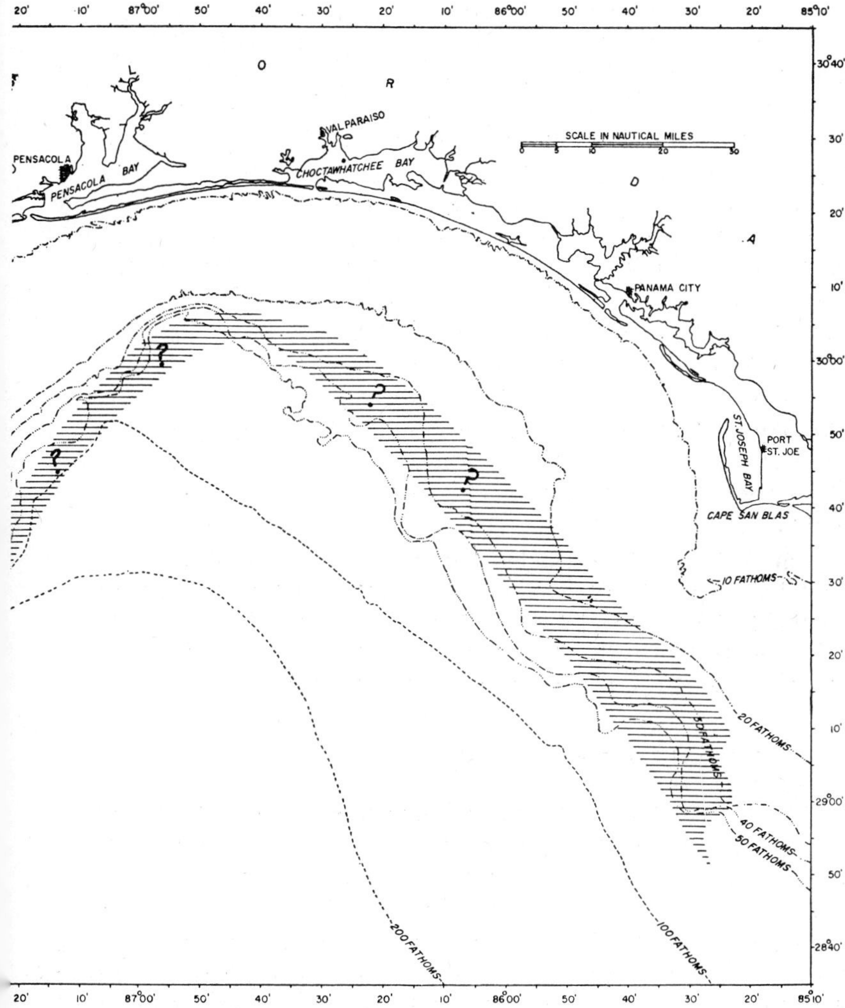

nonindigenous Foraminifera.

rence within the area indicated in Figure 22 is spotty and not continuous. The "brown fauna" is restricted to that portion of the continental shelf shoreward of the reef trend. The unusually large specimens of *Archais, Liebusella, Textulariella,* and *Cuneolina* occur only along the outer edge of the continental shelf and only on the seaward slope of the intensively sampled shelf-edge reef area off Mobile, Alabama. The process that led to the replacement and coloration of the "brown fauna" did not affect the shelf-edge fauna. The large *Amphistegina* fauna at the shelf edge may be related to a similar fossil fauna reported off the coast of central Florida in 98 fathoms (Gould and Stewart, 1955).

There is at present no direct quantitative method of separating nonindigenous species from indigenous species in the absence of living controls, that is, in fossil faunas. However, the nonindigenous faunas are easily recognizable in the northeastern Gulf of Mexico on the basis of (1) the large size and thickness of their tests relative to the indigenous fauna; (2) their brown color and preservation (replaced by secondary calcite or glauconitized); (3) their occurrence with abundant broken mollusk shells or calcareous algae; (4) their subdominant occurrences along with abundant indigenous species of different environmental implications; (5) the weathered appearance of most of the tests; and (6) their spotty distribution. One or more of these characteristics should aid in the recognition of nonindigenous species within an indigenous fauna.

Some relict species occur in large concentrations on the open continental shelf, and in a few cases may constitute 40% to 45% of the total benthonic foraminiferal fauna. The relationship of these species to faunal variability will aid in delineating them as nonindigenous species in areas where they dominate the benthonic fauna.

Foraminiferal Facies

Two types of foraminiferal facies exist in the area under consideration—geographic facies (east-west faunal variations) and depth facies (no causal relationship is intended in the use of "depth").

The most striking geographic facies are the *Nonionella* dominant zone, the *Epistominella* dominant zone (Figure 2) their disappearance toward the east, and the appearance of less dominant forms such as *Asterigerina, Peneroplis, Nodobaculariella,* and the abundant Miliolidae that occur indigenously in the eastern part of the area under consideration. The *Hanzawaia* dominant zone (Figure 2) appears to be isolated on the continental shelf off Alabama, but abundant specimens of *Hanzawaia* are known to occur off northern Florida, and it is believed that additional sample coverage to the east would extend this zone. The zone of dominant *Cassidulina* also appears to discontinue off Choctawhatchee Bay, Florida, but by the same token additional sample coverage might extend the zone farther to the east. The deeper water zones (deeper than 100 fathoms), even though they vary considerably in width, occur continuously around this portion of the Gulf of Mexico.

Depth facies can be defined best in terms of ranges of individual species. It is well established that individual species have discrete depth ranges over which they occur in addition to discrete distributions in the geographic sense just mentioned. Such depth distributions of species have been established in the area considered in this report by Parker (1954) and Phleger (1955).

The usefulness of recent ecological criteria to stratigraphic paleontologists depends, to a great extent, on the reliability of the data in terms of geologic time, that is, the ability of the criterion to bridge the gap between the recent and the ancient fauna and thus allow comparisons. Criteria based on species are the most rigorous but, due to evolutionary changes, are the most limited in terms of application to the geologic past due to restricted geologic ranges of species. Species characteristics are the last to be added and the first to be changed. Of the several hundreds of species that have been identified in the area, approximately 30 species, representing the 14 genera mentioned earlier, constitute by far the largest portion of the benthonic foraminiferal population in the entire area under consideration.

Depth facies, defined in terms of the most common genera, are more generally applicable to the paleoecologic interpretation of Tertiary faunas than facies based on species distributions. This is demonstrated in Part II of this paper. Generic dominance facies are shown in Figures 6 and 18. In Figure 6 the generic dominance depth facies of the marginal-marine fauna are shown. They include the coastal nonmarine facies, the intertidal facies, the intertidal to 2-fathom facies, and part of the 2- to 10-fathom facies.

The coastal nonmarine facies is a pure Thecamoebina fauna. The intertidal facies includes faunas dominated by the Thecamoebina and *Miliammina,* in addition to subdominant genera such as *Ammoastuta, Trochammina, Haplophragmoides,* and *Jadammina.* The intertidal to 2-fathom facies contains faunas dominated by the genera *Ammobaculites* and *Elphidium,* and the 2- to 10-fathom facies is the *Streblus* dominant zone that overlaps into the open-marine faunas.

Unlike the marginal-marine faunas, the open-marine faunas cannot be divided into depth zones without considering the geographic facies. A fauna from 15 fathoms off the Chandeleur Islands is not the same as a fauna from 15 fathoms off Horn Island, Mississippi, or off the coast of northern Florida.

The open-marine faunal facies are the 2- to 10-fathom, 10- to 30-

fathom, 30- to 100-fathom, 100- to 300-fathom, and the greater than 300-fathom facies (Figure 18). In addition to the *Streblus* dominant zone, the 2- to 10-fathom facies includes zones in which *Buliminella* and *Bolivina lowmani* dominate off the Chandeleur Islands. In the same manner, the 10- to 30-fathom depth zone contains the *Nonionella* dominant fauna off the Chandeleur Islands although it does not occur off Alabama and Florida. The 10- to 30-fathom facies off Alabama and Florida contains the *Rosalina* and *Hanzawaia* dominant zones. The 30- to 100-fathom facies contains the *Epistominella* dominant zone off the Mississippi River Delta and the *Cassidulina* dominant zone off Mississippi and Alabama. The 100- to 300-fathom and the deeper than 300-fathom facies include the *Bolivina* and the *Bulimina* dominant zones, respectively. These latter facies include common to abundant specimens of *Uvigerina* (Figure 16) and *Cassidulina,* as indicated in Figure 18, and do not appear to be affected by geographic facies changes.

It should be emphasized that the depths just listed can only be considered valid for the area under consideration, but the relative positions of the various dominance zones should remain constant. Likewise, the areal extent of the various dominance groups may vary considerably. It is interesting to note, however, that the marginal-marine fauna contains 5 generic dominance zones over an offshore distance of about 15 miles and a depth of 10 fathoms, while the open-marine fauna contains only 9 generic dominance zones between 10 and 1100 fathoms over an areal distance of at least 100 miles. This implies that, at least for this area, the rate of change of dominance zones is greater in the marginal-marine faunas than in the open-marine faunas.

Nonspecific Faunal Characteristics

The following portion of this paper is concerned only with those characteristics of foraminiferal faunas that are exclusive of specific or generic identifications. In contrast to criteria based on specific and generic characteristics, the following characteristics are free of such restrictions as evolutionary changes and changes in environmental tolerance of modern species and genera back through geologic history.

The basic ecological principle involved is that animal populations, regardless of their species composition, have characteristics that reflect the variability of their environment (i.e., the degree of variation of the many physical, chemical, and biological factors that characterize a particular environment). In modern oceans, environmental variability is related to distance offshore and depth of water—that is, as the shoreline (marginal-marine conditions) is approached and depth decreases, the environments become more variable. As shorelines and marginal-marine conditions have existed in all oceans throughout geologic time, modern faunal characteristics which result from the variability of the environment will be valid regardless of the species composition or geologic age of the fauna. The definition of these faunal characteristics on the pages which follow is a principal purpose of Part I of this paper.

Faunal Variability[1]

Faunal variability is based on the number of species of organisms that occurs in any given environment. With the Foraminifera, the number of benthonic species is inversely proportional to the variability of the environment. The areal distribution of numbers of benthonic species of Foraminifera in the area under consideration is shown in Figure 23. They vary from less than ten in the marginal-marine environments to over eighty near the edge of the continental shelf. Seaward of the shelf edge, the number of benthonic species decreases again. As can be seen in Figure 23, the zone of maximum number of species closely follows the edge of the continental shelf off Florida and eastern Alabama, but swings inland off western Alabama and Mississippi. This zone of maximum speciation is related to (1) the zone of nonindigenous fauna (Figure 22); (2) the distribution of maximum benthonic populations (Figure 19); (3) the distribution of maximum planktonic populations (Figure 20); and (4) the shelf-edge reef trend. These data suggest that the zone of maximum numbers of benthonic species of Foraminifera occurs in areas on the continental shelf where there is relatively little dilution of population by detrital sediments. The decrease in numbers of benthonic species off the continental shelf suggests that the deeper water, even though supporting a practically nonvariable environment, is like the extremely variable environments, not conducive to the formation of benthonic species. The decrease in number of species in deeper water could not be confused with the similar decrease in a shoreward direction, however, due to the abundant planktonic specimens in association with the former.

With regard to the major generic dominance faunal zones just described (Figures 6 and 18), averages of the numbers of species within

[1] The term "faunal diversity" has been suggested by John Imbrie as a better term for this faunal characteristic due to other implications of the term "variability." "Faunal diversity" is used in Part II of this paper.

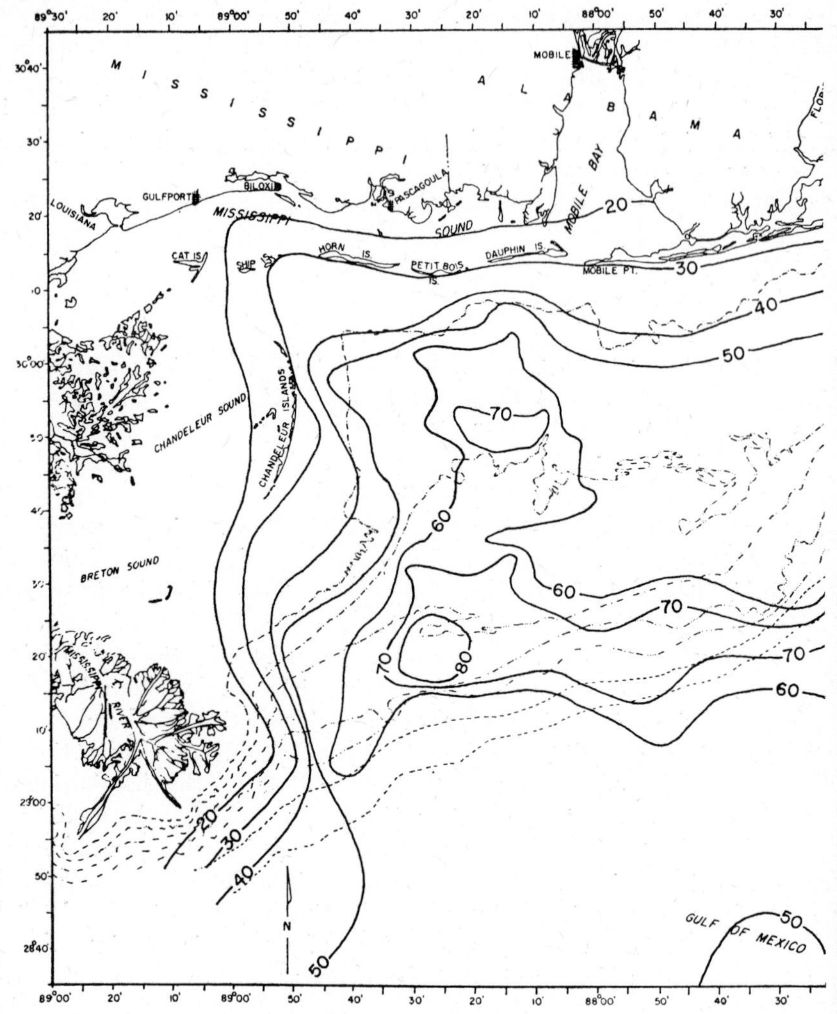

Fig. 23 Numbers of

each zone show the trend of increasing numbers of species offshore. The *Miliammina* dominant zone averages 7 species per sample; the *Ammobaculites* zone averages 13 species; the *Elphidium* zone, 14 species; the *Streblus* zone, 35 species; the *Buliminella* zone, 37 species; the *Nonionella* zone, 49 species; the *Epistominella* zone, 52 species; the *Rosalina* zone, 53 species; the *Hanzawaia* zone, 53 species; the *Cassidulina* zone, 69 species; the *Bolivina* zone, 63 species; and the *Bulimina* zone, 50 species.

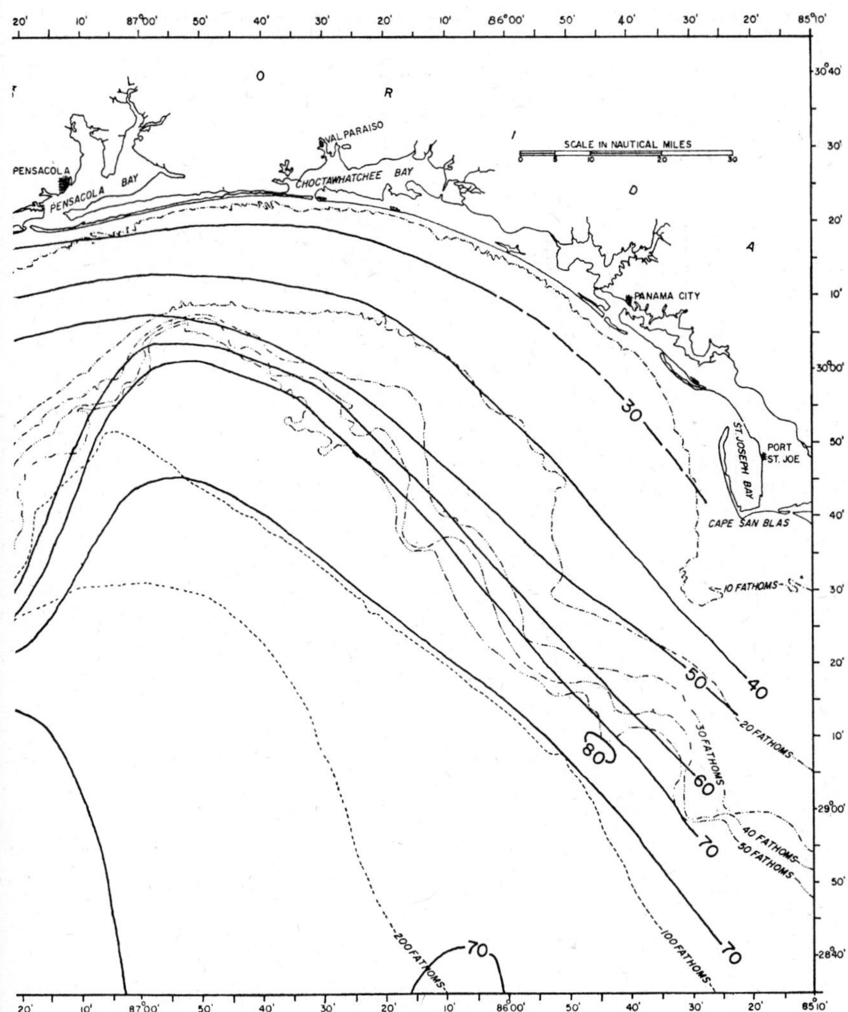

species of Foraminifera.

Many of the species included in the total species counts are rare or occur in small concentrations. The distributions of these species are so spotty that they are unreliable as environmental indicators. In addition, many nonindigenous species occur in the area in rare or spotted concentrations. These species are largely responsible for the variations in total species counts along the major profiles.

In order to further investigate the variation and significance of numbers of species in the various environments, a faunal character-

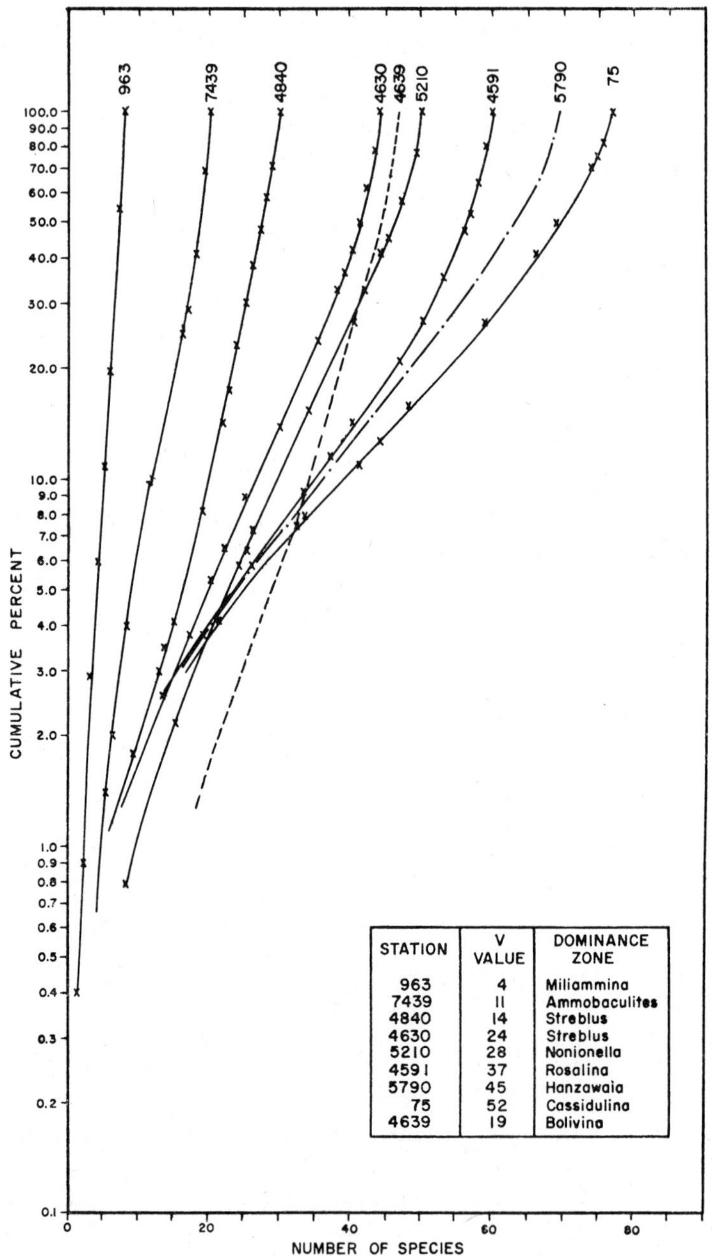

Fig. 24 Variability curves from major dominance zones.

istic which has been termed *faunal variability* has been established. Faunal variability is defined as *the number of ranked species of a counted or estimated foraminiferal population whose cumulative percentage constitutes 95% of the total population.* This characteristic is obtained by ranking the percentage occurrence of each benthonic species, cumulating the percentages, and plotting a curve of numbers of species against cumulative per cents. The variability value (V) is calculated from the curve by taking the difference between the number of species at the one-hundred percentile (NS_{100}) and at the five percentile (NS_5). These values have the same environmental significance as the total number of species but are not affected by those occurrences of rare species that constitute fractional percentages of the total populations. Several of the cumulative curves for foraminiferal populations with the generic dominance zones (Figure 2) are shown in Figure 24. Referring to Figure 24, the curves vary from a near vertical line (Station 963) in the *Miliammina* zone to a broad curve (Station *EG* 75) in the *Cassidulina* zone. The faunal variability value in the *Miliammina* zone is 4 in comparison with a (V) value of 52 in the *Cassidulina* zone. Deeper than the *Cassidulina* zone, the (V) values decrease and the curves tend to straighten out. The curve for Station 4639 in the *Bolivina* zone illustrates this tendency.

The areal distribution of (V) values in the area under consideration is shown in Figure 25. The distribution is similar to that of total numbers of species shown in Figure 23, in that the values increase in a seaward direction and reach a maximum near the edge of the continental shelf. The zone of largest (V) values does not swing inland off the coast of Alabama and Mississippi as does the zone of maximum numbers of total species, however, and is limited to the shelf edge. The computation of the (V) values eliminated the rare species and many of the nonindigenous species that occur in the central shelf area off Alabama and Mississippi. By eliminating these faunal elements a more valid representation of the increase in speciation across the continental shelf is obtained. The principal disadvantage to the (V) values is that percentage occurrences of all the species are required. In the absence of these data, however, total numbers of species are an adequate substitute.

A valuable aspect of the use of numbers of species or (V) values in environmental determinations is that no rigorous set of values need be established from modern faunas for application to fossil faunas. A relative decrease or increase in numbers of species or (V) values has environmental significance regardless of absolute values.

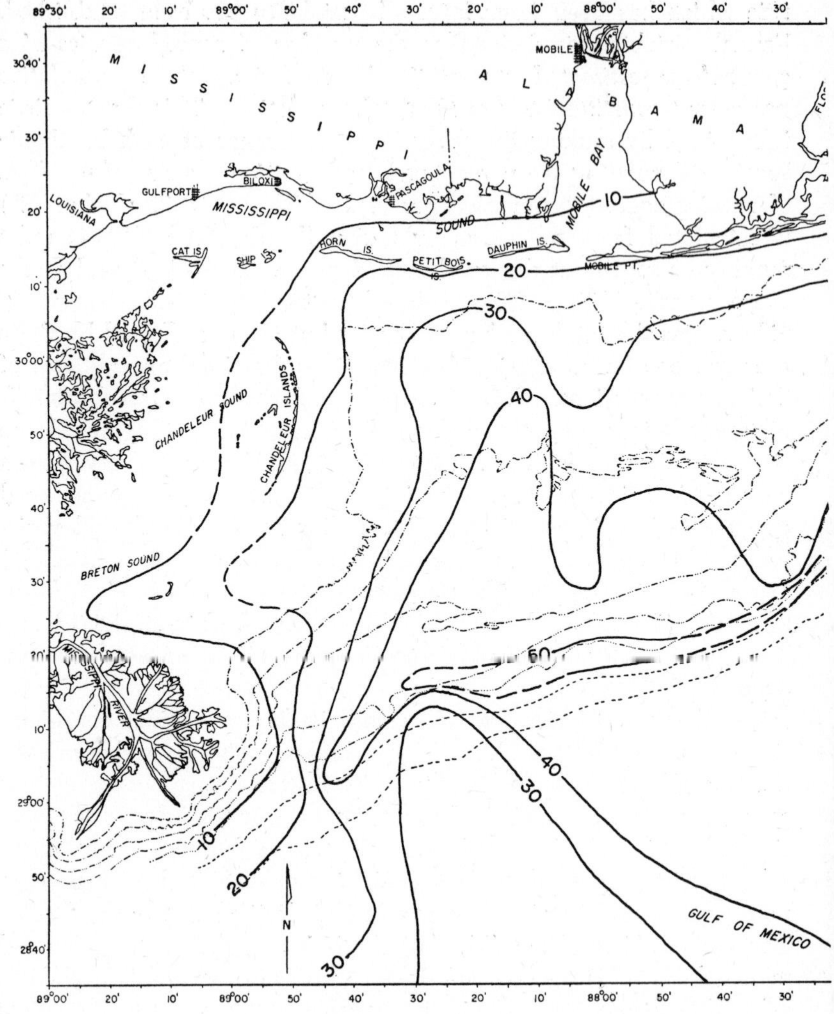

Fig. 25 Areal distribution of variability values (number of

In practical application, along any time line in the subsurface, a decrease in numbers of species of Foraminifera or (V) values indicates an approach toward marginal-marine conditions, and vice versa. Similarly, in any vertical section, a decrease in numbers of species or (V) values up the section indicates a marine regression. An increase in numbers of species or (V) values up the section indicates a marine transgression.

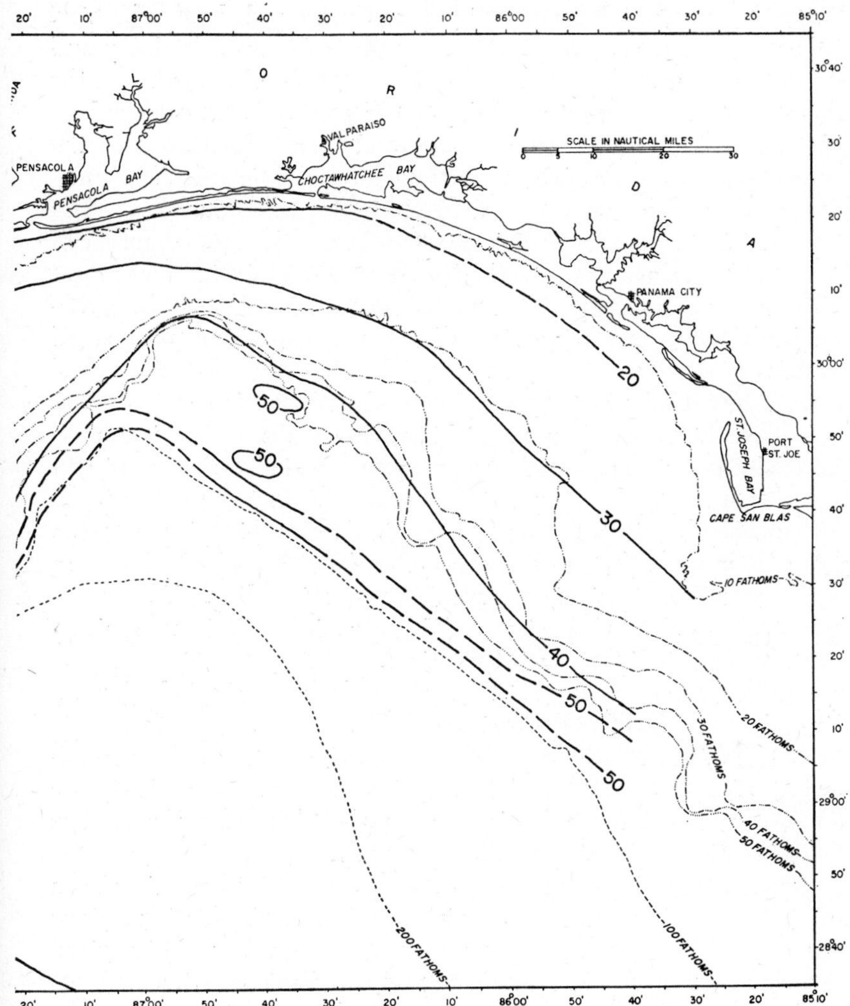

ranked species whose cumulative per cent exceeds 95%).

Faunal Dominance

Closely associated with faunal variability and speciation is another "nonspecific" population characteristic which has been termed "faunal dominance." *Faunal dominance* is defined as *the percentage occurrence of the most common species in a foraminiferal population.*

As with speciation, faunal dominance is related to the variability of the environment and thus to distance offshore and depth of water. Faunal dominance is inversely proportional to faunal variability and directly proportional to environmental variability. In brief, as the shoreline (marginal-marine conditions) is approached, total numbers of species and (V) values decrease, and faunal dominance or the percentage occurrence of the most dominant species increases. Faunal dominance varies from greater than 90% in the coastal marshes to less than 10% in the deeper waters off the edge of the continental shelf. Average dominance values in the faunal groups shown in Figure 2 are *Miliammina* faunal zone, 59%; *Ammobaculites* faunal zone, 54%; *Streblus* faunal zone, 38%; *Epistominella* faunal zone, 37%; *Nonionella* faunal zone, 28%; *Rosalina-Hanzawaia* faunal zone, 23%; *Cassidulina* faunal zone, 17%; *Bolivina* faunal zone, 16%; and *Bulimina* faunal zone, 14%.

In contrast to the faunal variability, faunal dominance is not affected by the occurrence of rare species or nonindigenous species in small concentrations. Large concentrations of nonindigenous species (where they dominate), such as occur in the *Amphistegina* zone, the *Cassidulina* zone, and in isolated areas in the central shelf off western Alabama and Mississippi, however, can be misleading. The associated total number of species or (V) value is useful in recognizing these large nonindigenous concentrations.

It is interesting to note that the most marked variation in both numbers of species and faunal dominance occurs across the *Streblus* dominant zone (the transition zone between open-marine and marginal-marine faunas). Total numbers of species average 35 species in the *Streblus* zone and 13 species in the *Ammobaculites* zone; the average faunal dominance is 38% and 54%, respectively.

As with faunal variability, the significance of faunal dominance in subsurface environmental determinations lies in the fact that it is not dependent on modern species or absolute values. In a given time plane, if a trend of increasing faunal dominance is noted, regardless of the species involved, an approach to marginal-marine conditions is indicated. If a decrease in faunal dominance is noted, an offshore open-marine trend is indicated. In a vertical section, an increase in faunal dominance up the section indicates a marine regression; a decrease in faunal dominance indicates a marine transgression.

Relationship between Faunal Variability and Faunal Dominance

The relation between numbers of species and per cent dominance is an interesting one and has useful environmental connotations. As has been stated, there is an inverse relationship between numbers of species and per cent dominance of the dominant species. A scattergram plot of total number of species against per cent occurrence of the most common species of a large group of populations produces a curve (Figure 26). The distribution of the samples on the curve with regard to numbers of species and the depth of the samples shows the following characteristics:

1. 100% of all faunas with less than 20 species occurs in water shallower than 10 fathoms.
2. 100% of all faunas with less than 30 species occurs in water shallower than 20 fathoms.
3. 80% of all faunas with 21 to 30 species occurs in water shallower than 10 fathoms (20% occurs between 10 and 20 fathoms).
4. 60% of all faunas with 31 to 40 species occurs between 10 and 20 fathoms (25%, less than 10 fathoms; 15%, 20 to 50 fathoms).
5. 46% of all faunas with 41 to 50 species occurs between 10 and 20 fathoms (7%, less than 10 fathoms; 29%, 20 to 50 fathoms; 18%, greater than 50 fathoms).
6. 36% of all faunas with 51 to 60 species occurs between 20 and 50 fathoms (4%, less than 10 fathoms; 31%, 10 to 20 fathoms; 23% greater than 50 fathoms; 4%, greater than 50 fathom reefs).
7. 68% of all faunas with 61 to 70 species occurs deeper than 50 fathoms (7%, 10 to 20 fathoms; 26%, 20 to 50 fathoms).
8. 91% of all faunas with 71 to 80 species occurs deeper than 50 fathoms (9%, 20 to 50 fathoms), thus 100% of all faunas with more than 71 species occurs deeper than 20 fathoms.
9. 100% of all faunas with more than 81 species occurs deeper than 50 fathoms.

With regard to per cent dominance and depth of the samples, the curve shows the following characteristics:

1. 100% of all faunas whose dominant species constitutes over 35% of the entire fauna occurs shallower than 10 fathoms.
2. 36% of all faunas with dominant species constituting 21% to 30% occurs between 10 and 20 fathoms (31%, less than 10 fathoms; 13%, from 20 to 50 fathoms; 21%, deeper than 50 fathoms).
3. 57% of all faunas with dominant species constituting 11% to 20% of the fauna occurs deeper than 50 fathoms (4%, less than 10 fathoms; 18%, 10 to 20 fathoms; 20%, 20 to 50 fathoms).
4. 92% of all faunas with dominant species constituting less than 10%

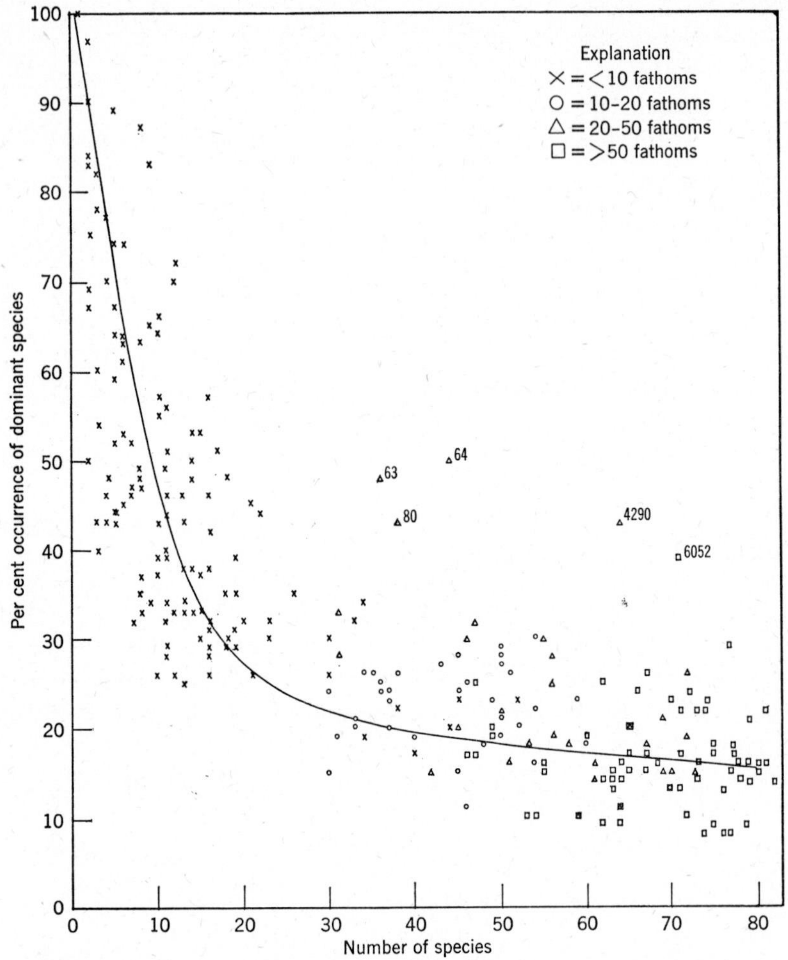

Fig. 26 Relationship between number of species and per cent dominance.

of the fauna occurs deeper than 50 fathoms (8%, from 20 to 50 fathoms).

In Figure 26, five samples (indicated by numbers) do not fall within the normal range of variation of the other points along the curve. These samples show an unusually high faunal dominance with regard to numbers of species. The samples occur in areas of predominantly nonindigenous species, and the unusually high percentage occurrences are nonindigenous species. Samples 63 and 64 (off Choctawhatchee Bay, Florida) are in the *Amphistegina* zone, and *Amphistegina lessonii* constitutes, respectively, 48% and 50% of the total benthonic population. Samples 4290 and 6052 (off Mobile Bay, Alabama) are in the *Cassidulina* dominant zone, and *Cassidulina subglobosa* constitutes, respectively, 43% and 39% of the total benthonic population. Station 80 (off Mobile Bay, Alabama) contains an anomalous *Planulina* fauna in the *Hanzawaia* dominant zone, in which *Planulina exorna* constitutes 43% of the total benthonic population. The anomalous location of these points and the fact that they result from nonindigenous populations suggests a possible criterion for recognition of reworked faunas in the subsurface. In the presence of abundant species (over 30), populations whose dominant species exceed 30% of the total benthonic population suggest the presence of nonindigenous species. This relationship may be an aid in recognizing nonindigenous populations along with the other criteria mentioned above.

Variability-Dominance Log

A consideration of the environmental significance of faunal variability and faunal dominance has led to the proposal of a paleontologic log which has been called the "Variability-Dominance Log." The only data required to prepare this log, in addition to those normally recorded on paleologs are (1) the total number of species present in any sample; and (2) an estimate of the percentage occurrence of the most dominant benthonic species.

An example of the proposed "Variability-Dominance Log" is shown in Figure 27. In it are three columns that can be added to existing paleologs—variability (numbers of species), dominance (in per cent), and the dominant genus. This idealized log was constructed from the population data of 42 recent surface sediment samples. The environments of deposition indicated in Figure 27 are the actual ones from which the samples were collected. The samples have been arranged in a vertical section to illustrate a hypothetical transgressive-regressive cycle and the associated variations in faunal variability and dominance. The bottom of the section is a fresh-water deposit and contains only abundant plant remains. This grades into a marsh environment at a hypothetical core depth of 41 to 42 units, which in turn grades into a shallow water bay or estuarine deposit. The fauna in this part of the section is almost totally arenaceous. On up the section, variability increases and dominance decreases across an open shelf environment to where faunal variability reaches a maximum value, and

CORE DEPTH	DOMINANT GENUS	REMARKS	ENVIRONMENT OF DEPOSITION
0–1	Miliammina	Abundant organic matter	Marsh
1–2	Miliammina	Abundant organic matter	
2–3	Ammobaculites	Silt & clay	Mississippi Sound (<2fms)
3–4	Ammobaculites	Sand	
4–5	Streblus	Sand	
5–6	Streblus	Sand	
6–7	Elphidium	Sand	
7–8	Elphidium	Sand	
8–9	Miliammina	Organic matter	Horn Island
9–10	No fossils	Clean quartz sand	
10–11	No fossils	Clean quartz sand	
11–12	Trochammina	Sand	Shallow Open -Marine (<10 fms)
12–13	Trochammina	Sand	
13–14	Streblus	Sand	
14–15	Streblus	Sand	
15–16	Streblus	Sand	
16–17	Streblus	Sand	
17–18	Streblus	Sand	
18–19	Rosalina	Sand	<50fms
19–20	Rosalina	Sand	

PERCENT OCCURRENCE OF MOST DOMINANT SPECIES (DOMINANCE)
10 20 30 40 50 60 70 80 90

REGRESSIVE

NUMBER OF BENTHONIC SPECIES (VARIABILITY)
10 20 30 40 50 60 70 80 90

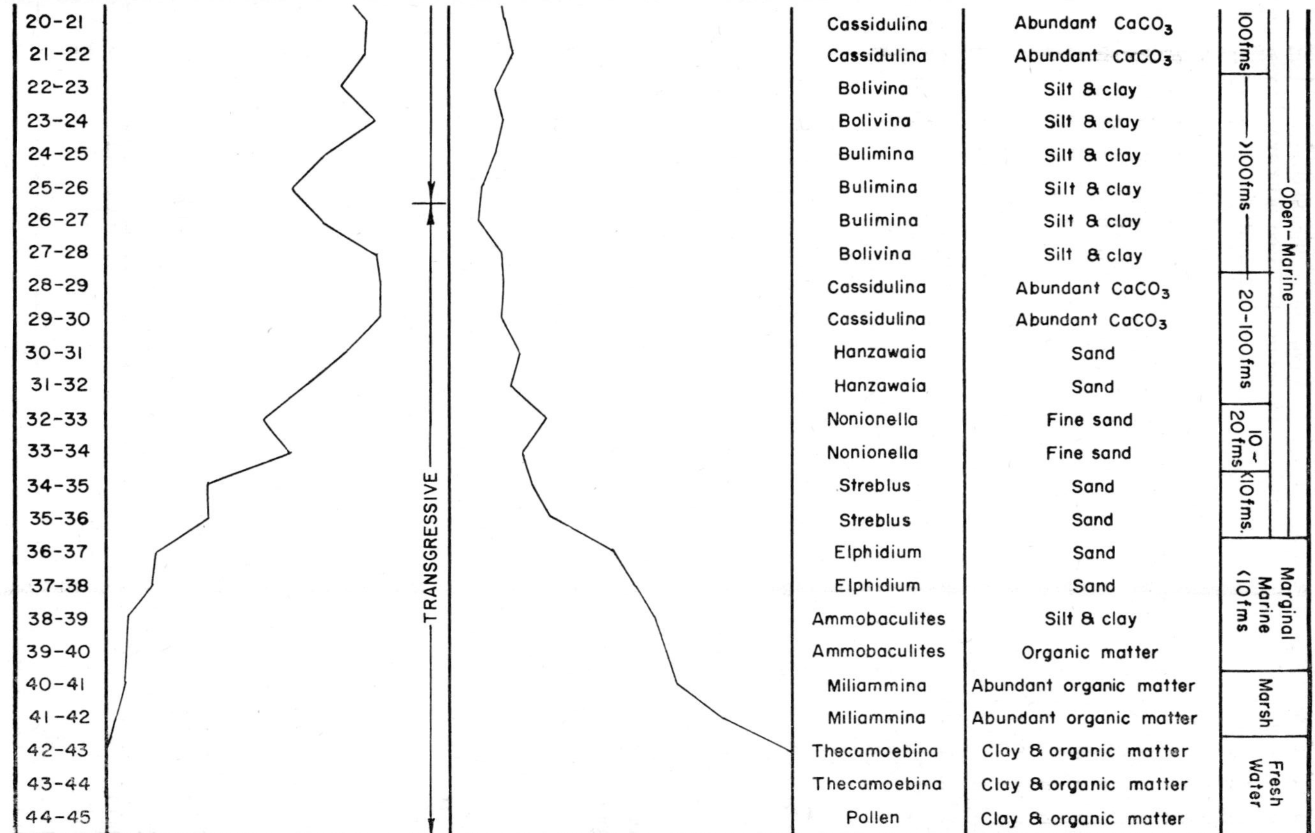

Fig. 27 Idealized variability-dominance paleontological log.

faunal dominance reaches a minimum value. This completes the transgressive phase of deposition. Above units 25 to 26 core depth, variability decreases, dominance increases, and sediments become more sandy to a core depth of 9 to 10 units, which is a clean, nonfossiliferous, quartz sand of a barrier island. On up the section, variability increases slightly and dominance increases into a dominantly arenaceous, brackish water, bay deposit at a core depth of 3 to 4 units. From core depth of 3 to 4 units, variability decreases, dominance increases, and the fauna is essentially an arenaceous one of a marsh deposit. This completes the regressive phase of deposition.

Data obtained from the study of modern foraminiferal assemblages in the northeastern Gulf of Mexico indicate that faunal variability and dominance recorded as indicated in Figure 27 can be a valuable aid in making paleoecologic interpretations of fossil foraminiferal assemblages.

Significance of Total Benthonic Foraminiferal Populations

The number of benthonic foraminiferal tests in a sediment is the product of many factors, the most important of which are rate of accumulation of detrital sediments, rate of production and accumulation of foraminiferal tests, and rate of removal and/or destruction of tests once deposited.

Data are not available at present to adequately evaluate the rate of production and accumulation of foraminiferal tests for all environments and all species. It is known, however, that reproduction is sporadic, rates of reproduction are not the same for every species, and rates of reproduction are not the same for every environment. Although measured living populations vary within relatively small areas by a factor of 10 or sometimes as much as 100, these are restricted occurrences. Measured living populations on the open continental shelf, however, show only slight variations over considerable distances. Highest measured living populations number approximately 1000 specimens per 100 cc wet sample volume, whereas some samples contain only a few specimens.

This variation is seemingly high, but in comparison to variations in total dead populations, it is insignificant. Recent data on living populations indicate that maximum production of Foraminifera occurs near the effluence of rivers into bays or the open ocean. In the northeastern Gulf of Mexico the greatest number of living specimens occurs within the depth range of 6 to 10 fathoms.

The effect of removal and/or destruction of foraminiferal shells is important but, as with production estimates, it is difficult to evaluate. The profound effects of transportation and mechanical accumulation of shells can be seen within the turbulent zone and around nearshore sedimentary forms where total populations vary from a few specimens to several thousand per unit volume sample over relatively short distances. Reworking of sediments by detritus feeding organisms may affect foraminiferal populations but no information is available to evaluate the degrees of destruction by such organisms.

It is known that burial and subsequent compaction of sediments destroy some foraminiferal tests, particularly those of predominantly arenaceous character. Well preserved marsh faunas as old as the Oligocene have been found, however. From all available evidence, it appears that the degree of dilution by detrital sediments is the principal control of the size of total benthonic populations.

There does not appear to be any direct relationship between zones of maximum productivity of living benthonic Foraminifera and zones of maximum abundances of empty tests. In areas where living populations have been studied, zones of maximum productivity do not coincide with maximum abundances of empty tests, the former always occurring in shallower nearshore waters. This appears to be due to the fact that areas of high productivity occur in areas of active sedimentation. If it is assumed that the production and accumulation of benthonic foraminiferal tests is relatively constant (the actual variation is of the magnitude of hundreds of specimens), the effect of the rate of accumulation of detrital sediments on total populations of empty tests is obvious.

The variability of the environment does not appear to affect the production of Foraminifera as there are species that will thrive and produce large numbers of foraminiferal tests in most all of the marine environments. Faunal variability (numbers of species) and faunal dominance are thus independent of total populations of empty tests. It is true, however, that the larger the total number of specimens in a given sample, the higher is the probability that the rare species will be encountered. Eliminating these rare species from the consideration, as in the calculated (V) values discussed earlier, does not appreciably affect faunal variability trends. Total numbers of specimens are, however, profoundly affected by the presence of nonindigenous faunas which result from previous accumulations or actual reworking of older faunas.

In summary, zones of maximum concentrations of empty tests of benthonic Foraminifera do not indicate zones of maximum productivity, but are primarily a result of slow accumulation of detrital sediments. On the open continental shelf there is a valid trend of increasing populations of benthonic Foraminifera in a seaward direction which, in the area under consideration, is augmented by the presence of large concentrations of nonindigenous species. Large concentrations of foraminiferal tests in the presence of relatively few species, however, indicate nearshore conditions. Total benthonic populations can be used as environmental indicators only in the presence of other criteria.

Significance of Total Planktonic Populations

The distribution of the total planktonic populations in the northeastern Gulf of Mexico are shown in Figure 20. This figure shows a wide belt of abundant (greater than 10,000 specimens/sample) specimens off Florida (deeper than 100 fathoms) constricting to a narrow belt (roughly between 40 and 100 fathoms) off Alabama at the edge of the continental shelf. Samples containing between 5000 and 10,000 specimens per sample occur in a halo around the more abundant zone and extend farther to the west toward the Mississippi River Delta in a narrow belt.

There are no data available on the production of planktonic Foraminifera but it is difficult to assign a distribution such as that shown in Figure 20 to differences in productivity. As with the total benthonic populations the size of total planktonic populations appears to be controlled principally by dilution with detrital sediments. Off Florida, numbers of planktonic specimens increase as a function of increasing depth. Off Alabama and Mississippi, however, this is true only to the edge of the continental shelf where they begin to decrease.

This tongue of anomalously high planktonic populations has interesting implications with regard to the relative ages of both the planktonic and benthonic faunas. It suggests that the zone along the edge of the continental shelf (between 40 and 100 fathoms) off western Alabama and Mississippi is older than either the area shallower than 40 fathoms or deeper than 100 fathoms. This zone of abundant planktonics is similar to total benthonic distribution (Figure 19) and to the distribution of nonindigenous Foraminifera, *Amphistegina* (Figure 13), *Cassidulina* (Figure 14), and *Liebusella* (Figure 21).

These data suggest that the concentration of planktonic Foraminifera in this area (many specimens of which are glauconitized) results from relatively less sedimentation at the shelf edge with respect to the areas to the shoreward and seaward sides.

In summary, total planktonic populations off northern Florida increase in a seaward direction. Off western Alabama and Mississippi they increase to the edge of the continental shelf and decrease in deeper water. These shelf edge concentrations are believed to represent less interrupted deposition of planktonic tests and less dilution with detrital sediments than the area to the landward or seaward of the shelf edge.

Environmental Significance of Shell Characteristics

In the course of this study, and from previous studies in this area, several characteristics of foraminiferal tests have been observed that appear to have environmental significance.

ARENACEOUS CHARACTER OF THE FAUNA. Phleger (1954) reported on the arenaceous character of the foraminiferal faunas in Mississippi Sound. This arenaceous fauna was in contrast to the predominantly calcareous fauna in the open Gulf of Mexico.

Later published works and this study have shown that these distributions are essentially correct. Shoreward of about 2 fathoms (the *Streblus-Ammobaculites* boundary, Figure 2), the fauna assumes a predominant arenaceous character which extends into the marsh and intertidal environment.

Some calcareous forms do occur along with these arenaceous faunas but their subdominance and shell characteristics mentioned below indicate a fringe distribution. These arenaceous faunas, characterized by relatively few species occur extensively in the northeastern Mississippi Delta area, the inner part of Chandeleur Sound, and the inner part of Mississippi Sound and Mobile Bay.

It can be stated that a principal characteristic of the marginal-marine faunas in this area (shoreward of the *Streblus* zone, Figure 2) is their arenaceous character, and further that predominantly arenaceous faunas indicate marginal-marine conditions.

SIZE OF FORAMINIFERAL TESTS. An interesting and significant feature of the foraminiferal faunas in the study area is the relative decrease in size of the calcareous species as the shoreline is approached. The *Nonionella, Epistominella, Buliminella,* and *Streblus* concentrations in the extreme western part of the study area (Figure 2), and the calcareous forms that occur in the predominantly arenaceous *Ammobaculites* zone, are much smaller than their counterparts in the open Gulf or offshore areas. In addition to the smaller size of these specimens, their shells are much thinner and more fragile.

These small, fragile shells are in sharp contrast to the large, heavily shelled, nonindigenous Foraminifera of West Indian origin, which are widespread on the continental shelf (Figure 22). The small thin-shelled forms appear to be limited to bays, sounds, and shelf areas that are near the effluence of large rivers, and it is believed that they result from the increased difficulty of precipitating calcium carbonate in waters of lower than normal salinity. Shallow areas of warmer, more saline water (such as the West Indies, southern Florida, and the bays and lagoons of southern Texas and Mexico) stimulate large, heavily shelled forms.

In brief, increases in percentages of arenaceous species and the presence of small, thin-shelled calcareous species indicate waters of less than normal salinity and proximity to sources of fresh water.

CHITINOUS-LIKE INNER LININGS. A third shell characteristic of the marginal-marine foraminiferal faunas that may have some environmental significance is the presence of a chitinous-like inner lining of the calcareous species. The shells of the arenaceous species contain varying amounts of chitin or a chitinous-like substance which is usually brown in color. It is significant that many of the nearshore calcareous species also have well-developed "chitinous" inner linings. Such forms would be expected on the fringes of the calcareous faunal zones where they grade into the predominantly arenaceous zones. The species which appear to have the best developed "chitinous" inner linings are *Streblus beccarii* vars., several species of *Elphidium,* and some miliolids.

Specimens of *Streblus* have the best developed linings. It is not known whether the animals can live within the linings in the absence of any calcareous material but this is suggested by the common occurrence of the linings along with other calcareous-coated forms in shallow water deposits. The significance of these linings in the shallow water Foraminifera is that they are practically indestructible and would be preserved even after the leaching of all calcareous material, probably in recognizable form.

PART II: PALEOECOLOGY OF THE SUBSURFACE OLIGOCENE IN COASTAL TEXAS

General Comments

Once environmental criteria are established from modern faunas and are accepted as diagnostic, the true test of usefulness to the geologist is the ease and practicability of application to fossil faunas.

In applying modern criteria to fossil faunas, practical problems arise which must be considered in evaluating the results.

As has been pointed out, distributions of species are the most diagnostic of environments. Most modern species are present in the Pleistocene, but direct analogies between modern and Tertiary species become fewer in older Tertiary sediments. The previously discussed generic distributions and gross population characteristics are less affected by the passage of geologic time and are valid in sediments at least as old as the Cretaceous. The Cretaceous limit, as far as this paper is concerned, is an arbitrary one created by the writer's lack of experience in older rocks. Applications of these paleoecologic criteria to older rocks are not precluded.

Perhaps the most serious problem of paleoecologic application is that of sample quality and fossil preservation. If cores or uncontaminated samples and perfectly preserved faunas were always available from the outcrop or subsurface, the job of the paleoecologist would be greatly simplified. Unfortunately, most subsurface work must be done from rotary cuttings rather than cores, and many outcrop faunas are poorly preserved.

The principal effect of sample quality and fossil preservation on paleoecologic interpretation is in decreasing the usefulness of quantitative analyses. This does not preclude the use of such quantitative analyses where sample quality and fossil preservation permit.

The second most common problem or question that arises is the validity of ecological criteria with increasing geologic time or the possibility of species or generic adaptation to environmental conditions changing with geologic time. As we are dealing here principally with criteria that are not based on species distributions, the writer's experience has been that this is not a serious problem. This is based on faunal associations and lithologic associations which substantiate the interpreted environments at least as far back as the Cretaceous. Generic distributions and gross population characteristics are considered the least likely to be affected by changes in tolerance of specific animals through geologic time. Just as certain oceanographic conditions have existed throughout geologic time to allow the deposition of clean sands and shales, sea water has been diluted nearshore, turbulence and turbidity have been greater nearshore, etc., to restrict the diversification of sessile benthonic organisms.

As with any rock characteristic, environmental interpretation of a sample or series of samples from a well or outcrop is unidimensional and does not constitute a map or a trend from which predictions of sand conditions or environmental conditions can be made. A serious limitation then of reconstructing the areal extent of a depositional sequence or a depositional surface, as with structure maps and isopach maps, is the difficulty in correlating a time horizon from outcrop-to-outcrop or from well-to-well in the subsurface. A map made on a particular lithologic unit or on a particular environmental zone does not usually constitute a surface suitable for paleogeographic mapping. A map of a rock unit, an environmental unit, or a fossil unit does not constitute a time-correlative surface except under certain conditions. It is necessary to have a time-correlative or near time-correlative unit to prepare a true paleogeographic or paleobathymetric map. At present, we have no rigorous criteria for making absolute time correlations in the subsurface. This creates a dilemma since it is necessary, as stated, to be able to map time-correlative units before paleobathymetric or paleogeographic mapping can be attempted. Time correlations are discussed more fully in a later section. The problem is mentioned here because it constitutes a serious problem in paleogeographic mapping.

Paleoecological Criteria

The purpose of Part I of this paper was to examine characteristics of modern foraminiferal faunas and determine which characteristics are most useful in interpreting paleoenvironments from fossil faunas. It was concluded that generic distributions, generic dominance, and the distributions of the most dominant genera, the diversity of the fauna, the arenaceous or calcareous nature of the fauna, and the abundance of planktonics constitute the most useful criteria for extrapolating modern environments into the geologic past. These criteria have been used to determine the environments of deposition of Tertiary sediments in the Gulf Coast of Texas and Louisiana, and particularly in the Oligocene Anahuac shale of South-Central Texas. Reconstructing the depositional history of the Anahuac shale and preparing paleobathymetric maps within the unit has been done exclusively from 30-foot rotary cuttings from wells drilled over the past 10 or 15 years. The samples were prepared using standard micropaleontological techniques.

Anahuac Shale Paleoecology (Oligocene)

The Anahuac shale was selected as an example of paleoecologic interpretation in the subsurface Tertiary. It is one of the most widespread transgressive shale wedges in the Gulf Coast Tertiary and is well described in the literature (Cushman and Ellisor, 1935; Ellisor, 1944; Meyer, 1939; Murray, 1947).

The Anahuac faunas are similar enough to modern faunas so that many direct analogies can be made. As the name implies, it is a shale wedge that is several thousand feet thick downdip and pinches out into nonfossiliferous, relatively massive sands updip. It does not outcrop and is described only from the subsurface, as are its contained faunas (Cushman and Ellisor, 1935; Ellisor, 1944). The area considered in this study includes portions of Refugio, Aransas, San Patricio, Nueces, Bee, Goliad, Victoria, and Calhoun Counties, Texas (Figure 28), where the Anahuac varies from 2000 feet to over 6000 feet below the surface. Thickness increases from the updip pinchout in Bee and Goliad Counties to over 3500 feet along the coast. It represents a general marine inundation of the Texas Gulf Coastal Plain and probably accounts for a considerable portion of Oligocene time.

Figure 29 is a portion of an electric log from the Tidewater No. 1 Richardson in San Patricio County, Texas, on which the interpreted paleoecology has been indicated. The Anahuac varies between 1000 and 1500 feet thick in this dip position. It is overlain by nonmarine sands of the Miocene age and underlain by nonmarine sands of the Oligocene Frio formation. The electric log shows sandy or silty streaks in the Anahuac which are characteristic in this dip position; it is a classic example of a subsurface transgressive-regressive wedge. The overlying Miocene and the underlying Frio immediately adjacent to the Anahuac shale contain no fossils and are predominantly sand. Fossil occurrence from 30-foot rotary cutting samples increases toward the middle of the Anahuac wedge, and Foraminifera are abundant at a subsurface depth of about 5500 feet.

Going up in this section, as the sediments were deposited, the transgression begins at about —6300 feet with a low faunal diversity dominated by the genera *Eponides, Nonionella,* and *Marginulina.* The diversity of the fauna increases to a maximum at about —5800 feet, and the fauna is dominated by species of *Uvigerina* and *Bolivina.* From this point, Anahuac deposition became regressive, faunal diversity decreased, and the fauna was successively dominated by shallower water genera to the upper limit of the marine phase at about —5100 feet. Reference should be made to Figure 27 which is an idealized log through a hypothetical transgressive-regressive sequence based on modern faunas. The interpreted environments in the Tidewater No. 1 Richardson are based on the dominant genera, faunal diversity, fossil abundance, and lithologic associations as in Figure 27. The similarity

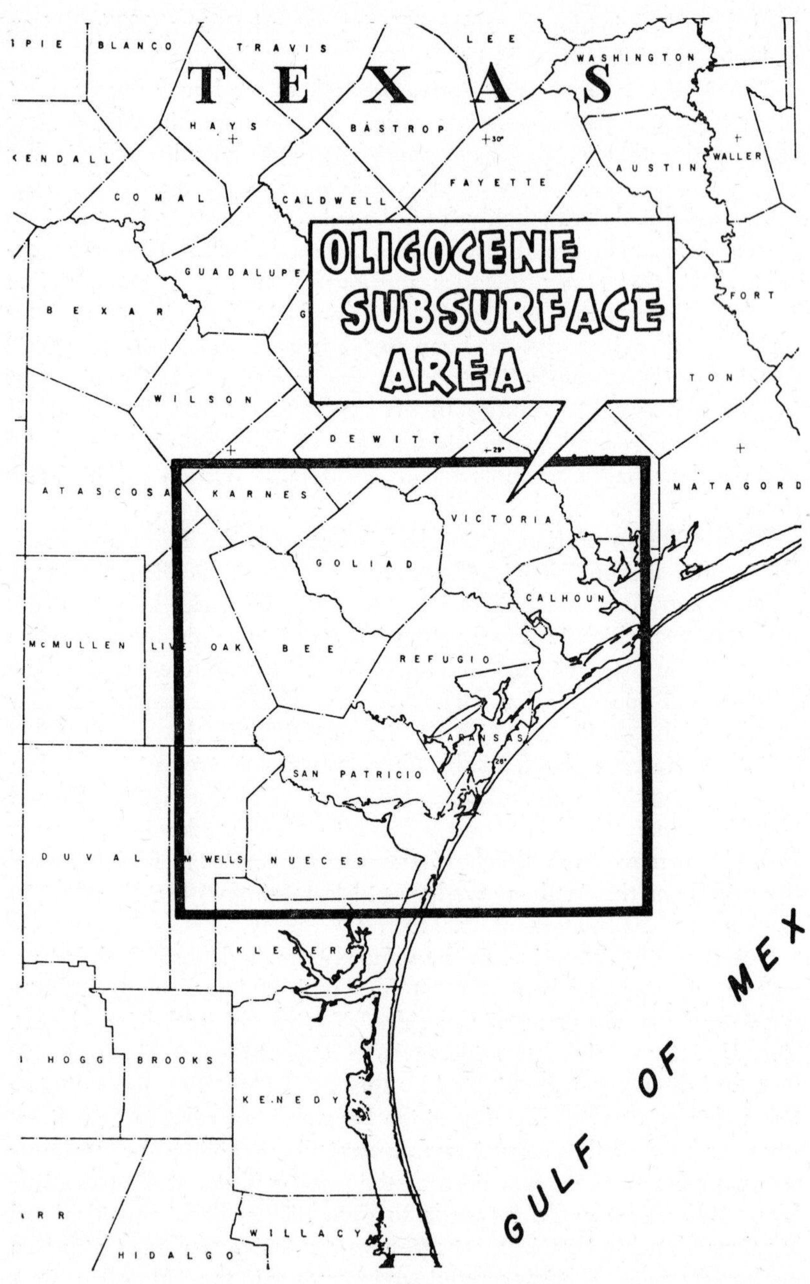

Fig. 28 Index map (of South Texas).

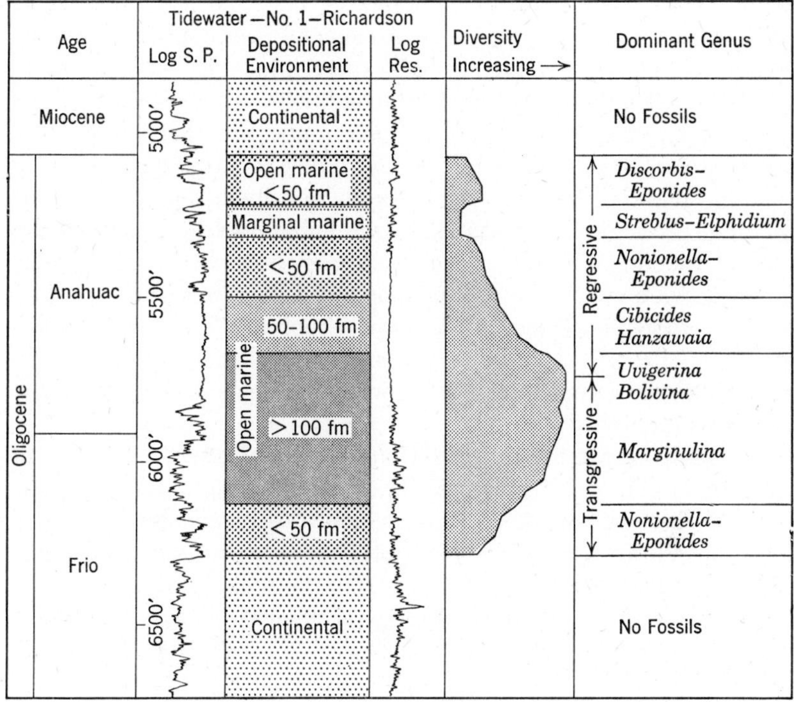

Fig. 29 Paleoecology of Anahuac formation.

between the two is striking with regard to faunal diversity, sediment associations, and dominant genera. Per cent dominance was not calculated in the subsurface samples due to sample quality.

It can be concluded, then, that paleoecologies of fossil foraminiferal faunas can be determined from subsurface or outcrop samples using a combination of criteria established from modern distributions. Paleoecological data on a series of wells or outcrop sections permit the reconstruction of the depositional history of an entire formation or stratigraphic unit. As mentioned before, one of the principal problems in constructing stratigraphic sections or paleogeographic maps is our inability to pick absolute time correlations in fossil sediments. Rock units, except under certain conditions, cannot be considered time correlative, as we know of no widespread environmental conditions that allow the deposition and preservation of the same lithologies. The principal exception is, of course, along depositional strike where similar rock units can be time correlative. The same is true in general of fossil units as we know of no organism that is not controlled in its distribution to some degree by environmental conditions. Along any time-correlative surface, we would expect lithologies and faunas to vary with changing environmental conditions. A most ideal fossil would be one that had a short geologic range, one that tolerated all environmental conditions from the shoreline to deep water equally well, and one that became extinct throughout its distribution at some instant in geologic time. As far as we know, such distributions are wishful thinking. However, many fossils had short stratigraphic ranges, a wide environmental tolerance, and became extinct within a relatively short period of geologic time. Such fossils, or combinations of such fossils, constitute by far the most reliable correlative surfaces and, while not completely satisfactory, most accurately approximate time correlations.

One such occurrence is the "*Heterostegina* Datum" in the Gulf Coast Oligocene. The foraminifer, *Heterostegina,* occurs in the Anahuac shale and became extinct within a relatively short period of time. In addition, certain species of *Heterostegina* had a relatively wide environmental tolerance and occur in sediments of nearshore origin to sediments deposited on the equivalent of our present middle-to-outer continental shelves. A time equivalent of *Heterostegina* in shallower brackish water is a species of *Elphidium.* Also a time equivalent of *Heterostegina* in deeper water is a species of *Bolivina.* A combination of these fossil occurrences which have overlapping environmental ranges but similar time extinctions approximates a time-correlative surface in the Oligocene. By using these fossil occurrences as a subsurface datum, the depositional history of a portion of the Anahuac can be inferred along a reasonably reliable time-correlative surface.

Figure 30 is a subsurface dip section of the Anahuac in San Patricio County, Texas constructed on the *Heterostegina* datum. The section is through six wells that penetrated the Anahuac; from updip to downdip they are Bridwell No. 1 Davis, Morgan No. 1 Grabb, Smith No. 1 Webb, Austral No. 1 State Tract 18 in Corpus Christi Bay, Atlantic No. 1 Wilson on Mustang Island, and Gulf No. 1 State Tract 774 offshore. The environments of deposition along this section have been indicated. The maximum point of transgression is along the *Heterostegina* datum in the updip wells and is slightly below in the downdip wells. The environmental determinations were made from rotary cuttings using the criteria previously discussed. The Anahuac is poorly developed as a shale in the Bridwell No. 1 Davis, the Morgan No. 1 Crabb, and the Smith No. 1 Webb. Samples and electric logs show the section to be

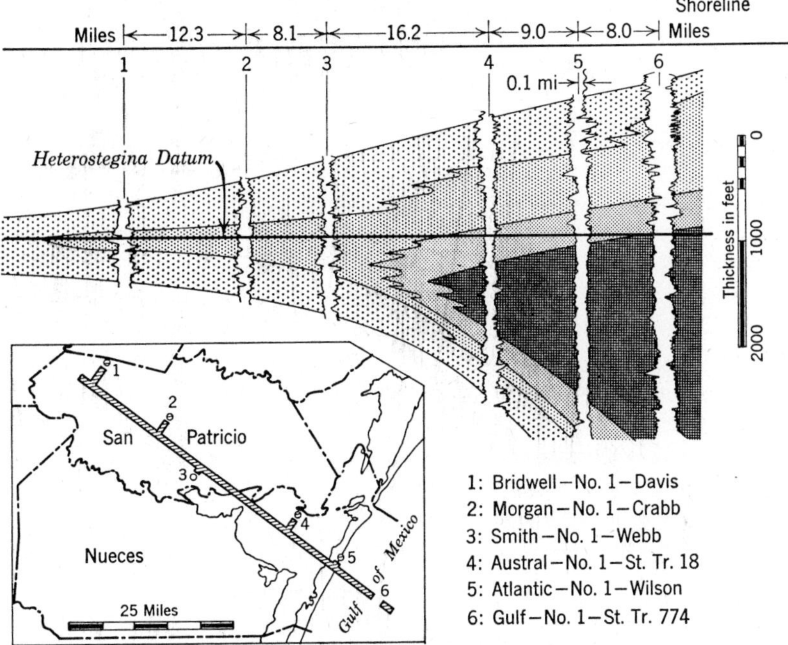

Fig. 30 Subsurface section through the Anahuac showing environments of deposition.

sandy, and Foraminifera indicate deposition in brackish to shallow marine waters. The Anahuac becomes well-developed shale in the three downdip wells and contains sediments deposited in outer continental shelf and upper slope water depths. All along the line of section, the marine Anahuac grades vertically into continental sands and shales and/or shallower marine sands and shales. This line of section is reasonably representative of the Anahuac depositional history throughout the Gulf Coastal Plain.

The ultimate purpose of subsurface paleoecology is the preparation of paleobathymetric maps along time-correlative surfaces. This leads to an understanding of the depositional history of a stratigraphic unit or sequence of units. Such a paleobathymetric map on the *Heterostegina* correlative surface is shown in Figure 31. This map is based on paleontological and paleoecological data from approximately 300 wells in Refugio, Aransas, San Patricio, Nueces, Bee, Goliad, Victoria, and Calhoun Counties, Texas. It is superimposed on a map of the present coast line for comparison. Indicated are (1) the *Hetero-*

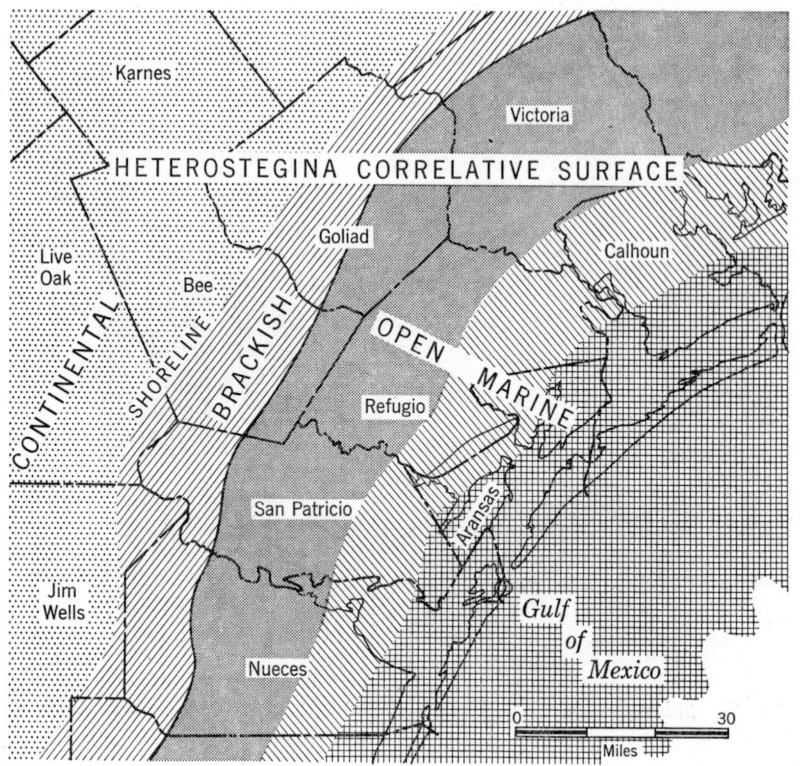

Fig. 31 Paleobathymetry of the Upper Oligocene (Anahuac).

stegina shoreline, the contact between continental and brackish water deposits; (2) a zone of shoreline, brackish water deposits similar to those being deposited in the present bays and lagoons; and (3) open marine deposits which vary from nearshore marine to outer continental shelf and upper slope deposits. A striking characteristic of the *Heterostegina* bathymetry is the similarity in the strike of the shoreline, size and distribution of brackish and marine deposits with the strike and distribution of equivalent deposits along the present coast. More complete subsurface control undoubtedly would allow the definition of bays, lagoons, and barrier islands on the *Heterostegina* surface. In addition, the paleobathymetry of the *Heterostegina* surface itself is evidence that the datum approximates a time-correlative surface. If it were not near time-correlative, such a sharp definition of environments from shoreline deposits to continental slope deposits would not be found. Such a succession of environments should always be present in a dip or offshore direction on a true time-correlative surface.

Conclusions

The question of the usefulness of modern faunal data and the environmental criteria thus developed in the interpretation of fossil faunas has long been a controversial one. Some have said such criteria will be useful only in the late Tertiary, or back to the mid-Tertiary; some say back through the Cretaceous. It has also been said that the quality of the samples available to the commercial paleontologist is so poor that only qualitative criteria are valid. The true tests of what is applicable and what is not, and how far back into geologic history modern faunal criteria will carry us, will come, of course, from detailed stratigraphic work attempting to apply modern criteria in sediments of all ages.

We need not delude ourselves into thinking, however, that it is, or ever will be, economically feasible or even desirable in many cases for commercial paleontologists to make detailed population counts or employ rigorous analytical methods. The time element and the quality of the samples most commercial micropaleontologists have to work with are the limiting factors. It would be useless to attempt detailed population counts on rotary cutting samples, which are usually the only ones available. Even in cored wells, the cores are usually small and so scattered so as to make detailed studies inconclusive.

The types of general observations we have discussed, which have been summarized from many different detailed studies by different workers, can be and have been applied to fossil faunas as far back as the Cretaceous. Such faunal characteristics are general enough to not be voided by evolutionary changes, and yet specific enough to be diagnostic. They are feasible with regard to time and can usually be made from good quality cuttings.

1. For stratigraphic purposes, benthonic foraminiferal faunas are defined best in terms of the three most common genera in a population.
2. Faunal zones based on the occurrence of the most abundant genera have environmental significance both with regard to depth and geographic distributions.
3. The largest number of living specimens of benthonic Foraminifera occur between 6 and 10 fathoms (approximately 1000 specimens per 10 cc wet samples).
4. The largest living populations occur near the mouth of the Mississippi River and Mobile Bay.
5. The most common living species in the area are *Nonionella opima, Nouria polymorphinoides,* and *Hanzawaia strattoni.*
6. Areas of maximum living populations do not coincide with, and occur shallower than, areas of maximum dead populations.

7. Areas of abundant *Rosalina, Cassidulina,* and *Amphistegina* are not supported by abundant living specimens and appear to be residual species from a previous environment. Smaller concentrations of *Planulina exorna, Nodobaculariella cassis, Peneroplis proteus, Archais compressus, Textulariella* spp., *Liebusella soldanii* var. *intermedia, Eponides repandus, Asterigerina carinata,* large miliolids, and *Cuneolina angusta* also are residual species.

8. Nonindigenous species in this area may be recognized by their relatively large, thick shells, their associated occurrences with nonindigenous mollusks and algae, their brown color and preservation, their spotty distribution, and, in some cases, their unusually large per cent dominance in the presence of numerous species.

9. Recognizable depth facies based on generic dominance in the study area are Thecamoebina, coastal nonmarine; *Miliammina,* intertidal; *Ammobaculites, Elphidium,* less than 2 fathoms; *Streblus, Bolivina lowmani, Buliminella,* 2 to 10 fathoms; *Nonionella, Rosalina-Hanzawaia,* 10 to 30 fathoms; *Epistominella, Cassidulina,* 30 to 100 fathoms; *Bolivina,* 100 to 300 fathoms; and *Bulimina,* greater than 300 fathoms.

10. Numbers of species of Foraminifera (faunal variability) are inversely proportional to the variability of the environment. As marginal-marine conditions are approached, the environment becomes more variable and numbers of species decrease. Numbers of species increase in an offshore direction, reach a maximum near the shelf edge, and decrease again deeper than 100 fathoms.

11. The percentage occurrence of the most common species in a foraminiferal population (faunal dominance) is directly proportional to the variability of the environment; that is, as marginal-marine conditions are approached, the environments become more variable and faunal dominance increases. Faunal dominance is a maximum in the intertidal zone marshes and decreases offshore to a minimum off the edge of the continental shelf.

12. Along any time plane in the subsurface, an increase in faunal dominance and a decrease in faunal variability indicate an approach to marginal-marine conditions, and vice versa.

13. In any subsurface section, an increase in faunal dominance and a decrease in faunal variability up the section indicate a marine regression, and vice versa.

14. The percentage occurrence of arenaceous species increases and constitutes the largest percentage of the fauna near the effluence of rivers.

15. Calcareous foraminiferal tests become smaller and thinner near sources of fresh water.

16. The tests of many calcareous species characteristic of brackish water have "chitinous" inner linings that are identifiable and would be preserved in completely decalcified sediments.

17. Paleoecologies can be determined and paleobathymetric maps can be made throughout the Gulf Coast Tertiary using criteria developed from modern faunas.

REFERENCES

Cushman, J. A. and Alva C. Ellisor, 1935, Foraminiferal fauna of Anahuac formation, *J. Paleo.*, v. 19, n. 6, pp. 545–572.

Ellisor, Alva C., 1944, Anahuac formation, *Bull. Am. Assoc. Petrol. Geologists,* v. 28, n. 9, pp. 1355–1375.

Gould, Howard R. and Robert H. Stewart, 1955, Continental terrace sediments in the northeastern Gulf of Mexico, *Soc. Econ. Paleontologists Mineralogists, Spec. Publ.,* No. 3, 1955.

Lowman, S. W., 1949, Sedimentary facies in Gulf Coast, *Bull. Am. Assoc. Petrol. Geologists,* v. 33, n. 12, pp. 1939–1997.

Ludwick, John C. and William R. Walton, 1957, Shelf-edge, calcareous prominences in the northeastern Gulf of Mexico, *Bull. Am. Assoc. Petrol. Geologists,* v. 41, n. 9, pp. 2054–2101.

Meyer, Willis, G., 1939, Stratigraphy of Gulf Coastal Plain, *Bull. Am. Assoc. Petrol. Geologists,* v. 23, n. 1, pp. 145–211.

Murray, Grover E., 1947, Cenozoic deposits of Central Gulf Coastal Plain, *Bull. Am. Assoc. Petrol. Geologists,* v. 31, n. 10, pp. 1825–1850.

Parker, F. L., 1954, Distribution of the Foraminifera in the northeastern Gulf of Mexico, *Bull. Museum Comp. Zool., Harvard Coll.,* v. 111, n. 10, pp. 452–588.

Phleger, Fred B., 1954, Ecology of Foraminifera and associated microorganisms from Mississippi Sound and environs, *Bull. Am. Assoc. Petrol. Geologists,* v. 38, n. 4, pp. 584–647.

——— 1955, Ecology of Foraminifera in southeastern Mississippi Delta area, *Bull. Am. Assoc. Petrol. Geologists,* v. 39, n. 5, pp. 712–752.

Walton, William R., 1954, Ecology of benthonic Foraminifera in the Tampa-Sarasota Bay Area, Florida (unpublished manuscript).

Sediments as Substrates

by Edward G. Purdy *Department of Geology, Rice University, Houston, Texas*

ABSTRACT

Many of the lithologic and all of the biologic attributes of sedimentary rocks are related to features of the depositional environment. Consequently it is not surprising to find that many recent and fossil organisms are associated with specific lithologies. Distribution patterns of aquatic benthos, for example, are correlated usually with the texture or, more specifically, with the silt and clay content of the sediment rather than with its mineral composition. This relationship results from the fact that current velocities not only determine the proportion of silt and clay in sediments, other factors being equal, but also control the ecologically important variables of substrate mobility and concentration of organic matter.

Sediments accumulating under conditions of relatively high current velocities are characterized by a shifting bottom containing a small proportion of mud and organic matter. The instability and low organic content of these substrates result in bottom communities dominated by vagile suspension feeders. In contrast, low current velocities generally result in nonshifting substrates containing considerable proportions of mud and organic matter. Here the ecological result is usually a bottom fauna dominated by deposit feeders, but containing suspension feeders which are sessile as well as vagile.

The writer is indebted to Robert Robertson of The Academy of Natural Sciences of Philadelphia, for information on the feeding types of some of the invertebrates found in and around Bahamian oolite shoals and for providing additional information on the fauna of the area. The facilities of the Lerner Marine Laboratory, a research station of the American Museum of Natural History at Bimini, British West Indies, made field work on Bahamian oolite faunas possible.

Introduction

The restriction of particular species of fossil organisms to specific sedimentary lithologies is a common phenomenon. Such fossils are known as facies fossils to distinguish them from guide fossils which are relatively unrestricted with respect to facies changes and hence more useful in establishing time relationships. Stratigraphers, long concerned with the problem of which fossils are guides to time, consequently have had to distinguish between facies fossils and guide fossils. In contrast, paleontologists usually have ignored the lithologic associations of fossils (e.g., see Weller, 1960, Fig. 68) and generally have made few attempts to determine the reasons for these associations. It is the purpose of this paper to consider briefly the nature of the correlations between sediment types and the distribution of Recent marine benthonic invertebrates and to indicate the paleoecological deductions that can be made from similar correlations in the geologic record.

Substrates and Bottom Faunas

A sediment substrate can be defined as an unconsolidated surface on or in which organisms live. No one has seriously doubted the importance of the substrate as an ecologic factor; however, there has been discussion concerning its importance *relative* to hydrographical factors such as salinity and temperature. For example, Petersen (1913) and Davis (1925) regard bottom type as more essential than hydrographical conditions in determining benthonic animal associations, whereas Molander (1928) and Shelford et al. (1935) believe the opposite to be true. It is noteworthy, as both Thorson (1957, p. 485) and Buchanan (1958, p. 36) have mentioned, that this difference of opinion has been expressed by individuals working in different areas. Those who advocate the primary ecologic importance of substrates have generally worked in open sea regions; those who believe hydrographical factors are more important have investigated areas such as fjords and sounds where variations in hydrographical conditions are apt to be more extreme than they are in the open sea. It would seem then, as Molander himself has stated, that "within the limits of similar hydrographic conditions . . . the animal communities are no doubt affected by divergent conditions of the bottom" (quoted in Buchanan, 1958, p. 36).

The best evidence for the correlation between bottom type and bottom fauna has been provided by Thorson's (1957) summary of

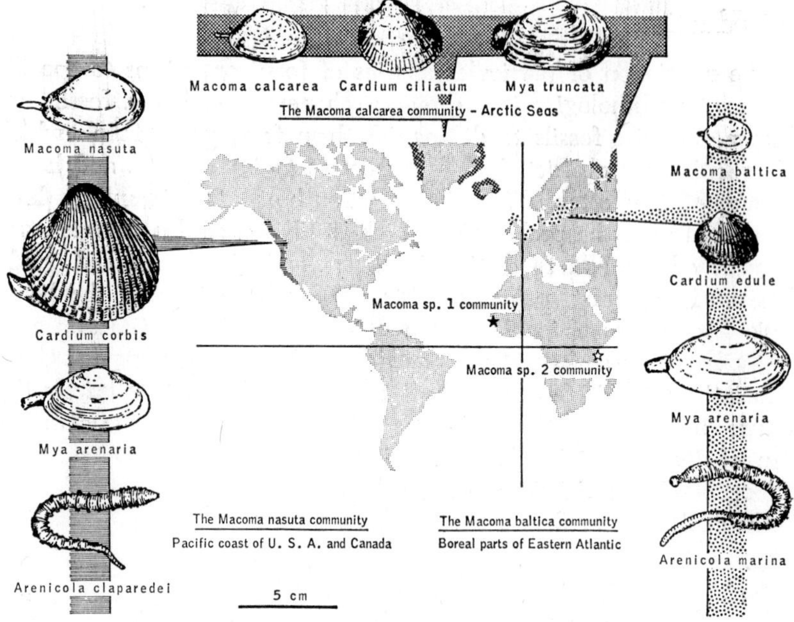

Fig. 1 Characterizing genera of the Arctic, boreal, and Northeast Pacific Macoma *communities. After Thorson, (1957).*

parallel, sublittoral, sediment bottom communities in different geographical regions.[1] These communities are parallel in the sense that they are characterized by the same genera inhabiting the same type of bottom at similar depths (Thorson, 1957, p. 521). The remarkable degree of taxonomic parallelism within these communities is evident in Figure 1 which illustrates the characterizing genera of the Arctic, Boreal, and Northeast Pacific *Macoma* communities. Indeed, the only notable lack of parallelism evident in this and other parallel communities is at the species level, where different species of the same genera replace one another with changing latitude. This replacement is apparently the result of temperature adaptations, the congeneric Arctic and tropical species having a similar though not identical metabolic rate (Thorson, 1957, p. 522).

In brief, if bottom type and, apparently to a lesser extent, depth are held constant, the same characterizing genera with the same ecologic role in the community will occur at different latitudes within the same

[1] Unless otherwise noted, the relationships discussed throughout this paper refer to the sublittoral environment.

zoogeographic province. Alternatively, differences in bottom type at the same latitude will be reflected by differences in the characterizing genera of the bottom faunas.

Substrates and Feeding Types

Having established the good correlation between bottom type and bottom fauna, it is now pertinent to consider some of the biological consequences of substrate changes which transcend taxonomic boundaries. One of the more ecologically important attributes of an invertebrate animal is the way in which it feeds. Basically three feeding types can be recognized: suspension feeders, deposit feeders, and carnivores (Hunt, 1925, pp. 567–568). Suspension feeders feed on microorganisms and/or organic detritus suspended in water, whereas deposit feeders feed on the same material on or in sediments; carnivores feed on other animals.

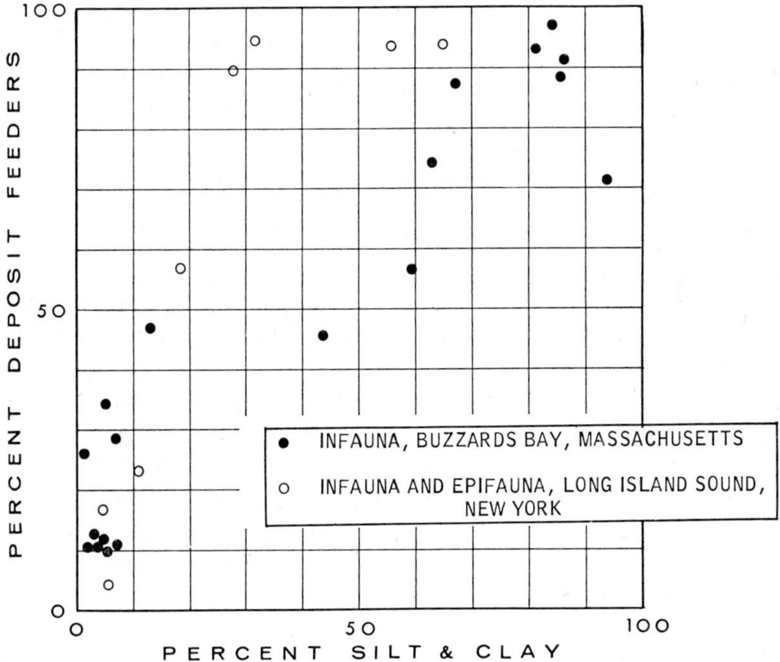

Fig. 2 Graph showing the correlation between the proportion of deposit feeders in the bottom fauna and the silt and clay content of the substrate. Data from Sanders (1956, 1958).

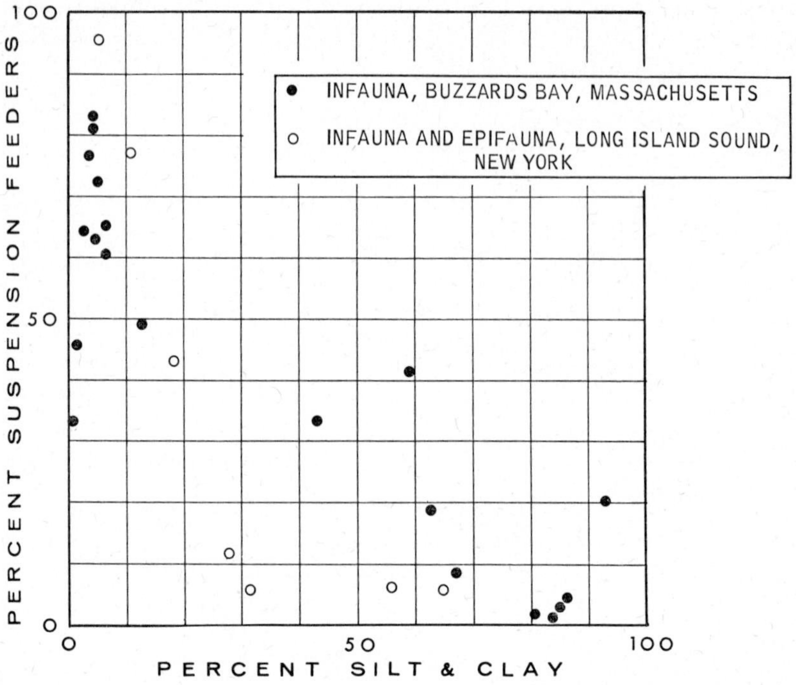

Fig. 3 Graph illustrating the relationship between the proportion of suspension feeders comprising the bottom fauna and the silt and clay content of the substrate. Data from Sanders (1956, 1958).

A relationship between feeding type and sedimentary texture has been recognized by several investigators. For example, Davis (1925, pp. 14–15) reported an association between the abundance of deposit feeders relative to suspension feeders and the texture of the sediment. Deposit feeders were most numerous in the finest-textured sediment; suspension feeders predominated in the coarsest sediment. This same correlation is evident in Thorson's (1957, p. 505) description of the general characteristics of the *Macoma* communities: ". . . increasing amounts of silt or mud will lead to dominance of the deposit feeders *Macoma* and *Arenicola,* increasing amounts of sand to dominance of the suspension feeder *Cardium.*" Sanders (1956, 1958) has quantified this relationship in Long Island Sound, New York, and Buzzards Bay, Massachusetts. His data are graphically illustrated in Figures 2 and 3. It is readily apparent (Figure 2) that the proportion of deposit feeders comprising the fauna increases as the sediment's silt and clay content increases; the opposite relationship is evident (Figure 3) with respect to suspension feeders. The question now arises as to whether these correlations indicate a causal relationship or are merely an expression of some higher-order factor controlling both the sediment's silt and clay content and the proportion of deposit and suspension feeders in the bottom fauna.

It is generally true that within any given depositional environment, fine-grained sediments contain more organic matter than coarse-grained deposits (Trask, 1955, pp. 433–434). This is evident, for example, in Figure 4 which illustrates the close parallelism between the organic carbon and silt and clay content of marine sediments off Accra, Ghana. These relationships result at least in part from the fact that the finely particulate organic matter in sea water can settle out of suspension only in areas attended by relatively low current velocities. Weak currents, of course, also favor the deposition of silt- and clay-sized particles and, in addition, prevent rapid removal of organic detritus formed at and below the sediment-water interface. Deposit feeders by definition feed on bottom deposits of nonliving organic detritus and on associated microorganisms. Consequently it is to be

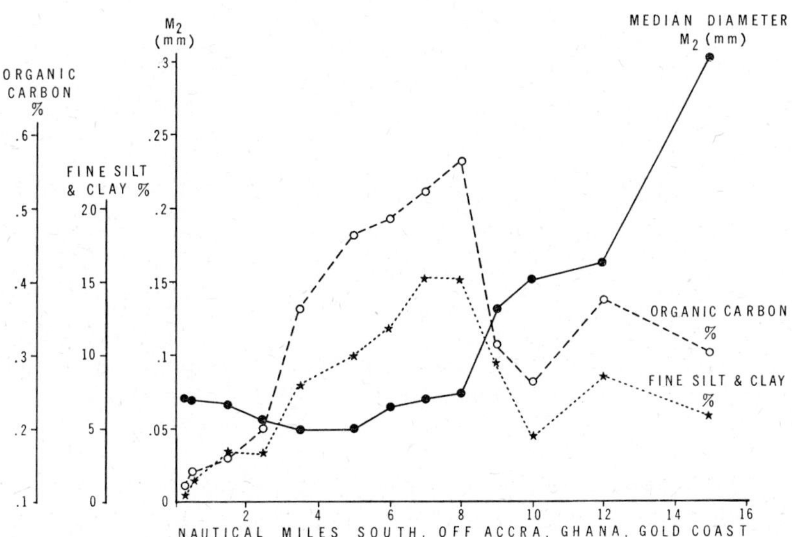

Fig. 4 Graph demonstrating the good correlation between the organic carbon and fine silt and clay content of marine sediments off Accra, Ghana. Note that the median diameter (M2) is a relatively poor indicator of the sediment's organic carbon content. After Buchanan (1958).

anticipated that the proportion of deposit feeders comprising the bottom fauna will increase as the organic content of the substrate increases. Because the organic content of the sediment also is highly correlated with the amount of silt and clay present, it follows that there will be a good correlation between the percentage of deposit feeders comprising the bottom fauna and the silt and clay content of the sediment. In brief, it is the organic content of the sediment and not the silt and clay content that is causally related to the proportion of deposit feeders in the bottom fauna.

In contrast to deposit feeders, the organic content of the sediment is of no direct consequence to suspension feeders, for by definition suspension feeders feed on microorganisms and organic detritus *suspended* in the surrounding water; it is rather the amount of food in the surrounding water which is of primary importance to suspension feeders.

> . . . Most suspension feeders filter about 15 l. of water for each millilitre of oxygen taken up. At this feeding rate the energy requirements for maintenance are covered if the available food in the water amounts to about 0.05 mg./l., whereas 0.15–0.20 mg./l. are needed to secure optimal growth. . . . It appears that during parts of the year these amounts of organic matter are contained in the phytoplankton, at least in coastal waters where all suspension feeders so far investigated live. During part of the year the amounts of phytoplankton may be 10–20 times the amounts required for optimal growth, or even more. When production is low, however, the amounts of phytoplankton may be too small to provide food enough even for maintenance. During such periods [organic] detritus may be of importance as a food source. In absolute amounts the detritus often exceeds the phytoplankton. . . . The food value of the detritus is not known. That it can be utilized as food appears from the fact that suspension feeders are also found living below the photosynthetic zone, which extends from the surface to a depth of at most 400 m. At greater depth, detritus is practically the only food source of the filter feeders.[2] The bacteria suspended in the water are probably too scarce to be of significance as food. . . . Suspension feeders living at great depths in the oceans, where the average content of particulate detritus is about 25 mg./l., must be able to filter some 100 l. of water or more for each millilitre of oxygen consumed (Jørgensen, 1955, pp. 440, 445).

Considering these facts from a population point of view, it is evident that rate of water renewal is of prime importance in determining the numbers of suspension feeders on a particular substrate. Large populations of suspension feeders would rapidly deplete the utilizable

[2] As used in this paper, the term "filter feeding" is synonymous with suspension feeding.

organic matter in the surrounding water were it not for the currents that constantly replace the filtered water with fresh sea water. Other factors being equal, the higher the current velocity, the greater the amount of usable organic matter brought to the suspension feeders per unit time and consequently the larger the suspension-feeding component of the bottom fauna. Relatively high current velocities are, of course, inimical to the deposition of large quantities of silt- and clay-sized particles; therefore large numbers of suspension feeders will be found on sediment substrates having a low silt and clay content. Alternatively, relatively low current velocities favor the deposition of silt and clay; hence few suspension feeders will be found on relatively fine-grained substrates. These relationships explain the negative correlation evident in Figure 3.[3]

Clays and Deposit Feeders

It will be noted in Figure 2 that there is considerable spread between the Buzzards Bay and Long Island Sound samples, suggesting that perhaps the silt and clay content of the sediment is not an adequate index of the abundance of deposit feeders in the bottom fauna. This discrepancy is made more apparent in Figure 5, which shows the observed range and weighted mean abundances of the deposit feeders *Nucula proxima*, a protobranchiate pelecypod, and *Nephthys incisa*, a polychaete worm, for Buzzards Bay and Long Island Sound. The weighted mean abundance of *Nucula* in Buzzards Bay occurs at a value of 81.96% silt and clay; in Long Island Sound the corresponding statistic is 57.47%. Thus there is approximately a 24% difference between the weighted mean abundance of *Nucula* in Buzzards Bay as compared to Long Island Sound. Similarly, an approximate 36% difference exists between the weighted mean abundances of *Nephthys* in these two regions. Sanders (1958), using a different method of graphical analysis, demonstrated that this difference in distributional pattern was reduced considerably by plotting the numerical abundance of these two species against clay percentage. This is evident in Figure 6, where the differences in weighted mean abundances between Buzzards Bay and Long Island Sound samples for *Nucula* and

[3] Of course, it could be argued that the observed correlations between silt and clay and feeding type result from larval selection of the substrate. This is the case, for example, for the polychaete *Ophelia bicornis* (Wilson, 1952). From an evolutionary point of view, however, it seems likely that such larval selectivity would develop as a consequence of or concomitantly with the substrate relationships noted for the adults.

Nephthys have been reduced to 7% and 0.8%, respectively. The strongly skewed character of the weighted mean abundances of *Nucula* and *Nephthys* in Buzzards Bay as compared to Long Island Sound (Figure 6) is due to the fact that samples taken in Buzzards Bay did not have a clay content above 20%, whereas Long Island Sound samples did (Sanders, 1956, p. 355; 1958, p. 247). This illustrates the important point that the ecology or paleoecology of an organism, even with respect to one variable, can seldom be ascertained from studying a single area or a single sedimentary unit, but rather must be pieced together from the data available from several such areas or units.

The data presented in Figures 5 and 6 suggest that the clay content

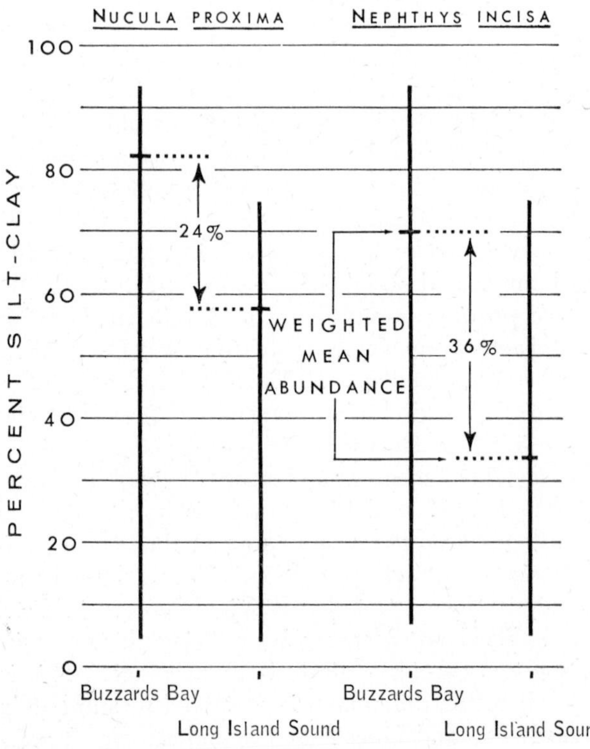

Fig. 5 Observed range and weighted mean abundance of two deposit feeding species in Buzzards Bay, Massachusetts and Long Island Sound, New York. The vertical lines indicate the observed range of each species with respect to silt and clay. The means are also expressed with respect to silt and clay so that the same number of individuals occur above the cross-bar representing the weighted mean abundance as below. Data from Sanders (1956, 1958).

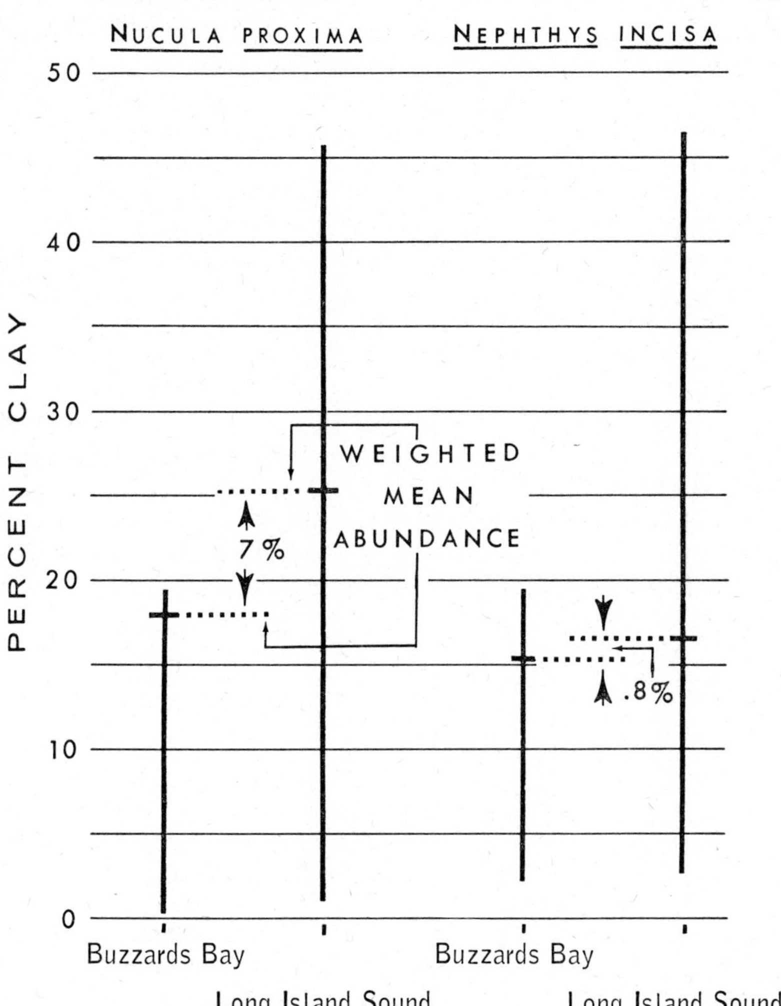

Fig. 6 Observed range and weighted mean abundance of two deposit feeding species in Buzzards Bay, Massachusetts and Long Island Sound, New York. The vertical lines indicate the observed range of each species with respect to clay. The means are also expressed with respect to clay so that the same number of individuals occur above the cross-bar representing the weighted mean abundance as below. Data from Sanders (1956, 1958).

of the substrate is a better index of the abundance of *Nucula* and *Nephthys* than silt and clay. If this relationship is true of deposit feeders in general, as Sanders (1958, p. 256) believes, then the spread evident between the Long Island Sound and Buzzards Bay samples of Figure 2 should be reduced considerably by plotting clay content against the number of deposit feeders in these same samples. This has been done in Figure 7, where it is obvious that there has been a considerable reduction in scatter. The rank correlation between the percentage of deposit feeders constituting the bottom fauna and the clay content of the substrate is +0.85, a value that is significant at the 1% confidence level. Thus Sanders' contention is supported by the available data.

The accumulation of clay-sized particles requires weaker currents than that of silts. Therefore the good correlation between the abundance of deposit feeders and the clay content of the substrate may be explained by assuming that weaker currents not only effect the deposition of large quantities of clay-sized material but also favor the settling of large amounts of finely dispersed particulate organic matter,

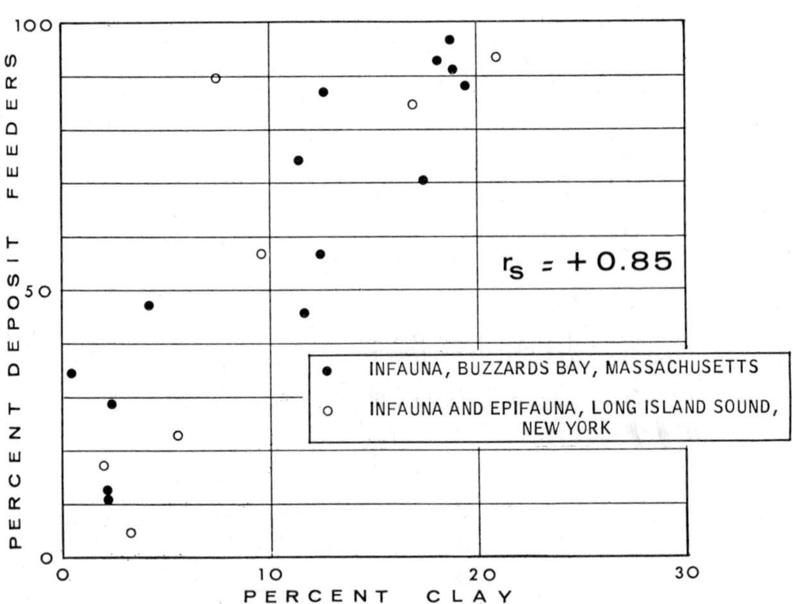

Fig. 7 Graph illustrating the correlation between the proportion of deposit feeders in the bottom fauna and the clay content of the substrate (compare with Fig. 2). Data from Sanders (1956, 1958).

the deposited organic detritus serving as food for deposit feeders. There is, however, an additional factor which ultimately may prove as important or more important than organic detritus in explaining the association between clays and deposit feeders.

The amount of dissolved organic matter in sea water ranges between 2.2 and 4.6 mg/l (Jørgensen, 1955, p. 445). Organic matter in this form is unavailable to deposit feeders but can be made potentially available through sorption on suspended sedimentary particles (Whitehouse, 1955; Bader and Jeffrey, 1958; Bader, Hood, and Smith, 1960; Bader, Rae, and Smith, 1960; Smith and Bader, 1961). The four mineral species which have been investigated show differential uptake with respect to the naturally occurring organic compounds—aspartic acid, alanine, glucose, sucrose, fructose, succinic acid, and glycine (Bader, Rae, and Smith, 1960). With respect to these compounds montmorillonite has the greatest sorption capacity, followed in order by illite, kaolinite, and quartz (Bader, Rae, and Smith, 1960). Thus the dissolved organic matter adsorbed and/or absorbed on clay minerals prior to deposition is a potential source of food for deposit feeders. Indeed, Bader, Rae, and Smith (1960) have found that bacteria, a link in the food chain of deposit feeders, and the deposit-feeding shrimp *Penaeus setiferus* and *Palaemonetes pugio* are capable of stripping organic compounds from clay minerals. The characteristics of clay minerals (e.g., see Bader, Rae, and Smith, 1960, p. 21) suggest that their sorption capacity is greater than that of other commonly occurring sedimentary minerals, and consequently clay minerals will afford deposit feeders a greater supply of adsorbed and/or absorbed food than nonclay minerals. This could be another reason for the good correlation between abundance of deposit feeders and clay content of the substrate. In this regard it is interesting to note that the clay fraction of the Buzzards Bay samples consisted predominantly of illite and chlorite, although montmorillonite, kaolinite, feldspar, and quartz also were present (Sanders, 1958, p. 246).

Decomposition of Organic Matter

The relationships considered thus far suggest that the abundance of deposit feeders increases with increasing organic content of the substrate, but this is not always the case. At Mt. Desert Island, Maine, Bader (1954) observed a decrease in pelecypod density when the sediment contained more than 3% organic matter. Bader (1954) assumed that the organic matter in the substrate was the principal food source for all the pelecypod species which he examined. This is an erroneous assumption, as Sanders (1956, pp. 402–403) has noted, because 10 of Bader's 16 pelecypod species are suspension feeders. With one exception, however, the suspension feeders comprise a numerically small proportion of the pelecypod fauna of each sample (Bader, 1952). Consequently the relationships Bader (1954) noted for pelecypod density are also evident for his deposit-feeding lamellibranchs. This is evident in Figure 8, where the number of deposit-feeding pelecypods, like pelecypod density, decreases as the substrate's organic content increases beyond 3%.

Bader (1954) reasoned that this decrease in pelecypod density might be the result of accumulation of toxic decomposition products and/or depletion in available oxygen by bacterial activity. The probability of this occurring increases with advancing stages of decomposition, other factors being equal. Therefore Bader (1954) computed a coefficient which was assumed to reflect the amount of decomposition in each of the substrates sampled. Comparing his samples with respect to their decomposition coefficient and pelecypod density, Bader (1954) observed that the samples could be divided readily into two groups, one having high pelecypod densities and low decomposition coefficients and the other showing the opposite relationship. This is

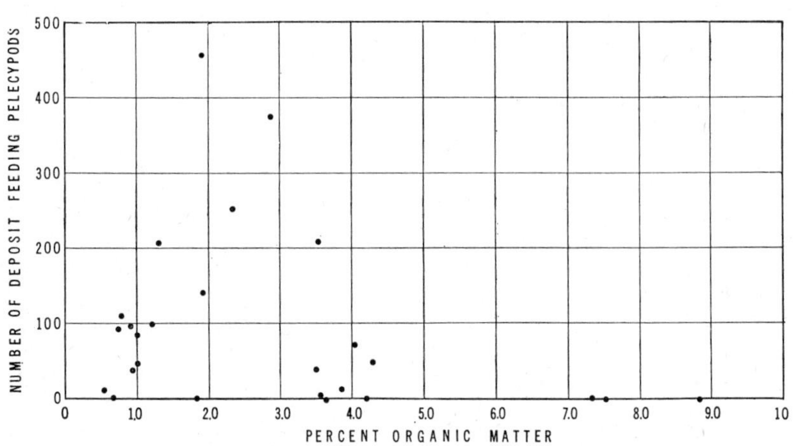

Fig. 8 Graph illustrating the curvilinear relationship between the number of deposit feeding pelecypods and the organic matter content of the substrate in the marine environments of Mt. Desert Island, Maine. Note the decrease in numbers of deposit feeders as the substrate's organic matter content exceeds 3 per cent. Data from Bader (1952).

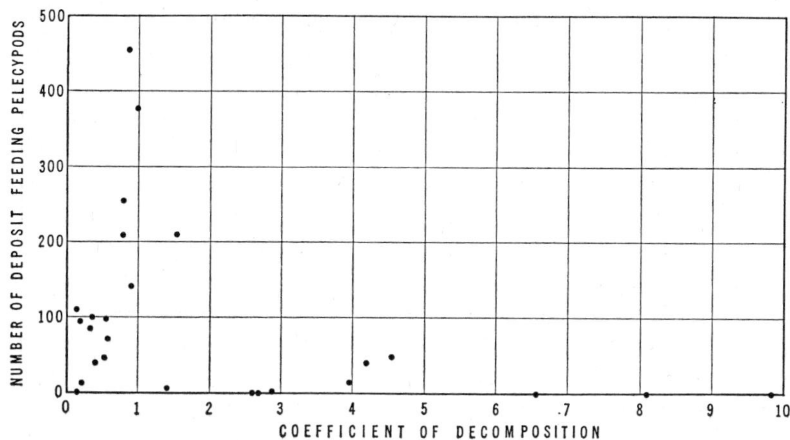

Fig. 9 Comparison between the number of deposit feeding pelecypods and the decomposition coefficient of samples collected in the marine environments of Mt. Desert Island, Maine. Note that two clusters of points are in evidence, the separation between the clusters occurring at a decomposition coefficient of 1.0. Data from Bader (1952).

also demonstrable with regard to the deposit-feeding lamellibranchs (Figure 9). The break between the two groups occurs at a decomposition coefficient of 1.0, the higher coefficients indicating a more advanced stage of decomposition. A comparison of the organic matter content and deposit-feeder density of the samples with a decomposition coefficient less than 1.0 reveals a linear trend, the rank correlation of +0.65 being significant at the 1% confidence level (Figure 10). The data suggest then that the depletion in available oxygen and/or accumulation of toxic decomposition products limit the distribution of deposit-feeding pelecypods in sediments containing more than 3% organic matter (Bader, 1954).

The organic matter in sediments is, of course, profoundly modified by postdepositional processes, and thus the original organic content of a sediment is seldom, if ever, preserved in the geologic record. Hence the importance of stage of decomposition in limiting the abundance of fossil deposit feeders must be ascertained in another way. It has been suggested previously that the clay and organic matter content of the substrate are closely correlated. Indeed, in Bader's samples a curvilinear relationship results regardless of whether the deposit-feeding pelecypod populations are compared with organic

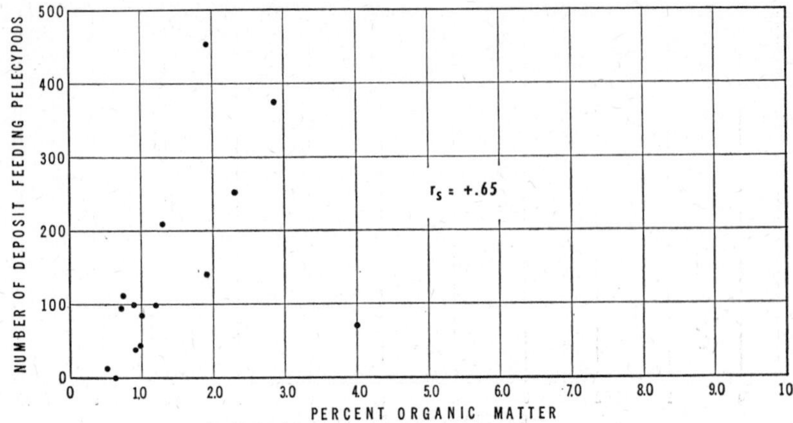

Fig. 10 Graph demonstrating the linear relationship between the number of deposit feeding pelecypods and the organic matter content of samples having a decomposition coefficient less than 1.0, Mt. Desert Island, Maine. Data from Bader (1952).

matter (Figure 8) or clay content (Figure 11).[4] The elimination of samples having a decomposition coefficient greater than 1.0 from the clay comparison (Figure 12) does not result in as good a correlation as it did previously (e.g., compare Figures 10 and 12). The inferior correlation is due largely to three samples which contain a relatively low number of deposit-feeding pelecypods and a high percentage of clay-sized particles. One of these samples also has an anomalous position in Figure 10 in that it contains 4% organic matter and only 72 deposit-feeding pelecypods. These three samples are thus characterized by a decomposition coefficient less than 1.0, a clay content greater than 50%, and a deposit-feeder population of less than 150 individuals. It can be hypothesized that the high clay content of these samples compensates for their relatively low stage of organic decomposition in limiting the abundance of deposit feeders. Sediments with a high clay content have relatively poor interstitial circulation; consequently a small amount of decomposition within these sediments probably would produce the same degree of toxicity as a more advanced stage of decomposition in sediments with fewer clay-

[4] The upper particle size limit of the clay-sized sample fraction plotted on the abscissas of Figures 11 and 12 is 0.0312 mm. The next coarser size grade determined by Bader (1952) includes both silt- and clay-sized particles; hence the restriction of the term clay with respect to Bader's (1952) samples to particles smaller than 0.0312 mm.

sized particles and hence better interstitial circulation. In this regard it is interesting to note that among the three anomalous samples previously mentioned, the sample having the greatest number of deposit feeders also has the *highest* decomposition coefficient but the *lowest* clay concentration.

It is apparent that the clay content of sedimentary rocks may prove useful in evaluating the importance of organic decomposition in limiting the distribution and abundance of fossil deposit feeders. A curvilinear relationship similar to that illustrated in Figure 11 would suggest that bacterial depletion of available oxygen and/or accumulation of toxic decomposition products ultimately limited the abundance of the fossil deposit feeders. Samples having few deposit feeders and an intermediate clay content (e.g., the samples in Figure 11 with less than 10 deposit feeders and clay concentrations approximating 48%) can be assumed to have experienced a relatively advanced stage of organic decomposition.

Substrate Mobility

It generally has been recognized that sand substrates support relatively sparse animal populations (e.g., Allee et al., 1950, p. 161; Yonge, 1949, p. 214). This relationship has been quantified for the shore

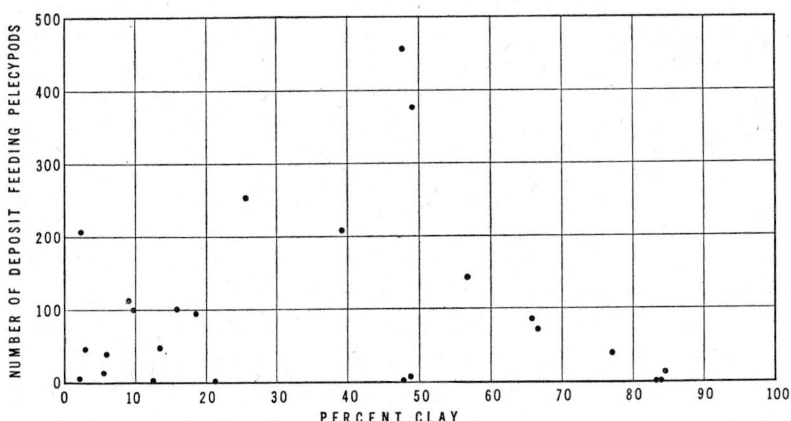

Fig. 11 Graph illustrating the curvilinear relationship between the number of deposit feeding pelecypods and the amount of clay-sized material in the Recent marine sediments of Mt. Desert Island, Maine (compare with Fig. 8). Data from Bader (1952).

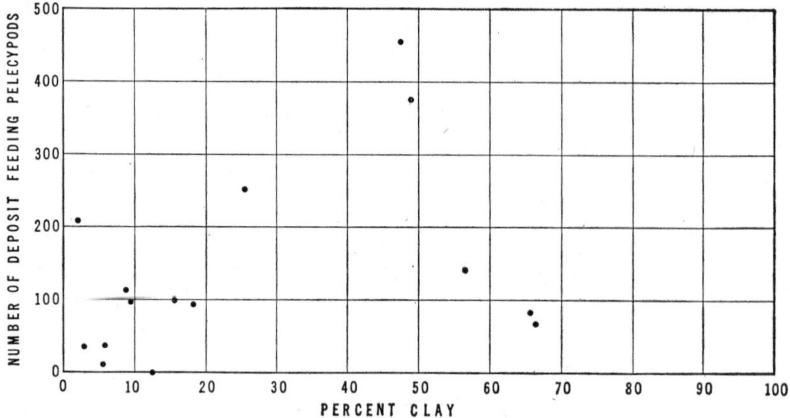

Fig. 12 Graph showing the relationship between the number of deposit feeding pelecypods and the amount of clay-sized material in samples having a decomposition coefficient less than 1.0, Mt. Desert Island, Maine. Note that the samples containing more than 50 per cent clay-sized material have relatively few deposit feeders (compare with Fig. 10). Data from Bader (1952).

fauna of western Lake Erie by Krecker and Lancaster (1933), who have noted that the number of individuals and number of species per square yard is least on a sand bottom (Figure 13). But why should sand substrates support less animal life than, for example, clay substrates (Figure 13)? It is true that the sand bottom fauna will consist largely of suspension feeders and the clay or mud bottom fauna largely of deposit feeders, but why should there be fewer numbers of suspension-feeding individuals and species per unit area on a sand bottom than deposit-feeding individuals and species on a mud bottom? The answer appears to be that sands, in contrast to muds, are usually characterized by a shifting bottom, and this substrate instability or mobility is an environmental attribute to which relatively few benthonic organisms have been able to adapt themselves.

An extreme example of the ecological consequences of substrate mobility is evident on the oolite shoals of the Great Bahama Bank. These shoals are of complex origin (Purdy, 1961), but their characteristics can be generalized in the form of the idealized profile shown in Figure 14. Bathymetrically the oolite shoals are bordered on either side by deeper water, the water on the seaward or outer platform side being deeper than that on the backward or shelf lagoon side. During flood tides the progressive decrease in water depth from the outer platform toward the shoal results in a concomitant increase in current velocity in the same direction. During ebb tides the same relationship is evident for water moving onto the shoal from the shelf lagoon. In these respects the shoal is analogous to a submerged barrier athwart the width of a stream, current velocities being accelerated as water moves over the barrier. With reference to the adjoining hydrographic provinces, the oolite shoal is characterized by relatively high current velocities, and these high current velocities, in turn, cause considerable substrate mobility. The oolite content of the shoals usually exceeds 90%. This fact in itself is indicative of relatively great substrate mobility, since the complete enclosure of nuclei by oolitic laminae necessitates considerable differential grain movement. The shifting nature of the oolite bottom, however, is also indicated directly

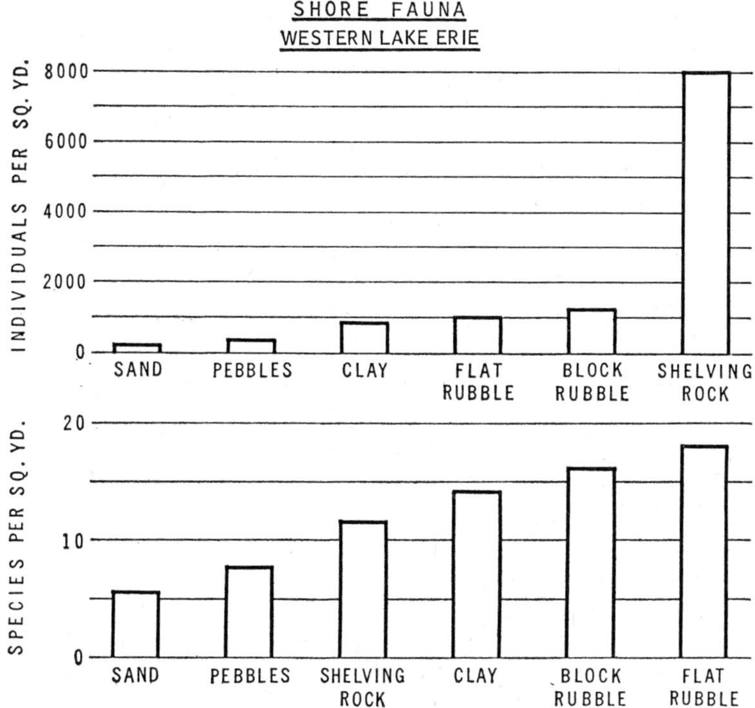

Fig. 13 Relationship between number of individuals and number of species per square yard with respect to substrate differences along the shore of Western Lake Erie. After Krecker and Lancaster (1933).

by the seemingly incessant rapid migration of small sand ripples and the abundance of large para-ripples.

The shallowest continually submerged portions of the oolite shoal are characterized by a paucity of benthonic organisms (Table 1 and Figure 14). Megascopically visible plants are absent, and the extremely few living invertebrates found in the area consist entirely of small, rapidly burrowing, suspension-feeding pelecypods of the species *Tivela abaconis.* Thus these regions of the shoal are veritable submarine deserts. The depth of water overlying the shoal increases toward the shelf lagoon (Figure 14), and concomitantly there is a gradual decrease in substrate mobility in the same direction. This

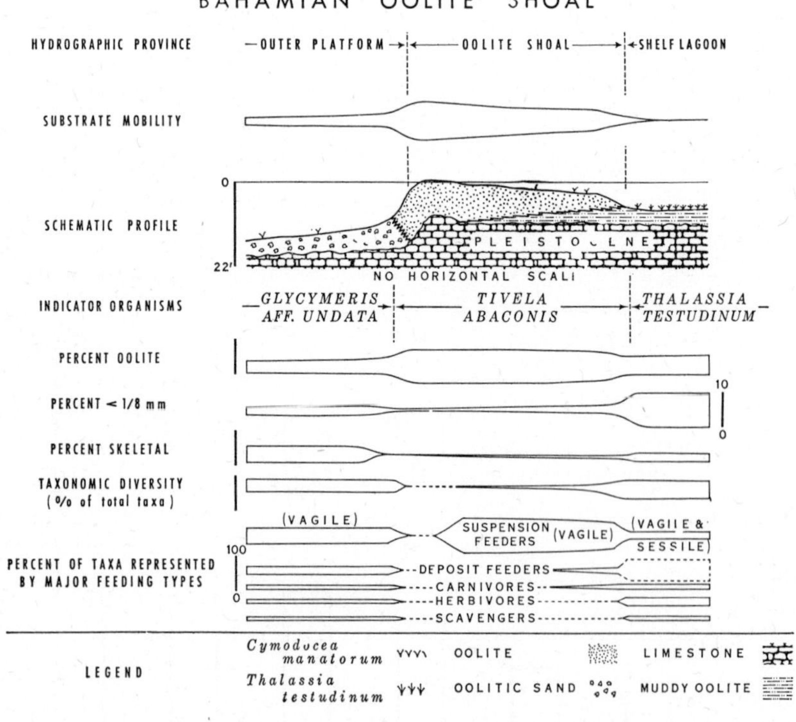

Fig. 14 Relative taxonomic abundance of invertebrate feeding types on an idealized Bahamian oolite shoal. Taxonomic diversity is expressed as a percentage of the total number of plant and animal species shown in Table 1. The percentages of oolite and skeletal grains are based on point-count analyses of thin sections. The percentages of material smaller than 1/8 mm. are based on sieve analyses. Unless otherwise designated, all vertical scales extend from 0 to 100 per cent.

TABLE 1. *Distribution of taxa, feeding types, and oolite on an idealized Bahamian oolite shoal**

		Oolite Shoal		
	Outer Platform	Outer Platform Side	Shelf Lagoon Side	Shelf Lagoon
Number of recognized plant and animal species	16	1	7	24
Number of recognized plant species	5	0	3	6
Number of suspension feeding invertebrate species	5	1	1	5
Number of deposit feeding invertebrate species	3	0	1	4
Number of species of invertebrate carnivores	1	0	1	2
Number of species of invertebrate herbivores	1	0	0	4
Number of species of invertebrate scavengers	1	0	0	1
Number of invertebrate species of unknown feeding habit	0	0	1†	2‡
Per cent oolite ($\overline{X}$)	42.8	95.8	95.4	60.3
Per cent skeletal grains ($\overline{X}$)	23.9	1.3	1.3	10.8
Per cent grains $< 1/8$ mm in size ($\overline{X}$)	2.7	1.8	2.1	12.2
Number of sediment samples point-counted and sieved	7	9	8	5

* The data presented in this table are based largely on seven dredge hauls and 29 Petersen grab samples taken on and adjacent to the S. Cat Cay-Sandy Cay oolite shoal on the western side of the Great Bahama Bank (see Newell, Purdy, and Imbrie, 1960, for the location of this area). This information has been supplemented by field observations in this and other oolite areas on the Great Bahama Bank.

† The starfish *Oreaster reticulatus.*

‡ The starfish *Oreaster reticulatus* and an unidentified species of the gastropod genus *Cantharus.*

increased substrate stability permits colonization of the bottom by a more varied biota. Sparse floral growths of the marine phanerogam *Cymodocea manatorum* appear along with an occasional representative of the algal codiacean genus *Penicillus.* More rarely stands of another marine phanerogam, *Thalassia testudinum,* occur. In addition to *Tivela abaconis,* the invertebrate fauna now includes the starfish *Oreaster reticulatus,* an unidentified sea anemone, and an unidentified worm. The feeding habit of the starfish in this area is unknown;[5] the sea anemone is a carnivore, and the worm, judging from the innumerable faecal pellets of aggregated sediment which surround each worm mound, is a deposit feeder. None of these animals is abundant.

The outer platform sediment adjacent to the shoal is also characterized by substrate mobility, although the movement of grains on the bottom is not as frequent or as rapid as on the shoal. This is suggested by the relative lack of para-ripples and the less frequent occurrence of small migrating sand ripples. It also is suggested by the smaller percentage of ooids as compared to the oolite shoal deposits (Figure 14). Here the taxonomic diversity of the biota is greater than that of the oolite shoal. *Cymodocea* and to a lesser extent *Thalassia* are again in evidence; the algae present include *Halimeda, Rhipocephalus,* and *Goniolithon,* as well as *Penicillus.* The invertebrate fauna consists largely of pelecypods, the most abundant and diagnostic form being the suspension-feeding lamellibranch *Glycymeris* aff. *undata.* The proportion of suspension-feeding taxa comprising the bottom fauna is still large, although the relative taxonomic importance of deposit feeders has increased compared to that of the oolite shoal.

The shelf lagoon sediments adjacent to the shoal are characterized by an even greater degree of bottom stability, as indicated by the absence of either large or small sand ripples and the relative abundance of grains smaller than ⅛ mm. The higher oolite content of the shelf lagoon sediments as compared to the outer platform deposits is a reflection of the fact that flood tidal currents on the bank are stronger than ebb currents, and consequently more ooids are transported bankward from their site of origin than seaward. The taxonomic diversity of the muddy oolite sediment is greater than that of either the oolitic sand deposits or the oolite deposits (Figure 14). In contrast to the other two facies, the muddy oolite bottom is densely covered by *Thalassia. Cymodocea* is relatively rare; and the algae

[5] Thomas (1960) has made observations on the feeding habit of *Oreaster* which suggest that it may be both a carnivore and a deposit feeder. Presumably the type of food available dictates its feeding habit at any one time.

present include *Penicillus, Halimeda, Rhipocephalus,* and less commonly *Acetabularia.* The proportion of suspension-feeding taxa comprising the fauna is reduced considerably from that of the oolitic sand of the outer platform. Moreover, the suspension feeders present are represented by sessile (e.g., sponges) as well as vagile forms, whereas only vagile suspension feeders were present in the oolite and oolitic sand deposits. The number of taxa feeding on plant material is increased largely due to the presence of such herbivores as *Strombus gigas, S. costatus,* and *S. raninus.* The number of deposit-feeding taxa also has increased slightly (Table 1). The dense cover of *Thalassia* on the muddy oolite bottom seriously hampered efforts to sample the fauna with either a Petersen grab sampler or a dredge; consequently it seems likely that a considerable number of deposit-feeding taxa escaped detection. For this reason the percentage of deposit-feeding taxa inhabiting the muddy oolite bottom has been increased somewhat in Figure 14 from the percentage given in Table 1. The speculative nature of this percentage is shown by a dashed line.

The ecological relationships evident on a Bahamian oolite shoal can be generalized in the form of the diagram shown in Figure 15. Increasing bottom current velocity results in increasing substrate mobility, which in turn has three ecological consequences. First, any organic matter produced *in situ* is rapidly winnowed out of the substrate as decompositional and disintegrational processes reduce the size of the organic particles to the point where they can be transported out of the environment by bottom currents. The strength of the bottom current itself prevents the deposition of organic detritus originating in other environments. Consequently the substrate contains a relatively low percentage of organic matter. (In this connection it is interesting to note that Kornicker [1958, p. 211] found that the oolite deposits in the vicinity of Bimini (Bahamas), British West Indies, contained the lowest percentage of organic matter of any sediment types in the area.) The same current velocities prevent the accumulation of excessive amounts of mud (silt and clay). The low organic content of the substrate limits the number of deposit feeders which the environment can support. This is true with respect both to the number of deposit-feeding individuals and the number of deposit-feeding taxa, the paucity of organic matter simply offering less ecologic opportunity for taxonomic exploitation.

Second, the shifting bottom effectively inhibits colonization of the substrate by many forms of marine plants, the substrate being too mobile for their attachment. This seriously limits the numerical and taxonomic abundance of the herbivores comprising the bottom fauna

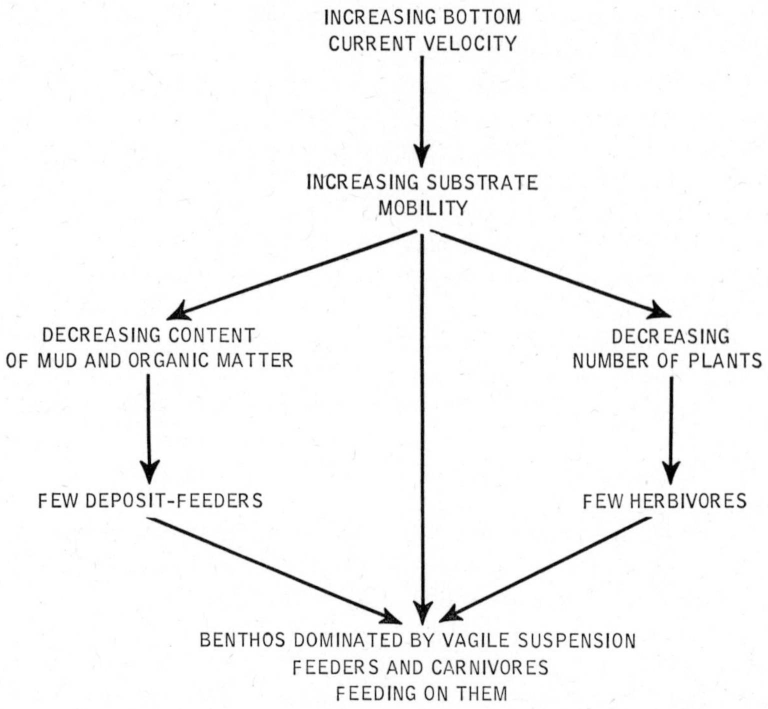

Fig. 15 Simplified diagram of the ecological consequences of increasing substrate mobility.

and further contributes to the sediment's dearth of organic matter. Thus the general lack of organic matter *in* the substrate and the poorly developed flora *on* the substrate results in a bottom fauna characterized chiefly by a relative abundance of suspension feeders and low taxonomic diversity. Substrate mobility, however, also has a third more direct consequence on the ecologic composition of the bottom fauna. Sessile suspension feeders such as sponges would be rapidly uprooted and/or buried by shifting sediment; hence shifting bottoms require mobile or, more properly, vagile suspension feeders for their colonization. This requisite, of course, further limits the taxonomic diversity of the bottom fauna, so that the end product of the extreme degree of substrate mobility shown by Bahamian oolite shoals is a benthos dominated by vagile suspension feeders and the carnivores which feed on them.

Fossil Oolite Faunas

Several instances of richly fossiliferous oolite have been noted in the geologic record. For example, the Mississippian Salem Limestone and the Pennsylvanian Drum Limestone in the mid-continent region of the United States and the Jurassic oolite formations of England all contain taxonomically diverse fossil assemblages. The diversity of these faunas contrasts markedly with the relatively few invertebrate species found living on Bahamian oolite shoals. This seemingly inconsistent relationship can be explained in terms of either the lack of a precise definition of the term oolite or the imperfect nature of the data on fossil oolite populations.

The indiscriminate use of the term oolite in geologic literature makes any evaluation of fossil oolite faunas difficult. Seemingly all that is necessary to designate a given lithologic unit as an oolitic formation is the presence of ooids, regardless of quantity. For example, the well-known Salem Limestone of Indiana has been frequently cited as an oolite limestone, and yet as Pettijohn (1949, pp. 301–302) has noted " . . . this designation is incorrect because ooliths form only a small part of the whole rock." An accurate comparison, however, between Bahamian oolite faunas and their ancient analogues presupposes nearly identical quantities of oolite. This presupposition is necessitated by the fact that considerable bottom agitation is a requisite condition for the formation of oolite (Newell, Purdy, and Imbrie, 1960). Increasing bottom agitation not only results in the formation of increasing amounts of oolite, other factors being equal, but also increases substrate mobility, which as previously mentioned, reduces the population density and taxonomic diversity of the bottom fauna. Thin sections prepared from sediment samples collected on Bahamian oolite shoals invariably contain more than 90% ooids. Consequently the fauna of these shoals should be compared with that of limestones containing more than 90% ooids in thin sections. Lesser amounts of oolite are indicative of a greater degree of substrate stability which would allow colonization of the bottom by a greater number and variety of organisms. This is true regardless of whether the ooids in these instances are regarded as autochthonous or allochthonous or both. Thus, depending on oolite content, many of the fossiliferous oolites cited in the literature may reflect environmental conditions more nearly analogous to the oolitic sands and muddy oolite of the outer platform and shelf lagoon (Figure 14), respectively, than that of Bahamian oolite shoals.

Perhaps even more important in explaining supposed occurrences of richly fossiliferous oolite is the imperfect nature of the data on oolite faunas. Faunal lists are generally given for an entire stratigraphic unit such as a formation or, more rarely, a member of a formation; however a vertical section of such a stratigraphic unit usually varies to some extent in its lithology. In the case of oolite formations, for example, thin beds of clay and massive limestone are found frequently interbedded with the more common oolite units of the formation (e.g., see the data presented by Wilson, 1949, on the Lower Corallian Rocks of the Yorkshire coast and Hackness Hills district of England). Faunal lists from such formations, in general, are given for the *entire formation,* and there is no attempt, at least in the literature, to present the faunal content of each lithologic entity within the larger stratigraphic unit. Such faunal lists are of little value to paleoecology, and it seems probable that some of the supposed instances of richly fossiliferous oolite are the result of this "faunal averaging."

The data presented for fossiliferous oolite units also fail to distinguish between transported and *in situ* faunal elements. On Bahamiam oolite shoals the probability of obtaining skeletal material in any one grab sample is rather small, and hence the thin sections prepared from such samples contain more than 90% ooids. A dredge haul across the same oolite shoals, however, yields a large number of invertebrate skeletons representing a taxonomically diverse fauna. With the exception of *Tivela abaconis* none of the organisms represented by these calcareous skeletons is found living on the shoals. In fact most of the organisms represented by skeletal material are found living in the oolitic sands of the outer platform, so that as successive dredge hauls are taken from the outer platform side of the shoal toward the shelf lagoon (Figure 14), the proportion of skeletons from these organisms decreases. The general lack of shelf lagoon skeletal material on the shoals results from the fact that flood tidal currents on the bank are stronger than ebb currents, producing a net movement of sediments toward the shelf lagoon. The dense covering of *Thalassia* on the muddy oolite sediments of the shelf lagoon (Figure 14) is probably equally important in inhibiting transportation of skeletal material from the shelf lagoon onto the shoals. The difference in depth between the oolite shoal and the adjoining hydrographic provinces (Figure 14) makes it seem likely that most of this exotic skeletal material is transported and deposited on the shoals during storms. Similar oolite deposits preserved in the geologic record would indeed be richly fossiliferous, but most of the fossil material would have originated in areas outside the oolite environment. Some evidence supporting this judgment is provided by the Pennsylvanian Drum Limestone. Sayre (1930, p. 75), in reporting on the fauna of this formation, states that "in the northern area of its outcrop the upper one-half to two-thirds is oolitic and is like most of the oolitic limestone of North America in that it contains a dwarfed molluscan fauna . . . ." Tasch (1957, p. 382) has noted that Sayre's dwarfed fauna contains abundant juveniles of the pelecypod *Nuculana bellistriata* and consequently believes that the so-called dwarfing of the Drum fauna and of oolite faunas in general can be explained best ". . . in terms of selective bottom sorting *without recourse to dwarfing.*" The so-called dwarfed faunas would thus represent accumulations of juvenile forms which have been selectively transported to and deposited in the oolite environment.

The Interstitial Fauna

Thus far, attention has been directed toward the relationships between sediments and the benthonic macrofauna (the macrobenthos of Mare, 1942). There are, however, a large number of smaller organisms (the meiobenthos and microbenthos of Mare, 1942) which live on or in sediments. Many of the smaller species are ecologically united by the fact that they inhabit water-filled spaces between sediment particles and move around by sliding within this interstitial space system (Weiser, 1959, p. 192). These characteristics distinguish the interstitial fauna from other small animals which are not confined to interstices and which move through the sediment by burrowing or pushing aside grains (Weiser, 1959, p. 192). "The distinction between the two types is by no means sharp. Animals which in fine sand are burrowers might in coarse sand slide through interstitial spaces" (Weiser, 1959, p. 192).

Gradual filling of sediment interstices causes a reduction in the interstitial fauna's living space or *Lebensraum.* Ideally this should result in a decrease in the number of species constituting the interstitial fauna, if for no other reason than the physical impossibility of large interstitial species occupying small interstices. This has proven to be the case for bacteria in the Texas Laguna Madre tidal flats where Oppenheimer (1960, pp. 251–252, Fig. 5) has demonstrated that the interstices of sand contain a greater variety of bacteria types than clay.

The large interstitial spaces of sand or shell provide a living space for most types of bacteria and allow free movement of organisms by motility and density currents. Clays with particles of 1 μ or less have very small interstitial spaces (unless highly hydrated). The small pore spaces afford living room for only the smaller types of bacteria and the migration of the bacteria and the diffusion of food and metabolic wastes are inhibited (Oppenheimer, 1960, p. 251).

Wieser (1959, p. 192) has suggested that a median diameter of approximately 200 μ is a critical grain size for most interstitial organisms because it is ". . . around this grain size [that] the interstitial spaces which exist in coarser sand are beginning to fill up with fine material." He has speculated further that "sands with a median diameter of 120 μ might be the finest in which interstitial life is possible for any kind of organism" (Wieser, 1959, p. 192). It thus seems that sediments have a critical particle size above which the development of an interstitial fauna takes place and below which the interstitial fauna is greatly impoverished. There is, however, little reason to believe that substrates with a median diameter approximating 200 μ are always going to be as effective a barrier in limiting the distribution of interstitial organisms as Weiser (1959) found them to be in the beaches of Puget Sound. The important point, of course, is the size of the organisms with respect to the size of the interstices. Bacteria, for example, can live in much smaller interstices than those required by nematodes and are almost certain to be found in the interstices of sediments having a median diameter less than 120 μ. Larger interstitial organisms require larger interstitial spaces, but the size of these interstices is determined not only by the sediment's median diameter but also by its grain shape, sorting, skewness, and packing. Therefore it seems likely that different sediments will have different critical median diameters for the same interstitial organisms. Moreover, the same sediment probably will have different critical grain sizes for at least some of the interstitial species.

At first glance it seems that these relationships are of little importance to paleoecology, since the probability of preservation of such known interstitial forms as nematodes, copepods, oligochaetes, and gastrotrichs is extremely small. However, relatively little is known about marine interstitial faunas, and the available information is concerned largely with marine beaches. It is thus conceivable that some of the common microfossils in the geologic record were part of the interstitial fauna. This could be the case, for example, for some of the smaller species of Foraminifera or Ostracoda. In this regard, it is interesting to note Pennack's (1950, p. 476) belief that some minute ostracod species are regular members of interstitial marine beach faunas.

The occurrence of microfossils in the interstitial fauna would partially explain their distribution patterns. Increasing quantities of silt and clay would effectively reduce the size of sedimentary interstices and therefore ultimately would restrict the distribution of interstitial microfossil populations to coarser-grained sediments. On the other hand microfossils which were not part of the interstitial fauna but which moved through the sediment substrate by burrowing or displacing sediment particles would be relatively restricted to finer-grained deposits, the smaller and/or lighter grains being more readily displaced than larger and/or heavier ones. For example, Kornicker (1957) has reported some preliminary experiments which suggest that ostracodes prefer to burrow in less dense sediment than oolite, ooids having a greater weight-to-surface area ratio than most other similar sized particles. Thus the critical texture of the substrate could conceivably separate a microfossil population consisting largely of interstitial sliders from one containing a large proportion of burrowing forms, just as it does with the small invertebrates which inhabit the beaches of Puget Sound (Weiser, 1959).

Permeability

The interstices of sediments are also ecologically important from the standpoint of interstitial circulation. Webb and Hill (1958) have found that the distribution of the lancelet *Branchiostoma nigeriense* in Lagos Lagoon, Western Nigeria, is limited by the permeability of the substrate. The adult lancelets are suspension feeders which are found only in relatively undisturbed sands containing less than 1.5% silt or less than 25% sand smaller than 0.2 mm. (Webb and Hill, 1958.) Normally the lancelets are completely buried and therefore require adequate interstitial circulation to replenish consumed oxygen and remove waste products. Apparently the presence of more than 1.5% silt or 25% fine sand is sufficient to reduce permeability to the point where interstitial circulation is inadequate to meet these ecological demands, and hence *B. nigeriense* is absent (Webb, 1958; Webb and Hill, 1958).

Poor permeability not only limits the distribution of burrowing organisms dependent on interstitial circulation for oxygen replenishment and waste products removal (Webb, 1958), but also apparently dictates the depth to which they will burrow. For example, Pratt and Campbell (1956) have shown that the depth of burial of the pelecypod *Mercenaria mercenaria* is correlated with the permeability of the substrate. The average depth of burial was found to be greater for highly permeable sands than poorly permeable muds; moreover the pelecypods maintained a more well-defined burrow in the muds as compared to the sands (Pratt and Campbell, 1956). The livelihood of these organisms is dependent upon pumping water over gill surfaces. In a sand with good interstitial circulation, *M. mercenaria* can maintain its vital pumping activities while completely covered with sediment; in a mud the poorer interstitial circulation requires that the pelecypods maintain direct contact with the overlying water mass. Thus *M. mercenaria* compensates for the poorer permeability of fine-grained sediments by living closer to the sediment-water interface and maintaining a more well-defined burrow (Pratt and Campbell, 1958).

Morphology

Differences between substrate habitats are sometimes reflected by differences in skeletal morphology. A case in point is that described by C. M. Yonge (1937) for two species of the gastropod genus *Aporrhais*. *Aporrhais pes-pelecani* and *A. serresiana* are burrowing deposit feeders which have a similar mode of life (Figure 16) on different substrates (Yonge, 1937). "*A. pes-pelecani* . . . occurs on comparatively firm bottoms of muddy gravel, but *A. serresiana* is an inhabitant of softer bottoms of fine mud found in deeper water" (Yonge, 1937, p. 699). Correlated with these differences in substrate habitat are differences in skeletal morphology. The shell of *A. serresiana* is characterized by a greatly expanded lip and a long, narrow terminal digitation; in contrast *A. pes-pelecani* has a heavier shell with a considerably less expanded lip and a broad, blade-like terminal digitation (Figure 16). The terminal digitations of both species are used as aids in burrowing. The short, bunt terminal digitation of *A. pes-pelecani* is well suited for pushing aside the gravel particles in its muddy gravel habitat, whereas the elongated, pointed terminal digitation of *A. serresiana* is equally well adapted to burrowing in soft mud (Yonge, 1937, p. 699). Apparently the expanded lip and lighter shell of *A. serresiana* function to prevent the animal from sinking too far into the mud. These are adaptations which are unnecessary for life on the firmer, muddy gravel substrate of *A. pes-pelecani.*

Intraspecific as well as interspecific morphologic attributes can sometimes be related directly to substrate differences. Pratt (1953) and Pratt and Campbell (1956) found that populations of *Mercenaria mercenaria* grew considerably faster in sand as compared to mud. The growth retardation in the mud-inhabiting individuals appears

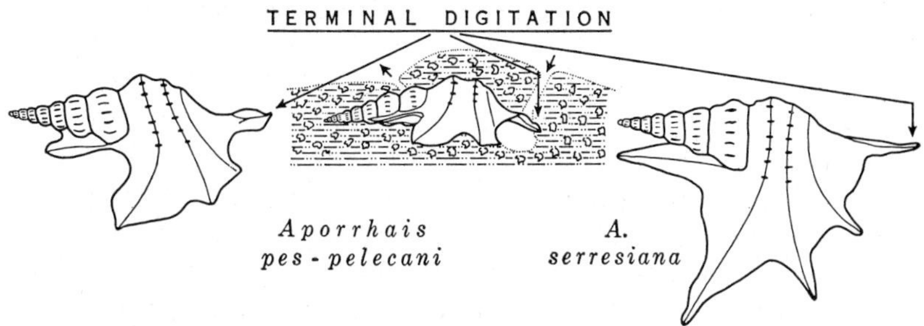

Fig. 16 Shell morphology of Aporrhais pes–pelecani *and* A. serresiana. *Compare the expanded lip and elongate, pointed terminal digitation of* A. serresiana *with the less expanded lip and broad, bladelike terminal digitation of* A. pes–pelecani. *The center diagram shows the position of* A. pes-pelecani *when buried in its muddy gravel substrate. The arrows show the direction of inhalent and exhalent currents. Magnification of all three drawings is × 1⅓. After Yonge (1937).*

largely to result from interruptions in feeding and excessive expenditures of energy (Pratt and Campbell, 1956). The mud-inhabiting individuals inadvertantly take in large quantities of suspended silt and clay, as well as food particles, through their inhalent siphons. The accumulation of silt and clay within the animal ultimately would clog the feeding surfaces of the gills were it not for inorganic material that is separated from the animal's food and expelled as pseudofaeces. "This process must result in an additional expenditure of energy, a reduction in actual feeding time, and probably the loss of some nutritive particles incompletely separated from the indigestible matter expelled" (Pratt and Campbell, 1956, p. 15). In *M. mercenaria* the average expulsion rate of pseudo-faeces increases with the silt and clay content of the substrate; consequently it seems likely that the slower growth rate of this pelecypod in muds is primarily the result of the additional expenditure of energy and reduction in feeding time accompanying the increased rate of formation and expulsion of pseudo-faeces (Pratt and Campbell, 1956).

Presumably this same relationship between sediment texture and growth rate can be applied to suspension feeders other than pelecypods. In these cases, of course, pseudofaeces might not be formed, but the additional expenditure of energy necessary to keep ciliary feeding surfaces unclogged and the consequent reduction of actual feeding time should result in small-sized suspension feeders inhabiting predominantly fine-grained substrates. This association between size and texture should be evident in the fossil record as well as in Recent environments.

Conclusions

Thus far the ecological relations between sediments and organisms have been examined with respect to either sands or muds. It is evident, however, that these sediments are part of a textural continuum extending from substrates composed entirely of sand-sized grains to those formed entirely of clay-sized material. It is therefore, appropriate to summarize here the ecological changes paralleling the textural changes along this continuum, other factors being equal.

In rapidly shifting sand deposits the invertebrate fauna is characterized by low population density and few species. This is true of the microfauna as well as the macrofauna. The invertebrates present consist largely of suspension feeders, the paucity of deposit feeders resulting from the dearth of organic matter in the substrate. The shifting nature of the sand imposes the additional ecological requirement that the invertebrates present be vagile rather than sessile forms.

Sand deposits accumulating under less current-agitated conditions are typified by a greater degree of substrate stability. This stability is reflected by the presence of greater quantities of silt- and clay-sized grains. The macrofauna and microfauna are characterized by an increased number of species and greater population density, the latter group being represented mainly by the interstitial fauna. The reduced current velocities which favor the accumulation of silt- and clay-sized grains also allow the deposition of organic detritus; consequently the proportion of deposit feeders comprising the fauna increases. Suspension feeding, however, remains the dominant feeding type, and the suspension feeders present are sessile as well as vagile.

As the texture of the substrate becomes finer, the proportion of suspension feeders comprising the fauna decreases and concomitantly the abundance of deposit feeders increases until finally the deposit feeders are more numerous than the suspension feeders. These relationships result primarily from two facts. First, the weaker bottom currents associated with the accumulation of finer-grained deposits transport less suspended food material over a given bottom area per unit time and therefore reduce the population density of suspension feeders. (The increased turbidity of the water also may decrease the numbers of suspension feeders present.) Second, the same currents allow the deposition of increased amounts of organic detritus and fine-grained particles with sorbed organic matter and consequently increase the population density of deposit feeders. The decreasing grain size of the substrate also results in a progressive impoverishment of the interstitial fauna, principally because of the decrease in the size of the interstices. Thus the microfauna is now represented largely by burrowing deposit feeders and in this respect is similar to the macrofauna.

In extremely fine-grained deposits the fauna is generally characterized by low population density and low taxonomic diversity. This relationship can be attributed mainly to poor interstitial circulation, which results in the accumulation of toxic decomposition products and/or depletion of available oxygen. Such substrates are usually quite soft due to their high water content, so that most invertebrates experience difficulty in moving across them. This may be an additional factor contributing to the general paucity of invertebrate life in very fine-grained deposits. The invertebrate fauna present consists mainly of deposit feeders. This is true of the microfauna as well as the macrofauna.

It is thus evident that both ends of the sand-to-mud textural continuum represent stress habitats for most invertebrates. Consequently it is not surprising to find that the species occurring at either end of the gradient are more restricted with respect to habitat than the species occurring on substrates between these two environmental extremes (Davis, 1925, p. 14).

These considerations leave little doubt of the paleoecological importance of considering sediments as substrates.

REFERENCES

Allee, W. C., A. E. Emerson, O. Park, T. Park, K. P. Schmidt, 1950, *Principles of Animal Ecology:* Philadelphia, W. B. Saunders Co., 837 pp.

Bader, R. G., 1952, A quantitative study of some physical, chemical, and biological variants of modern marine sediments: Ph.D. dissertation, University of Chicago, 75 pp.

——— 1954, The role of organic matter in determining the distribution of pelecypods in marine sediments: *J. Marine Res.*, v. 13, pp. 32–47.

Bader, R. G., and L. M. Jeffrey, 1958, The exchange capacity, organic adsorption, and differential flocculation of clay minerals as related to radioactive waste disposal: Texas A. and M. Research Foundation, *Project 142,* Ref. 58-2A, Part V, pp. 1–25.

Bader, R. G., D. W. Hood, and J. B. Smith, 1960, Recovery of dissolved organic matter in seawater and organic sorption by particulate material: *Geochim. Cosmochim. Acta,* v. 19, pp. 236–243.

Bader, R. G., K. M. Rae, and J. B. Smith, 1960, A study of some factors concerning radioactive materials in the sea: Texas A. and M. Research Foundation, *Project 142,* Ref. 60-2A, pp. 1–78.

Buchanan, John B., 1958, The bottom fauna communities across the continental shelf off Accra, Ghana (Gold Coast): *Proc. Zool. Soc. London,* v. 130, pp. 1–56.

Davis, F. M., 1925, Quantitative studies on the fauna of the sea bottom, no. 2. Southern North Sea: *Gt. Brit. Fish. Invest.,* Ser. II, v. 8, n. 4, pp. 1–50.

Hunt, O. D., 1925, The food of the bottom fauna of the Plymouth fishing grounds: *J. Marine Biol. Assoc. U. K.,* v. 3, pp. 560–599.

Jørgensen, C. B., 1955, Quantitative aspects of filter feeding in invertebrates: *Biol. Reviews,* v. 30, pp. 391–454.

Kornicker, L. S., 1957, Ecology and taxonomy of Recent marine ostracodes in the Bimini area, Great Bahama Bank: Ph.D. thesis, Columbia University, 221 pp.

________ 1958, Ecology and taxonomy of Recent marine ostracodes in the Bimini area, Great Bahama Bank: *Publ. Inst. Mar. Sci. Univ. Tex.,* v. 5, pp. 194–300.

Krecker, F. H., and L. Y. Lancaster, 1933, Bottom shore fauna of western Lake Erie; A population study to a depth of six feet: *Ecology,* v. 14, pp. 79–93.

Mare, M., 1942, A study of a marine benthic community with special reference to the microorganisms: *J. Marine Biol. Assoc. U. K.,* v. 25, pp. 517–554.

Molander, A. R., 1928, Animal communities on soft bottom areas in the Gullmar Fjord: *Kristinebergs Zoologiska Stat.* 1877–1927, n. 2, Uppsala, pp. 1–90.

Newell, N. D., E. G. Purdy, and J. Imbrie, 1960, Bahamian oolitic sand: *J. Geology,* v. 68, pp. 481–497.

Oppenheimer, C. H., 1960, Bacterial activity in sediments of shallow marine bays: *Geochim. Cosmochim. Acta,* v. 19, pp. 244–260.

Pennak, R. W., 1950, Comparative ecology of the interstitial fauna of fresh-water and marine beaches: *Colloque Internat. Centre Nat. Rech. Scient. Ecol. Paris,* 1950, pp. 449–480.

Petersen, C. G., Joh., 1913, Valuation of the sea, II; The animal communities of the sea bottom and their importance for marine zoogeography: *Rep. Danish Biol. Stat.,* v. 21, pp. 1–44.

Pettijohn, F. J., 1949, *Sedimentary Rocks:* New York, 1st edition, Harper and Brothers, 526 pp.

Pratt, D. M., 1953, Abundance and growth of *Venus mercenaria* and *Callocardia morrhuana* in relation to the character of bottom sediments: *J. Marine Res.,* v. 12, pp. 60–74.

Pratt, D. M., and D. A. Campbell, 1956, Environmental factors affecting growth in *Venus mercenaria: Limnol. and Oceanog.,* v. 1, pp. 2–17.

Purdy, E. G., 1961, Bahamian oolite shoals, in J. A. Peterson, and J. C. Osmond (eds.), *Geometry of Sandstone Bodies:* Am. Assoc. Petroleum Geologists, Special Volume, pp. 53–62.

Sanders, H. L., 1956, Oceanography of Long Island Sound, 1952–1954, X; The biology of marine bottom communities: *Bull. Bingham Oceanogr. Coll.,* v. 15, pp. 345–414.

________ 1958, Benthic studies in Buzzards Bay, I; Animal-sediment relationships: *Limn. and Oceanogr.,* v. 3, pp. 245–258.

Sayre, A. N., 1930, The fauna of the Drum limestone of Kansas and western Missouri; *Bull. Univ. Kansas,* v. 31, pp. 75–203.

Shelford, V. E., A. O. Weese, L. A. Rice, D. I. Rasmussen, and A. MacLean, 1935, Some marine biotic communities of the Pacific Coast of North America, Part I; General survey of the communities: *Ecol. Monogr.,* v. 5, pp. 251–332.

Smith, J. B., and R. G. Bader, 1961, Preliminary investigations of the association of organic material and carbon dioxide with sedimentary particles: Texas A. and M. Research Foundation, *Project 142,* Ref. 61-8T, pp. 1–221.

Tasch, P., 1957, Fauna and paleoecology of the Pennsylvanian dry shale of Kansas, in H. S. Ladd (ed.), *Treatise on Marine Ecology and Paleoecology,* v. 2, Paleoecology: Mem. Geol. Soc. Amer., n. 67, pp. 365–406.

Thomas, L. P., 1960, A note on the feeding habits of the West Indian sea star *Oreaster reticulatus* (Linnaeus): *Quart. J. Florida Acad. Sci.,* v. 23, pp. 167–168.

Thorson, Gunnar, 1957, Bottom communities, in J. W. Hedgpeth (ed.), *Treatise on Marine Ecology and Paleoecology,* v. 1, Ecology: Mem. Geol. Soc. Amer., no. 67, pp. 461–534.

Trask, P. D., 1939, Organic content of recent marine sediments, in P. D. Trask (ed.), *Recent Marine Sediments:* Soc. Econ. Paleontologists and Mineralogists Spec. Pub. 4, pp. 428–453.

Webb, J. E., 1958, The ecology of Lagos Lagoon, V; Some physical properties of lagoon deposits: *Phil. Trans. Roy. Soc. London,* ser. B., v. 241, pp. 393–419.

Webb, J. E., and M. B. Hill, 1958, The ecology of Lagos Lagoon, IV; On the reactions of *Branchiostoma nigeriense* Webb to its environment: *Phil. Trans. Roy. Soc. London,* ser. B, v. 241, pp. 355–391.

Weller, J. Marvin, 1960, *Stratigraphic Principles and Practice:* New York, Harper and Brothers, 725 pp.

Whitehouse, U. G., 1955, Preliminary consideration of selected chemical and oceanographic factors influential in the formation of the alumino-silicate fraction of some recent sediments: Ph.D. dissertation, A. and M. College of Texas, 197 pp.

Wieser, W., 1959, The effect of grain size on the distribution of small invertebrates inhabiting the beaches of Puget Sound, Washington: *Limnol. and Oceanog.,* v. 4, pp. 181–194.

Wilson, D. P., 1952, The influence of the nature of the substratum on the metamorphosis of the larvae of marine animals, especially the larvae of *Ophelia bicornis* Savigny: *Ann. Inst. Oceanog. Monaco,* v. 27, pp. 49–156.

Wilson, V., 1948, The Lower Corallian rocks of the Yorkshire coast and Hackness Hills: *Proc. Geol. Assoc.* v. 16, pp. 235–271.

Yonge, C. M., 1937, The biology of *Apporrhais pes-pelecani* (L.) and *A. serresiana* (Mich.): *J. Marine Biol. Assoc. U. K.,* v. 21, pp. 687–704.

Yonge, C. M., 1949, *The Sea Shore:* London, Collins, 311 pp.

Sedimentary Structures

as Approaches

To Paleoecology

Inorganic Sedimentary Structures

by Edwin D. McKee *U. S. Geological Survey, Federal Center, Denver, Colorado*

ABSTRACT

Ancient environments may be interpreted, at least in part, from primary structures in sedimentary rocks. Because such structures are largely developed during deposition, they provide information on the processes involved and on the general geologic and climatic setting. Unfortunately, many sedimentary structures are poorly understood; numerous data are required from the observation of modern sediments and of controlled experiments before positive conclusions can be drawn concerning rock genesis.

Stratification and cross-stratification of 13 principal types are described with reference to environments in which they are known to have developed. Some of these structures are typical of more than one environment; other structures are represented by two or more varieties in a single environment. Thus, information on natural combinations or associations of structures is especially valuable for paleoecological interpretation.

Publication authorized by the Director of the U. S. Geological Survey. Examples of stratification and cross-stratification in sand illustrated in this paper are restricted to those actually examined by the writer or recorded in detail by some of his associates. In this connection, acknowledgment is made to Messrs. J. C. Harms, D. G. MacKenzie, and D. C. McCubbin, of Ohio Oil Research Laboratory, for the use of illustrations and for information on structures in point bars on the Red River, near Shreveport, Louisiana, and to Mr. George Merk, of Adams State College, Alamosa, Colorado for data on structures in the Great Sand Dunes, Colorado. In order to fill certain gaps in the classification, however, some references to modern bedding structures as described in the literature have been added.

Introduction

The types of layering in a sedimentary rock are useful in the interpretation of its depositional environment. Both stratification and cross-stratification reflect ecological conditions at the time of deposition, and several related structures, such as mottling, contorted bedding, and recumbent cross-strata included in this discussion, are mostly penecontemporaneous or developed very soon after deposition. These primary structures, therefore, have special value in environmental interpretation and in this respect are more significant than most compositional and textural features normally developed prior to deposition.

During the past decade modern environments of sedimentation have been described in terms of their primary structures by a number of geologists (Moore and Scruton, 1957; McKee, 1957*b;* Van Straaten, 1959). In the present study the problem of stratification analysis is approached from the opposite direction. Bedding structures in sand are discussed according to type, based on shape, size, dip, and other features that can be treated objectively; under each of these types are described or listed the principal sedimentary environments in which the structure has been recorded. Only those structures developed in *modern* sediments for which ecological factors are known, or those formed in the experimental laboratory, are included. Many other examples will doubtless be added as more information is obtained.

Twelve principal types of layering in sand, together with structureless sand or that without layers, constitute the categories recognized in this treatment. Ultimately these may be fitted into a classification, but other major varieties probably will be recognized and most of those listed will be divided into distinguishable subtypes. In any event, the types discussed here are structures that any field geologist can readily recognize in ancient rocks and can use, especially in their association with other features, in the identification of depositional environments. Combinations of structures, rather than any one structure, probably should be used wherever possible.

The discussion that follows is organized to show for each of the 13 categories of bedding structure the environment or environments in which it is known to occur. Included in this summary, also, are data on types of stratification commonly associated with those described, information on localities from which the structures have been recorded, and data on probable causes of their development. Illustrations have been selected to show characteristics of the principal structural types referred to, and some of the modern environments in which these have been recorded are indicated in Table 1.

TABLE 1. *Some environments of deposition and associated sedimentary structures that have been observed and illustrated by the writer (X = Modern deposits; O = Laboratory)*

	Alluvial Fans	Alluvial Plains	River Floodplains, Bank Overflow	Rivers, Point-bar	Dunes, Wind Deposits	Deltas, Upper Part (interdistributary)	Delta Cones	Tidal Flats, Lower	Beach, Foreshore	Beach, Backshore	Bars, Offshore	Marine, Shore Face Terrace
Flat, horizontal stratification			X		X	X		X				
Ripple stratification			X			X						
Trough cross-stratification	X			XO	X					X		
Low-angle, simple or planar cross-stratification	X								XO		XO	
Tabular-planar cross-stratification, intermediate angle		X					X				XO	O
High-angle, wedge-planar cross-stratification					XO		X					
Graded bedding												
Recumbent fold structures							O					
Contorted bedding												
Convolute bedding												
Irregular bedding								X				
Mottled structures												
Structureless, homogeneous bodies						X						

Flat, Horizontal Stratification

This type of structure is one of the most abundant in sedimentary rocks. It ranges from thin, even laminae to beds of considerable thickness and of diversity in texture and composition. Probably several significant subtypes will ultimately be recognized within this category; certainly it would be desirable to distinguish between laminated varieties (<1 cm) and bedded varieties (>1 cm).

A good illustration of horizontal lamination is the widespread, stratified sand distributed over floodplains on the upper part of the Colorado River Delta in Mexico and commonly associated with ripple lamination (Plate 1, Figure 1). It also occurs on the floodplain of Indian Creek in Lavender Canyon, Utah (Plate 1, Figure 2). Horizontal stratification on "upper delta front slopes" of the Fraser, Mississippi, Orinoco, and Rhone Rivers is reported by Van Straaten (1959, p. 213), but he does not state whether laminae or thicker strata are involved.

Well-developed horizontal lamination is preserved in remnants of once-extensive sand units that are associated with trough cross-stratification in point bars of the Red River in Louisiana, according to J. C. Harms, D. G. MacKenzie, and D. C. McCubbin (1963, p. 576–577).

Surprisingly, uniform, horizontal laminae also occur in wind-formed interdune deposits within the sand seas of Libya in Africa (Plate 1, Figure 3). These structures are in areas between the long crests of longitudinal or seif dunes and apparently form from sand grains being moved along essentially horizontal surfaces. Bore holes indicate that the sand body is hundreds of feet deep and extends for many tens of miles.

Intertidal laminated silt and sand, in which strata are flat-lying, have been described and illustrated from the Wash in England (Kindle, 1930, p. 10, fig. 4); and also in the horizontally bedded sand from top-set beds below the level of mean low tide on the delta of the Fraser River in British Columbia (Johnston, 1922, p. 121).

Flat beds are common on the tidal flats at Cholla Bay, Sonora, Mexico, but these are not laminated. They consist of alternating layers of coquina and quartz sand, each of which is one or more inches thick (Plate 1, Figure 4). Lower tidal flats on the Wadden Sea, especially in channel banks, behind coastal barriers, and in estuaries are referred to this type of bedding by Van Straaten (1959, p. 212). He attributes the structure to strong variations in competency of tidal currents. In both Cholla Bay and the Wadden Sea tidal areas, small lateral continuity is a characteristic of the bedding. In the latter area it is associated with ripple lamination and with clay pebble beds.

Environments, other than those just described, from which horizontal-type stratification has been reported are hypersaline lagoons and low-salinity lagoons (Van Straaten, 1959, pp. 213–214) and shallow marine waters surrounding deltas (Moore and Scruton, 1957, p. 2733).

Figure 1

Figure 2

Figure 3

Figure 4

Figure 5

Figure 6

Plate 1 Fig. 1—Horizontal stratification, associated with ripple lamination, delta plain of Colorado River, Sonora, Mexico. Fig. 2—Horizontal stratification, floodplain of Indian Creek, Lavender Canyon, Utah. Fig. 3—Horizontal stratification, wind deposits in area between seif dunes near Sebha, Libya. Fig. 4 —Horizontal stratification consisting of coarse layers of coquina and quartz sand, tidal flats, Cholla Bay, Sonora, Mexico. Figs. 5 and 6—Ripple stratification, floodplain bordering Colorado River, Arizona.

Many of these horizontal strata presumably are laminae; others are thicker, but they apparently include clay and silt as well as sand.

Ripple Stratification

Ripple stratification is a type of small-scale cross-stratification forming a complex pattern where many layers of ripple-marked sand are preserved in superposition (McKee, 1939, p. 72). Such structures are abundant in some deposits formed by rivers and may occur in other places where ripple marks develop, but because many such structures apparently are not permanently preserved in sand, caution must be used in attributing them to certain environments.

In interdistributary areas on the upper part of the Colorado River Delta, where the parallel-type ripple is commonly formed from sheets of water moving across the flats, ripple stratification is developed (Plate 1, Figure 1). In such areas it is associated with the sloping foreset beds of local cones or small deltas that form planar cross-bedding. Ripple stratification is also reported from the Rhone and Mississippi Deltas (Van Straaten, 1959, p. 213).

Floodplains along the Colorado River where it has overflowed its banks during flood periods are composed over considerable areas of ripple-laminated sand (Plate 1, Figures 5, 6) like that on the delta. The parallel-type ripple is the common variety involved (McKee, 1938, p. 80). Other illustrations of ripple stratification in river deposits are from the Klarälven in Sweden (Sundborg, 1956, figs. 20, 49) where this structure occurs in transverse bars and in a point bar, and from Billtal near Bergedorf, Germany (Illies, 1949, table 2).

Similarly, ripple marks of the cusp type (crescentic), in contrast to those of the parallel type, commonly develop in stream deposits. Laminae formed from such ripple marks are recorded from point bars of the Red River in Louisiana (Harms, MacKenzie, and McCubbin, *id.*, p. 575). These structures are easily recognized in plan view where not eroded, but are like "rib-and-furrow" as described by Stokes (1957, p. 1872) when beveled (Plate 2, Figure 1) and present a miniature "festoon" pattern in cross section (Plate 2, Figure 2).

Ripple stratification has also been stated (Van Straaten, 1959) to form in low salinity lagoons, the vegetationless lower parts of tidal flats, areas behind bars, and in estuaries, but it is not illustrated from these places so there is uncertainty as to whether the markings persist as lamination structures in all these environments.

Trough Cross-Stratification (Including Festoon)

Scours filled with subsequent deposits are probably common in many environments, yet relatively few actual modern examples are well documented and illustrated in geological literature. Possible variations in form and pattern are numerous, depending on the shape of the trough, the plunge of its axis, and the manner of fill (McKee and Weir, 1953, p. 388). Thus, numerous subtypes of this kind of cross-stratification will probably be recognized ultimately.

Stream deposits, as might be expected, include excellent examples of scour-and-fill structures. Deposits from the lower Red River in Louisiana contain numerous troughs which, when cut normal to the axis, are seen to be well rounded and are filled with sand in which the structure roughly conforms to curvature of the scour (Plate 2, Figure 3). These troughs form a succession of structures, one cutting another in a festoon pattern (Harms, MacKenzie, and McCubbin, *id.*, pp. 570–575). Somewhat similar structures (Plate 2, Figure 4) are formed by stream currents in the experimental laboratory, where variations in the pattern of fill are produced by differences in depth of water and direction of current (McKee, 1957*a*, p. 133).

One variety of trough cross-stratification developed by stream currents in the laboratory consists of essentially horizontal laminae filling the trough, as seen in section normal to the axis (Plate 2, Figure 5), but of parallel dipping strata as viewed in longitudinal section (Plate 2, Figure 6). This structure apparently forms where the surface of the water is below the rim of the trough and the current deposits a succession of foresets down the channel. Probably when more information is available, the recognition of certain environments will be possible through distinctive types of scour-fills.

Backshore beaches commonly contain buried channels which are roughly parallel to the beach crest or berm. Such channels are typically irregular and the sand that fills them is deposited with irregular structure (Plate 3, Figures 1, 2). Common also are such unassorted materials as pieces of charcoal, shells, or debris, and, in places, intraformational conglomerate formed of weakly coherent, laminated lumps of beach sand, all of which are distributed here and there in the channel-fill.

Tidal flats on the coast of the North Sea at Wilhelmshaven, Germany, are described (Bucher, 1938, pp. 731–734, table 12) as containing abundant "channel cross-bedding of the silty muds." Ap-

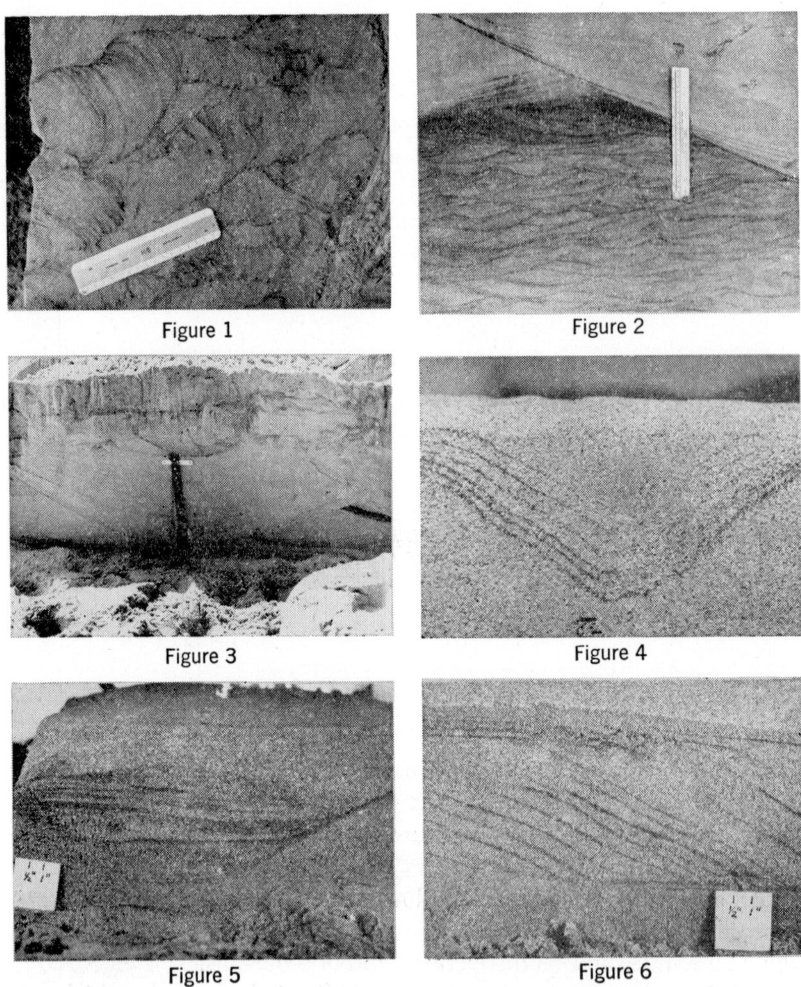

Plate 2 Figs. 1 and 2—Ripple stratification, (1) beveled surface of plan view, flow direction, right to left, (2) cross-section, (trough cross-strata above), point bar of Red River, Louisiana. Photographs by D. C. McCubbin. Fig. 3—Trough cross-stratification, lower Red River, Louisiana. Photograph by D. C. McCubbin. Fig. 4—Trough cross-stratification, University of Arizona Laboratory, Tucson. Figs. 5 and 6—Trough cross-stratification, (5) cross-section, (6) longitudinal section, U.S. Geological Survey Sedimentation Laboratory, Denver,

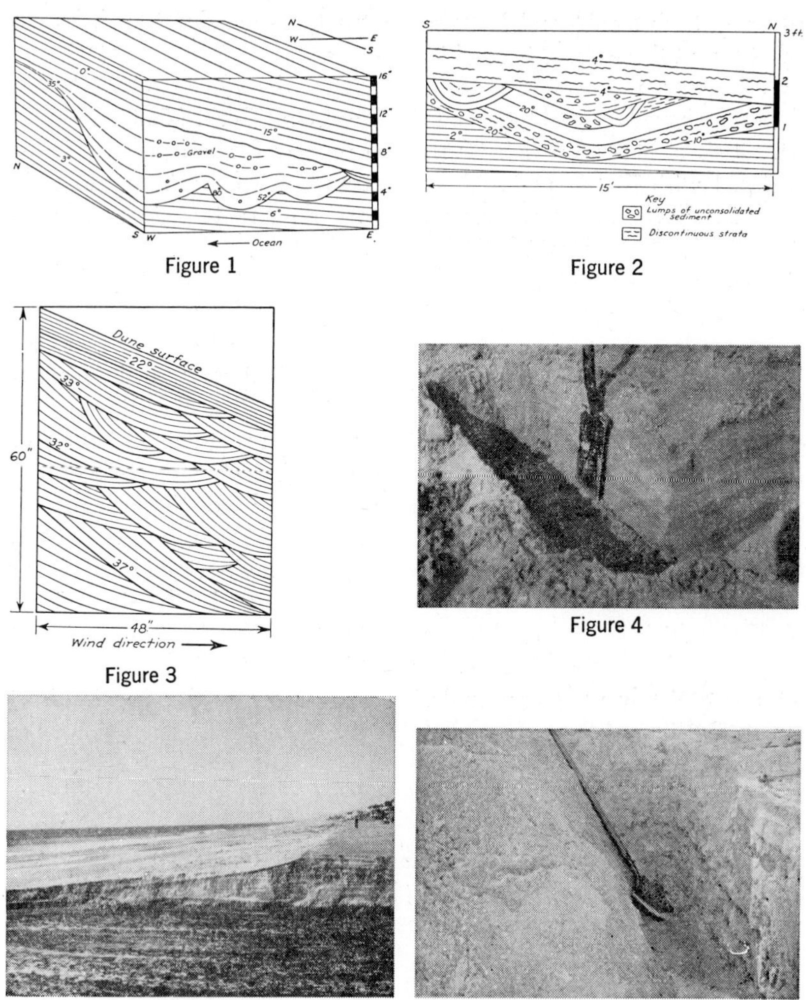

Figure 1

Figure 2

Figure 3

Figure 4

Figure 5

Figure 6

Plate 3 Figs. 1 and 2—Trough cross-stratification, parallel to strand, backshore beach, Laguna Beach, California. Fig. 3—Trough cross-stratification in anchored dune associated with high angle wedge structures, Gulf Coast near Corpus Christi, Texas. Figs. 4, 5, and 6—Low angle, planar cross-stratification, foreshore beach, (4) Mustang Island, Texas, (5) Oceanside, California, (6) Kapingamorangi Atoll, Caroline group.

parently both small- and large-scale structures are developed, but to what extent these occur in sand is not clear.

A variety of trough cross-stratification has been observed in dunes anchored by vegetation on the Texas Gulf Coast (Plate 3, Figure 3). This structure, which forms an irregular festoon pattern, is associated with high-angle wedge structures such as normally form in barchan dunes. Another variety of trough structure is in alluvial fans (McKee, 1957*b*, p. 1730, table 12).

Low-Angle (<12°) Simple [or] Planar Cross-Stratification

Low-angle simple or planar cross-stratification[1] seems to be formed largely where topset deposits develop with small initial dip, in contrast to intermediate and high-angle cross-strata that consist largely of foreset beds. Because low-angle cross-strata are characteristic of certain environments, however, and normally can be distinguished from horizontal strata without difficulty, they are considered a distinct type.

Foreshore beaches are composed of low-angle simple or planar cross-strata. The angle of dip is controlled in part by the slope of the shelf on which it forms and in part by the type of sediment of which it is composed. Quartz sand beaches of the Gulf Coast (Plate 3, Figure 4) are typically very low angle, whereas those of the Pacific Coast (Plate 3, Figure 5) are somewhat steeper; shell beaches commonly are considerably steeper (Plate 3, Figure 6) (McKee, 1957*b*, p. 1715).

Emergent offshore bars or barriers have seaward slopes which actually are beaches superimposed on bars. The cross-strata of these are low angle like those of ordinary beaches, as shown in a typical sample at Bimini in the Bahamas (Plate 4, Figure 1), but these strata commonly are associated with steeper dipping beds of the bar that face shoreward. In the experimental laboratory this combination of structures is shown to be characteristic of bars that are constantly fed sand from seaward as though by longshore currents (Plate 4, Figure 2).

Most alluvial fans contain low-angle cross-stratification. It is formed, in general, of poorly sorted sediment and commonly contains many gently dipping lenses and beds of gravel. The cross-strata are extremely variable and little similarity exists between them and long, even foreshore beach strata. Stratification of a typical fan in southern

[1] Planar cross-strata are differentiated from simple cross-strata according to the type of lower bounding surface (McKee and Weir, 1953, p. 385). In the planar type a surface of erosion is involved; in the simple type a depositional contact only.

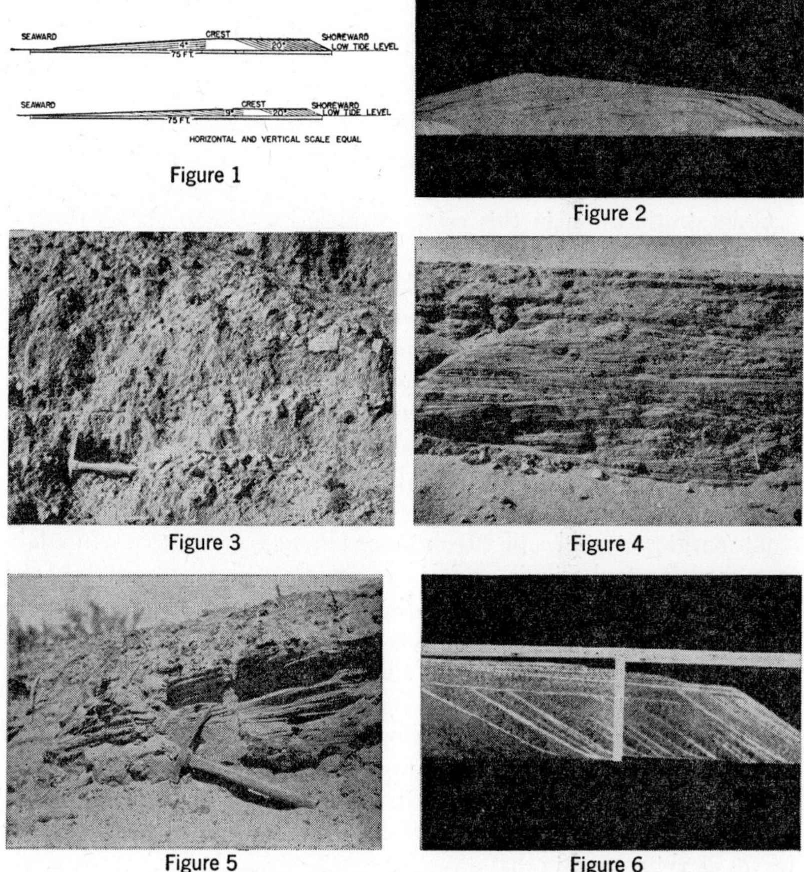

Figure 1

Figure 2

Figure 3

Figure 4

Figure 5

Figure 6

Plate 4 Fig. 1—Low angle, planar cross-stratification, associated with reverse-dipping, higher angle cross-strata, off-shore bar, Bimini Island, Bahamas. Fig. 2—Low angle, planar cross-stratification, seaward (left) side of off-shore bar, U.S. Geological Survey Sedimentation Laboratory, Denver. Figs. 3 and 4—Low angle cross-stratification, associated with beds and lenses of gravel in alluvial fan, (3) near Ubari in the Fezzan, Libya, and (4) northwest of Santa Catalina Mountains, Arizona. Fig. 5—Tabular, planar cross-stratification of intermediate angle, upper part of Colorado River delta, Sonora, Mexico. Fig. 6—Tabular, planar cross-stratification of intermediate angle, delta deposit, U.S. Geological Survey Sedimentation Laboratory, Denver.

Libya is shown in Plate 4, Figure 3; and one near the Santa Catalina Mountains of Arizona is shown in Plate 4, Figure 4.

Tabular Planar Cross-Stratification of Intermediate Angle (Generally 18° to 28° but Locally Less)

Cross-stratification in this category includes most varieties formed as foresets of small deltas or cones and has been referred to in earlier literature as "torrential" crossbedding. These structures consist of sets of uniformly dipping strata bounded above and below by essentially horizontal planes and commonly are formed by a sudden decrease in the velocity of sediment-transporting currents where an abrupt increase in water depth occurs.

Tabular planar cross-stratification is characteristic of delta deposits. Cones of sediment forming on the surface of the Colorado River Delta during flood periods develop long, sloping foresets along their front margins at angles of 20° or more (Plate 4, Figure 5). In a laboratory delta tank similar structures are formed where an artificial stream drops its load into a standing body of water (Plate 4, Figure 6). The degree of dip on the foresets depends on the speed of the current introducing the sediment and, to a less extent, on the physical properties of the sand.

Offshore bars commonly develop tabular planar cross-strata, as illustrated by a dissected sample at Bimini Island (Plate 4, Figure 1) and by laboratory experiments. In these bar structures, unlike those of deltas, the strata dip shoreward for they are formed by advancing waves carrying sand in that direction.

Structures of shore-face terraces formed out from the beach where deposits of the seafloor develop a relatively steep face have not been recorded from direct observation. Laboratory experiments clearly indicate, however, that these structures consist of planar cross-stratification forming tabular sets of seaward-dipping strata (Plate 5, Figure 1).

Alluvial sand plains, including those formed by sheet floods and those by glacier waters, apparently form some extensive deposits of planar cross-stratification. An example of the sheet-flood type from the wide sandy valley near Cow Springs in the Navajo Indian Reservation in Arizona is shown in Plate 5, Figure 2. Local development of planar-type structure is also illustrated in point-bar deposits of the Klarälven River in Sweden (Sundborg, 1956, figs. 47, 49).

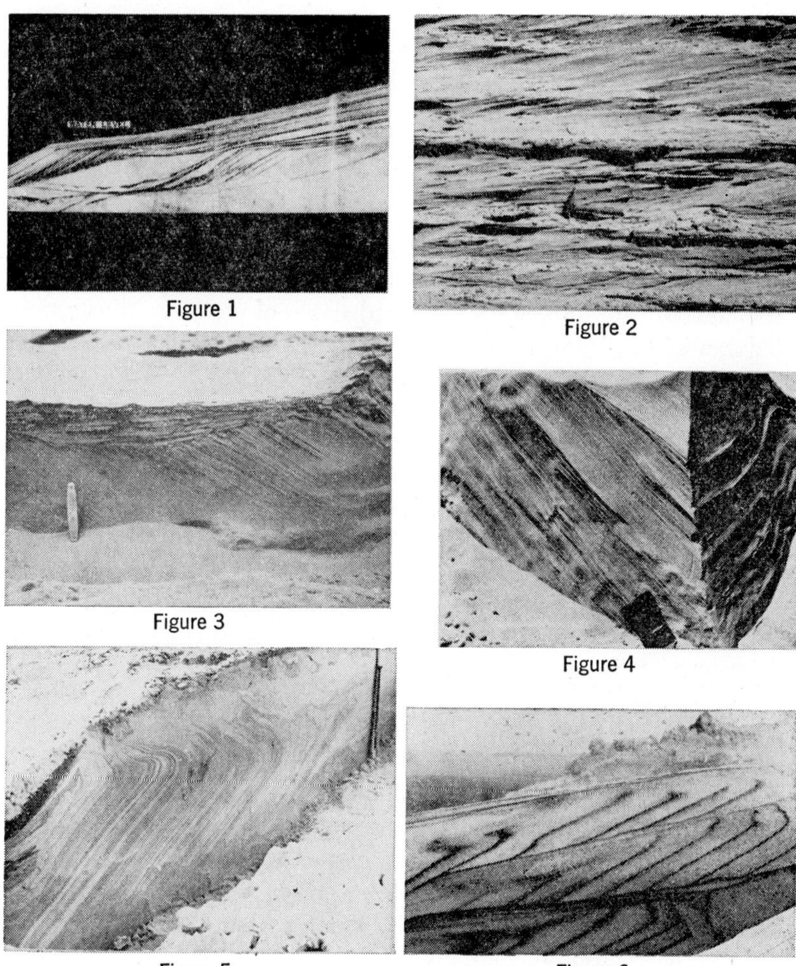

Figure 1

Figure 2

Figure 3

Figure 4

Figure 5

Figure 6

Plate 5 Fig. 1—Planar cross-strata of intermediate angle, shore face terrace (lower, left), U.S. Geological Survey Sedimentation Laboratory, Denver. Fig. 2—Tabular, planar cross-stratification of intermediate angle, sand plain developed by sheet floods, Cow Springs on Navajo Indian Reservation, Arizona. Figs 3 and 4—High angle, wedge-planar, cross-stratification, (3) section near base of windward slope, (4) section across horn, barchan dune, near Leupp, Arizona. Fig. 5—Intraformational recumbent fold structures, point bar deposits, Red River, Louisiana. Photo by D. G. MacKenzie. Fig. 6—Recumbent fold structures, V-shaped type from sudden movement, U-shaped type from slower movement, U.S. Geological Survey Sedimentation Laboratory, Denver.

High-Angle (24 to 34°) Wedge-Planar Cross-Stratification

Structures of this type, on a large scale with individual cross-strata extending 30 to 60 feet or more, are especially characteristic of dune deposits as shown in sections of barchan dunes near Leupp, Arizona (Plate 5, Figures 3, 4), and by longitudinal (seif) dunes examined by the writer in the Fezzan of Libya. The steep bedding planes, forming tangents with underlying surfaces, represent the "slip faces" or lee sides of the dunes; the low-angle planes that bound each wedge or set commonly are formed as windward slopes of erosion. Illustrations of dunes at Seyistan in Persia also show these characteristic features (Huntington, 1907, pl. 38).

The wedge-planar type of cross-stratification is not restricted to eolian deposits. With moderately high angles (up to about 28°), this type has been developed in the laboratory as the product of compound delta development where one set of foresets overlaps another. Likewise, it has been observed on the Colorado River Delta where the foresets of some overlapping cones (although not as long as many dune slopes) have lengths of 25 to 35 feet.

Graded Bedding

This structure is generally attributed to the environment of turbidity currents (Kuenen and Migliorini, 1950) where it is common, but it may occur elsewhere. It is formed by settling from suspension, as well as from decreasing competence of current. Volcanic eruptions, sandstorms, and wave turbulence are suggested as methods probably also responsible for graded bedding (Kuenen and Menard, 1952, pp. 91, 94). It has been noted in salt marshes by Van Straaten (1959, p. 212) and doubtless develops also in a number of other environments.

Because most turbidities have apparently formed in the sea at relatively great depths, samples of modern graded bedding are known chiefly from cores (Bramlette and Bradley, 1942; and many others). Those deposits on subsea fans and on submarine canyon floors, called "discontinuous sediments" by Gorsline and Emery (1959, p. 285), probably are typical. They are interpreted by those geologists to be the result of "geologically instantaneous deposition of coarser than usual sediment," and are described as containing, in addition to graded beds, laminated sand, contorted beds, and some gravel.

Many data on the manner in which sediment becomes graded by turbidity currents and on the mechanisms involved have been obtained experimentally by Kuenen and Migliorini (1950) and by Kuenen and Menard (1952). Results of experimental work on high-density currents and some distinctions between the deposits formed by them and those by other agents of transport are discussed by Kuenen (1951).

Recumbent Fold Structures

Dipping cross-strata within a set may be overturned or folded in sequence to form a series of U's or V's lying on their sides; such structures are especially characteristic of the tabular planar type of crossbedding. Although not a part of the original depositional pattern, these folds evidently form soon after deposition and before overlying sediments are laid down, because strata above and below are unaffected by the folding. Thus the structures must be considered intraformational and are characteristic of the environment in certain depositional areas.

Intraformational recumbent folds have been observed in point-bar sand deposits of the Red River in Louisiana (Plate 5, Figure 5), where they occurred within the uppermost layer among planar cross-strata of intermediate dip (Harms, MacKenzie, and McCubbin, *id.*, p. 577). Other examples are from flood deposits of the Colorado River in Arizona (Plate 6, Figures 2, 3, 4). Furthermore, they have been formed in the experimental laboratory of the U. S. Geological Survey at Denver, Colorado, where surface accumulations of sand are pushed forward by a sudden rush of water across the surface of a submerged set of foreset beds (Plate 5, Figure 6; Plate 6, Figure 1). The hydraulic force was introduced to simulate conditions of a flash flood.

Convolute Bedding

Convolute or crinkled bedding consists of a series of rounded anticlinal folds, with or without beveled crests, that are overlain and underlain by undisturbed beds of mud. Its origin is not fully understood (Kuenen and Menard, 1952, p. 91; Kuenen, 1952, p. 31), but it is commonly associated with rocks having graded bedding, and in such places is considered to be related to an environment of turbidity flows. Convolute bedding in sands of a tidal delta at San Miguel Lagoon, Baja California illustrated by Stewart (1956, fig. 2), is associated with flat sand laminae and with contorted bedding (Stewart, pp. 153–154). Additional data concerning its distribution in modern sediments would be useful.

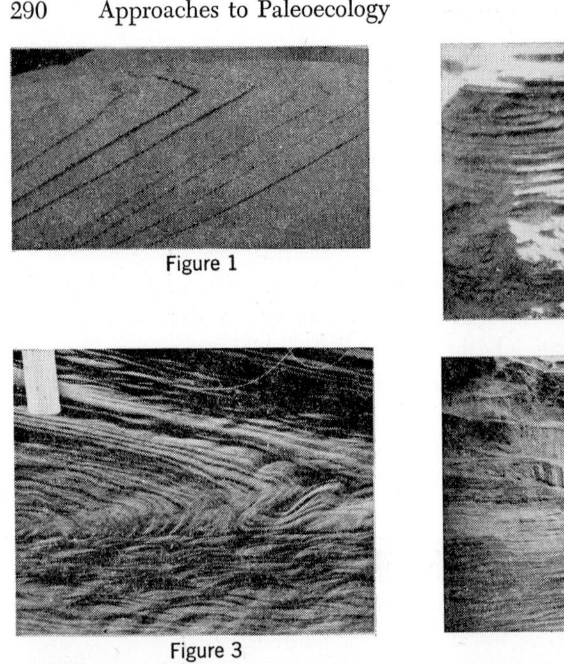

Figure 1

Figure 2

Figure 3

Figure 4

Figure 5

Figure 6

Plate 6 Fig. 1—Recumbent fold structure formed by stream in tanks, U.S. Geological Survey Sedimentation Laboratory, Denver. Figs. 2 and 3—Recumbent fold structures, flood plain deposits of Colorado River, Arizona. Fig. 4—Thrust faults associated with recumbent folding, flood plain deposits of Colorado River, Arizona. Fig. 5—Contorted bedding, slip faces of cross-strata in dune sand, Great Sand Dunes, Alamosa, Colorado. Photo by George Merk. Fig. 6—Structureless homogeneous sand in which original ripple stratification has been largely destroyed by the roots of plants, upper part of Colorado River delta, Sonora, Mexico.

Contorted Bedding

The terms "contorted bedding" and "gnarly bedding" are commonly applied to intraformational features in which strata or cross-strata within a single set have been *irregularly* bent, twisted, or otherwise contorted. Many examples have been cited in geologic literature and apparently are not uncommon in both sandstones and mudstones. Furthermore, a large number of varieties has been reported (e.g., Nevin, 1936, p. 212; Fairbridge, 1946, p. 84) with scales ranging from a few millimeters up to many feet. Unfortunately, as yet, little is known concerning which environments and processes are responsible for each of the types.

Laboratory experiments by Rettger (1935, pp. 275–282) illustrate methods by which some types of contorted bedding are formed. Certain characteristic structures developed by him were caused by the oversteepening of a delta front (subaqueous slumping), and others were obtained by differential movement caused by rotational forces. Experiments by Kindle (1917, figs. 6, 7) show deformation, produced by differential loading, in clay and sand beds.

Much contorted bedding has been attributed to "slumping" of sediment during the movement of turbidity flows (e.g., Kuenen and Migliorini, 1950; Kuenen, 1952, p. 32). Such structures are observed in sample cores (Gorsline and Emery, 1959, p. 285) and commonly develop during experimental work on turbidity flows (Natland and Kuenen, 1951, p. 88; Kuenen and Menard, 1952, p. 88) but little seems to be known concerning differences, if any, between these structures and contorted beds formed in other environments. They probably develop under many different conditions as shown by examples in delta sands within San Miguel Lagoon in Baja California (Stewart, 1956, p. 153), in the Colorado River flood-plain deposits, and even in dry sand as illustrated by contorted bedding recorded by George Merk (written commun., 1961) within cross-strata of the Great Sand Dunes at Alamosa, Colorado (Plate 6, Figure 5).

Irregular Bedding

Structures assigned to this category include beds that were deposited on an original irregular or uneven surface such as one covered with vegetation and also strata that have been locally disturbed but not completely destroyed by roots or by burrowing animals. Irregular bedding, as recognized in drill cores, is distributed over the open shelf off the coast of Texas at depths of 30 to 65 feet and, also, seaward of the Mississippi Delta at 6 to 360 feet (Moore and Scruton, 1957, p. 2735). In these areas it seems to represent a transition type between regularly layered structures to shoreward and mottled or structureless varieties on the seaward side. It also was found in some bays on the Texas coast.

Other environments from which irregular bedding has been reported (Van Straaten, 1959, pp. 212–213) are (1) salt marshes on the shoreward side of tidal flats bordering the Dutch and German Wadden Sea; (2) hypersaline lagoons at Laguna Madre, Texas; and (3) interdistributary bays and other sheltered parts of the Rhone Delta platform. As might be supposed, such structures where derived from partial destruction of other types of stratification are locally associated with both ripple-laminated and horizontally bedded structures.

Laboratory experiments, by Solowiew (1924) with the worm *Tubifex* and by Parker (in Moore and Scruton, 1957, p. 2742, fig. 11) in which burrowing clams and shrimp were used, have demonstrated the manner in which strata may be disorganized. They illustrate some of the nonuniform, lenticular, and disrupted varieties of bedding structure that result.

Mottled Structures

Mottled structures in modern sediments have been described by several observers and, in view of the not uncommon occurrence of mottling in ancient rocks, this feature is included here. It is considered by Moore and Scruton (1957, p. 2727) to develop in various ways, especially through the filling of animal burrows and surface irregularities and by incomplete destruction of earlier structures. Its distribution is described as seaward of the area of irregular layering, at 50 to 300 feet off the Texas coast and at 15 to 350 feet in the open Gulf off the Mississippi Delta. It is also said to occur in Texas coastal bays at depths of 2 to 9 feet and in Breton Sound, Louisiana, at 4 to 20 feet.

Mottled structures in shelf areas off Trinidad, western Guiana, and the Paria and Rhone Deltas, are reported by Van Straaten (1959, p. 213). The mottling is attributed by him to burrowing animals in areas of little deposition and little reworking and occurs in proximity to homogeneous structureless deposits.

Structureless, Homogeneous Deposits

Many modern sand deposits, as well as ancient sandstones, including some of considerable thickness, seem to be devoid of any well-defined stratification or cross-stratification. Examination under favorable conditions of etching and lighting, however, demonstrates that in many examples of this feature the supposed lack of structures is more apparent than real. Furthermore, the study of sandstones using an X-ray technique recently developed by Hamblin (1961) has shown that many apparently structureless rocks have definite stratification. Thus considerable caution should be used in assigning any particular sediment or rock to this class.

True structureless sand deposits may result from uniformity of source material (Natland and Kuenen, 1951, p. 93) or from continuous deposition under uniform conditions. Most of them are, however, believed to result from the elimination of original structures through the growth of plants or by the burrowing activities of organisms. Illustrations of original cross-stratified sands in which structures have been partly or entirely destroyed through the growth of root systems are common on the topset plain of the Colorado River Delta (Plate 6, Figure 6). In this warm, wet environment fast-growing shrubs such as salt cedar and arrow weed form dense stands following deposition during flood periods, effectively obliterating the underlying stratification in some places.

Sand deposits believed to have become structureless through burrowing by worms or other animals are reported from both marine and marginal environments. Based on examination of drill cores, such sands are described by Moore and Scruton (1957, p. 2736) from seaward of barrier islands off the Texas coast, nearshore to depths of 30 to 45 feet, and off the Louisiana coast to depths of 75 to 90 feet; also, they are recorded from beneath very shallow water of lagoons inside the barrier islands. They are reported by Van Straaten (1959, pp. 212–213) in the high parts of tidal flats of the Wadden Sea and on the lower delta front of the Rhone, Orinoco, and other rivers.

Conclusions

Primary structures in ancient rocks are an important aid in the interpretation of environments of deposition. In order to use these structures most effectively, however, knowledge of all the environments in which a particular structure may be found and of other structures with which it may be associated is needed. The classification presented in Table 1, therefore, is but a very incomplete example of the type of objective data needed. With systematic additions from further studies of modern sediments and from laboratory experiments, it may be expanded into a significant and useful tool in making accurate interpretations.

REFERENCES

Bramlette, M. N., and W. H. Bradley, 1942, Lithology and geological interpretations, Pt. 1 *of* Geology and biology of North Atlantic deep-sea cores between Newfoundland and Ireland: *U. S. Geol. Survey Prof. Paper 196,* pp. 1–34.

Bucher, W. H., 1938, Key to papers published by an institute for the study of modern sediments in shallow seas: *J. Geol.,* v. 46, n. 5, pp. 726–755.

Fairbridge, R. W., 1946, Submarine slumping and location of oil bodies: *Am. Assoc. Petroleum Geologists Bull.,* v. 30, n. 1, pp. 84–92.

Gorsline, D. S., and K. O. Emery, 1959, Turbidity-current deposits in San Pedro and Santa Monica basins off southern California: *Geol. Soc. America Bull.,* v. 70, n. 3, pp. 279–290.

Hamblin, W. K., 1961, X-ray radiographs in the study of structures in homogeneous rocks [abs.]: *Geol. Soc. Am. Program Ann. Meetings,* p. 66A.

Harms, J. C., D. B. MacKenzie, and D. G. McCubbin, 1963, Stratification in modern sands of the Red River, Louisiana: *J. Geol.,* v. 71, no. 5, pp. 566–580.

Huntington, Ellsworth, 1907, Some characteristics of the glacial period in nonglaciated regions: *Geol. Soc. Am. Bull.,* v. 18, pp. 351–388.

Illies, Henning, 1949, Die Schrägschichtung in fluviatilen und littoralen Sedimenten, ihre Ursachen, Messung und Auswertung: *Hamburg, Mitt. Geol. Staatsinst.,* n. 19, pp. 89–109.

Johnston, W. A., 1922, The character of stratification of the sediments in the recent delta of Fraser River, British Columbia, Canada: *J. Geol.,* v. 30, n. 2, pp. 115–129.

Kindle, E. M., 1917, Deformation of unconsolidated beds in Nova Scotia and southern Ontario: *Geol. Soc. Am. Bull.,* v. 28, pp. 323–334.

________ 1930, The intertidal zone of the Wash, England, in *Report of the Committee on Sedimentation, 1928–1929:* Nat'l. Research Council, reprint and circular series, n. 92, pp. 5–21.

Kuenen, Ph. H., 1951, Properties of turbidity currents of high density: in *Turbidity Currents and the Transportation of Coarse Sediments to Deep Water—a Symposium:* Soc. Econ. Paleontologists and Mineralogists Spec. Pub. 2, pp. 14–33.

________ 1952, Paleogeographic significance of graded bedding and associated features: *Amsterdam, Koninkl. Nederl. Akad. Van Wetens., Proceed.,* ser. B, v. 55, n. 1, pp. 28–36.

________ and H. W. Menard, Jr., 1952, Turbidity currents, graded and nongraded deposits: *J. Sediment. Petrol.,* v. 22, n. 2, pp. 83–96.

________ and Migliorini, C. I., 1950, Turbidity currents as a cause of graded bedding: *J. Geol.,* v. 58, n. 2, pp. 91–127.

McKee, E. D., 1938, Original structures in Colorado River flood deposits of Grand Canyon: *J. Sediment. Petrol.,* v. 8, n. 3, pp. 77–83.

________ 1939, Some types of bedding in the Colorado River Delta: *J. Geol.,* v. 47, n. 1, pp. 64–81.

________ 1957*a,* Flume experiments on the production of stratification and cross-stratification: *J. Sediment. Petrol.,* v. 27, n. 2, pp. 129–134.

________ 1957*b,* Primary structures in some Recent sediments [U. S. and Mexico]: *Am. Assoc. Petroleum Geologists Bull.,* v. 41, n. 8, pp. 1704–1747.

________ and G. W. Weir, 1953, Terminology for stratification and cross-stratification in sedimentary rocks: *Geol. Soc. Am. Bull.*, v. 64, n. 4, pp. 381–389.

Moore, D. G., and P. C. Scruton, 1957, Minor internal structures of some recent unconsolidated sediments [Gulf of Mexico]: *Am. Assoc. Petroleum Geologists Bull.*, v. 41, n. 12, pp. 2723–2751.

Natland, M. L., and Ph. H. Kuenen, 1951, Sedimentary history of the Ventura Basin, California, and the action of turbidity currents: in *Turbidity Currents and the Transportation of Coarse Sediments to Deep Water—a Symposium:* Soc. Econ. Paleontologists and Mineralogists Spec. Pub. 2, pp. 76–107.

Nevin, C. M., 1936, *Principles of Structural Geology:* New York, John Wiley and Sons, Second Edition, 348 pp.

Rettger, R. E., 1935, Experiments on soft-rock deformation: *Am. Assoc. Petroleum Geologists Bull.*, v. 19, n. 2, pp. 271–292.

Solowiew, M. M., 1924, The influence of *Tubifex tubifex* in the formation of organic mud: *Intern. Rev. Hydrobiol.*, v. 12, p. 90.

Stewart, H. B., Jr., 1956, Contorted sediments in modern coastal lagoon explained by laboratory experiments: *Am. Assoc. Petroleum Geologists Bull.*, v. 40, n. 1, pp. 153–161.

Stokes, W. L., 1957, Rib-and-furrow, a primary directional structure of sedimentary rocks [abs.]: *Geol. Soc. Am. Bull.*, v. 68, n. 12, pt. 2, pp. 1872–1873.

Sundborg, Åke, 1956, The river Klarälven; a study of fluvial processes: *Uppsala Univ., Geog. Inst., Medd.*, ser. A, n. 115, pp. 125–316.

Van Straaten, L. M. J. U., 1959, Minor structures of some littoral and neritic sediments: *Geologie en Mijnbouw, N. W.* ser., 21 e, Jaargang, pp. 197–216.

Biogenic Sedimentary Structures

by Adolf Seilacher *Georg-August Universität, Göttingen, Germany*

Trace Fossils as Paleontological Objects

It is generally agreed that biogenic sedimentary structures are true fossils and that their study (ichnology or palichnology) is part of paleontology. Accordingly, they should be described, classified, and named like other fossils. The ordinary procedures of systematic paleontology, however, are difficult to apply to such structures, the shapes of which are controlled more by the depositional environment than by the shapes of the animals producing them. Therefore, some general considerations necessarily have to precede the paleoecological evaluation of these structures.

Definition

Traces are sedimentary structures resulting from biological activity. This excludes agglutinated tests like those of Pectinaria and Foraminifera, as well as marks left by dead bodies drifting or rolling over the ground.

Preservation affects other fossils mainly in a negative sense, that is, by various degrees of secondary solution, disintegration, or deformation. Trace fossils, however, improve rather than suffer through diagenetic processes. Chemical differentiation tends to "develop" minor structural differences in originally more homogeneous sediments and to make them visible much as in photographic printing. Markings on bedding planes, almost inaccessible in recent cores, can be easily observed after selective cementation of the coarser layers. Even erosion, although usually destructive, may in certain cases preserve biogenic structures. For example, a mud structure may be eroded and a cast made by subsequent coarser sedimentation (Figure 1). In addition to secondary changes, a surprising variety of

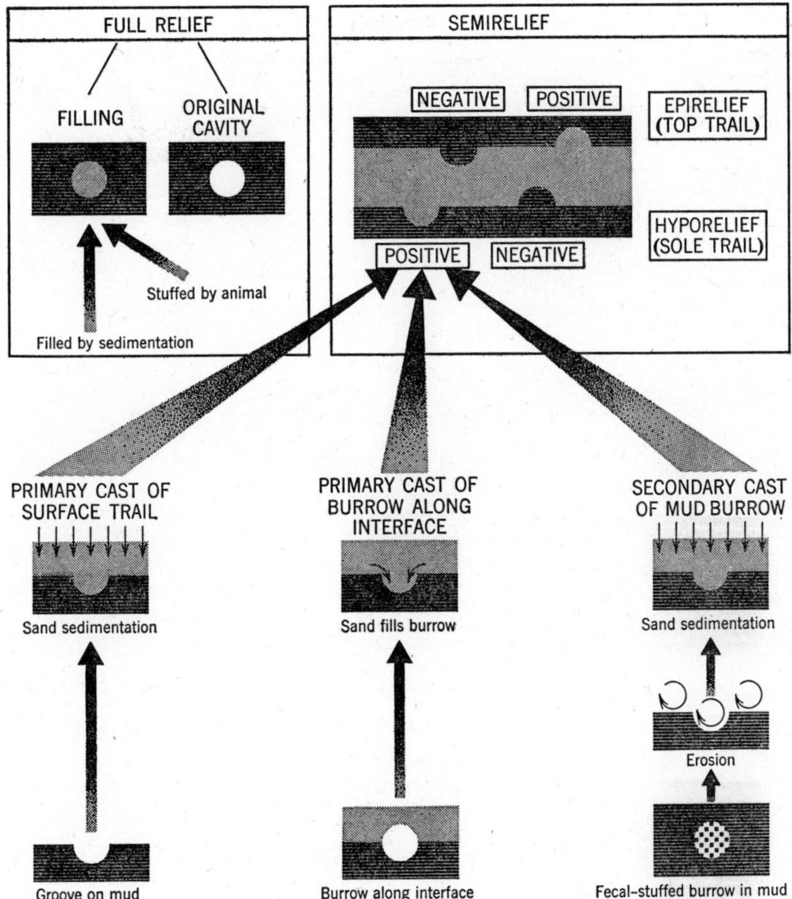

Fig. 1 Preservation of trace fossils. *Since the preparation of this chart a somewhat modified terminology has been suggested to the Committee for the Nomenclature of Sedimentary Structures. This includes the following new terms:* Convex *for positive, and* concave *instead of negative semireliefs.* Exogene *for actual surface trails, versus* endogene *for primary casts of internal origin, and pseudexogene for the secondary casts. Active fill, if burrow was stuffed by the animal,* passive *fill, if it was filled by sedimentation.*

traces may result from the same activity of the one animal, depending on the plasticity of the sediment and the site of the activity at surface or inside the sediment. If such differences are not realized and eliminated, nearly every specimen may be considered as a new "species." Some significant types of preservation and their possible origin are shown in Figure 1.

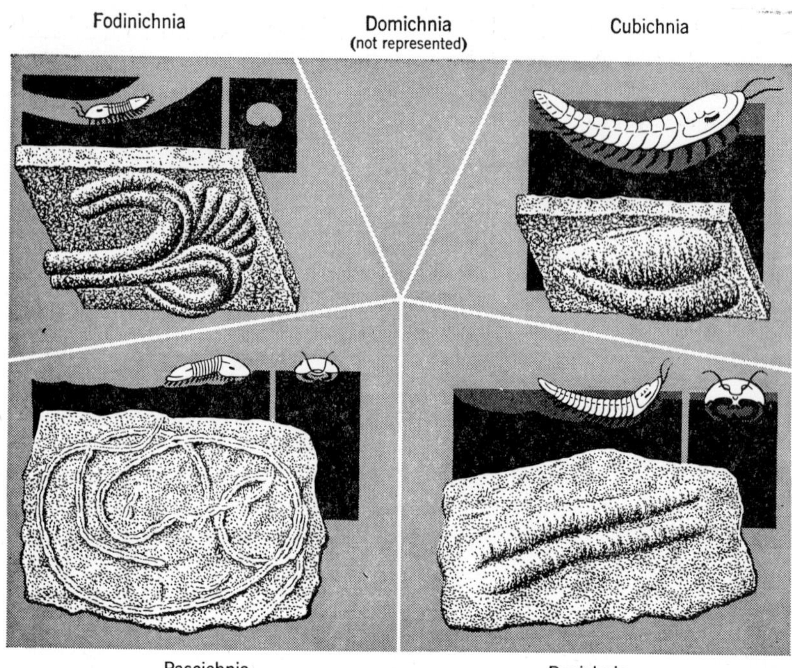

Fig. 2 Main ethologic groups of trace fossils, illustrated by trilobite burrows (sole faces of beds and restorations). Cubichnia: (Rusophycus) *Trace corresponds to outline of animal. Repichnia:* (Cruziana) *Trace formed by repetition or extension of* Rusophycus. *Pascichnia: Circling variety of the latter (Ordov., North Iraq), reflects search for food. Fodinichnia:* (Cruziana ancora Lessertisseur) *From the Silurian of Equatorial Africa, a branching burrow. Domichnia referable to trilobites have not been found so far.*

Ethological Elements in Trace Morphology

Having sorted out accidental elements in trace morphology, we still have to separate features that express function from those reflecting the morphology of the animals. Since function is inherently involved in any trace, this separation is more difficult. The recognition of five ethological groups (Seilacher, 1953*a*) has so far proved to be satisfactory (Figure 2):

1. REPICHNIA: Trails or burrows left by vagile benthos during directed locomotion.
2. PASCICHNIA: Winding trails or burrows of vagile mud eaters

which reflect a "grazing" search for food by covering a given surface more or less efficiently and avoiding double coverage.

3. FODINICHNIA: Burrows made by hemisessile deposit feeders. They reflect the search for food and at the same time fit the requirements for a permanent shelter.

4. DOMICHNIA: Permanent shelters dug by vagile or hemisessile animals procuring food from outside the sediment as predators, scavengers, or suspension feeders.

5. CUBICHNIA: Shallow resting tracks left by vagile animals hiding temporarily in the sediment, usually sand, and obtaining their food as scavengers or suspension feeders.

Nonfunctional (Taxonomic) Elements of Trace Morphology

The final step in the analysis of trace fossils should be the recognition of features which are directly related to the morphology of particular animals. These features link the traces with other fossil remains and allow their identification in terms of systematic paleontology. While this goal is commonly reached in vertebrate ichnology, the analysis of invertebrate trace fossils can very rarely go that far, although it may happen that the body of an animal is preserved in its very track or burrow like *Limulus* in the Solnhofen Limestone (Caster, 1940). In other cases the body has left identifiable impressions, for instance, of cephalon and pleura in trilobite burrows or of distinctive claws in many arthropod tracks. Resting tracks of asteroids and ophiurians, which have long been mistaken for the bodies of the starfishes themselves, may be mentioned as another example, (Seilacher, 1953*b*). Compared to the host of well-recognized, but systematically unidentified trace fossils, however, these are only rare exceptions. Even if by further studies, more and more revealing "fingerprints" are found, this situation will not essentially change in the future.

Classification and Nomenclature

A threefold determination including preservational, ethological, and taxonomic characters is necessary to describe any trace fossil adequately. As a base for nomenclature, however, only *one* classification can be used.

Hundt (1932), Desio (1940), and Lessertisseur (1955) have proposed ichnological systems, in which the main distinction is made between surface trails and burrows, while functional (ethological), ecological, or taxonomic differences are used for subordinate grouping. In practice these classifications are difficult to apply, because surface tracks and burrows are fundamentally different only to our eyes. For many benthonic animals it makes little difference whether they creep at the surface or along bedding planes inside the sediment, and for the paleontologist it is often impossible to differentiate these two types of motion. Therefore, most German authors (Richter, 1927; Krejci-Graf, 1932, and Abel, 1935) have based their classifications completely on ethology. A compromise solution was proposed by Seilacher (1953*a*). The higher categories of his ichnological system should be based on ethologic interpretations; the lower ones (ichnospecies) on taxonomic interpretations.

Meanwhile experience has shown that a hybrid system inevitably leads to difficulties. Preservation, ethology, and taxonomy do not have equivalent relative importance in different groups of trace fossils. Tetrapod tracks often reflect the morphology of their producers clearly enough to be placed in certain families, or even genera. Ethologically, however, they would all belong to the same group, Repichnia. "Worm" trails, on the other hand, very rarely permit further taxonomic distinction, but they show remarkable ethologic diversity. Other groups range between these two extremes. The burrows of Figure 2 are all made by trilobites. Some can be attributed even more specifically to Illaenids. This natural group must be split into four different genera if an ethological classification is rigidly applied. Ichnological names—not recognized according to the International Rules of Zoological Nomenclature—should express individual morphology rather than the interpretation of trace fossils. The recent issue, by W. Häntzschel, of the *Treatise on Invertebrate Paleontology*, has made the recognition of individual types much easier. Eventually, more and more taxonomic differences in trace morphology will emerge which may help to give invertebrate trace fossils a similar, though less defined, taxonomic status as tetrapod tracks have in vertebrate classification.

Trace Fossils as Paleoecologic Guides

General Remarks

It is generally believed that ecological interpretation of fossil assemblages becomes more and more difficult as we go further back in geologic history. This rule does not fully apply to trace fossils. A Tertiary shell fauna can still be interpreted in terms of recent animals and their environments. Tertiary trace fossils, however, have little more resemblance to known Recent traces than do Mesozoic or even Paleozoic examples (Figure 3). Nevertheless there may be very close similarity between the Tertiary and Paleozoic trace fossils. This does not mean that the fossil types no longer exist in Recent seas. Rather, sedimentary structures, and particularly the internal ones, are much easier to study in consolidated rocks than in soft sediments where special preparations are needed to make them visible. What we know from Recent sea floors are mainly surface trails which would be rarely preserved as fossils, while internal structures have so far been inadequately studied, that is, in single sections (Reineck, 1958; Moore and Scruton, 1957). We could say that in ichnology the present has rarely provided actual keys to the past; however, it has taught us how the locks work. Here is still an open field for future exploration by marine geologists.

Although they cannot yet be directly translated into terms of recent taxonomy and biogeography, trace fossils nevertheless have considerable advantages.

1. LONG TIME RANGE. Trace morphology reflects certain functions and behaviour patterns rather than body shapes. Different animals acting alike may leave almost the same type of traces. Partly for this reason many gross types of trace fossils occur through many periods, or even eras, of geologic history. This may be a disadvantage for stratigraphic use, but it considerably facilitates long-range facies comparison.

2. NARROW FACIES RANGE. The recorded actions are often direct responses to environmental conditions. Significant types of trace fossils therefore are restricted to certain facies, irrespective of what animals have produced them.

3. NO SECONDARY DISPLACEMENT. Sedimentary structures obviously cannot be reworked like other fossils. Every ichnocoenosis represents part of an actual benthic community that lived in a single area and usually at the same time.

4. PREFERENCE FOR CLASTIC SEDIMENTS. Ichnofossils may occur in any type of sediment, but they are most abundant and best preserved in clastic series, particularly where sandy and shaly beds alternate.

All these circumstances together make trace fossils promising as paleoecologic guides. They will be particularly useful in clastic sediments poor in other fossils and in the more ancient rocks where other fossils are too different from Recent animals to justify the simple application of uniformitarianism.

For the purpose of this paper we may distinguish three main direc-

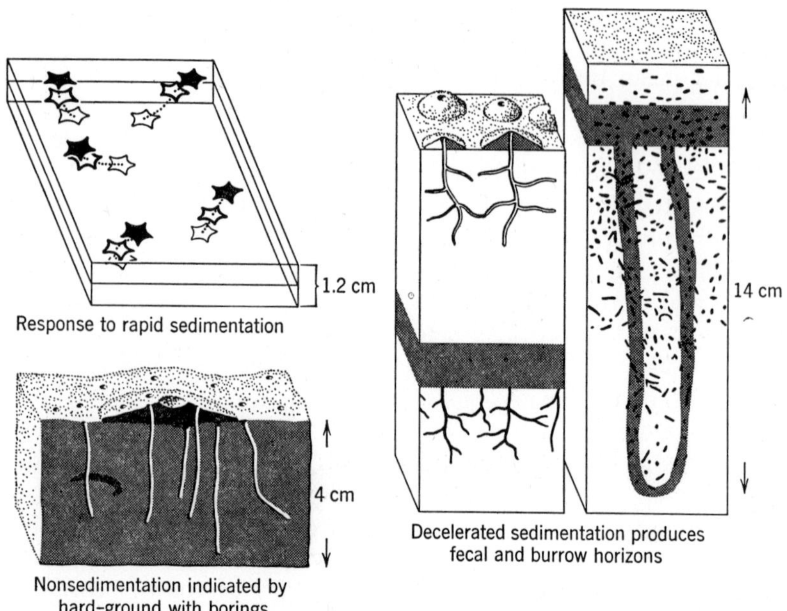

Fig. 3 Upper left: *Reacting to fast deposition of new sand layers, epipsammonic ophiurans have followed the rising surface. They left corresponding, but not congruent, impressions* (cubichnia of Asteriacites type) *on subsequent laminae. Lower Triassic Seiser beds, Tyrol. In Rhaetic ss. of S. Germany, corresponding impressions may be found on lower and upper face of beds up to 7 cm thick (Seilacher, 1953b).* Right: *During a time of retarded mud sedimentation, deposit feeders had a chance to riddle the top part of the mud with burrows* (fodinichnia) *and form a dark fecal layer at the contemporary surface. Note that* Chondrites *burrows (small spots) do not reach as deeply as the U-shaped* Corophioides, *except in the reworked septum ("Spreite") between the shafts of the latter. Deviations of burrows around mollusk shells indicate that the sediment was still soft. After a time interval, sedimentation continued at the original rate and formed the upper part of the calcareous mudstone bed in which the bioturbate layer is now included. (Lias γ, S. Germany). Similar bioturbation zones have been observed in experiments with recent worms (Schäfer, 1952: left block).* Lower left: *Simple burrows* (domichnia) *of suspension feeders originate from a sharp but uneven surface which was already hard enough to serve as a substrate for crinoid roots. These as well as shells in the sediment were pierced by the boring animals just as easily as the matrix. "Hard grounds" of this type indicate longer periods of nondeposition and form good marker horizons, Lower Muschelkalk (M. Trias.). (From A. H. Müller, 1956).*

tions of research in this field. The first aims at recognition of individual environmental factors; the second is concerned about minor facies variations in limited sections; and the third tries to recognize general trace associations, or types of ichnocoenoses, representing certain facies with a long geologic range.

Individual Environmental Factors

It is obvious that environmental conditions directly control animal actions to a large extent. In some cases individual environmental factors can be recognized in the fossil record of such actions.

Aeration

Whenever discussion arises about euxinic or noneuxinic origin of sediments, lack of trace fossils is a strong argument in favor of euxinic conditions, while their occurrence is the best possible proof against such conditions. The black Devonian Hunsrück Shales of Western Germany contain exceptionally well-preserved and complete fossils, and this fact was long considered to be a result of euxinic conditions. In this particular case, euxinic origin was ruled out by Rudolf Richter, who discovered a variety of trails indicating a rich bottom life. Autochthonous benthos and complete preservation are not incompatible. For example, complete trilobite specimens with legs and even tiny preserved setae are associated with burrows of *Chondrites*, which must have been made when the trilobite body lay only 1 or 2 cm below the bottom surface (Seilacher, 1962).

On the other hand, the Liassic Posidonia Shales of Holzmaden (Western Germany), famous for skin-bearing Ichthyosaur fossils, contain no trails or burrows except in one or two distinct layers close to the upper and at the lower boundaries of the unit.

Sedimentation

Trace fossils may tell about the relative speed of sedimentation in several ways; for example, by the response to sedimentary deposition shown by certain resting tracks of ophiuroids. Like most cubichnia, they are made by epipsammonic species that hide themselves in the sand just under the surface. If covered in experiments with more sand, ophiuroids dig their way up until the sensory organs (at the arm tips) reach the surface again. Vertical repetition of resting tracks, as occurs particularly in current-lineated sandstones, records

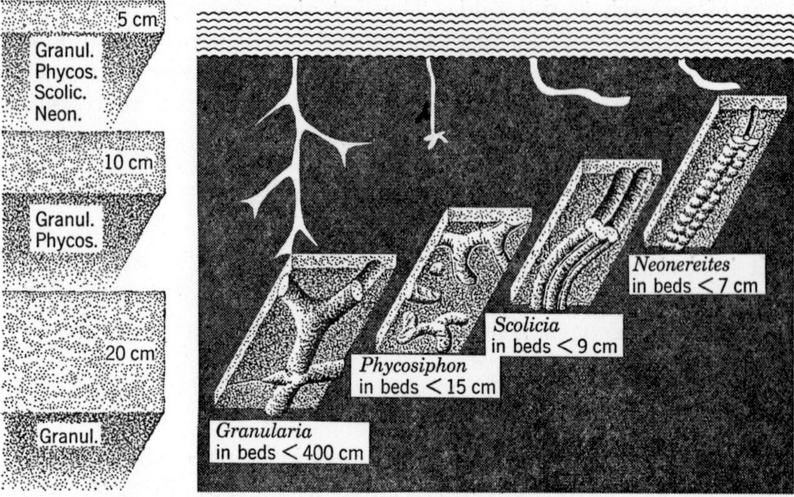

Fig. 4 Trails indicating turbidity sedimentation: Among the sole trails of flysch greywacke beds the listed types are postdepositional. They are made by animals that penetrated the sand layer and moved along the interface between sand and mud. These trails are never found in beds beyond a certain thickness, probably corresponding to the depth to which the particular species used to burrow. This relation was tested in several hundred beds and is considered a proof for instantaneous sedimentation of each bed by a turbidity current (Seilacher, 1962).

such reaction to the deposition of a corresponding sand layer on top of the buried animal. As epipsammonic animals usually leave the sand to gather their food, this deposition must have happened between two meals—that is, rather rapidly.

Retarded sedimentation gives burrowing deposit feeders a chance to riddle the top layer more intensively. In addition, fecal pellets may accumulate at the surface. Both burrow horizons and fecal layers can be traced within otherwise homogeneous beds (Figure 3).

Periods of nondeposition produce in pelitic deposits more compact and firm surface layers ("hard grounds," Voigt, 1959). In hard grounds, suspension feeders have their burrows from which to feed in the turbulent water. These burrows, however, are mainly shelters (domichnia) dug or drilled perpendicular to the surface, rather than complicated feeding burrows (fodinichnia) as mentioned earlier.

An extremely rapid type of deposition has been suggested for sandy beds of the flysch, and for other supposed turbidites. Figure 4 illustrates how this concept was confirmed ichnologically in the Spanish flysch. There is no contradiction in the fact that one type of sole trails (*Granularia*) occurs in beds up to 4 m. In modern deep-sea sands, which are aerated to a greater depth than shallow-water sands, worms actually dig that deeply (Bezrukov and Romankevič, 1960).

Currents

Compared to the large number of inorganic current markings, biogenic indicators of current have no real importance. Nevertheless, they should be mentioned as a paleontological contribution to the study of paleocurrents. Currents not only affect the movements of animals crawling on the sea floor (Figure 5), but also control the orientation of suspension feeders and other animals hidden in the

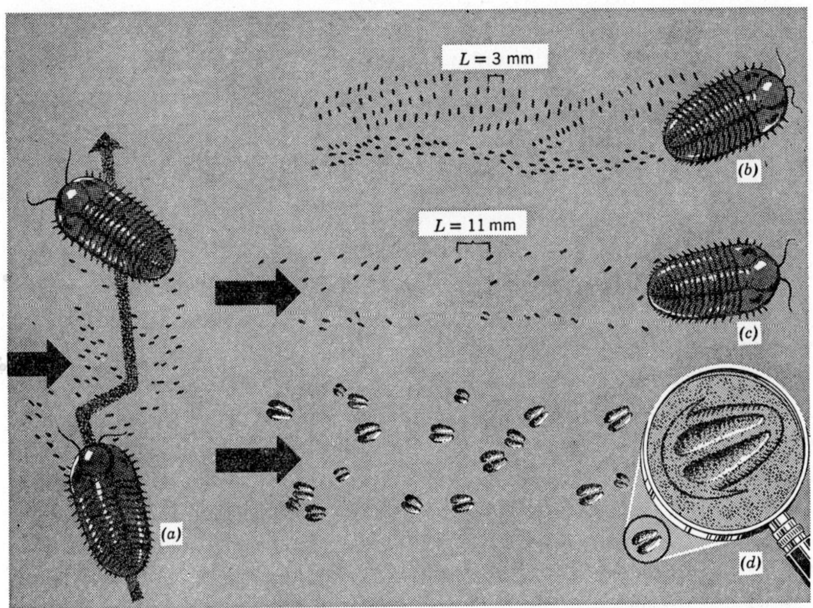

Fig. 5 a-c Trilobite tracks from Lower Devonian Hunsrück shales, Germany (Seilacher, 1960, fig. 13). (a) Lateral current (recorded by groove casts) has displaced the walking trilobite from it's original path, (b) normal trackway, (c) current from the rear (groove cast indication) has considerably increased the pace, (d) coffeebean-shaped resting tracks from the Purple Sandstone (Lower Cambrian) of Pakistan (Seilacher, 1955). They record the rheotactic orientation of trilobites or phyllopods dug in the sand with their heads against the current (indicated by current lineation). Size and orientation of the animals are assumed.

sand. Many crustaceans and gastropods tend to face the current, while some other crustaceans have filter mechanisms that require an orientation downstream, or even at right angles to the current (Seilacher, 1961). The umbo of digging pelecypods, if oriented at all, points downstream, so that the inhaling siphon faces the current. As a result, the resting tracks left on underlying bedding planes are subparallel to each other (Figure 5).

Minor Facies Variations within a Given Series

In recent tidal flats the different types of burrows and surface trails and their relative abundance are used to distinguish and to map minor variations in sediment type, exposure, etc. There is no reason why a similar procedure should not be applied to trace lateral and vertical changes in ancient sediments.

Particular associations of faunal and lithological elements occur in almost any series of sedimentary deposits. As recurrent facies types, they reflect certain conditions that have controlled either the original or postmortem distribution of organisms and their remains. Trace associations, or ichnocoenoses, however, may be destroyed but never secondarily changed by later events. They form a more adequate record of original benthic communities. For the given purpose it makes little difference whether the trace fossils dealt with are fully understood or not. They must not even belong to generally recognizable types, if they can only be told apart from other trace fossils of that particular formation.

Figure 6 illustrates an example from the Upper Carboniferous Ruhr Basin, where trace fossils have been successfully used to further subdivide the additional members of paralic cyclothems. None of the types represented is really diagnostic. *Planolites montanus* is a simple sand-filled burrow, *Gyrochorte carbonaria* a bilobate gallery that might occur in any formation. *Sinusites* trails may be formed through sinuose locomotion of almost any worm; they are found alike in Cambrian or Jurassic marine sandstones, as well as in Recent beach sands and pond muds. Even *Planolites ophthalmoides* becomes less diagnostic, if the eye-like halo is understood as a zone of slight alteration or cementation around a galley, made visible by subsequent tectonic compression. Nevertheless, within the limits of the Ruhr Basin and of the Pennsylvanian section, each type corresponds to a particular, though unknown, species of burrowing animal, each with distinct requirements as to salinity and other environmental factors.

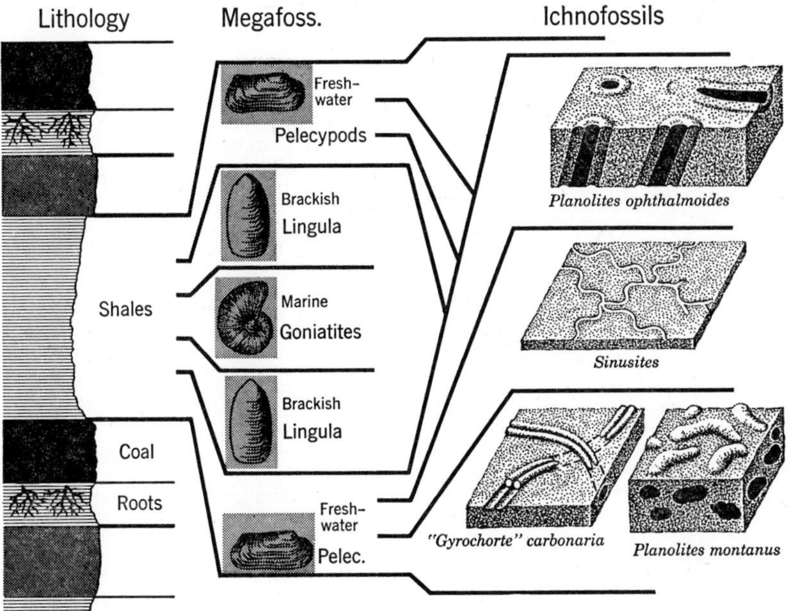

Fig. 6 Within lithologic cyclothems in paralic deposits of the Ruhr Basin, more members can be recognized with the help of trace fossils. For this purpose it makes no difference that these trace fossils belong to rather insignificant types which in other formations may occur in dissimilar types of facies. (Based on data by Fessen and others).

Universal Types of Marine Ichnofacies

In the preceding section, each trace fossil was considered as a substitute for the unknown species of animals from which it came. The conclusions, therefore, are not valid beyond the vertical and horizontal range of that particular species.

Comparison between many ichnocoenoses of various geologic ages has shown, however, that there is a more general, supraspecific relation between the ethological character of trace fossils and the geologic facies indicated by lithology and inorganic sedimentary structures. In a gross way, the difference is expressed by the ichnospectrum, that is, by the relative abundance in which the various ethotypes (domichnia, cubichnia, etc., (see Fig. 2)) are represented in each trace

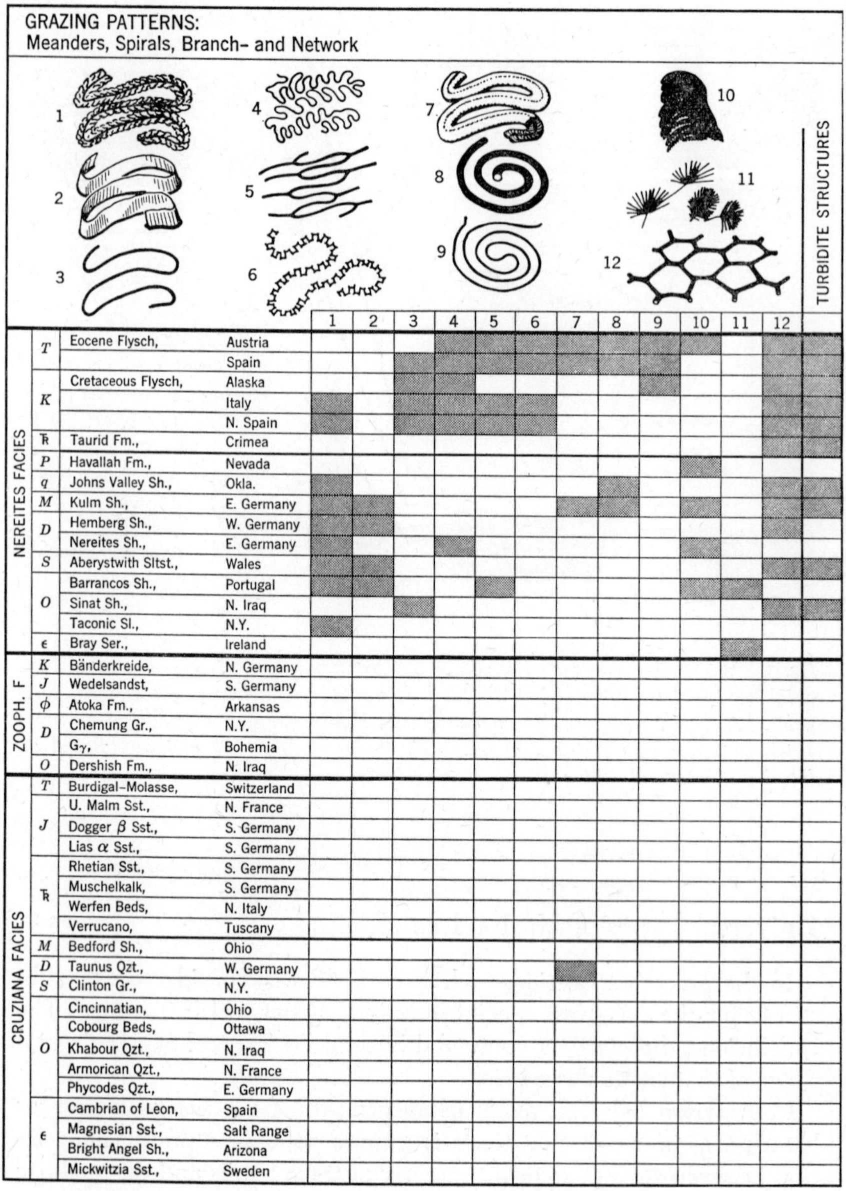

GRAZING PATTERNS:
Meanders, Spirals, Branch- and Network

Facies	Age	Formation	Locality	1	2	3	4	5	6	7	8	9	10	11	12	TURBIDITE STRUCTURES
NEREITES FACIES	*T*	Eocene Flysch,	Austria				■	■	■	■	■	■	■		■	■
			Spain			■	■	■	■	■	■	■			■	■
	K	Cretaceous Flysch,	Alaska			■	■					■			■	■
			Italy	■		■	■	■	■						■	■
			N. Spain	■		■	■	■	■						■	■
	Ꞧ	Taurid Fm.,	Crimea												■	■
	P	Havallah Fm.,	Nevada										■			
	q	Johns Valley Sh.,	Okla.	■							■				■	■
	M	Kulm Sh.,	E. Germany	■	■					■	■		■		■	■
	D	Hemberg Sh.,	W. Germany	■	■										■	
		Nereites Sh.,	E. Germany	■			■						■			
	S	Aberystwith Sltst.,	Wales	■	■										■	■
	O	Barrancos Sh.,	Portugal	■	■			■					■	■		
		Sinat Sh.,	N. Iraq			■									■	■
		Taconic Sl.,	N.Y.	■												
	ϵ	Bray Ser.,	Ireland											■		
ZOOPH. F	*K*	Bänderkreide,	N. Germany													
	J	Wedelsandst,	S. Germany													
	ϕ	Atoka Fm.,	Arkansas													
	D	Chemung Gr.,	N.Y.													
		Gγ,	Bohemia													
	O	Dershish Fm.,	N. Iraq													
CRUZIANA FACIES	*T*	Burdigal-Molasse,	Switzerland													
	J	U. Malm Sst.,	N. France													
		Dogger β Sst.,	S. Germany													
		Lias α Sst.,	S. Germany													
	Ꞧ	Rhetian Sst.,	S. Germany													
		Muschelkalk,	S. Germany													
		Werfen Beds,	N. Italy													
		Verrucano,	Tuscany													
	M	Bedford Sh.,	Ohio													
	D	Taunus Qzt.,	W. Germany							■						
	S	Clinton Gr.,	N.Y.													
	O	Cincinnatian,	Ohio													
		Cobourg Beds,	Ottawa													
		Khabour Qzt.,	N. Iraq													
		Armorican Qzt.,	N. France													
		Phycodes Qzt.,	E. Germany													
	ϵ	Cambrian of Leon,	Spain													
		Magnesian Sst.,	Salt Range													
		Bright Angel Sh.,	Arizona													
		Mickwitzia Sst.,	Sweden													

*Fig. 7 All communities of trace fossils, regardless of geologic age, can be assigned to one of three major types of ichnofacies which show parallel differences in lithology and inorganic sedimentary structures. See Table 1 for more details. The three facies represent major environments differing in depth and sedimentary regime. Sources of information: Hundt, 1941 (*Phycodes *Quartzite); Wilson 1948 (Cobourg); J. Hall, 1850 (Clinton;* Asteriacites *in Albany museum);*

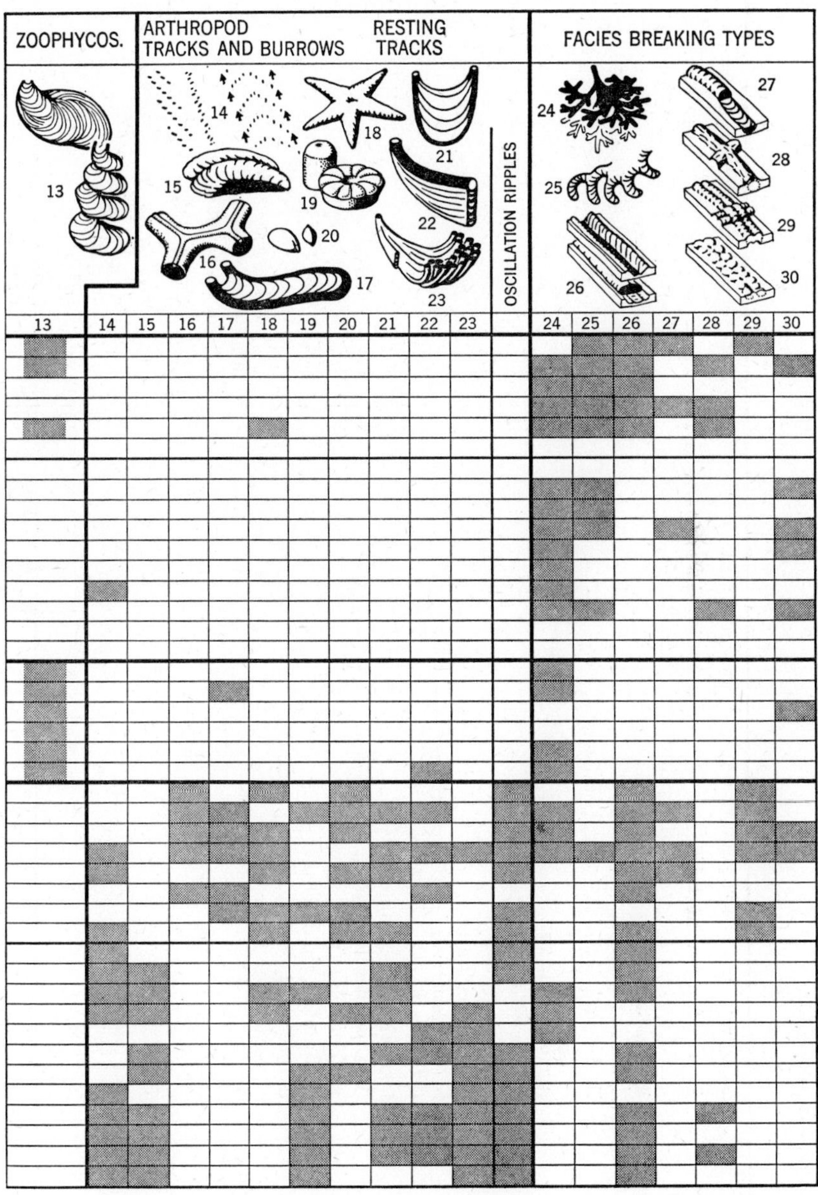

Fucini, 1936–38 (Verrucano); M. Schmidt, 1934; Leonardi, 1935, (Werfen); J. Hall, 1852 (Chemung); L. Henbest, 1960 (Atoka); Voigt and Häntzschel, 1956 (Bänderkreide); Emmons, 1844 (Taconic; similar types in Maine); Keeping, 1882 (Aberystwyth); S. W. Muller (unpublished specimens from Havallah); O. S. Vialov, 1960 (Taurid). Other data are based mainly on personal observations.

TABLE 1. *Universal ichnofacies*

	Nereites-Facies	*Zoophycos*-Facies	*Cruziana*-Facies
Some diagnostic trace fossils (Fig. 7):	Internal, meandering pascichnia: 1. *Nereites* (w. lateral flaps) 2. *Dictyodora* (w. vertical septum) 3. *Helminthoida crassa* 4. *Cosmorhaphe* (plain, sec. cast) 5. *Urohelminthoida* (w. appendices; sec. cast) 6. *Paleomaeandron* (sec. cast) 7. *Taphrhelminthopsis* (gastrop.-trail, stuffed) Spiral pascichnia: 8. *Ceratophycus* (+ *Spirodesmos*) 9. *Spirorhaphe* (sec. cast) Branching pascichnia: 10. *Lophoctenium* (prim. cast) 11. *Oldhamia* (prim. cast; left: Cambr.; right: Ord.) 12. *Paleodictyon* (sec., rarely prim. cast)	Fodinichnia: 13. *Zoophycos* (only flat, nonspiral variety)	Arthropod tracks and burrows: 14. Tracks of Trilobites (left), Limulids (right), and other Arthropods 15. *Cruziana* and *Rusophycus* (Trilobite burrow, inverted cast) 16. *Thalassinoides, etc.* (Anomuran burrows) 17. *Rhizocorallium* (septate burrows, probably of crustaceans) Cubichnia (all inverted casts): 18. *Asteriacites* (of Asterozoans) 19. left: *Bergaueria;* right: *Solicyclus* (of Coelenterates) 20. *Pelecypodichnus* (of pelecypods) Septate Fodinichnia: 21. *Corophioides* (U-shaped with septum) 22. *Teichichnus* (similar, but irregular) 23. *Phycodes* (palmate)

Dominant groups:	Pascichnia of vagile, endobiotic deposit feeders	Fodinichnia of deposit feeders	Cubichnia of epipsammon Domichnia of suspension feeders (mainly in shallow, turbulent zone) Fodinichnia of deposit feeders (mainly in deeper zone)
Diagnostic inorganic sedimentary structures:	Load casts, convolute lamination and other turbidite structures	Bedding and lamination poor	Oscillation ripples
Dominant lithology:	Lutites, alternating with graded greywackes or pelagic marls	Impure, crumbly silt-stones to shales	Well sorted sandstones to shales, quartzites; detrital limestones to marls
Probable depth:	Bathyal with turbidite sedimentation	Sublittoral to bathyal, below wave base and without turbidite sedimentation	Littoral to sublittoral, above wave base
Nondiagnostic trace fossils of Fig. 7:	24. *Chondrites* (root-like, branching fodinichnia)	25. *Phycosiphon* (small, looped, and septate fodinichnia or pascichnia)	26. *Scolicia* (gastropod trails like Nr. 7, but without meanders)
	27. *Münsteria* (stuffed linear burrows)	28. *Fucusopsis* (burrows cracking the interface; inverted) 30. *Scalarituba* (= *Neonereites;* burrows like Nr. 1, but without meanders; inverted)	29. *Gyrochorte* (positive epireliefs, repeating in adjacent laminae)

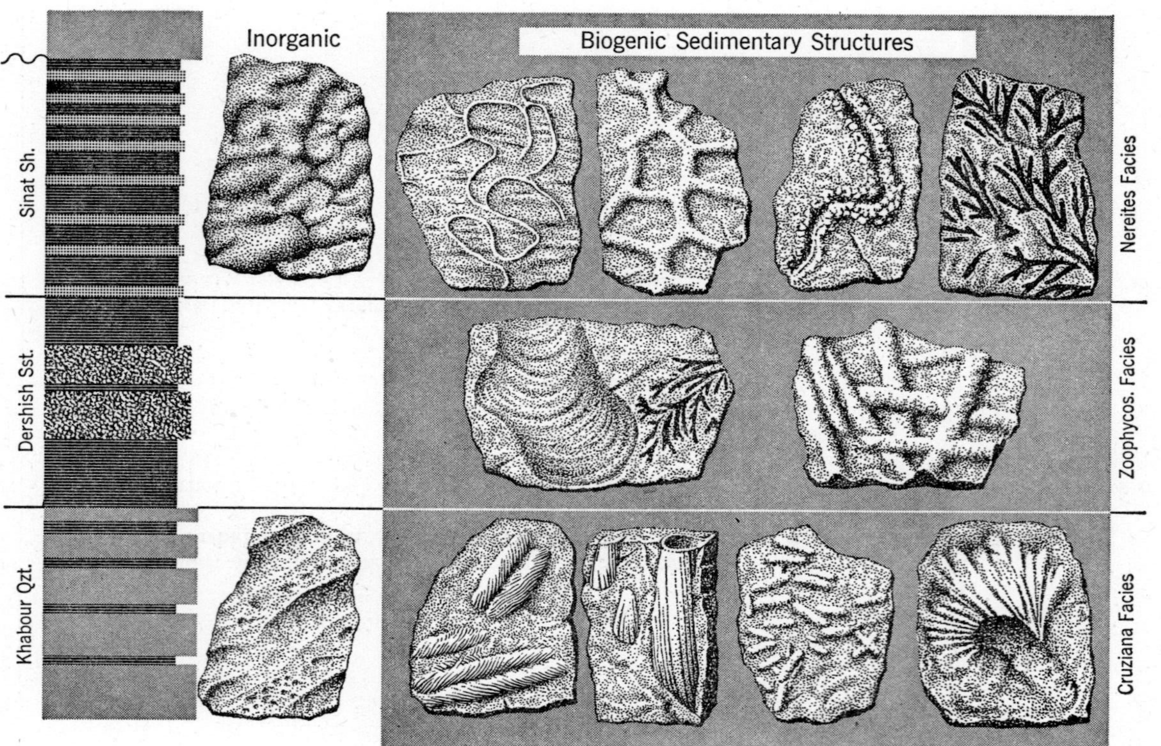
Inorganic
Biogenic Sedimentary Structures
Sinat Sh.
Dershish Sst.
Khabour Qzt.
Nereites Facies
Zoophycos. Facies
Cruziana Facies

association (Seilacher, 1958, fig. 1). In a most general way, this relation may be described and interpreted as follows:

1. To benthic animals of littoral and very shallow water environments, physical protection is a major concern. Vagile animals and suspension feeders which prevail in this turbulent zone either bury themselves temporarily under the surface, leaving shallow resting tracks (cubichnia), or they produce deep and vertical burrows (domichnia) for shelter. In a slightly deeper and quieter zone in which the food particles settle, deposit feeders become more important. Most of them are hemisessile and produce feeding burrows (fodinichnia). Cubichnia and domichnia are still found. Repichnia left by vagile epibenthos occur in either of the two zones.

2. Deep-sea animals gain little by hiding in the sediment. Domichnia and cubichnia almost disappear from the trace spectrum. Instead, complicated fodinichnia and internal grazing tracks (pascichnia) with intricate patterns become more common. The deposit feeders that make them are largely vagile and have particular locomotion patterns to insure systematic coverage of possible food-rich layers.

The quantitative ichnospectrum is not the only way to classify a given ichnocoenosis. Most trace fossils are more or less restricted to one type of ichnofacies. In Figure 7 the diagnostic types are separated from the more ubiquitous forms, while the formations are grouped according to their lithofacies. In both respects three universal types of facies are recognized and named after significant trace fossils. These three facies are most obvious in psammitic rocks, but they apply also to pelitic sediments. The significant features of each are listed in Table 1.

It should be remembered that our ichnological facies concept was

---

Fig. 8 The Ordovician section of Sinat, N Iraq, can be subdivided into three formations, named after nearby villages. These formations correspond by lithology as well as inorganic and biogenic sedimentary structures to the Cruziana-, Zoophycos-, *and* Nereites-*facies and indicate the subsidence of the region from above wave base to deep geosynclinal conditions with turbidity currents in a relatively short time. Subsequent uplift is shown by lack of Silurian and deposition of littoral and continental Devonian beds on top. (For more details see Seilacher, 1963). Illustrated specimens (from field photographs):* KHABOUR QUARTZITE *(left to right): oscillation ripples with flattened crests;* Cruziana, × 1/10 Dacdalus halli, × 1/3; *basal parts of* Diplocraterion, × 1/2; Phycodes, *cf.* circinatum *Richter,* × 1/3. DERSHISH SANDSTONES: Zoophycos *and* Chondrites, × 1/7; Teichichnus (*hyporelief*), × 1/4. SINAT SHALES AND GREYWACKES: *Load casts,* × 1/4; Helminthoida (*secondary hyporelief*), × 1/10; Palaeodictyon (*second. hyporelief*), × 1/4; Neonereites (*primary epirel.*), × 2/3; Chondrites, × 2/3.

primarily derived from the comparison of given fossil ichnocoenoses. New discoveries have meanwhile confirmed this classification and its environmental interpretation.

A most striking example may be cited from the mountains of northern Iraq, where clastic Ordovician rocks crop out underneath thick limestones of the later Iranidian geosyncline. They have been considered so far as one single formation (Khabour Quartzites and Shales, Lexique Stratigraphique, Iraq, p. 147). At one place, however (Sinat), the Ordovician section consists of three distinct formations which clearly correspond to our *Cruziana-*, *Zoophycos-* and *Nereites-*facies, one grading vertically into the other (Figure 8). Sedimentary facies and associated volcanic rocks confirm the picture of a rapidly subsiding geosyncline that preceded the late Paleozoic and Mesozoic one in this place. No angular unconformity can be observed between the two cycles, but there is an abrupt change from the Ordovician turbidites (*Nereites*-Facies) to a very pure quartzite of unknown age that contains oscillation ripples and numerous vertical burrows. It is considered here as the littoral or fresh-water (*Scolithus*) facies that indicates the beginning of the new depositional cycle after a major uplift.

While the Iraq section illustrates a transition in time, lateral transition between the three ichno-facies can be most perfectly studied in the Paleozoic fold belts of the eastern and central United States and their forelands. In the Ouachita Mountains, for instance, the Johns Valley turbidites (Cline and Shelburne, 1959) correspond in every respect to our *Nereites* facies (Figure 7). North of the Ouachita Mountains, at Tenkiller Dam, Atoka siltstones of approximately the same age are impure and poorly bedded and contain *Zoophycos* ("*Taonurus*") and *Scalarituba*, a *Nereites*-like, but less-meandering burrow. There is no doubt that still further toward the craton this *Zoophycos* facies would eventually grade into the *Cruziana* facies including littoral deposits.

REFERENCES*

Abel, O., 1935, *Vorzeitliche Lebensspuren:* Fischer, Jena.

Bezrukov, P. L., and A. Romankevič, 1960, Stratigraphy and lithology of the sediments in the northwest Pacific Ocean: *Dokl. Akad. Nauk SSSR,* 130, pp. 417–420, 3 Abb., 12 plates.

Caster, K. E., 1940, Die sogenannten Wirbeltierspuren und die Limulusfährten der Solnhofener Plattenkalke: *Paleont. Z.*, v. 22 pp. 12–29.

Cline, L. M., and O. B. Shelburne, 1959, Late Mississippian-early Pennsylvanian stratigraphy of the Ouachita mountains, Oklahoma: *Ouachita Symposium,* Dallas Geol. Soc., pp. 175–207.

* For more complete bibliography, see Lessertisseur (1955).

Desio, A., 1950, Sulla nomenclatura delle vestigia problematiche fossili: *Riv. Ital. Paleont.*, v. 56, plates 1–5.

Emmons, E., 1844, *The Taconic System:* Albany, plate II.

Fucini, A., 1936, 1938, Problematica verrucana I and II, *Palaeontographica Italica,* Appendice I–II, Pisa, 148 T.

Hall, J., 1850, On trails and tracks in the sandstone of the Clinton group: *Proc. Amer. Ass. Adv. Sci.*, v. 2.

Hall, J., 1852, *Natural History of New York,* Palaeontology of New York: v. 2, Albany, New York.

Häntzschel, W., 1962, Trace fossils and problematica: *Treatise on Invertebrate Paleontology,* part W., pp. W177–W245, fig. 109–149.

Henbest, L., 1960, Fossil spoor and their environmental significance in Morrow and Atoka series, Pennsylvania, Washington County, Arkansas: *U.S. Geol. Survey Prof. Paper,* v. 400, pp. 383–384, fig. 177.

Hundt, R., 1932, *Eine Monographie der Lebensspuren des unteren Mitteldevons Thüringens: (M. Weg, Leipzig).*

_______ 1941, *Das mitteldeutsche Phycodesmeer:* (Fischer, Jena).

Jessen, W., G. Kremp, and P. Michelau, 1951, Gesteinsrhythmen und Faunenzyklen des Ruhrkarbons und ihre Ursachen: v. 3, *Congrès Stratigr. Géol. Carbonifère,* pp. 289–294.

Jessen, W., and G. Kremp, 1954, Feinstratigraphisch-mikrofaunistische Profilbeschreibung mit Fundstücken von Gyrochorte carbonaria Schleicher im Oberkarbon (Westfal A) am Niederrhein: Neues *Jb. Geol. Paläont., Monatsh.,* pp. 284–286.

Keeping, W., 1882, On some remains of plants, Foraminifera and Annelida, in the Silurian Rocks of Central Wales: *Geol. Magaz.,* (2), v. 9, pp. 485–491, plate 11.

Krejci-Graf, K., 1932, Definition der Begriffe Marken, Spuren, Fährten, Bauten, Hieroglyphen und Fucoiden: *Senckenbergiana,* v. 14, pp. 19–39.

Lenoradi, P., 1937, Il trias inferiore delle Venezie: *Mem. Ist geol. Univ. Padova,* v. 11, 136 pp., 8 plates.

Lessertisseur, J., 1955, Traces fossiles d'activité animale et leur signification paléobiologique: *Mem. Soc. geol. France,* v. 74, pp. 7–150, plate 11.

Moore, D. G., and P. C. Scruton, 1957, Minor internal structures of some recent unconsolidated sediments: *Bull. Amer. Ass. Petrol. Geol.,* v. 41, pp. 2723–2751.

Müller, A. H., 1956, Weitere Beiträge zur Ichnologie, Stratinomie und Ökologie der germanischen Trias: *Geologie,* v. 5, pp. 405–423.

Reineck, H., 1958, Wühlbau-Gefüge in Abhängigkeit von Sediment-Umlagerungen: *Senckenbergiana leth.,* v. 39, pp. 1–14, 5 plates.

Richter, R., 1927, Die fossilen Fährten u. Bauten der Würmer, ein Überblick über ihre biologischen Grundformen u. deren geologische Bedeutung: *Paleont. Z.,* v. 9, pp. 193–235.

_______ 1936, Marken und Spuren im Hunsrück-Schiefer, II; Schichtung und Grund-Leben: *Senckenbergiana,* v. 18, pp. 215–244, 4 figs.

Schäfer, W., 1952, Biogene Sedimentation im Gefolge von Bioturbation: *Senckenbergiana,* v. 33, pp. 1–12.

Schmidt, M., 1934, *Cyclozoon philippi* und verwandte Gebilde: *Stz. Ber. Heidelberger Akad. d. Wiss., Math.-naturwiss.* Kl., 31 pp., 4 plates.

Seilacher, A., 1953, Studien zur Palichnologie. I. Über die Methoden der Palichnologie: *Neues Jb. Geol. u. Paläontol.,* v. 96, pp. 421–452, 14 figs., 2 plates.

——— 1953, Studien zur Palichnologie, II; Die fossilen Ruhespuren (Cubichnia): *Neues Jb. Geol. u. Palaeontol.*, v. 98, pp. 87–124, 5 figs., plates 7–13.

——— 1958, Zur ökologischen Charakteristik von Flysch und Molasse: *Eclogae geol. Helv.*, v. 51, pp. 1062–1078, 1 fig., 3 tables.

——— 1961, Krebse im Brandungssand: *Natur u. Volk*, v. 91, pp. 257–264, 8 figs.

——— 1962, Paleontological studies on turbidite sedimentation and erosion: *J. Geol.*, pp. 227–234.

——— 1963, Kaledonischer Unterbau der Irakiden: *Neues Jb. Geol. u. Palaeont. Mh.*, pp. 527–542, 3 figs.

Vialov, O. S., and B. T. Golev, 1960, K sistematike Paleodictyon: *Dokl. Akad. Nauk SSR 1960*, v. 134, n. 1, pp. 175–178.

Voigt, E., 1959, Die ökologische Bedeutung der Hartgründe ("Hardgrounds") in der oberen Kreide: *Palaeont. Z.*, v. 33, pp. 129–147, 4 plates.

——— and W. Häntzschel, 1956, Die grauen Bänder in der Schreibkreide Nordwest-Deutschlands und ihre Deutung als Lebensspuren: *Mitt. Geol. Staatsinst. Hamburg*, v. 25, pp. 104–122, plates 15–16, 2 figs.

Wilson, A. E., 1948, Miscellaneous classes of fossils, Ottawa Formation, Ottawa-St. Lawrence Valley: *Geol. Survey Bull., Canada*, v. 11, 116 pp.

Diagenetic Approaches to Paleoecology

Diagenesis and Paleoecology: A Survey

by R. G. C. Bathurst *Department of Geology, University of Liverpool, England*

ABSTRACT

This paper is a brief survey of recent work on diagenesis as it impinges on the study of paleoecology. Diagenetic processes are considered in the light of their ability to preserve or change paleontological evidence, and to supply new indirect evidence. Matters discussed include cementation, organic compounds in sediments and fossils, solution, ion migration, the deposition of silica, dolomitization, recrystallization, bacterial activity, compaction and the growth of iron minerals.

Introduction

The remains of living things, if they are to be preserved as fossils, must normally be buried in sediment. This applies as much to skeletons on the sea floor, as to burrows and impressions in mud, and to amino acids in pore water. Yet this very act of burial sets off a train of chemical and physical processes which can radically disguise the fossil record and may end by destroying it. The study of these diagenetic changes, as they affect the interpretation of past ecologies, is the subject of this article.

What follows is not meant to be exhaustive. Work in the Russian language has very regretfully been left almost unheeded; so also have the highly specialized fields of coal and oil genesis. Even within the remaining compass there are few papers specifically on diagenesis. Much of the work is scattered in publications devoted largely to other

I am indebted to my wife for her criticism of the manuscript and to Dr. J. C. Harper, Dr. N. Rast, and Mr. P. J. Brenchley for helpful discussion.

matters, so that its discovery has been somewhat haphazard and uncertain. Most attention is paid to recent works, and those with useful bibliographies. The aim of this paper is to review, in a very general way, the present state of knowledge in this field of geology and to indicate current trends of thought.

Pettijohn's definition (1957, p. 649) of diagenesis will be taken as a guide. He refers to the post-depositional processes of cementation, authigenesis, differentiation, segregation, metasomatism, solution, and compaction. In this review, the making of burrows is excluded but bacterial activity is considered; the growth of algal structures is not examined but their preservation is noted. These various aspects of diagenesis are conveniently though arbitrarily arranged in three groups: (1) the preservation of primary fabrics and materials; (2) their modification or destruction; (3) new fabrics or products which, nevertheless, show indirect evidence of the primary ecological situation.

Preservation of Primary Fabrics and Materials

Cementation

Chemical deposition of crystalline material from solution on preexisting surfaces (as drusy fabric or cement) provides mechanical support for delicate skeletons, for the empty molds of aragonite shells, for burrows, and for a variety of cavities in calcilutites. The sites now occupied by drusy fabric or cement may have been the pores in a sandstone, the chambers of an ammonite, or the tubes remaining after the decay of algal filaments. The origin of cement is closely bound up with the preferential solution of aragonite skeletons and their redeposition. In the past the recognition of these chemically deposited materials has been difficult, even controversial. Now they can generally be determined in thin section and distinguished from recrystallization products through the fabric studies of Schmidegg (1928) and Sander (1936, 1951), elaborated by Bathurst (1958, 1959*a*).

Much chemical deposition is increasingly believed to take place in a fresh-water interstitial environment, although it is clear that this restriction cannot be applied to all cemented sediments, because, at depth, pressure-solution and redeposition must play an important role. Support for this idea has come mainly from the studies of Pleistocene and Recent reef limestones (Ladd et al., 1953; Emery et al., 1954; Ginsburg, R. N., 1957; Schlanger et al., 1963). Gross (1964) has compared the O^{18}/O^{16} and C^{13}/C^{12} ratios of calcite cements and drusy casts of mollusks in the Pleistocene limestones of Bermuda with those of the associated Recent carbonate sediments which are in equilibrium with sea water. The cements and casts show a trend toward equilibrium with fresh water. Studies of the environment of cementation owe much to the detailed descriptions of reef fabrics by Skeats (1902), Cullis (1904), and Newell (1955).

The growth of drusy mosaic or cement is still something of a mystery. Maxwell's work (1960) on the cementation of sands under various conditions of pressure and temperature, with its emphasis on the importance of a moving pore solution, is interesting. Weyl's examination of the solution physics of calcium carbonate (1958, 1959*a*, *b*) has done much to clarify the nature of the process. Studies with Weyl's saturometer (1961) should eventually add greatly to our knowledge both of the degree of saturation of natural waters for different minerals and of the conditions necessary for crystal growth. Valuable help comes also from the new outlook on carbonate complexes involving Na^+, Mg^{2+}, HCO_3^-, CO_3^{2-}, and on the importance of magnesium as an indirect control of calcium carbonate solubility (Garrels et al., 1961; Garrels and Thompson, 1962). Combined chemical and fabric studies in thin section are becoming increasingly practicable with the staining techniques of Friedman (1959) and their further refinement by B. Evamy (1963).

Cementation is not entirely inhibited on the sea floor. Illing (1954, p. 25) refers to the hardening, and consequent preservation, of fecal pellets of aragonite mud and "grains of aragonite matrix," on the Great Bahama Bank, by the deposition of aragonite cement. The cementation of these aggregates, and of his "grapestone," indicate the attainment of suitable conditions for crystal growth in localized microenvironments which are isolated in a manner unknown from the main chemical environment on the sea floor. On an intertidal oolite shoal between Sandy Cay and Brown's Cay on the west edge of the Great Bahama Bank, flattish pieces of lamellibranch and echinoid lying on the sand commonly have a few grains cemented to their undersurfaces (author's observations). In Bimini lagoon the chambers and pores of dead Foraminifera and *Halimeda* are commonly filled with micritic aragonite. Ellenberger (1947) offers fabric evidence for the early cementation of chalk, possibly in the upper few centimeters of the sediment. The whole question of subaqueous cementation is examined in two thoughtful papers by Jaanusson (1961) and Lindström (1963). Despite Jaanusson's clear demonstration that the weight of evidence is against subaqueous cementation as a general method of lithification, it cannot be denied that Lindström's detailed analysis of sedimentary structures argues strongly for widespread lithification under an early Ordovician sea in Scandinavia.

It is remarkable that the only calcium carbonate known to be precipitated from sea water is *aragonite,* whereas calcite *cement* is formed from fresh water. Cloud's papers (1962*a* and *b*) are the most recent of many thoughtful studies of this problem. He proposes that any and all factors favoring the attainment of high apparent supersaturation also favor the initial precipitation of the more soluble, higher energy polymorph. In other words, aragonite should precipitate from solutions that are supersaturated for both aragonite and calcite, but calcite should form between the saturation levels for the two minerals. Trace elements (such as magnesium) do not influence the primary mineralogy.

There is a persistent output of papers on concretions and the preservation of their contained fossils, with emphasis on the time relationship between growth and compaction. Coal-balls are examined in some detail by Stopes and Watson (1909), M. Bellière (1919), Stainier (1924), Raistrick and Marshall (1939), and Leclercq (1952). The growth processes of concretions and the accompanying impoverishment of the surrounding sediment appear to have been little studied, though Avias (1956) and Weeks (1957) discuss the role of decaying organic matter in the precipitation of the carbonate. Freyer and Tröger (1959) describe the syngenetic growth of phosphorite-bituminous, fossiliferous concretions in terms of their contents of quartz, chalcedony, gypsum, apatite, and sericite, and by analyses of various trace elements. Important advances in understanding of chert nodules are referred to in the section on *Silicification.*

Organic Compounds

One of the outstanding advances in the last decade has been the growing list of organic compounds discovered in sediments, sedimentary rocks, and fossil skeletons—a development made possible by new techniques in microchemistry, particularly chromatography. The isolation of porphyrins by Treibs (1934) and Dhéré and Hradil (1934) was followed by the work of Abelson (1954, 1959) on amino acids. Other recent papers are by Forsman and Hunt (1958) on kerogen, Jones and Vallentyne (1960) on polypeptides and amino acids, Blumer and Omenn (1961) on uncomplexed chlorins, and Swain (1961) on furfurals and amino acids. Two papers by the same team (Prashnowsky et al., 1961; Degens et al., 1961) give data on sugars and amino acids in sediment cores off Southern California. They include discussions of the source of the substances, their preservation, and their vertical redistribution after burial. ZoBell (1946*a*) stresses the significance of new organic compounds synthesized in the sediment pores in bacterial protoplasm.

These researches must increasingly add to our appreciation of the structures of proteins, chlorophylls, celluloses, and other organic compounds in ancient animal and plant tissues. They may throw light on kinds of life which leave no otherwise recognizable remains. It is also possible that they may help in the understanding of past taxonomic relationships.

Bader (1956) notes the apparent great stability of lignin in marine sediments, and ZoBell and Stadler (1940) discuss its oxidation by lake bacteria. Jodry and Campau (1961) report on the indestructibility of chitinous and resinous microfossils.

Plant Impressions

Voigt (1956) has an interesting paper on the preservation of imprints of Cretaceous algae and marine grasses on their epifaunas which had hard parts. In the epifauna there are Foraminifera, sponges, bryozoa, annelids, lamellibranchs, etc.

Modification or Destruction of Primary Fabrics and Materials

Solution

Within the last decade there has appeared a new conception of the diagenetic history of carbonate sediments in terms of the mobility of the magnesium, strontium, and other substitute ions in the calcite and aragonite of the skeletons of mollusks, foraminifera, algae, ostracods, echinoids, corals, bryozoa, etc. (Degens, 1959). Chave (1954*a, b*) showed that the mineralogy of modern carbonate skeletons is limited to aragonite and a range of magnesium calcites with as much as 25% of magnesium carbonate. Those calcites with more than about 4% of magnesium carbonate, distinguished as high-magnesium calcites, are probably not stable at surface temperatures and pressures (Jamieson, 1953; Harker and Tuttle, 1955; Graf and Goldsmith, 1955; Schlanger, 1957; Goldsmith and Heard, 1961). The magnesium carbonate content of a calcareous marine skeleton is dependent, above all, on the mineralogy, the taxonomic position, and the water temperature.

While aragonite rarely contains more than 1%, calcite generally has more.

One of the challenging problems facing the carbonate petrologist today is the way in which a two-component marine sediment of aragonite and high-magnesium calcite changes to a two-component rock of low-magnesium calcite and dolomite (Chave, 1954*b*; Stehli and Hower, 1961). The last two authors have studied diagenetic changes with reference to three end-members. These are aragonite, low-magnesium calcite, and high-magnesium calcite. Their comparison of Recent sediments with Pleistocene limestones confirms a trend in composition toward low-magnesium calcite which is already becoming familiar (Lowenstam, 1954; Lowenstam and Epstein, 1954; Odum, 1957) and is massively supported by the data of Friedman (1964). Gross (1964) has found that the Pleistocene limestones of Bermuda have developed from sediments of aragonite and high-magnesium calcite, by solution of the aragonite, chemical redeposition of the carbonate as low-magnesium calcite cement and casts, and loss of magnesium by diffusion from the high-magnesium calcite. Whereas Gross records that the magnesium is leached out from the skeletons of calcareous algae, foraminifera, mollusks, echinoids, etc., Chave, on the other hand, notes (this volume) that Tertiary and Quaternary skeletons of high-magnesium calcite are commonly either mineralogically unchanged or represented by molds and casts. The loss of aragonite from carbonate sediments, though generally achieved by solution, can take place by alteration to calcite in place, though not necessarily by polymorphic inversion (p. 331). The loss of strontium from the aragonite of corals is investigated by Siegel (1960), and its loss from carbonate sediments by Stehli and Hower (1961), who have also studied the mobility of barium and manganese. Siegel suggests that strontium may inhibit inversion of aragonite to calcite, as indicated by some experiments of Zeller and Wray (1956) and Wray and Daniels (1957). The possibility that aluminum, magnesium, and manganese can be taken up by the skeleton after burial arises from the data of Krinsley (1959) and Krinsley and Bieri (1959).

Implicit in all this work is the need for care in the study of the mineralogy and chemistry of fossil skeletons. In these the aragonite and high-magnesium calcite may have been dissolved and replaced by a calcite cast, the existing calcite may be in part a replacement *in situ* of aragonite, and the primary elemental composition may have been modified.

In the recognition of facies, these chemical and mineralogical considerations may be of some use. Turekian and Armstrong (1960) show that the amounts of magnesium, strontium, and barium in modern molluscan shells are more strongly related to taxonomic position than to temperature and aragonite-calcite ratio. Siegel (1960) and Stehli and Hower (1961) stress a threefold relationship in carbonate sediments between the level of magnesium and strontium, the amounts of aragonite and the various calcites, and the geographic environment of deposition (e.g., position in the back reef, depth of water). Different modern communities reveal pronounced contrasts in bulk chemistry and mineralogy. These are further affected by the temperature dependence of the aragonite-calcite ratio (Lowenstam, 1954) and of the magnesium and strontium contents (Lowenstam, 1961).

When estimating paleotemperatures by measurement of O^{18}/O^{16}, possible diagenetic changes in the ratio have to be considered. Lowenstam (1961) has gone carefully into this problem in an examination of modern and fossil brachiopods. He relates $SrCO_3$ and $MgCO_3$ in turn to O^{18}/O^{16}, and finds that, for Recent shells, the correction of the isotope ratio for the O^{18} content of the water makes only minor differences for shells from waters having salinities which are normal or above normal. There is a big difference between corrected and uncorrected data for shells from waters with salinities below normal. On this basis Lowenstam concludes that fossil brachiopods from waters with salinities equal to or greater than normal can be compared safely with modern ones, even though their O^{18}/O^{16} ratios have not been corrected for the composition of the water with which they were presumably in equilibrium. He then compares modern brachiopods with fossil forms of various ages back to the Mississippian. There is fair agreement throughout for the relationship $SrCO_3:O^{18}/^{16}$. There is also fair agreement in the relationship $MgCO_3:O^{18}/O^{16}$ for the Pliocene and one Permian shell. For the Cretaceous, for the other Permian samples, and for the Mississippian there is none. The agreement between the $SrCo_3:O^{18}/O^{16}$ ratios for modern and fossil shells is taken to mean that the isotope ratios have not been seriously changed. Therefore, the lack of agreement between the $MgCO_3:O^{18}/O^{16}$ ratios must be the result of a loss of magnesium from the fossil brachiopods.

O^{18}/O^{16} ratios have not always been stable. Indeed, Degens (1959) proposes a change of O^{18}/O^{16} as an indication of diagensis in marine carbonates and cherts. Turekian and Armstrong (1961) record an increase of strontium in some Cretaceous mollusks. This, they feel, may well have been accompanied by an exchange with subsurface water having an isotope ratio lighter than sea water. Gross (1964) shows that the bulk diagenesis of Pleistocene limestones in Bermuda involved a change to more negative values of both O^{18}/O^{16} and C^{13}/C^{12}. This occurred largely as a result of the redeposition of dissolved aragonite, as calcite cement and calcite casts of mollusks, from fresh water. But it also owes something to exchange of ions in otherwise undissolved skeletal particles. Turekian and Armstrong (1961) refer to the likelihood of modification of the test of a mollusk, for example, as a result of syntaxial addition of carbonate to the primary crystals in the shell wall, in the spaces left by the removal of organic material. Such a change might be impossible to detect optically in thin section.

Deposition of Silica

In the study of chert lie the answers to many problems of the conservation and destruction of fossil biota. Among these are the processes of limestone replacement, the growth of gels on the sea floor, the sedimentation and solution of diatomites, the deposition of flint, and the mobility of silica in a compacting sediment. After a quarter of a century of quiet progress, with the advantages of X-ray diffraction, rapid methods of chemical analysis, and electron microscopy, the outlines of a general theory of silica deposition are becoming clear.

The new outlook has its roots in the mineralogical studies of chalcedony and opal in the thirties. Correns and Nagelschmidt (1933) confirmed that the fibers of chalcedony are composed of quartz crystals with their *c* axes normal to the long axis of the fiber and arranged spirally about it. To account for the low refractive indices and specific gravity, and the high water content, they suggested a matrix of opal in between the crystallites. However, a detailed study by Donnay (1936) shed some doubt on this, and X-ray work by Midgley (1951) and Tovborg et al. (1957) indicated quartz and micropores but no opal. The electron photomicrographs of Folk and Weaver (1952) revealed spherical pores probably filled with cation-rich water. Pelto (1956), applying the ideas of dislocation theory, drew attention to the association of water with the regions of angular misfit and elastic strain at the intercrystalline boundaries. The crystalline structure of opal was demonstrated by Levin and Ott (1933), whose work, extended by Flörke (1955), established the presence of low-temperature cristobalite. The nature of the disorder in this mineral has been studied by Flörke, and also by Braitsch (1957), and it is apparent that the high degree of disorder, compared with quartz or even tridymite, is maintained by the presence of interstitial foreign cations (Buerger, 1954) within the lattice.

Parallel with the developments in mineralogy there has evolved a deeper understanding of the behavior of silica in solution and as a colloid. Notable work has been done in this field by Alexander et al. (1954), Iler (1955), Krauskopf (1956), and Okamoto et al. (1957). The various threads of this now much expanded subject have been drawn together in three comprehensive papers by Siever (1957, 1959) and Krauskopf (1959). It is now clear that silica in natural waters is not normally in colloidal suspension but in true molecularly dispersed solution as unionized H_4SiO_4. The solubility of silica gel below pH 9 is virtually independent of pH, and only above 9 does it increase with pH as the H_4SiO_4 ionizes. Only when the concentration exceeds about 130 ppm does the surplus silica polymerize below pH 9. Flocculation in nature seems to be a rare phenomenon, and silicification of limestones must proceed as ion-by-ion replacement. Molecularly dissolved silica is peculiar in that it yields a colloidal suspension unusually readily on becoming supersaturated. This suspension may remain dispersed for months before precipitating as gel or gel flocs. The extreme slowness of this change has not always been appreciated by petrologists. The rate of polymerization increases with pH in the range 2 to 9. Siever (1962) discusses in detail the bearing of the new data on the precipitation of various forms of silica in sediments after deposition.

The third line of advance was foreshadowed by some interesting ideas of Deicha (1946) and Vatan (1947) on the effect of different degrees of disequilibrium of crystals with their environment during growth. This aspect has been followed up by Millot (1960) who, at the end of an extremely full and interesting paper (to which this review is greatly in debt), sets out the main factors which appear to govern the form in which silica is laid down. Of the three crystalline forms of silica in sediments—quartz, chalcedony, and opal—quartz is the least disordered. There is a transition through microcrystalline quartz to chalcedony with an increasingly irregular arrangement of the crystals and crystallites caused partly by a corresponding rise in the content of impurities. In opals the SiO_4 tetrahedra are disordered by the presence of cations in solid solution, stabilizing the cristobalite lattice. Yet foreign cations are not the only influence. Rapidity of growth hinders the development of the better ordered crystallites and crystal lattices. Quartz grows from pure, dilute solutions. Its growth is slow and unimpeded and characteristically takes place in the pores of sands, generally as syntaxial overgrowths on existing grains. Microcrystalline quartz and chalcedony grow from highly concentrated solutions rich in cations and available nuclei (e.g., in the pore water of a limestone), with a high nucleation rate, all leading to the rapid growth of very fine-grained mosaics. Chalcedony is deposited predominantly in carbonate rocks. Opal is laid down from highly concentrated solutions, typically in clays, where the obstacles to the growth of well-ordered crystals are greatest.

Vatan (1947) suggests that the normal order of crystallization in any one environment is opal-chalcedony-quartz, corresponding to a decrease in the amount of disequilibrium, a fall in the concentration of the solution, an increasing purity of the solution, and a slowing down of the rate of nucleation and growth. Hoss (1957) shows how very probable it is that, in time and given the right conditions, opal will recrystallize to chalcedony, and chalcedony to quartz. A fourth type of silica, the gel, may perhaps grow from even more concentrated solutions in which the silica is polymerized, but this condition is probably unusual. Above all, Millot emphasizes that the form in which silica is deposited depends primarily on the chemistry, the fabric, and the mineralogy of the host rock, a theme beautifully illustrated with microfabrics by Walker (1960, 1962).

Application of the new physicochemical data to the study of particular cherts seems to be limited mainly to the examples examined briefly by Millot, but progress has been made in other directions in a number of papers based on field and petrographic evidence. There is an immense fund of information, especially petrographic, in two long papers by Storz (1928, 1931). The importance of solution and redeposition of the silica of diatoms in the formation of the Monterey cherts of California has been demonstrated by Bramlette (1946). Pittman (1959) suggests that the silica in the Edwards Limestone in Texas may be derived from sponge spicules. Lewin (1960) has made a special study of the solution of silica in diatom walls.

Regarding the place of silica deposition, there is a growing feeling that the process commonly takes place at or near the sediment surface as a result of the solution of opaline silica and its redeposition from upward-moving water during compaction, in an environment of decomposing organic matter. This view is evident in the work of Illies (1949*a*, *b*, 1954), Müller (1956), and Defretin (1958) on flint in chalk, and of Emery and Rittenberg (1952) on cores in marine sediments off Southern California. Gripp (1954) stresses the influence of chemical soil-forming processes in the making of flint, when the chalk surface was above water. There is a general discussion of the silicification process by Hellmers (1949).

Arrhenius (1952, p. 85) has information on the solution of diatom and radiolarian tests on the floor of the East Pacific, and on cementation by silica at the present sediment surface. Field and petrographic data lead Humphries (1957) to conclude that the chert in some Lower Cretaceous sandstones in the south of England was formed as a gel on the sea floor. Sujkowski (1958), also, supports the idea of a gel origin for flint in chalk on the basis mainly of field evidence. Emery and Rittenberg (1952) discuss the changes of chemical and bacterial environments with depth on the basis of their cores from the California Basin.

Dolomitization

To the paleoecologist dolomitization is mainly a nuisance, and Murray (p. 388) has done well to emphasize that useful paleontological evidence commonly survives dolomitization. This must encourage further research on the many apparently hopeless but profoundly interesting dolomitized reefs. He makes plain the need for close scrutiny of small fabrics. It is possible to detect predolomitization molds which have survived the dolomitization of their matrix. There are also molds which develop by solution of skeletons after these have escaped the dolomitization of the enclosing sediment. Detailed preservation of skeletal fabric can be brought about by the deposition of dolomite fabrics which are nicely correlated with those of the host. Banner and G. V. Wood (1964) find that resistance to dolomitization is a function of the biological affinity of the skeleton.

Dolomites are sometimes mistakenly identified when, as a result of dedolomitization, the fabric is, in fact, largely or wholly calcitic. A recent paper on this subject with helpful illustrations and references to earlier work is by Shearman et al. (1961).

Recrystallization in Carbonate Sediments and Rocks

This dumping ground for mysterious processes seems to be filling more quickly than it can be emptied. As more geologists are drawn to the study of modern sediments, so the examples of different processes of skeletal change multiply. These commonly show a complexity which makes the recrystallization fabrics in some older limestones seem simple by comparison.

Consolidated limestones are known to show evidence of solution and redeposition, dominantly a reflection of the greater solubility of aragonite than calcite, although this may appear to be a simplification when more is known about the behavior of high-magnesium calcites. Bathurst (this volume) has attempted to organize the fabric data in this field. He also deals with the change of aragonite shells to calcite *in situ,* a subject more intensively studied by Hudson (1962). There is valuable information on the recrystallization of the tests of fossil Foraminifera in papers by A. Wood (1949) and Cummings (1961). Banner and G. V. Wood (1964) have shown that the microbiota of Miocene limestones in Papua recrystallize (by crystal enlargement) in an order related to taxonomic affinity.

Bathurst has also proposed (1958, 1959*a*) that calcite mudstones and similarly fine-grained calcite mosaics undergo a patchy coarsening of crystal size by a process which seems to be akin to the "grain growth" of metallurgists. Whatever the nature of the process may eventually turn out to be, it evades silt grade or coarser mosaic, including cement. When pellets of calcite mudstone enclosed in calcite cement have been recrystallized in this way, in Pennsylvanian limestones of Kansas, there is a sudden change in the fabric of the coarse mosaic across the pellet boundary, from grain growth mosaic inside, to cement outside (author's observation). The grain growth mosaics described do not appear to have attained equilibrium. The intercrystalline boundaries are very irregular, although these irregularities commonly have an arrangement which looks as though it may be related in some systematic way to the orientations of the two crystal lattices. By contrast, at the contact between the coarse mosaic and the unaltered calcite mudstone, the larger crystals of the coarse mosaic show what appear to be plane boundaries against the calcite mudstone. These resemble crystal faces, but are too small to be determined with a universal stage. Yet such a texture is not characteristic of grain growth in metals, where the intercrystalline boundaries are curved. In fact, this anomaly points the main dilemma. Grain growth in the metallurgical sense is an anhydrous process and, although the evidence from limestones favors recrystallization in a lithified (consolidated) limestone, the role of water may be important.

The action of grain growth (metallurgical sense) in calcite mudstone was demonstrated by Griggs et al. (1960, pp. 29, 36), who noted also that the behavior of calcite during recrystallization in general conforms to the pattern established for metals. A specimen of Solenhofen limestone was heated without initial strain to 800°C at 5 kilobars for one hour under purely hydrostatic pressure in CO_2. Apparently the energy of the intercrystalline boundaries was alone sufficient driving force for recrystallization to take place by grain growth. The resultant mosaic is a good deal coarser than the grain growth mosaics in Carboniferous and Pennsylvanian limestones (crystal diameters 150 μ instead of 20 μ), and the crystals have simple polygonal outlines.

Some experiments by Hathaway and Robertson (1961) show that by confining Bahamian aragonite mud at pressures up to those equivalent to burial at 5000 ft, at temperatures up to 400°C, and for as long as 63 days, a rock is produced which closely resembles natural calcite mudstones, when examined with an electron microscope. The two materials even match each other in the abundant occurrence of apparently plane intercrystalline boundaries (author's observations on Hathaway's enlargements). Yet a natural calcite mudstone might have developed plane intercrystalline boundaries entirely by rim cementation. Can this fabric arise in two ways?

A variety of obscure processes of recrystallization affects the components of modern carbonate sediments. Eardley (1939) noted the change of aragonite in ooliths to a coarse-grained calcite. Bumps on the oolith surface he attributed to the 8% increase in volume. Revelle (1944, p. 47) and Emery et al. (1954, p. 88) have referred to recrystallization of calcite Foraminifera by crystal enlargement; and Illing (1954, p. 49) described the calcitization of aragonite ooliths and pellets with an eventual coarsening of the calcite. A number of workers have referred informally to a process whereby microcrystalline skeletons of aragonite and calcite recrystallize to an even finer-grained mosaic. As a reduction in crystal size cannot take place in a closed system (since the free energy cannot increase), there must have been an exchange of some kind with the environment. Emery et al. (1954) have so far detected no mineralogical alteration in recrystallized aragonite tests, and no change in strontium content. However, in their examples, it is not apparent that a reduction in grain size was involved. Siegl (1960), on the other hand, has demonstrated a negative correlation between strontium content and the degree of calcitization in Pleistocene corals. From cores in the Bikini reef Emery et al. (1954) describe the crystal enlargement of coral and molluscan skeletons so that their outlines are only distinguishable by a dust line from the surrounding carbonate.

Chalkification is described by Nelson (1959, pp. 66–67) from the Edwards Limestone in Texas. Skeletons change to a "soft white microgranular calcite." Emery et al. also record chalkification of buried corals and mollusks in the Bikini cores. The nature of this process has not been explained. Bathurst (p. 365) has described the replacement of modern skeletal particles by micrite deposited in empty tubes vacated by boring algae.

There are valuable petrographic data on the Funafuti cores by Cullis (1904), who postulates recrystallization of aragonite cement to calcite. Newell (1955), too, suggests that the fibrous drusy calcite in some Permian reef limestones may be an alteration of a primary drusy aragonite. Cullis's descriptions and drawings of diagenetic fabrics remain unsurpassed after sixty years.

Recrystallization in Greywackes

A recent paper by Cummins (1962) may influence thinking on the whole greywacke-turbidite problem. He suggests that much of the "mud" fraction is a recrystallization product of postdepositional origin. This makes it necessary to re-examine the suitability of the original sediments as substrates for mud-feeding, possibly burrowing, benthonic life.

Postdepositional Origin for Some Calcilutite

The likelihood of a postdepositional origin for some microcrystalline calcite, similar now in appearance to calcilutite, is indicated by several lines of evidence. These include chalkification, the occurrence in many sediments of shells which are soft enough to be cut with a knife (presumably owing to the decay of conchiolin or other organic cement between the crystals), and the formation of micrite in empty algal bores. These processes might yield products optically indistinguishable from detrital calcilutite.

Bacterial Activity

Bacteria are so difficult to resolve with a microscope and their study requires such specialized techniques that progress in this field has not shown the more dramatic advances of some other aspects of diagenesis. The quantitative importance of bacteria in modern sediments has been indicated by Reuszer (1933) in an areal study of the muds off Cape Cod. ZoBell (1946*a*) has done quantitative research and added data about the main groups of bacteria (aerobic and anaerobic) at various depths in marine sediments, and about the associated physicochemical conditions. ZoBell and Feltham (1942) published some of the earliest information on vertical changes of Eh in cores (also ZoBell 1946*b*). Shepard and Moore (1955) have added to this and have shown how complex the vertical distribution (and redistribution) can be. They stress the importance of a reliable environmental control in the interpretation of these changes. It is certain that bacterial activity in general yields CO_2, NH_3, and H_2S. The accompanying uptake of O_2 has been studied by Liagina and Kuznetzow (1937), ZoBell and Stadler (1940), and ZoBell and Feltham (1942). That bacteria can be important in the precipitation of carbonates has been demonstrated by Black (1933), Monaghan and Lytle (1956), and LaLou (1957). Work on bacterial decomposition of organic materials has been done by Waksman et al. (1933), and ZoBell and Stadler (1940); the relation of this decomposition to pelecypod density has been indicated by Bader (1954). A paper by Morita and ZoBell (1955) refers to living bacteria, 8 meters below the sediment surface in the mid-Pacific, which may be about one million years old.

Work on fossil bacteria has entered a new phase with the use of the electron microscope, with which Barton and Jones (1948) have demonstrated bodies similar to bacteria (or their spores), fungi and algae in rocks of Oligocene, Tertiary, Mesozoic, and Paleozoic ages. In earlier investigations with the optical microscope, Walcott (1915) reported on fossil bacteria in Algonkian algal limestones. Renault (1899) made many studies in coal and carbonaceous sediments, and Moodie (1923) discovered fossil bacteria in Permian and Devonian vertebrate remains.

Compaction

The main importance of compaction to the study of paleoecology seems to be its ability to flatten organic structures and to cause the migration of oil, gas, water, and salts. The postdepositional redistribution of various substances has been touched upon in earlier sections. Here it is convenient to refer to two useful summaries of present knowledge about compaction in papers by Hamilton (1959) and Weller (1959). Data on the consolidation of carbonate muds are still very scarce, although at last Ruth Terzhagi's (1940) much quoted paper has been augmented by some recent work by Laughton (1957). From this it seems that the consolidation behavior of these muds is not always so close to terrigenous clays as Terzhagi's data had indicated. The work of Hathaway and Robertson (1961) on the fabrics produced by the artificial and very rapid consolidation of aragonite mud, at elevated temperature, is described earlier.

Indirect Evidence from New Fabrics and Materials

Pyrite and Other Iron Minerals

It is now generally realized that the presence of pyrite in a sediment is by itself no indication that the water above the sediment was poorly oxygenated or that benthonic life was impeded. The chemistry of iron minerals has progressed to the extent that it is now possible to draw reasonable conclusions about the chemical environment in which the minerals grew, in terms of Eh and pH. This subject is dealt with in a paper by Huber (1958) who with Garrels (1960) has done so much to clarify this vital aspect of diagenesis.

Van Straaten (1955, p. 38) has described the early formation of pyrite in the lutites of the Waddenzee, Netherlands. Hemingway (1951) has compared some Liassic sediments of Yorkshire to some of the deposits of the Black Sea, and Morreti (1957) has discussed petrological implications of the presence of pyrite in limestones. Certain tiny pyrite spheres have been shown by Love (1958) and Love and Zimmerman (1961) to be part fillings and part overgrowths of microfossils.

Ericson et al. (1961) record that hydrotroilite, possible precursor of pyrite, is normally present only below the top few decimeters of Atlantic deep-sea sediments and is commonly associated with organic matter. That the overlying water is well oxygenated is shown by the abundant foraminifera and active burrowing benthos. They have also found marcasite, in fecal pellets and inside diatom frustules, in the Neogene clays of the Hudson submarine canyon.

The Structure "Stromatactis" in Knoll Reefs

Masses of coarsely crystalline calcite, sheet-like in form and no more than a few centimeters thick, in the fossiliferous calcilutites of Devonian knoll reefs in Belgium, were first interpreted by Dupont (1881, p. 268) as an organic structure, possibly a stromatoporoid. Lecompte (1937) in his detailed work gave no enthusiastic support to this hypothesis, but Lowenstam (1950) recorded organic-like structures in similar materials in the Silurian of the Great Lakes region. J. Bellière (1953) proposed that the coarse calcite had grown as a result of a double exchange between the calcium salts of sea water and the ammonium carbonate evolved in a decomposing organism. These coarse mosaics were shown to be drusy fillings of cavities by Bathurst (1959*b*) and he tentatively put forward the idea that the cavities might have been the molds of a decayed organism. More recently Schwarzacher (1961) has made a quantitative analysis of the orientations of the cavity floors in relation to the old reef surfaces. His results suggest that the cavities formed along planes of shear failure during creep, slumping, or compaction.

General Works

Useful discussions of diagenetic matters in general are contained in Newell et al. (1953), Strakhov (1953), Revelle and Fairbridge (1957), R. N. Ginsburg (1957), Sujkowski (1958), Illing (1959), Murray (1960), and I. I. Ginsburg (in press). Chilingar (1958) summarizes some data from Soviet literature. There is a very full summary of the geochemistry of carbonate sediments and rocks by Graf (1960) and papers from a symposium on the subject by Ingerson et al. (1960), and a thorough treatment of the colloid chemistry of silica by Iler (1955). Essential data on skeletal mineralogy are contained in Bøggild's (1930) work on mollusks, with additional information by Piveteau (1952), and Raup's (1959) examination of the crystallography of echinoid calcite. Details of the mineralogy of Foraminifera are given by Blackmon and Todd (1959), and there is information on wall structure in fossil forms by Wood (1949) and Cummings (1961). The elemental composition of marine organisms is very widely dealt with by Vinogradov (1953), and there is also the earlier survey by Clarke and Wheeler (1922). Nicholls et al. (1959) give spectographic analyses of marine plankton for seventeen elements including boron, lead, and vanadium. Taylor (1964) has lately produced a stimulating general survey of diagenesis.

Summary

It must be apparent from the foregoing notes that diagenetic studies are still in the embryonic stage, and it is hardly surprising, therefore, to discover that the influence of these studies on the researchers of the paleoecologist is rather a question of promise than of achievement. Nevertheless, one outcome of the progress of the last few years is clear. In the future, more of the faded, tattered, and tantalizing pages of ecological history will successfully be reconstructed than would ever have been the case without the help of this ancillary discipline. No matter whether the paleoecologist is concerned with the quantities of different organisms in a past community or, indeed, with their very existence, or with the temperature of the environment or the food potential of a substrate, he is continually faced with the consequences of solution, redistribution, recrystallization, replacement, compaction, and authigenesis.

Certain lines of research seem both to be particularly appropriate and to have made outstanding progress during the last few years. There has been a great development of the whole subject matter of solution, redeposition, ion migration, dolomitization, and the selective removal of certain kinds of skeletons. Useful signposts in these studies of subsurface chemical environments are the iron minerals. Closely related to these fields is the new understanding of the complex problems of silicification, again with its implication of wholesale solution of skeletons and its interesting illumination of the questions of primary-versus-secondary cherts, and the formation of gels on the sea floor. Ion migration is also relevant to the estimation of paleotemperatures and to the comparison of the elemental compositions of fossil skeletons with those of modern groups. The value of a biochemical approach to paleoecology is being realized thanks to the stirrings, still faint but persistent, of the potentially rich field of paleobiochemistry. It may be that a bridge between this line of advance and the study of fossil bacteria will lead to valuable discoveries.

REFERENCES

Abelson, P. H., 1954, *Annual Report of the Director of the Geophysical Laboratory, 1953–1954:* Carnegie Inst. Washington Year Book, v. 53, pp. 97–101.

________ 1959, Geochemistry of organic substances: in *Researches in Geochemistry:* New York, John Wiley and Sons, pp. 79–103.

Alexander, G. B., W. M. Heston, and H. K. Iler, 1954, The solubility of amorphous silica in water: *J. Phys. Chem.,* v. 58, pp. 453–455.

Arrhenius, G., 1952, Sediment cores from the East Pacific: *Swedish Deep-Sea Exped. (1947–1948) Repts.,* v. 5, fasc. 1, 227 pp.

Avias, J., 1956, Le problème des nodules pétrifiés des mangroves néocalédoniennes: *4th Int. Quaternary Assoc. Cong., Rome–Pisa,* actes 1, pp. 245–249.

Bader, R. G., 1954, The role of organic matter in determining the distribution of pelecypods in marine sediments: *J. Marine Res.,* v. 13, pp. 32–47.

________ 1956, The lignin fraction of marine sediments: *Deep-Sea Research,* v. 4, pp. 15–22.

Banner, F. T., and G. V. Wood (in press) Recrystallization in microfossiliferous limestones: *Geol. J.*

Barton, H. M., and D. J. Jones, 1948, Electron microfossils: *Science,* v. 108, pp. 745–746.

Bathurst, R. G. C., 1958, Diagenetic fabrics in some British Dinantian limestones: *Liverpool Manchester Geol. J.,* v. 2, pp. 11–36.

________ 1959*a,* Diagenesis in Mississippian calcilutites and pseudobreccias: *J. Sed. Petrol.,* v. 29, pp. 365–376.

________ 1959*b,* The cavernous structure of some Mississippian *Stromatactis* reefs in Lancashire, England: *J. Geol.,* v. 67, pp. 506–521.

Bellière, J., 1953, Note sur le calcaire Famennien de Baelen et ses *Stromatactis: Soc. Géol. Belg. Ann.,* tm. 76B, pp. 115–128.

Bellière, M., 1919, Sur la présence de concrétions du type des coal balls dans le terrain houiller belge: *Soc. Géol. Belg. Ann.,* tm. 42B, pp. 126–132.

Black, M., 1933, The precipitation of calcium carbonate on the Great Bahama Bank: *Geol. Mag.,* v. 70, pp. 455–466.

Blackmon, P. D., and R. Todd, 1959, Mineralogy of some Foraminifera as related to their classification and ecology: *J. Paleontol.*, v. 33, pp. 1–15.

Blumer, W., and G. S. Omenn, 1961, Fossil porphyrins: uncomplexed chlorins in a Triassic sediment: *Geochim. Cosmochim. Acta,* v. 25, pp. 81–90.

Bøggild, O. B., 1930, The shell structure of the mollusks: *K. Danske Vidensk. Selsk. Skr. Naturvidensk. Math. Afd.*, raek. 9, v. 2, pp. 231–326.

Braitsch, O., 1957, Über die natürlichen Faser- und Aggregationstypen beim SiO_2, ihre Verwachsungsformen, Richtungsstatistik und Doppelbrechung: *Heidelberger Beitr., Min. Petrog.*, bd. 5, pp. 331–372.

Bramlette, M. N., 1946, The Monterey formation of California and the origin of its siliceous rocks: *U.S. Geol. Survey Prof. Paper 212,* 57 pp.

Buerger, M. J., 1954, The stuffed derivatives of the silica structures: *Am. Mineralogist,* v. 39, pp. 600–614.

Chave, K. E., 1954*a*, Aspects of the biogeochemistry of magnesium: 1, Calcareous marine organisms: *J. Geol.*, v. 62, pp. 266–283.

________ 1954*b*, Aspects of the biogeochemistry of magnesium: 2, Calcareous sediments and rocks: *J. Geol.*, v. 62, pp. 587–599.

Chilingar, G. V., 1956, Relationship between Ca/Mg ratio and geologic age: *Am. Assoc. Petrol. Geologists Bull.*, v. 40, pp. 2256–2266.

________ 1958, Some data on diagenesis obtained from Soviet literature: a summary: *Geochim. Cosmochim. Acta,* v. 13, pp. 213–217.

Clarke, F. W., and W. C. Wheeler, 1922, The inorganic constituents of marine invertebrates: *U.S. Geol. Survey Prof. Paper 124,* 62 pp.

Cloud, P. E., Jr., 1962*a*, Behaviour of calcium carbonate in sea water: *Geochim. Cosmochim. Acta,* v. 26, pp. 867–884.

________ 1962, Environment of calcium carbonate deposition west of Andros Island Bahamas: *U.S. Geol. Survey Prof. Paper 350,* 138 pp.

Correns, C. W., and G. Nagelschmidt, 1933, Über Faserbau und optische Eigenschaften von Chalzedon: *Zeitsch. Kristall.*, bd. 85, pp. 199–213.

Cullis, C. G., 1904, The mineralogical changes observed in the cores of the Funafuti borings: in *The Atoll of Funafuti,* Royal Society of London, pp. 392–420.

Cummings, R. H., 1961, The foraminiferal zones of the Carboniferous sequence of the Archerbeck borehole, Canobie, Dumfriesshire: *Geol. Survey Great Britain Bull.*, n. 18, pp. 107–128.

Cummins, W. A., 1962, The greywacke problem: *Liverpool Manchester Geol. J.*, v. 3, pp. 51–72.

Defretin, S., 1958, Suite à une communication de Ch. Barrois du 15 décembre 1909 et hypothèses sur la génèse de certains silex de la craie: *Soc. Géol. Nord. Ann.*, tm. 78, pp. 89–99.

Degens, E. T., 1959, Die Diagenese und ihre Auswirkungen auf den Chemismus von Sedimenten: *Neues Jahr. Min. Geol. Paläont. Mh.*, h. 2, pp. 72–84.

________ A. Prashnowsky, K. O. Emery, and J. Pimenta, 1961, Organic materials in recent and ancient sediments, II: amino acids in marine sediments of Santa Barbara Basin, California: *Neues Jahr. Geol. Paläont. Mh.,* h. 8, pp. 413–426.

Deicha, G., 1946, Individualité pétrographique et faciès cristallographique: *Soc. Géol. France C. R. Som.*, n. 12, pp. 220–222.

Dhéré, C., and G. Hradil, 1934, Fluoreszenzspektrographische Untersuchungen an Oelschiefern: *Schweiz. Min. Petr. Mittlng.*, bd. 14, pp. 279–294.

Donnay, J. D. H., 1936, La biréfringence de forme dans la calcédoine: *Soc. Géol. Belg. Ann.*, tm. 59, pp. 289–302.

Dupont, E., 1881, Sur l'origine des calcaires dévoniens de la Belgique: *Acad. Roy. Sci. Belg.*, ser. 3, v. 2, pp. 264–280.

Eardley, A. J., 1939, Sediments of Great Salt Lake, Utah: *Am. Assoc. Petrol. Geologists Bull.*, v. 22, pp. 1359–1387.

Ellenberger, F., 1947, Le problème lithologique de la craie durcie de Meudon: *Soc. Géol. France Bull.*, ser. 5, v. 17, pp. 255–274.

Emery, K. O., and S. C. Rittenberg, 1952, Early diagenesis of California Basin sediments in relation to origin of oil: *Am. Assoc. Petrol. Geologists Bull.*, v. 36, pp. 735–806.

________ J. I. Tracey, Jr., and H. S. Ladd, 1954, Geology of Bikini and nearby atolls: *U.S. Geol. Survey Prof. Paper 260-A*, 265 pp.

Ericson, D. B., M. Ewing, G. Wollin, and B. C. Heezen, 1961, Atlantic deep-sea sediment cores: *Geol. Soc. America Bull.*, v. 72, pp. 193–285.

Evamy, B. D., 1963, The application of chemical staining technique to a study of dedolomitisation: *Sedimentology*, v. 2, pp. 164–170.

Flörke, O. W., 1955, Zur Frage des "Hoch"-Cristobalit in Opalen, Bentoniten und Gläsern: *Neues Jahr. Min. Mh.*, h. 10, pp. 217–223.

Folk, R. L., and C. E. Weaver, 1952, A study of the texture and composition of chert: *Am. J. Sci.*, v. 250, pp. 498–510.

Forsman, J. P., and J. M. Hunt, 1958, Insoluble organic matter (kerogen) in sedimentary rocks: *Geochim. Cosmochim. Acta*, v. 15, pp. 170–182.

Freyer, G., and K.-A. Tröger, 1959, Über Phosphoritknollen im vogtländisch-ostthüringischen Silur: *Geologie*, jahr. 8, pp. 168–188.

Friedman, G. M., 1959, Identification of carbonate minerals by staining methods: *J. Sed. Petrol.*, v. 29, pp. 87–97.

Friedman, G. M., in the press, Geochemical implications of early diagenesis in carbonate rocks: *J. Sed. Petrol.*

Garrels, R. M., 1960, *Mineral Equilibria:* New York, Harper and Bros., 254 pp.

________ M. E. Thomson, and R. Siever, 1961, Control of carbonate solubility by carbonate complexes: *Am. J. Sci.*, v. 259, pp. 24–45.

________ and M. E. Thompson, 1962, A chemical model for sea water at 25°C and one atmosphere total pressure: *Am. J. Sci.*, v. 260, pp. 57–66.

Ginsburg, I. I., 1961, Basic problems in the formation of crusts of weathering and their importance in prospecting for mineral deposits: *Geol. Rudnikh Mestorozhdenii*, n. 5, pp. 21–36 (English translation: *Econ. Geol. U.S.S.R.*, in press).

Ginsburg, R. N., 1957, Early diagenesis and lithification of shallow-water carbonate sediments in South Florida: in *Regional Aspects of Carbonate Deposition*, Soc. Econ. Paleontologists Mineralogists, Special Pub. 5, pp. 80–99.

Goldsmith, J. R., and H. C. Heard, 1961, Subsolidus phase relations in the system $CaCO_3$-$MgCO_3$: *J. Geol.*, v. 69, pp. 45–74.

Graf, D. L., 1960, Geochemistry of carbonate sediments and sedimentary carbonate rocks: *Illinois State Geol. Survey*, Circulars 297, 298, 301, 308, 309.

________ and J. R. Goldsmith, 1955, Dolomite-magnesium calcite relations at elevated temperatures and CO_2 pressures: *Geochim. Cosmochim. Acta*, v. 7, pp. 109–128.

Griggs, D. T., M. S. Patterson, H. C. Heard, and F. J. Turner, 1960, Annealing recrystallization in calcite crystals and aggregates: *Geol. Soc. Am. Mem. 79*, pp. 21–37.

Gripp, K., 1954, Kritik und Beitrag zur Frage der Enstehung der Kreide-Feuersteine: *Geol. Rundschau*, bd. 42, pp. 248–262.

Gross, G. (in press), Variations in the O^{18}/O^{16} and C^{13}/C^{12} ratios of diagenetically altered limestones in the Bermuda Islands: *J. Geol.*

Hamilton, E. L., 1959, Thickness and consolidation of deep-sea sediments: *Geol. Soc. Amer. Bull.*, v. 70, pp. 1399–1424.

Harker, R. I., and D. F. Tuttle, 1955, Studies of the system CaO-MgO-CO_2: *Am. J. Sci.*, v. 253, pp. 274–282.

Hathaway, J. C., and E. C. Robertson, 1961, Microtexture of artificially consolidated aragonitic mud: *U.S. Geol. Survey Prof. Paper 424-C*, pp. 301–304.

Hellmers, J. H., 1949, Der Vorgang der Verkieselung: *Geol. Landes. Berlin Abh.*, h. 218, pp. 1–15.

Hemingway, J. E., 1951, Cyclic sedimentation and the deposition of ironstone in the Yorkshire Lias: *Yorkshire Geol. Soc. Proc.*, v. 27, pp. 67–74.

Hoss, H., 1957, Untersuchungen über die Petrographie kulmischer Kieselschiefer: *Beiträge Min. Pet.*, bd. 6, pp. 59–88.

Huber, N., 1958, The environmental control of sedimentary iron minerals: *Econ. Geol.* v. 53, pp. 123–140.

Hudson, J. D., 1962, Pseudo-pleochroic calcite in recrystallized shell-limestones: *Geol. Mag.*, v. 99, pp. 492–500.

Humphries, D. W., 1957, Chert: its age and origin in the Hythe Beds of the western Weald: *Geologists Assoc. London Proc.*, v. 67, pp. 296–313.

Iler, H. K., 1955, *The Colloid Chemistry of Silica and Silicates:* Ithaca, New York, Cornell University Press, 324 pp.

Illies, Von H., 1949*a*, Über die erdgeschichtliche Bedeutung der Konkretionen: *Zeitsch. Deutsch. Geol. Ges.*, bd. 101, pp. 95–98.

________ 1949*b*, Zur Diagenese der südbaltischen Schreibkreide: *Geol. Fören. Förhandl.*, bd. 71, pp. 41–50.

________ 1954, Zur Entstehung der Kreide-Feuersteine: *Geol. Rundschau,* bd. 42, pp. 262–264.

Illing, L. V., 1954, Bahaman calcareous sands: *Am. Assoc. Petrol. Geologists Bull.*, v. 38, pp. 1–95.

________ 1959, Deposition and diagenesis of some Upper Palaeozoic carbonate sediments in Western Canada: *5th World Petroleum Cong.*, Sect. 1, pp. 23–50.

Ingerson, E., et al., 1960, Papers from a symposium on geochemistry of sedimentary carbonate rocks: *Geochim. Cosmochim. Acta,* v. 26, pp. 811–903.

Jaanusson, V., 1961, Discontinuity surfaces in limestones: *Geol. Insts. Univ. Uppsala Bull.*, v. 40, pp. 221–241.

Jamieson, J. C., 1953, Phase equilibrium in the system calcite-aragonite: *J. Chem. Phys.*, v. 21, pp. 1385–1390.

Jodry, R. L., and D. E. Campau, 1961, Small pseudochitinous and resinous microfossils: new tools for the subsurface geologist: *Am. Assoc. Petrol. Geologists Bull.*, v. 45, pp. 1378–1391.

Jones, J. D., and J. R. Vallentyne, 1960, Biogeochemistry of organic matter—I; Polypeptides and amino acids in fossils and sediments in relation to geothermometry: *Geochim. Cosmochim. Acta,* v. 21, pp. 1–34.

Krauskopf, K. B., 1956, Dissolution and precipitation of silica at low temperatures: *Geochim. Cosmochim. Acta,* v. 10, pp. 1–26.

——— 1959, The geochemistry of silica in sedimentary environments: in *Silica in Sediments,* Soc. Econ. Paleontologists Mineralogists, Special Pub. No. 7, pp. 4–19.

Krinsley, D., 1959, Manganese in modern and fossil gastropod shells: *Nature,* v. 183, pp. 770–771.

——— and R. Bieri, 1959, Changes in the chemical composition of pteropod shells after deposition on the sea floor: *J. Paleontol.,* v. 33, pp. 682–684.

Ladd, H. S., et al., 1953, Drilling on Eniwetok Atoll, Marshall Islands: *Am. Assoc. Petrol. Geologists Bull.,* v. 37, pp. 2257–2280.

LaLou, C., 1957, Studies on bacterial precipitation of carbonates in sea water: *J. Sediment. Petrol.,* v. 27, pp. 190–195.

Laughton, A. S., 1957, Sound propagation in compacted ocean sediments: *Geophysics,* v. 22, pp. 233–260.

Leclercq, S., 1952, Sur la présence de coal-balls dans la couche Petit-Buisson (Assise de Flénu) du Bassin houillier de la Campine: *IIIe Congr. Avanc. Étude Strat. Carb. C.R.,* tm. 2, pp. 397–400.

Lecompte, M., 1937, Contribution à la connaissance des récifs du Dévonien de l'Ardenne. Sur la présence de structures conservées dans des efflorescences crystallines du type *"Stromatactis": Mus. Roy. Hist. Nat. Belg. Bull.,* t. 13, n. 15, pp. 1–14.

Levin, I., and E. Ott, 1933, X-ray study of opals, silica glass and silica gel: *Zeitsch. Kristall.* bd. 85, pp. 305–318.

Lewin, J. C., 1960, The dissolution of silica from diatom walls: *Geochim. Cosmochim. Acta,* v. 21, pp. 182–198.

Liagina, N. M., and S. I. Kuznetzow, 1937, The determination of the intensity of respiration of some species of water bacteria at various temperatures under laboratory conditions (Russian: English summary): *Mikrobiol.,* v. 6, pp. 21–27.

Lindström, M., 1963, Sedimentary folds and the development of limestone in an early Ordovician sea: *Sedimentology,* v. 2, pp. 243–276.

Love, L. G., 1958, Microorganisms and the presence of syngenetic pyrite: *Geol. Soc. London Quart. J.,* v. 113, pp. 429–437.

——— and D. O. Zimmerman, 1961, Bedded pyrite and microorganisms from the Mount Isa Shale: *Econ. Geol.,* v. 56, pp. 873–896.

Lowenstam, H. A., 1950, Niagaran reefs of the Great Lakes area: *J. Geol.,* v. 58, pp. 430–487.

——— 1954, Factors affecting aragonite-calcite ratios in carbonate secreting marine organisms: *J. Geol.,* v. 62, pp. 284–322.

——— 1961, Mineralogy, O^{18}/O^{16} ratios, and strontium and magnesium contents of Recent and fossil brachiopods and their bearing on the history of the oceans: *J. Geol.,* v. 69, pp. 241–260.

——— and S. Epstein, 1954, Paleotemperatures of the post-Aptian Cretaceous as determined by the oxygen-isotope method: *J. Geol.,* v. 62, pp. 207–248.

Maxwell, J. C., 1960, Experiments on compaction and cementation of sand: *Geol. Soc. Am. Mem. 79,* pp. 105–132.

Midgley, H. G., 1951, Chalcedony and flint: *Geol. Mag.,* v. 88, pp. 179–184.

Millot, G., 1960, Silice, silex, silicifications et croissance des cristaux: *Serv. Carte Géol. Alsace Lorraine Bull.,* tm. 13, pp. 129–146.

Monaghan, P. H., and M. A. Lytle, 1956, The origin of calcareous ooliths: *J. Sed. Petrol.,* v. 26, pp. 111–118.

Moodie, R. L., 1923, *Paleopathology: An Introduction to the Study of Ancient Evidences of Disease:* Urbana, University Illinois Press, 567 pp.

Moretti, F. J., 1957, Observations on limestones: *J. Sediment. Petrol.,* v. 27, pp. 282–292.

Morita, R. Y., and C. E. ZoBell, 1955, Occurrence of bacteria in pelagic sediments collected during the Mid-Pacific expedition: *Deep-Sea Research,* v. 3, pp. 66–73.

Müller, A. H., 1956, Die Knollenfeuersteine der Schreibkreide, eine foühdiagenetische Bildung: *Geol. Ges. Deutsch. Dem. Rep.,* bd. 1, pp. 136–144.

Murray, R. C., 1960, Origin of porosity in carbonate rocks: *J. Sediment. Petrol.,* v. 30, pp. 59–84.

Nelson, H. F., 1959, Deposition and alteration of the Edwards Limestone, Central Texas: in *Symposium on Edwards Limestone in Central Texas,* Austin, University of Texas Publ. 5905, 235 pp.

Newell, N. D., 1955, Depositional fabric in Permian reef limestones: *J. Geol.,* v. 63, pp. 301–309.

________ et al., 1953, *The Permian Reef Complex of the Guadalupe Mountains Region, Texas and New Mexico:* San Francisco, Freeman and Company, 236 pp.

Nicholls, G. D., H. Curl, Jr., and V. T. Bowen, 1959, Spectrographic analyses of marine plankton: *Limnol. Oceanog.,* v. 4, pp. 472–478.

Odum, H. T., 1957, Biochemical deposition of strontium: *Inst. Marine Sci.* (Univ. Texas), v. 4, pp. 38–114.

Okamoto, G., T. Okura, and K. Goto, 1957, Properties of silica in water: *Geochim. Cosmochim. Acta,* v. 12, pp. 123–132.

Pelto, C. R., 1956, A study of chalcedony: *Am. J. Sci.,* v. 254, pp. 32–50.

Pettijohn, F. J., 1957, *Sedimentary Rocks:* New York, Harper and Bros., 718 pp.

Pittman, J. S., 1959, Silica in Edwards Limestone, Travis County, Texas: in *Silica in Sediments,* Soc. Econ. Paleontologists Mineralogists, Special Pub. No. 7, pp. 121–134.

Piveteau, J., 1952, *Traité de paléontologie,* Tm. 2: Paris, Masson et Cie., 790 pp.

Prashnowsky, A., E. T. Degens, K. O. Emery, and J. Pimenta, 1961, Organic materials in recent and ancient sediments—I: Sugars in marine sediments of Santa Barbara Basin, California: *Neues Jahr. Geol. Paläont. Mh.,* h. 8, pp. 400–413.

Raistrick, A., and C. E. Marshall, 1939, *The Nature and Origin of Coal and Coal Seams:* London, English University Press Ltd., 282 pp.

Raup, D. M., 1959, Crystallography of echinoid calcite: *J. Geol.,* v. 67, pp. 661–674.

Renault, B., 1899, Sur quelques microorganisms des combustible fossiles: *Soc. Industrie Min. Bull.,* v. 13, pp. 865–1169.

Reuszer, H. W., 1933, Marine bacteria and their role in the cycle of life in the sea—III, The bacteria in the ocean waters and muds about Cape Cod: *Woods Hole Biol. Bull.,* v. 65, 48–97.

Revelle, R. R., 1944, Marine bottom samples collected in the Pacific Ocean by the Carnegie on its seventh cruise: *Carnegie Inst. Washington Publ.* 556, 196 pp.

________ and R. W. Fairbridge, 1957, Carbonates and carbon dioxide: *Treatise on Marine Ecology and Paleoecology,* v. 1: Geol. Soc. America Mem. 67, pp. 239–296.

Sander, B., 1936, Beiträge zur Kenntnis der Anlagerungsgefüge (Rhythmische Kalke und Dolomite aus der Trias): *Min. Petr. Mittlng.*, bd. 48, pp. 27–209.

——— 1951, Contributions to the study of depositional fabrics: rhythmically deposited Triassic limestones and dolomites: Tulsa, *Am. Assoc. Petrol. Geologists*, 207 pp.

Schlanger, S. O., 1957, Dolomite growth in coralline algae: *J. Sed. Petrol.*, v. 27, pp. 181–186.

——— et al., 1963, Subsurface geology of Eniwetok Atoll: *U.S. Geol. Survey Prof. Paper 260-BB*, 1066 pp.

Schmidegg, O., 1928, Über geregelte Wachstumsgefüge: *Jahr. Geol. Reichsanst. Bundesanst.*, bd. 78, pp. 1–52.

Schwarzacher, W., 1961, Petrology and structure of some Lower Carboniferous reefs in northwestern Ireland: *Am. Assoc. Petrol. Geologists Bull.*, v. 45, pp. 1481–1503.

Shearman, D. J., J. Khouri, and S. Taha, 1961, On the replacement of dolomite by calcite in some Mesozoic limestones from the French Jura: *Geologists Assoc. London Proc.*, v. 72, pp. 1–12.

Shepard, F. P., and D. G. Moore, 1955, Central Texas coast sedimentation: characteristics of sedimentary environment, recent history and diagenesis: *Am. Assoc. Petrol. Geologists Bull.*, v. 39, pp. 1463–1593.

Siegel, F. R., 1960, The effect of strontium on the aragonite-calcite ratios of Pleistocene corals: *J. Sediment. Petrol.*, v. 30, pp. 297–304.

Siever, R., 1957, The silica budget in the sedimentary cycle: *Am. Mineralogist*, v. 42, pp. 821–841.

——— 1959, Petrology and geochemistry of silica cementation in some Pennsylvanian sandstones: in *Silica in Sediments*, Soc. Econ. Paleontologists Mineralogists, Special Pub. No. 7, pp. 55–79.

——— 1962, Silica solubility, 0°–200°C., and the diagenesis of siliceous sediments: *J. Geol.*, v. 70, pp. 127–150.

Skeats, E. W., 1902, The chemical composition of limestones from upraised coral islands, with notes on their microscopical structures: *Mus. Comp. Zool.*, v. 42, pp. 53–126.

Stainier, X., 1924, Nodules dolomitiques avec végétaux à structure conservée du houiller belge: *Soc. Belge Géol. Bull.*, tm. 34, pp. 26–30.

Stehli, F. G., and J. Hower, 1961, Mineralogy and early diagenesis of carbonate sediments: *J. Sed. Petrol.*, v. 31, pp. 358–371.

Stopes, M. C., and D. M. S. Watson, 1909, On the present distribution and origin of the calcareous concretions in coal-seams, known as coal balls: *Roy. Soc. London Phil. Trans.*, ser. B, v. 200, pp. 167–218.

Storz, M., 1928, Die sekundäre authigene Kieselsäure in ihrer petrogenetisch-geologischen Bedeutung—I, Verwitterung und authigene Kieselsäure fuhrende Gesteine: *Monogr. Geol. Palaeont.*, ser. II, h. 4, pp. 1–137.

——— 1931, Die sekundäre authigene Kieselsäure in ihrer petrogenetisch-geologischen Bedeutung—II, Die Einwirkung der sekundären authigenen Kieselsäure auf vorhandene Gesteine (Einkieselung und Verkieselung): *Monogr. Geol. Palaeont.*, ser. II, h. 5, pp. 139–479.

Straaten, van, L. M. J. U., 1955, Composition and structure of recent marine sediments in the Netherlands: *Leidse Geol. Mededelingen*, d. 19, pp. 1–108.

Strakhov, N. M., 1953, Diagenesis of sediments and its significance in sedimentary ore formation: *Izvest. Akad. Nauk S.S.S.R. Ser. Geol.*, n. 5, pp. 12–49, (English translation) East Orange, New Jersey, Assoc. Tech. Services Ltd.

Sujkowski, Zb. L., 1958, Diagenesis: *Am. Assoc. Petrol. Geoolgists Bull.*, v. 42, pp. 2692–2717.

Swain, F. M., 1961, Stratigraphic distribution of furfurals and amino compounds in Jurassic rocks of Gulf of Mexico region: *Am. Assoc. Petrol. Geologists Bull.*, v. 45, pp. 1713–1720.

Taylor, J. H., 1964, Some aspects of diagenesis: *Advancement Sci.*, v. 20, pp. 417–436.

Terzhagi, R. D., 1940, Compaction of lime mud as a cause of secondary structure: *J. Sed. Petrol.*, v. 10, pp. 78–90.

Tovborg, J. A., C. J. Wohlk, K. Drenck, and E. Andersen, 1957, A classification of Danish flints etc., based on X-ray diffractometry: *Danish Nat. Inst. Building Research Prog. Rep.*, ser. D, n. 1.

Treibs, A., 1934, Über das Vorkommen von chlorophyllderivaten in einem Oelschiefer der oberen Trias: *Liebigs Ann.*, bd. 509, pp. 103–114.

Turekian, K. K., and R. L. Armstrong, 1960, Magnesium, strontium, and barium concentrations and calcite-aragonite ratios of some recent molluscan shells: *J. Marine Res.*, v. 18, pp. 133–151.

________ 1961, Chemical and mineralogical composition of fossil molluscan shells from the Fox Hills Formation, South Dakota: *Geol. Soc. America Bull.*, v. 72, pp. 1817–1828.

Vatan, A., 1947, Remarques sur la silicification: *Soc. Géol. France C. R. Som.*, n. 5, pp. 99–101.

Vinogradov, A. P., 1953, *The Elementary Chemical Composition of Marine Organisms:* (English translation) New Haven, Sears Foundation Marine Research, 647 pp.

Voigt, E., 1956, Der Nachweis des Phytals durch Epizoen als Kriterium der Tiefe vorzeitlicher Meere: *Geol. Rundschau*, v. 45, pp. 97–119.

Waksman, S. A., C. L. Carey, and H. W. Reuszer, 1933, Marine bacteria and their rôle in the cycle of life in the sea—I, Decomposition of marine plant and animal residues by bacteria: *Woods Hole Biol. Bull.*, v. 65, pp. 57–79.

Walcott, C. D., 1915, Discovery of Algonkian bacteria: *Nat. Acad. Sci. Proc.*, v. 1, pp. 256–257.

Walker, T. R., 1960, Carbonate replacement of detrital crystalline silicate minerals as a source of authigenic silica in sedimentary rocks: *Geol. Soc. Amer. Bull.*, v. 71, pp. 145–152.

________ 1962, Reversable nature of chert-carbonate replacement in sedimentary rocks: *Geol. Soc. Amer. Bull.*, v. 73, pp. 237–242.

Weeks, L. G., 1957, Origin of carbonate concretions in shales, Magdalena valley, Colombia: *Geol. Soc. Amer. Bull.*, v. 68, pp. 95–102.

Weller, J. M., 1959, Compaction of sediments: *Am. Assoc. Petrol. Geologists Bull.*, v. 43, pp. 273–310.

Weyl, P. K., 1958, The solution kinetics of calcite: *J. Geol.*, v. 66, pp. 163–176.

________ 1959*a*, The change in solubility of calcium carbonate with temperature and carbon dioxide content: *Geochim. Cosmochim. Acta*, v. 17, pp. 214–225.

________ 1959*b*, Pressure solution and the force of crystallization—a phenomenological theory: *J. Geophys. Research*, v. 64, pp. 2001–2025.

________ 1961, The carbonate saturometer: *J. Geol.*, v. 69, pp. 32–44.

Wood, A., 1949, The structure of the wall of the test in the Foraminifera; its value in classification: *Geol. Soc. London Quart. J.*, v. 104, pp. 229–252.

Wray, J. L., and F. Daniels, 1957, Precipitation of calcite and aragonite: *Am. Chemical Soc. J.*, v. 79, pp. 2031–2034.

Zeller, E. J., and J. L. Wray, 1956, Factors influencing precipitation of calcium carbonate: *Am. Assoc. Petrol. Geologists Bull.*, v. 40, pp. 140–152.

ZoBell, C. E., 1946*a*, Occurrence and activity of bacteria in marine sediments: in *Recent Marine Sediments*. Am. Assoc. Petrol. Geologists, pp. 416–427.

________ 1946*b*, Studies on redox potential of marine sediments: *Am. Assoc. Petrol. Geologists Bull.*, v. 30, pp. 477–513.

________ and C. B. Feltham, 1942, The bacterial flora of a marine mud flat as an ecological factor: *Ecology*, v. 23, pp. 69–78.

________ and J. Stadler, 1940, The oxidation of lignin by lake bacteria: *Hydrobiol. Plankt. Arch.*, v. 37, pp. 163–171.

The Solution Alteration of Carbonate Sediments and Skeletons

by P. K. Weyl *Dept. of Oceanography, Oregon State University, Corvallis, Oregon*

ABSTRACT

The geologist normally approaches carbonate rocks as a historian in that he wishes to discover the origin and diagenesis of a sediment from the information contained in the rock. The physical scientist on the other hand approaches nature as a prophet in that he wishes to predict the future behavior from the original state of the sediment and the chemical, physical, and biological processes that are going on. In studying solution alteration, we wish to be able to predict how a sediment, which consists of an intimate mixture of many impure phases, is transformed by interaction with the interstitial solutions into a carbonate rock. So far our knowledge of these processes is very limited and more often than not leads to predictions which are clearly contradicted by the geologic evidence. For example, one would expect recrystallization of a mixture of finely divided particles of different carbonates to proceed much more rapidly than is observed. The use of the carbonate saturometer is beginning to give us some understanding of the complexities of the kinetics of this recrystallization process in natural carbonate systems. We observe that an initially rapid rate of precipitation is followed by a greatly reduced rate in the same water. This study is continuing and we hope that it will lead to better prediction of geologic processes.

Introduction

In a study of solution alteration of carbonate sediments two approaches are possible. In the classical geological approach, the geologist looks at nature as a historian. From the evidence seen in a limestone, he attempts to discover the environment of deposition and the subsequent history of the rock. The physical scientist, on the other hand, approaches nature as a prophet. Given a particular initial state and the forces acting on the system, he would like to predict the evolution of the system in time. In our problem, given a particular sediment and its subsequent history of burial and hydrology, we should like to predict the transformation of the sediment under the particular conditions.

The advantage of the physical, predictive method is that it must lead to a unique answer—a given system (if all the forces acting on it are specified) can evolve in only one way. The geological method, however, can never establish that there is one and only one way in which a given rock can be produced. The difficulty of the predictive method results from the disparity between the human and geologic time scales. We are able to study processes that take place during 1 μsec; we can hardly wait millions of years for a geologic experiment to be completed. We must therefore turn to the historian to check our predictions.

The historian, in the meanwhile, after studying a piece of rock, has decided that it resulted from a particular process. Before we can have confidence in this interpretation, we must be convinced that the proposed mechanism could yield the observed result in the time available. We must be able to predict that the proposed mechanism could indeed have transformed the sediment into the piece of rock.

An understanding of the solution alteration of carbonate sediments will therefore require both the predictive and the historical approach. We must investigate the physics and chemistry of model systems that simulate nature, and then compare the predicted results with observations of nature. If we are good prophets, our predictions will be reasonable approximations of what is actually observed. If we are false prophets, our predictions will be repudiated by nature. In that case, we shall have learned that the model, which we have assumed, is incorrect. This is negative knowledge; nevertheless, we have made a step forward in that we have eliminated a model. Without working out in detail the consequences of the model, we could not have proved its incorrectness.

Let us now consider some model carbonate systems and investigate their physics and chemistry. Our sediment consists of mixtures of the minerals calcite and aragonite. In addition, dolomite, gypsum, quartz, and trace minerals may be present. These minerals will not be pure chemical compounds. The calcite, for instance, may contain magnesium in solid solution in varying amounts up to 20 mole %.

In addition to the solid mineral phases, the pore space will be permeated by fluids. Below the water table, the fluids will generally be a concentrated solution of ions. Sodium, magnesium, calcium, potassium, strontium, chloride, sulfate, bicarbonate, and carbonate ions are frequently present in appreciable concentrations. Dissolved atmospheric gases usually must be considered, and other ions and compounds may also be important.

We shall restrict our attention to mechanisms of solution alteration —that is, changes in the sediments produced by an interaction between the solid minerals and the interstitial solutions. In a consideration of the solution alteration of carbonate sediments, two types of environments must be considered—that in which a sediment particle is surrounded by essentially an infinite volume of solution, and that in which the pore space of the sediment is filled with solution.

Environment I—Sediment Particle in Contact with an Infinite Volume of Water

EXAMPLES. A calcareous test sinking to the bottom of the ocean; fine grained carbonate sediments brought into dilute suspension by physical (e.g., by wave action) or biological (e.g., by fish) forces; coarser grained sediment particles saltating over the water-sediment interface.

In this environment, the aqueous phase can be considered an open system, and its bulk composition will be controlled by large-scale physical, biological, and chemical processes. Dissolution of, or precipitation on, the sediment particle will affect the water only in a very limited zone of diffusion about the particle.

PROBLEMS. In this environment, we must determine (*a*) the degree of supersaturation or undersaturation of the water with respect to the sediment particle; (*b*) the rates of precipitation or dissolution; and (*c*) the morphology of the precipitate or the leached product.

Environment II—Sediment with Interstitial Water

EXAMPLES. A carbonate sand beneath the sea; a lime mud below the sea; a limestone-dolomite mixture below the water table.

In this environment, most of the matter present, other than water, is in the solid phase. For example, a calcium carbonate sediment which has 50% porosity, which contains 1 mole % of magnesium and strontium, and whose pore space is filled with sea water, will have the following composition:

Ion	Concentration, Millimoles/cc Sediment Solid	Liquid
Ca^{2+}	13.23	0.0050
Mg^{2+}	0.135	0.0260
Sr^{2+}	0.135	0.0001
Total CO_2	13.5	0.0012

The water composition will adjust to the solid phases present. The Eh and pH of the water will be the result of chemical changes taking place at the solid-liquid interfaces and of biological (bacterial) reactions. The Eh and pH are dependent, rather than independent, variables. For example, the presence of calcium carbonate will adjust the pH to some equilibrium value. The presence of calcium carbonate is not the result of the pH of the interstitial water. It is important to stress this point, because some writers give the impression that pH and Eh are independent variables similar to the physical variables, temperature, and pressure:

> A good many chemical reactions which influence the diagenesis and morphology of sediments are influenced by the redox potential. The redox potential determines the physiological activity of bacteria (ZoBell, 1946).

> In many such natural systems the chemical reactions involved may be controlled almost entirely by pH and Eh of the environment (Huber, 1958).

The pH and Eh of the water are symptoms. Changes in these variables indicate that chemical or biological reactions are taking place. For example, a change in pH of the interstitial water in a carbonate may be the result of solution or precipitation of carbonate. This fact is used in the principle of the carbonate saturometer (Weyl, 1961). A change in Eh may be the result of bacterial activity. For example, sulfate-reducing bacteria may be reducing the original sulfate in the sea water to sulfide or elemental sulfur.

Apart from equilibrating with the sediment, the composition of the water may be changed by diffusion due to concentration gradients and by fluid flow.

PROBLEMS. The original sediment will be a mixture of many impure phases. This mixture is determined by the carbonate-secreting organisms present and by the physical forces that affect sedimentation. The organic community will produce calcites containing varying amounts of magnesium and aragonites of varying impurity content. The physical forces may or may not select particular size fractions. The mixture produced will, in general, not be in thermodynamic equilibrium. At an arbitrary magnesium-to-calcium ratio in the water, one and only one of these impure calcium carbonates can be the least soluble and thus be the stable phase. A particular calcium carbonate and a particular dolomite can coexist in thermodynamic equilibrium only at a particular calcium-to-magnesium ratio. Since the sediment originally is not an equilibrium assemblage, we should like to be able to predict the final equilibrium product and the kinetics of recrystallization. How will this recrystallization alter the morphology of the sediment? If the interstitial water is in motion in the direction of solubility gradients, how much cementation or leaching will take place?

The Physics and Chemistry of Solution Alteration

Conservation of Mass

Except for the radioactive elements, the mass of each of the chemical elements in a closed system must be conserved. This basic principle is a powerful tool. It permits us to relate a change in chemical composition to the net amount of material transported into the system.

Mechanisms of Transport in Solution

Material can be transported in the interstitial water either by diffusion or by fluid flow. In diffusion, the ions move through the water because of concentration gradients, and the transport is proportional to the concentration gradient. The net amount added by diffusion to a given volume element of the sediment is proportional to the second space derivative of the concentration. The following laws apply to diffusion in a porous medium:

$$j = \frac{D}{F} \nabla C$$

$$\frac{\partial C}{\partial t} = \frac{D}{\phi F} \nabla^2 C + \frac{A}{\phi}$$

where j is the mass of material diffusing across unit cross-sectional area of the sediment in unit time,

D is the diffusion constant (of the order of 10^{-5} cm/sec^2 for ions in aqueous solution),

F is the formation resistivity factor (the ratio of the resistance across the solution-filled sediment to the resistance of a similar geometry in the free solution),

C is the concentration of the solution in mass per unit volume,
ϕ is the fractional porosity of the sediment,
A is the mass of material dissolving per unit time per unit volume of the sediment ($-A$ is precipitation),
∇ is the gradient operator

$$i\frac{\partial}{\partial x} + j\frac{\partial}{\partial y} + k\frac{\partial}{\partial z}$$

∇^2 is the Laplace operator

$$\frac{\partial^2}{\partial x^2} + \frac{\partial^2}{\partial y^2} + \frac{\partial^2}{\partial z^2}$$

In the case of fluid flow, the amount of cementation or leaching depends on the first space derivative of the concentration:

$$\frac{\partial m}{\partial t} = -q \cdot \nabla C$$

where m is the mass of solids per unit volume of the sediment,
q is the flow vector in volume per unit sediment area per unit time.

These equations will apply to the total mass of dissolved matter in the water as well as to any one chemical constituent which is conserved.

Solubility of Minerals

Of primary importance in solution alteration is the solubility of the various constituents of the sediment in the interstitial solution. An idealized version of this problem has been studied by the physical chemist, who studies the equilibrium of a heterogeneous system consisting of two or more phases. A phase is a homogeneous mass having uniform physical and chemical properties which is separated from other phases in the system by well-defined bounding surfaces. For example, a piece of pure calcite in an aqueous solution is a two-phase system; one phase is the calcite; the other is the solution. The boundary between the two phases is the solid-solution interface. When the phases are brought together, either the calcite will dissolve or precipitation will take place until the two phases are in equilibrium. Upon dissolving, the calcite will be converted to calcium and carbonate ions in solution. The law of mass action states that at equilibrium, the product of the calcium and carbonate ion activities in solution divided by the activity of solid calcium carbonate will be a constant, the equilibrium constant, which depends only on the temperature and pressure of the system. The theory implicitly assumes that any precipitate formed on the calcite will have the same chemical composition as the original calcite.

The activities involved in the equilibrium constant are thermodynamic concentrations. They differ from the actual concentration by a factor—the activity coefficient. At infinite dilution, the activity coefficient approaches unity. For most waters of geologic interest, however, the activity coefficients differ significantly from one and depend on the detailed composition of the solution and on the temperature and pressure.

A possible approach to the study of the solution equilibria of minerals is to determine the equilibrium constants of the various minerals as a function of temperature and pressure. In addition, one must be able to determine the activity coefficients of the various ionic species in any geologic waters as a function of temperature and pressure. This approach has been pursued by many investigators and has been developed most rigorously by Garrels (1960). It is the classical approach of the physical chemist to the study of solutions. As geologists, we wish to obtain specific answers to geological problems and are not primarily concerned with understanding the details of solution chemistry. We must therefore ask to what extent the classical approach has obtained answers to geological problems and to what extent this approach gives promise of obtaining such answers in the future.

Let us now consider how the classical approach can be used in a specific case and what alternative methods are available. Assume that we are standing on a carbonate sand beach of a tropical island. The sea water is moving over the strand line in waves and is constantly moving the sand particles about. We should like to determine whether calcium carbonate is being precipitated on the sand or whether it is slowly being dissolved by the sea water—in other words, whether the sea water is over- or undersaturated with respect to the carbonate sand. The fact that there is beach sand indicates that the sea water is not either grossly supersaturated or grossly undersaturated. If it were grossly undersaturated, the sand would have dissolved long ago. If it were highly supersaturated, the precipitation would have cemented the sand into a solid rock. The difference from saturation must therefore be slight.

To determine the difference from saturation by the classical method, we proceed as follows:

1. Obtain a sample of the carbonate sand, and determine its phase—calcite, aragonite, or impure calcite of what composition.
2. Look up the solubility product of the carbonate at the particular water temperature. If it has not previously been determined, measure it by determining the solubility in distilled water plus carbon dioxide.
3. Obtain an analysis of the major constituents of the sea water. If we were dealing with normal sea water, this would not be necessary.
4. Determine the pH of the water.
5. Determine the total CO_2 content of the water.
6. Look up the first and second dissociation constants of carbonic acid at the temperature of the water.
7. Look up or determine the activity coefficients of carbonate, bicarbonate, and dissolved CO_2 at the temperature of the water. Due to the specific interaction of carbonate with cations, particularly calcium and magnesium, the activity coefficient is not merely a function of the ionic strength of the solution.
8. Look up or determine the activity coefficient of calcium in the water and compute the calcium activity.
9. Compute the activity product of calcium carbonate in the water, and compare that product with the equilibrium constant of the solid calcium carbonate on the beach.
10. Make a detailed error analysis to determine whether the difference between the equilibrium constant and the activity product is significant. If it is, we have determined whether the water is over- or undersaturated and by approximately how much. If it is not, within the errors of our determinations the water is in equilibrium. In view of the many constants involved in the calculation, the error is likely to be quite large.

It can be seen that the classical procedure is very involved. It is still relatively simple in the case of sea water, because the analysis of sea water is well known and much work has been done on the estimation of the activity coefficients in sea water. In different types of water, however, the procedure is much more complicated.

What alternative procedure is available? Using the carbonate saturometer technique (Weyl, 1961), we can proceed as follows:

Using a modification of the pH meter, we take a sample of water at the beach and place it in our portable saturometer. We set the potential reading to zero, drop a sample of the carbonate sand into the water sample, and note the change in potential. If it is positive, the water is supersaturated; if it is negative, the water is undersaturated. From the deflection, we can estimate the difference from saturation. With sea water, an approximate calibration has been published. If we are dealing with a different water, we must perform a calibration. The saturometer technique is quick and straightforward. With sea water, we can determine differences from saturation of 1 part per million. What do these measurements show?

First, we take a sample of the sand from the surf zone and find a slight supersaturation of a few parts per million. Next, we take a sample of the sand higher on the beach and find a supersaturation of slightly over 10 parts per million in the same water. Apparently, the immediate history of the carbonate particles affects their solubility in sea water. The grains that have recently been contacted with fresh sea water (Environment I) show little supersaturation, whereas those that have been quiescent on the beach (Environment II) show a much larger supersaturation in the same water. This observation is in conflict with the simple solution chemistry model. If we are dealing with a distinct carbonate phase in sea water at a particular temperature and pressure, there should be only one solubility independent of the past history.

The empirical saturometer measurement has thus demonstrated that nature is not so simple as we might have hoped. This fact would never have been discovered by the classical solution chemistry approach. X-ray analysis of the carbonate sand from the surf zone and from higher up on the beach would have shown the same bulk phase to be present. Thus, we would have assumed that their solubilities in sea water are the same.

The saturometer measurements indicate that the carbonate sediment particle is not a single phase as defined by the chemist. Apparently, the calcium carbonate precipitated differs in apparent solubility from the previously precipitated solid. Nature thus violates the requirement of homogeneity. Although we do not yet understand the detailed mechanism of carbonate precipitation on the beach, it is clear that we cannot hope to investigate it by the classical methods of solution chemistry.

Solution Kinetics of Carbonates

In addition to knowing the equilibrium solubility of carbonates, we must know something about the rates at which equilibrium is reached. From a study of the solution kinetics of calcite in water containing CO_2 (Weyl, 1958), the rate of solution was found to be limited only by the rate of diffusion of the solute away from the solid-liquid interface where the solution was saturated. Work with the saturometer in sea water, however, has shown that things are much more complicated: the rates of equilibration are much slower than would be expected if equilibration were limited only by the rate of diffusion. In addition, the past history of the carbonate particles affects the apparent solubility.

Recrystallization in a Carbonate Sediment

A carbonate sediment consists of various organically or otherwise derived pieces of calcium carbonate in an intimate, fine-grained mixture. This mixture should recrystallize to the thermodynamically most stable phase(s). Ultimately, recrystallization takes place, since after a few hundred million years only relatively pure calcite and dolomite are found. Recrystallization is obviously a very important mechanism in the transformation of carbonate sediments into carbonate rocks. At what rate should this process take place? Let us first consider an idealized system consisting of a fine-grained mixture of calcite and aragonite.

Calcite-Aragonite Mixture

Assume a mixture of calcite and aragonite grains of 0.5-mm size, and a small difference in solubility of 1 ppm in the interstitial water. If each aragonite grain has at least one calcite grain adjacent to it with a separation of 0.2 mm, the concentration gradient will be 5×10^{-4}/gm cm^3/cm. If we assume that the rate of recrystallization depends only upon the rate of diffusion from the aragonite to the calcite surface, then, during each second, the grain will loose 1.25×10^{-11} gm. Since it contains 3.5×10^{-4} gm, recrystallization will be completed in about 3×10^7 seconds, or about 1 year.

This model suggests that recrystallization in a sand-size, mixed carbonate sediment should take place within about a year. Finer grained sediments should recrystallize even faster. Although recrystallization from aragonite to calcite does take place, the time required is more on a scale of tens of thousands to millions of years. Our simplified model thus results in a prediction that is grossly in error. We must therefore conclude that the rate of recrystallization is inhibited by mechanisms other than diffusion.

Magnesian Calcite-Calcite Mixture

Recent experiments in carbonated water and sea water (Garrels, Chave, Deffeyes, and Weyl, 1962) have shown that magnesian calcites are considerably more soluble than pure calcite. A sediment composed of a mixture of magnesian calcite (fragments of red algae) and relatively pure calcite would tend to recrystallize to pure calcite. The solubility contrast in this case is much larger than in the case of the aragonite-calcite conversion. For the same size of sediment particles, recrystallization should take place even faster. During recrystallization, magnesium carbonate will be added to the interstitial water.

Let us assume that each cc of sediment contains 0.5 cc interstitial water, 0.25 cc pure calcite, and 0.25 cc calcite containing 16 mole % magnesium carbonate. If all of the magnesium carbonate remains in solution after recrystallization, the water will have the following composition:

	Concentration, Millimoles/cc Sediment	
Ion	Initial Water	Final Water
Ca^{2+}	0.0050	0.0050
Mg^{2+}	0.0260	1.106
Total CO_2	0.0012	1.081

The magnesium carbonate concentration in the water after recrystallization would thus be enormous. Long before recrystallization has been completed, the solubility of dolomite must be exceeded. We would thus expect a rapid recrystallization of the mixed sediment to a mixture of calcite and dolomite. Again, the geologic evidence indicates that, although recrystallization eventually does take place, the time involved are very much longer than would have been predicted.

Conclusion

In discussing the solution alteration of carbonates, I have done little but share my ignorance with you. Let us hope that a knowledge of our ignorance is the first step toward understanding. It appears that the means by which nature transforms carbonate sediments into limestones and dolomites are not as simple as we might have hoped. We have much to learn before we can make reliable predictions and become true prophets.

REFERENCES

Chave, K. E., Deffeyes, K. S., Weyl, P. K., Garrels, R. M., Thompson, M. E., 1962, Observations on the solubility of skeletal carbonates in aqueous solutions: *Science*, v. 137, pp. 33–34.

Garrels, R. M., 1960, *Mineral Equilibria*, New York, Harper and Bros., 254 pp.

Huber, N. King, 1958, The environmental control of sedimentary iron minerals, *Econ. Geol.*, v. 53, p. 123.

Weyl, P. K., 1958, The solution kinetics of calcite, Shell E & P Research Pub. 119, *J. Geol.*, v. 66, p. 163.

——— 1961, The carbonate saturometer, Shell E & P Research Pub. 235, *J. Geol.*, v. 69, p. 32.

ZoBell, Claude E., 1946, Redox potential of marine sediments, *Bull. Amer. Assoc. Petroleum Geol.*, v. 30, p. 477.

The Replacement of Aragonite by Calcite in the Molluscan Shell Wall

by R. G. C. Bathurst *Department of Geology, University of Liverpool, England*

ABSTRACT

Where the aragonite of molluscan shells has been replaced by calcite, it can be shown that the resultant fabrics have evolved in one of two ways: by solution, yielding a mold which was subsequently filled by a cast of drusy calcite; or by recrystallization *in situ.* Solution-deposition is indicated by the drusy fabrics of the calcite mosaic and the collapse of micrite envelopes that have partly replaced many shells. Recrystallization *in situ* is apparent from the absence of drusy fabrics and the preservation of lamellar structure. These events are related to the sequence of shell fracture during compaction and the early and late stages of cementation.

It is also suggested that solution of molluscan aragonite can remove large quantities of shell debris without trace, yield important amounts of dissolved carbonate as a source of calcite cement, and cause a significant development of secondary porosity. A new criterion, the enfacial junction, is put forward for the recognition of granular cements and drusy mosaics.

Introduction

Although it is widely believed that many fossil molluscan shells are now composed of a calcite mosaic that has replaced the primary

It has been my particular good fortune to have been able to discuss the question of drusy replacement with Heinz Lowenstam and Grant Gross in the California Institute of Technology; and with Lloyd Pray, Jack Wray, Coy Squyres, Phil Choquette, and Alan Horowitz of the Marathon Oil Company. I acknowledge with pleasure my wife's help in the writing of the manscript and the valuable advice of John E. Hemingway of the University of Durham, and Philip Brown of Continental Oil Company.

aragonite, there is no general agreement about the process, or processes, by which the aragonite was supplanted. Opinions favor, for the most part, either solution with replacement by drusy[1] calcite or inversion of aragonite in the solid state. Yet no body of fabric[2] evidence has been offered in support of these contentions, no criteria developed systematically for the recognition of the resultant fabrics. Above all there is need for a method of distinguishing between the calcite mosaics formed in the shell wall by different diagenetic processes. So prodigious is the role of molluscan shells in limestone building that this neglected field of diagenesis marks a serious gap in the area of our understanding. This is particularly serious because the most common process, solution-deposition, involves mass transport, and the development of secondary porosity and release of calcium carbonate in solution on a very large scale.

In this paper fabric criteria are proposed by which the processes of aragonite replacement can be determined in general terms. Data from the molluscan shells examined confirm to a large extent the earlier views, that one of two processes operated: either solution-deposition or recrystallization *in situ.* In most of the shells, the aragonite dissolved and gave rise to a mold (secondary porosity). The mold was then filled with a cast of drusy calcite. In others, calcite replaced the aragonite *in situ,* there was no cavity stage, and various internal wall structures are now preserved. It is not at the moment possible to say whether this second process is inversion, that is to say, a true polymorphic transformation.

The results presented here are based mainly on the examination of acetate peels and thin sections of Purbeckian (top of Jurassic) and Dinantian (Mississippian) limestones of the British Isles. A less detailed study has been made of Cambrian to Recent limestones from various parts of the Middle East and the United States.

The Possibility of Aragonite Inversion

Aragonite is stable only above a hydrostatic pressure of about 4 kb at 25°C, rising to about 14 kb at 600°C (Clark, 1957). At lower

[1] *Drusy mosaic* arises in the same way as cement. Nevertheless, by convention, "cement" is applied to material which binds particles of sediment together. Therefore some other term is needed to describe the crystalline material (otherwise identical with cement) which fills, for example, the chamber of a gastropod or the cavity remaining after solution of a mollusk shell.

[2] *Fabric* is defined in the A.G.I. Glossary (1960) as follows: "The spatial arrangement and orientation of rock components, whether crystals or sedimentary particles, as determined by their sizes, shapes, etc."

pressures, in the stability field of calcite, it is metastable and inverts to calcite on heating (Johnston, Merwin, and Williamson, 1916; Lander, 1949; Jamieson, 1953; 1957; MacDonald, 1956; Clark, 1957). During inversion, which is a solid-state reaction, the CO_3 groups rotate and the Ca ions change their positions. The presence of water is irrelevant. In considering the possibility that inversion may have occurred in some calcitised molluscan shells, there are two factors that should be taken into account. For a sediment at the surface of the earth, the only imaginable pressure change is a positive one through burial, and this would serve to increase the stability of aragonite. Heat as a cause of the inversion seems improbable because unaltered and altered molluscan shells occur in adjacent beds. It appears, then, that a lattice reorganization brought about by changes of pressure or temperature is unlikely to be the means by which the molluscan shells acquired their calcite—unless other factors were involved. It is significant that aragonite skeletons, in rocks as old as the Carboniferous, have been isolated from meteoric water.

Replacement by Drusy Calcite

General

In most limestones studied, secondary calcite mosaics in the molluscan walls show a remarkable uniformity of fabric (Plate 1, Figures 1 and 2) with the characteristics of drusy mosaic (Bathurst, 1958, pp. 14–20, or summarized in Bathurst, 1959*a*, *b*). They grew, therefore, on free surfaces in supersaturated solutions. Of the two forms of drusy mosaic, only one has so far been found in the shell walls. Unlike radiaxial mosaic (Bathurst, 1959*b*, p. 511), which was not seen, the crystals in this mosaic have plane intercrystalline boundaries and uniform (as distinct from undulose) extinction. This kind of chemically deposited mosaic, typical of cement and cavity fillings in general, will for convenience be called *para-axial mosaic* (Plate 1, Plate 2, Plate 3) to distinguish it from the less common radiaxial mosaic.

Another line of evidence also points to the need for a cavity stage during replacement. Many shells were replaced, before burial, by a thin micrite (Folk, 1959, p. 8) envelope. Seen now in thin section the arrangement of the broken pieces of some of these envelopes indicates that they have collapsed inward (Plate 2, Figures 1 and 2). This evidence is discussed in detail later.

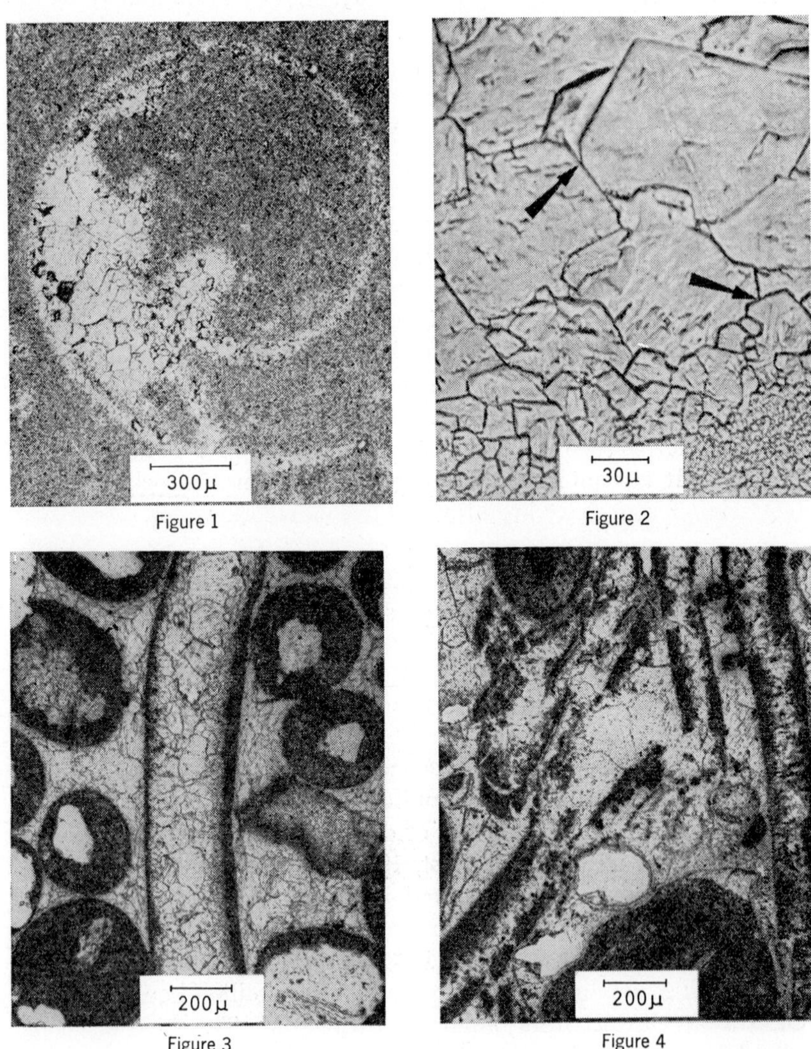

Figure 1

Figure 2

Figure 3

Figure 4

Plate 1 Fig. 1 Test of gastropod, replaced by drusy calcite, in calcilutite. Mississippian. New Mexico (Peel). Fig. 2 Part of wall of gastropod, replaced by drusy calcite, in calcilutite (bottom right). Two of many enfacial angles by arrow. Mississippian. New Mexico (Peel). Fig. 3 Abraded fragment of molluscan shell, replaced by drusy calcite, enclosed in micrite envelope, in cement. Inferior Oolite, Jurassic. Gloucestershire (Slice). Fig. 4 Fragments of molluscan shell (many bored), replaced by drusy calcite, enclosed in micrite envelopes, in cement. Inferior Oolite, Jurassic. Yorkshire (Slice).

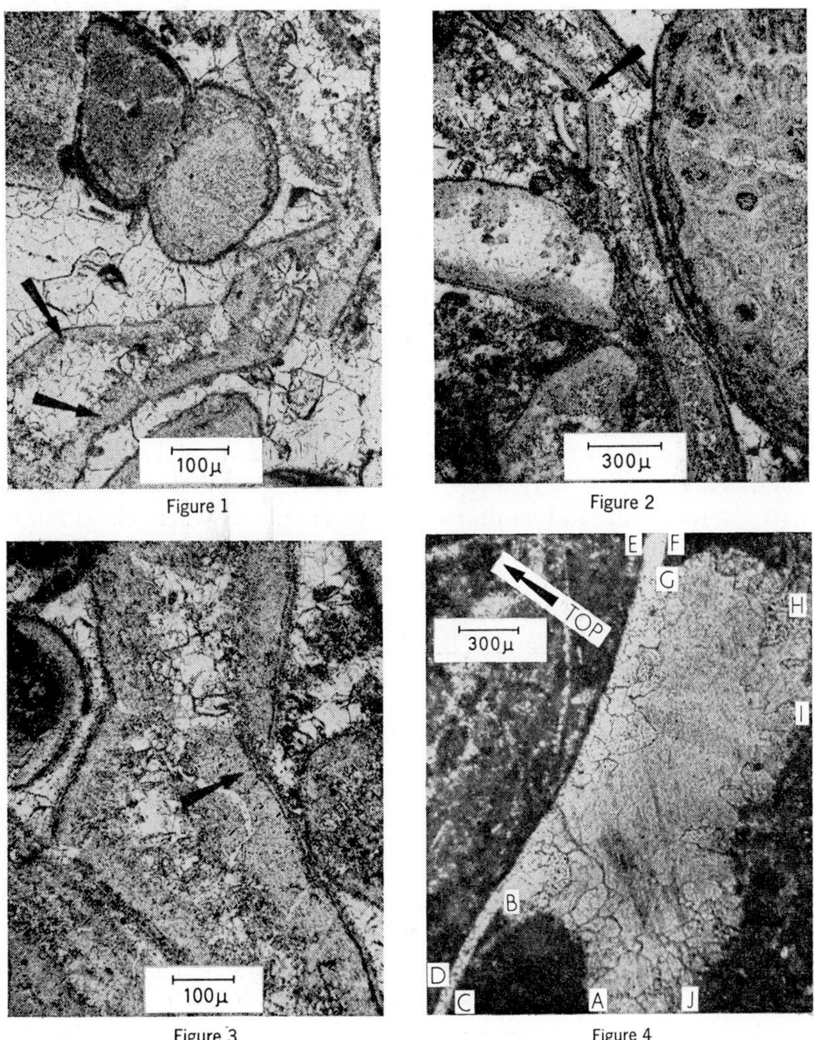

Figure 1 Figure 2 Figure 3 Figure 4

Plate 2 Fig. 1 Collapsed micrite envelope (arrows) enclosing what remains of a drusy-filled cavity once occupied by a fragment of molluscan shell, in cement. Inferior Oolite, Jurassic. Yorkshire (Peel). Fig. 2 Same as Fig. 1. Fig. 3 Same as Fig. 1, but showing one fragment of envelope thrust over another (by arrow). Fig. 4 Cavity in calcilutite roofed originally by a lamellibranch valve which was later dissolved. Knoll-reef in Carboniferous Limestone. Lancashire.

The Mosaic

The criteria which have been most useful in the recognition of para-axial drusy mosaic are described below and illustrated in Plate 1, Figures 1 and 2.

1. The mosaics show an increase of crystal size inward from the outer margins of the shell wall. Particularly noticeable is the sudden change in size near the margin, so that around the periphery of the mosaic there is commonly a concentration of little crystals.

2. Single crystals extinguish uniformly (unlike those in radiaxial drusy mosaic which show undulose extinction).

3. The intercrystalline boundaries are made up of a number of plane interfaces (compromise boundaries of Buckley [1951, p. 127] and overgrown crystal faces).

4. In addition to these criteria which have been catalogued before (Bathurst, 1958, p. 18), there is another texture that can be used. A study was made in two dimensions of the places where three intercrystalline boundaries meet, using magnifications of at least 450× with peels (Table 1). In drusy mosaics, more than half of these triple junctions have one of the three angles equal to 180° (Plate 1, Figure 2). In grain growth mosaic (Bathurst, 1958, p. 24) and in the calcite mosaic evolved *in situ* from aragonite shell walls (as described later), the proportion of 180° triple junctions is less than 5% (Table 1).

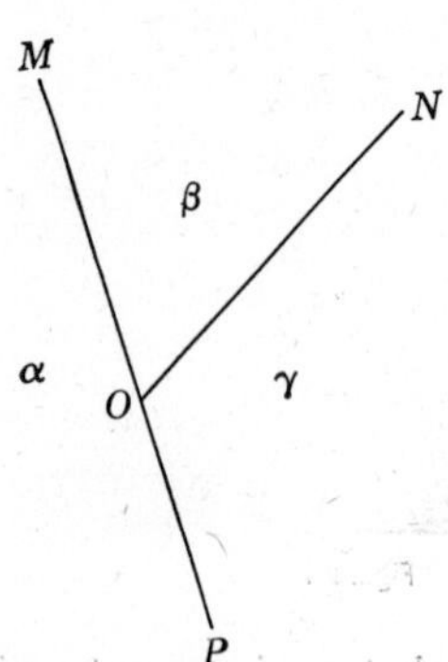

Fig. 1 Enfacial junction: MP being a face of the crystal α, and NO either a compromise boundary between crystals β and γ, or a face of β or γ.

It follows, therefore, from the data in Table 1, that a new textural criterion is available for the recognition of para-axial drusy mosaic. This texture has been found in the secondary calcite mosaics of the molluscan shells here being considered.

The formation of the 180° triple junctions can be discussed with the help of Figure 1, where the plane intercrystalline boundaries *MO*, *NO* and *PO* separate the crystals α, β, and γ. *MP* is a straight line.

Although it is theoretically possible that *MP* is the result of a geometrical coincidence whereby two compromise boundaries, *MO* and *PO*, happened to form a continuous line in the plane of the peel, the odds against this being a common occurrence are extremely high.

TABLE 1. *Triple junctions with angles of 180°, in calcite mosaics*

Type of Mosaic	Horizon, Location, and Catalogue Number of Sample	Number of Triple Junctions with All Angles < 180°	Number of Triple Junctions with One Angle = 180°
Drusy Calcite and Cement	Purbeckian, Dorset, England (20,225)	65	55
	Callovian, Isle of Wight, England (25,638)	124	83
	Bajocian, Lincolnshire, England (13,964)	100	57
	Bajocian, Lincolnshire, England (13,660)	101	51
	Bajocian, Lincolnshire, England (13,661)	74	57
	Lower Carboniferous, Anglesey, Wales (B 451)	41	50
	Lower Carboniferous, Yorkshire, England (13,979)	80	50
	Mississippian, New Mexico, U.S.A. (E 24)	67	59
	Locality unknown (CT 1)	103	44
Drusy-Replaced Molluscan Shell	Purbeckian, Dorset, England (20,225)	103	77
	Bajocian, Lincolnshire, England (13,661)	113	70
	Mississippian, New Mexico, U.S.A. (E 24)	36	50
Molluscan Shell Recrystallized *in situ*	Wealden, Sussex, England (8327)	79	3
	Purbeckian, Dorset, England (21,786)	171	8
	Purbeckian, Dorset, England (18,700)	174	6
	Purbeckian, Dorset, England (21,766)	177	3
Grain Growth Mosaic	Pennsylvanian, New Mexico, U.S.A.	174	6
	Lower Carboniferous, Yorkshire, England (4453 A)	174	6
	Lower Carboniferous, Yorkshire, England (4453 B)	175	5

Similarly it is unlikely that *MP* consists of a face *MO* and a compromise boundary *PO* (or vice versa). It is also improbable that *MO* and *PO* are the faces of the crystals β and γ, which were overgrown by α. Such coincidences are by their very nature exceedingly rare and cannot account for the observed high frequency of 180° triple junctions in para-axial drusy mosaic. There is, however, one other possible event which does satisfy the conditions. The boundary *MP* can be a face of the crystal α which did not grow while crystals β and γ were growing against it. Under these conditions, the face *MP* (of crystal α) would have been a stationary barrier during the development of the intercrystalline boundaries *MO* and *PO*. This event is the only one which is not dependent on an improbable geometrical coincidence. It will be assumed, therefore, that such an event was responsible for the growth of this special kind of junction. This 180° triple junction, in a chemically deposited fabric, will be called an *enfacial* junction (from the French *en*, Latin *in*, meaning "against").

Support for this interpretation of the enfacial junction comes from measurements of the angle between the optic axis of the crystal α (Figure 1) and the pole of its supposed face, also of the angle between this pole and cleavage which is parallel to $(10\bar{1}1)$. Data from a drusy cavity of calcite in the Carboniferous Limestone of Great Orme, Denbighshire, are given in Table 2. Bearing in mind the ac-

TABLE 2. *Crystallographic orientations of the face* MP *of the crystal* α *(Figure 1).*

Measurements with Universal Stage		Nearest Common Face
$c \wedge$ Pole of Face	Face $\wedge$ Cleavage	
(*a*) 88°		Prism: 90°
(*b*) 59°30′		$(35\bar{8}4)$: 59°55′
(*c*)	1°42′	$(10\bar{1}1)$
(*d*)	1°24′	$(10\bar{1}1)$
(*e*) 25°		$(01\bar{1}2)$: 26°15′
(*f*) 55°30′		$(35\bar{8}4)$: 59°55′
(*g*) 44°		$(10\bar{1}1)$: 44°36′
(*h*)	3°	$(10\bar{1}1)$
(*i*)	1°54′	$(10\bar{1}1)$
(*j*) 47°36′		$(10\bar{1}1)$: 44°36′

Data from drusy cavities in Carboniferous Limestone, Great Orme, Denbighshire (means of five readings).

curacy of measurements with the universal stage (c within 2° to 3° according to Turner, 1949), the identification of the crystal faces is clear for nine out of the ten results where the measured angle is within 3° of the expected. Even the value for f is probably as close as can be expected, considering that the errors of two angular measurements are involved.

In the location of optic axes Turner (1949) was followed ($c \wedge$ pole of face was determined on a stereographic net).

The Micrite Envelope and its Rupture

In many limestones some or even all of the skeletal particles are confined in thin envelopes of calcite micrite (Plate 1, Figures 3 and 4). This enclosing sheath is commonly between 10 and 50 μ thick (true thickness). In its undamaged state it adheres to the shell wall. It is of special interest that these envelopes clothe both brachiopods and mollusks, irrespective of whether the mollusk is still aragonite or has been replaced by drusy calcite or has been calcitized *in situ.* Whole particles are entirely enclosed, but the envelope only covers those fracture surfaces which were made before deposition. Fracture surfaces which developed during compaction are free. It is the spatial relationship of this envelope to the enclosed drusy calcite that is germane to the understanding of the process of aragonite replacement.

The micrite envelope differs from an oolitic coat in that it is not an encrusting addition to the shell, but is a replacement and cuts across the original shell fabric where this is preserved. Also it is unlaminated. Where only poorly developed, it consists of a collection of tubes filled with micrite. This arrangement is closely similar to that seen in modern Bahamian skeletal sands, and a detailed comparison was made with grains from Bimini lagoon. In these, the boring algae invade the skeleton and, when they die, the tubes are filled with fine-grained carbonate. This process can lead eventually to the total replacement of the skeleton by a grey-looking micrite.

It is important to note that the micrite envelope is unlikely to be an alteration product of molluscan aragonite as both mollusks and brachiopods are affected. It is also clear, from the sharpness of its fracture surfaces, that the envelope was rigid and brittle.

Many envelopes are fragmentary, and the broken pieces have been displaced, showing signs of inward collapse. This indicates the existence at some time of cavities within these envelopes. These signs of collapse are absent from the envelopes around brachiopods. There is

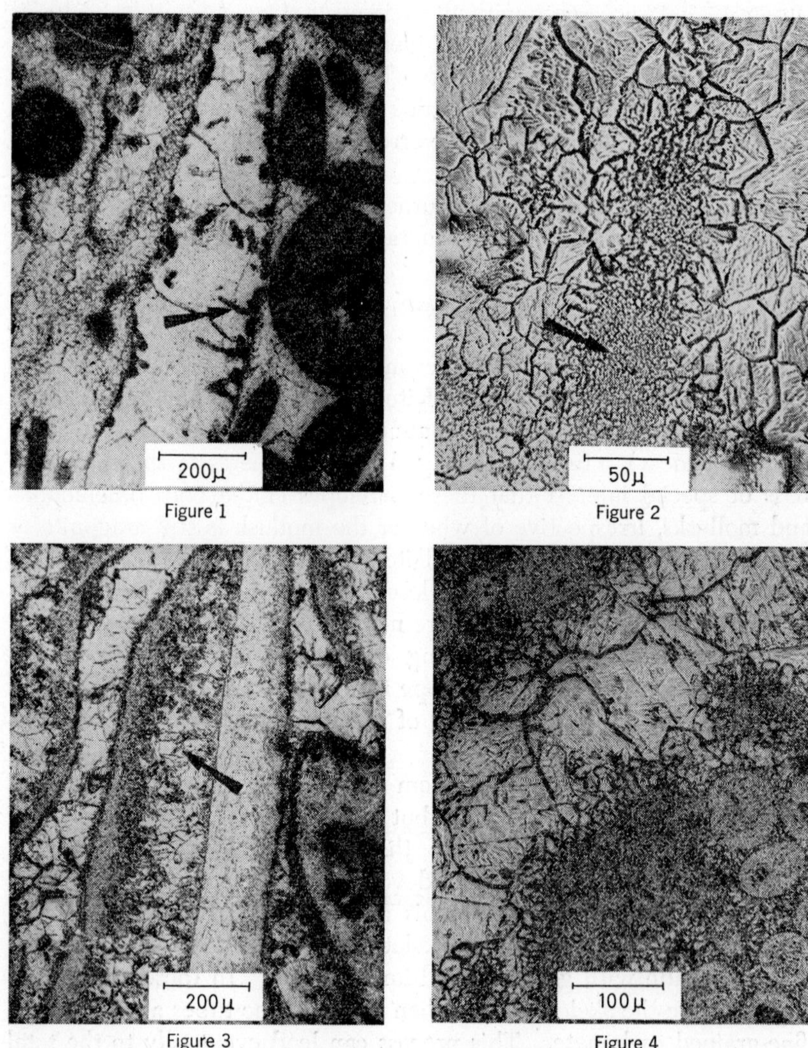

Plate 3 Fig. 1 Fragment of molluscan shell, replaced by coarse drusy calcite and containing micrite-filled bores (one by arrow); in cement. Purbeckian, Jurassic. Dorset (Slice). Fig. 2 Longitudinal section of a micrite-filled bore (arrow) in molluscan shell wall with enclosing drusy calcite. Mississippian. New Mexico (Peel). Fig. 3 Fragment of molluscan shell, enclosed in a micrite envelope with bores, and lying in cement. The aragonite layer has been replaced by drusy calcite (arrow), but the calcite layer (to the right of it) is intact. Inferior Oolite, Jurassic. Yorkshire (Peel). Fig. 4 Fragment of molluscan shell, replaced by drusy calcite, in oolite.

also evidence of another kind of rupture which, although it could be interpreted as exfoliation from a solid shell wall, is also absent from the envelopes of brachiopods.

INWARD COLLAPSE. Where fragments of the micrite envelope are displaced in such a way as to indicate that they now lie within the region formerly occupied by the solid shell wall, it is concluded that they collapsed into a cavity (Plate 2, Figures 1 and 2). Except for fracture, the envelope is entire. It does not show the reduction of volume which would be expected if its fragments had been forced into the solid shell wall during pressure solution nor does it interrupt the drusy fabric of the wall. In many examples the inward displacement of the envelope can be seen to coincide with the juxtaposition of another detrital particle (e.g., an oolith). This is so placed as to suggest that it forced the envelope inward and so caused the rupture. Yet another pattern shows displacement of a kind which can only have evolved by the thrusting of one part of an envelope over another (Plate 2, Figure 3). Care is needed here to insure that the disturbance arose by thrusting in the envelope alone and not by thrusting of one piece of solid shell wall over another.

Where broken pieces of envelope have early cement crystals on their outer and inner surfaces, but not on the fracture surfaces, it is concluded that fracture took place after cementation had started both on the outer micrite surface and within the mold (Plate 4, Figure 4).

ABSENCE OF COLLAPSED ENVELOPES ON BRACHIOPODS. The envelopes around brachiopods are not displaced. Otherwise they have similar textures and thicknesses to those on mollusks. This is consistent with the hypothesis that solution of the molluscan shell wall preceeded collapse.

OUTWARD DISPLACEMENT OF THE ENVELOPE. Commonly some broken parts of a molluscan envelope have been displaced outward away from their apparent original position. The difficulty about this type of evidence is that it could be interpreted as showing exfoliation of a loosely attached envelope. Yet, here too, displacements of this kind are not seen on brachiopod shells, on which the envelope is firmly fixed everywhere. This evidence is consistent with, though it does not clinch, the argument that solution of the molluscan shell released a thin and readily shattered micrite envelope. The case for solution is, however, strengthened by the fact that outwardly displaced envelopes and those showing inward collapse occur together in the same thin section and even at different places on and in the same molluscan valve. They differ simply in the direction of displacement of the envelope. The general impression, in thin section, is of an accumula-

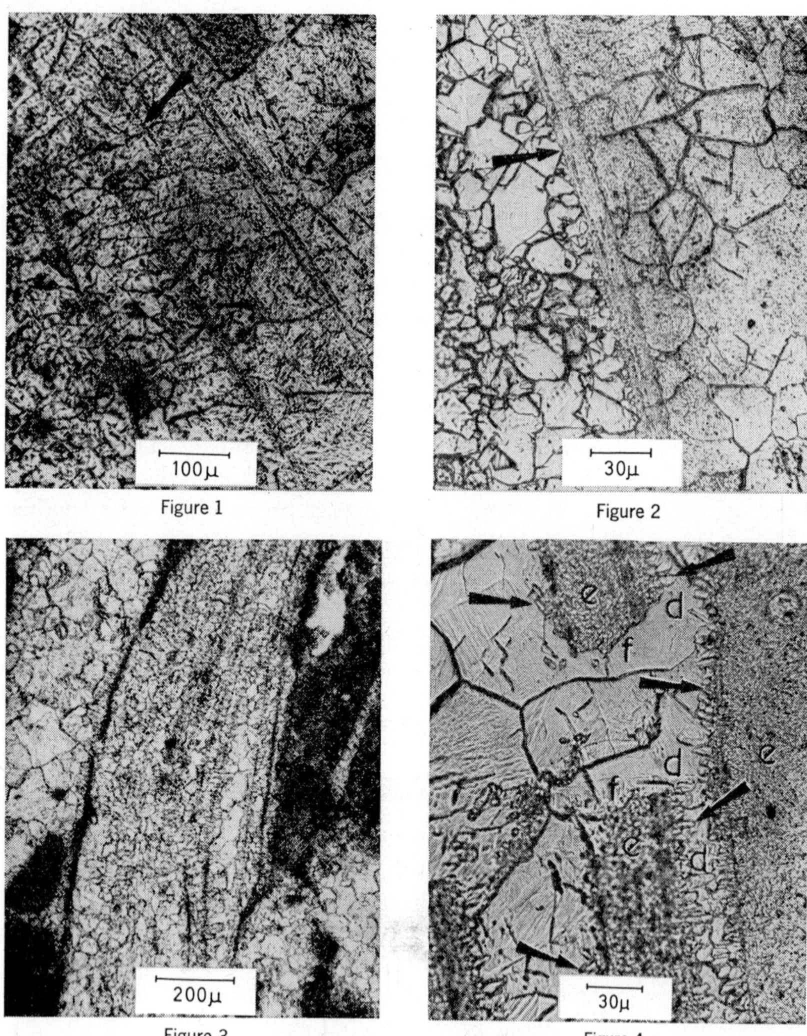

Figure 1
Figure 2
Figure 3
Figure 4

Plate 4 Fig. 1 Part of shell wall of the fresh-water gastropod Viviparus, *recrystallized* in situ. *Arrow shows line of inclusions cutting across intercrystalline boundary of calcite mosaic. Wealden, Lower Cretaceous. Sussex (Peel). Fig. 2 Part of shell wall of* Viviparus *(right), recrystallized* in situ. *Junction with cement (left) shown by arrow. Wealden, Lower Cretaceous. Sussex (Peel). Fig. 3 Part of molluscan shell wall, recrystallized* in situ, *in cement. Purbeckian, Jurassic. Dorset (Slice). Fig. 4 Fragments (e) of micrite envelope enclosing the remains of a drusy-filled cavity (d) formed by solution of molluscan aragonite. Early cement crystals (arrows) on outer and inner surfaces of envelope but not on fracture surface. (f). Inferior Oolite, Jurassic. Yorkshire (Peel).*

tion of envelopes, some undamaged, but others shattered by compaction and showing a complex arrangement of fragments depending on whether they burst inward, outward, or both.

Molluscan Valves Lining Cavities in Calcilutite

These yield useful evidence of replacement by solution-deposition. In Plate 2, Figure 4 a molluscan valve *DEFGBC* (now all calcite) lies partly embedded in calcilutite. Under a part of the valve, however, there is no calcilutite but, instead, the drusy filling of a cavity *ABGHIJ* of unknown origin. The following evidence shows that the valve was removed in solution, giving rise to a continuous cavity with walls (partly outside the figure) *ABCDEFGHIJ* which was later filled with para-axial drusy calcite.

1. Everywhere along the line *ABCDEFGHIJ* there is an increase in crystal size away from the calcilutite.
2. All the mosaic within the line *ABCDEFGHIJ* exhibits plane intercrystalline boundaries.
3. The small, early drusy crystals lining the cavity along the walls *AB, GH,* and *IJ* are indistinguishable in appearance from those projecting downward from the upper margin of the valve *DE* and upward from its lower margin along *CB* and *GF*.

If the valve had always been solid, then the roof of the cavity must have lain along *BG*. Yet the small, early drusy crystals which would have adhered to this roof are absent.

Absence of Relics of Internal Structure

Cases of recrystallization *in situ* of the molluscan shell are described later. Internal structures are preserved in these shells which are relics of those in the original aragonite shell. The absence of this kind of relic in the replaced aragonite shells considered here is contistent with the action of a process whereby internal structures are removed, as, for example, by solution.

Discussion

The existence, at one time, of an empty mold in place of the aragonite shell wall is indicated, first of all, by the drusy appearance of the secondary calcite. Nevertheless, it might be argued that there may exist some process of calcitization *in situ* which acts in much the same way as dolomitization, and gives a mosaic which mimics drusy fabric. Just as some dolomite crystals develop plane compromise boundaries, so also might this secondary calcite. If the calcitization were to spread inward from the margins of the shell wall, then competition for space might give rise to an increase of crystal size in the same direction. Yet this hypothesis will not stand examination on two counts. After dolomitization of limestone, relic structures commonly remain, but there are no relics in the shell walls in question. Even more important is the impossibility of equating any hypothesis of calcitization *in situ* with the evidence for inward collapse of the micrite envelope. These collapse structures form, with the drusy fabrics, the main foundations for the hypothesis of solution-deposition. Useful evidence also derives from the fabrics of replaced mollusks which once formed the walls of cavities in calcilutites.

There is other evidence which, though not conclusive, is consistent with this hypothesis. This evidence includes the absence of collapse structures on brachiopods, the outward displacement of envelopes on molluscan shells, and the absence of relic structures in the secondary calcite.

Taken together, these seem to be reasonable grounds for concluding that the aragonite shell was dissolved and that its mold was wholly or partly supported by the surrounding micrite envelope or the matrix of calcilutite and later filled with drusy calcite.

Recognition of the drusy filling of the shell mold is in some instances rather difficult owing to the local absence of a sharp boundary between the micrite envelope and the drusy mosaic. There is, instead, a gradational passage and the picture is often complicated by the presence of a good deal of micrite mixed up with the drusy mosaic. Some micrite patches float in two dimensions in the drusy mosaic (Plate 1, Figure 4; Plate 3, Figure 1). These areas of micrite within the shell wall were regarded, in the early course of this work, as possible relics of primary shell structure showing that recrystallization had occurred *in situ.* The true nature of the pattern became clear when Dr. Grant Gross showed, at the California Institute of Technology, sections of Pleistocene molluscan shells in which the distributions of micrite-filled bores (perhaps algal) closely resembled those seen in the Dinantian and Jurassic shells discussed here. The similarity between ancient micrite envelopes and Recent ones formed by the deposition of micrite in algal bores was noted later and has already been mentioned. Careful examination of many thin sections and peels in the ancient limestones has confirmed that the micrite areas seen in thin section are commonly sections through roughly cylindrical masses such as would be formed by bores filled with micrite (Plate 3, Figure

2). Concentrations of these around the margins of the shell wall lead to an untidy gradation between micrite and drusy mosaic. The larger bores are, in places, very clearly encrusted by a layer of small crystals like those of the early drusy mosaic in the rest of the shell wall. The filled bores were apparently sufficiently cemented and insoluble enough to remain when the aragonite went into solution. Sections of walls consisting mainly of this micritic material are interpreted as glancing sections nearly parallel to the wall surface.

The results of solution-deposition are visible in mollusks with mixed aragonite and calcite layers. Plate 3, Figure 3 shows a rounded molluscan fragment with the original calcite intact but with an adjacent layer of drusy calcite which, it must be assumed, has replaced aragonite. The fragment is enclosed in a micrite envelope and is extensively bored along its margins.

Where the drusy-replaced mollusk has no micrite envelope and is embedded in cement, its outline is revealed either by a dust line or by the position of the small early drusy crystals. These lie against the early crystals of the neighbouring cement.

Recrystallization *In Situ*

General

A few of the molluscan walls which were studied are without drusy characteristics, although they are composed of a calcite mosaic. This mosaic is undoubtedly secondary since there is no trace of the finer structure described by Bøggild (1930) for the Mollusca, by Newell (1942) for the late Paleozoic Pelecypoda, or figured for the Mollusca by Piveteau (1952). In many, a linear pattern of inclusions cuts across the mosaic (Plate 4, Figure 1), continuing with no deviation across the intercrystalline boundaries. These patterns are seen in section either as lines of inclusions in a clear mosaic or as lines of higher or lower density of inclusions in mosaics which are otherwise uniformly dusty with inclusions. Linear arrangements of intercrystalline boundaries also occur. All the patterns of lines are similar to those seen in sections through the lamellar structures of unaltered molluscan shell walls. It is assumed, therefore, that they are relics of original structure. It follows that the shell has been recrystallized *in situ.*

The Mosaic

The characteristics of this secondary calcite mosaic in thin section and peel are given below and illustrated in Plate 4, Figures 1–3.

1. The crystals vary in maximum visible diameter mainly from 10 to 300 μ when equant, the columnar crystals having lengths up to 500 μ. In range the crystal sizes are similar to those in drusy mosaic.

2. The smallest crystals are commonly, but not invariably, concentrated along the margins of the shell wall.

3. The intercrystalline boundaries are either consertal, gently curved or, uncommonly, plane.

4. Triple junctions with one angle equal to 180° are rare (see Table 1).

5. The patterns of inclusions are described above. They stop abruptly at the broken edge of a shell wall.

6. In some walls there are curved lines, commonly discontinuous and roughly parallel to the wall margins, which are formed of a broken series of intercrystalline boundaries, each of which forms a part of the curve. The line is made up of the intercrystalline boundaries of those crystals which touch it but do not cross it. Other crystals lie across the line so causing it to be discontinuous. It is not clear whether the surface (of which the line is a section) obstructed the growth of crystals or acted as a starting place for growth, or both. Its function as a starting place is suggested by the concentration, in some shells, of small crystals against this surface. Indeed, the coarseness of the mosaic commonly increases away from these lines.

7. In some molluscan walls (e.g., of the Purbeckian in the south of England) the mosaic is pale brown and pleochroic. J. D. Hudson (1963), who is working independently on these fabrics in great detail, has discovered that the color is related to the nature of the inclusions.

8. Some crystals have undulose extinction. A crystal 150 μ long may have a maximum range of extinction of as much as 10°.

9. There is, in some shells, a preferred orientation of the longer visible axis normal to the margins of the wall.

10. Commonly, where shells have been broken after deposition and their parts separated, the crystals on either side of the fracture would, if reunited, form continuous lattices. This means that recrystallization took place before fracture and before cementation had made the necessary movement impossible.

11. Where the shells are encased in micrite envelopes, like those described earlier, these envelopes do not show collapse structures.

Discussion

The fabric details show that the calcite mosaic has evolved *in situ;* whether directly or via an intermediate stage, it is not possible to say.

Brown (1961) has recorded molluscan walls consisting of a secondary, coarse aragonite mosaic (Purbeckian of Dorset, England). This may be an earlier stage. The process seems, at least in some limestones, to have begun before the sediment was cemented to a rigid framework, while shell fracture was still possible. The mechanism of the process is not obvious and it would be improper to describe it as inversion without more evidence. Replacement of aragonite by calcite via a water film across which material moves in solution is a possibility.

Time

An order of events is apparent for both processes of replacement. The fracture of shells after their calcitization *in situ* indicates that the replacement was completed before cementation had yielded a rigid framework. At this stage, also, some shells in micrite envelopes dissolved and their envelopes collapsed under load. The fracture surfaces of both the recrystallized shells and of the envelopes are usually unadorned by small, early cement crystals, even though these are present on the shell wall and on both outer and inner surfaces of the envelope (Plate 4, Figure 4). The corollary that fracture occurred, in both cases, after the early stages of cementation but before the final deposition of the coarse cement, emphasizes the duration of this important, though little understood, interval of time in cementation history.

This interval of time between early and late cementation, in limestones generally, is revealed in other ways. It is accentuated by chemical differences where, for example, the late cement is relatively iron-rich. It is also clear that the larger crystal size of the late-stage cement is not simply a result of survival in the competition for space of a few, more favorably oriented crystals of the early-stage cement. Where shells or micrite envelopes have been broken after deposition of early stage cement, as in Plate 4, Figure 4, the later cementation on the fracture surfaces has not proceeded by growth of many tiny crystals (as in the early cement). This is in spite of the many available nuclei in the fracture surfaces of these multicrystalline materials. In other words, there was a lower nucleation density in the later stage, although the wall (shell or envelope) was similarly fine grained at both stages. Is it, instead, possible that the coarseness of the late cement is a product of reduced supply of dissolved carbonate, brought about by a lowering of permeability during early cementation? Or is late-stage nucleation hindered because of chemical differences between late and early cement so great that one will not grow syntaxially on the other?

Where a drusy cast of a shell wall now lies with no envelope, simply encased either in cement or in calcilutite, the aragonite can only have been dissolved after enough cement had been laid down to support a mold. Doubtless complete cementation was unnecessary. Even where the shell had a micrite envelope some degree of cementation may have been necessary to give this the support to resist crushing.

The solution of molluscan aragonite is strikingly demonstrated in limestones by the great volume of drusy replacements. The sight of heaps of discarded and broken envelopes encourages the suspicion that enormous quantities of molluscan shell may have disappeared without leaving even this record of their former presence. It is necessary to consider how many were removed in solution before a viable mold had been developed either by the formation of a micrite envelope, the cementation of a calcilutite, or the deposition of pore cement. The present molluscan content of limestones may be very small compared with the initial content, much of which has gone without a trace.

Space: Aragonite Solution and the Growth of Calcite

The movement of large quantities of dissolved aragonite, out of the developing molds into other parts of the sediment, has implications which must now be examined. There is no doubt that some molds were totally emptied of solid material, because some micrite envelopes have been so crushed that their opposing sides met.

The carbonate sediments, in which molluscan debris is replaced in this way, may be considered crudely as mixtures of aragonite and calcite. As aragonite is the more soluble polymorph, the pore water is likely to be saturated for this mineral and supersaturated for calcite. There will, therefore, be a tendency for ions to leave aragonite surfaces and to grow either on existing calcite lattices or to form fresh calcite nuclei. There is no question, here, of a general solution of all the carbonate. The primary calcite skeletons show no sign of solution. In some sediments as old as the Permian the aragonite is preserved intact, though only where the shells are embedded in a matrix of low permeability, such as clay, shale, or pitch. It is also preserved (with little or no calcite cement) in marine carbonate sediments containing connate pore water, and in those which lie above the meteoric water-table. Yet, where the sediment has been immersed in ground water (derived from rain), aragonite has been dissolved and drusy calcite deposited. The example of the Late Pleistocene Miami Oolite (Ginsberg, 1957, p. 96) is one of a growing number of records which illustrates this principle. Where the oolite "is still in the marine environment or above the ground-water table it is so friable that it can easily be broken down into individual ooliths." At the exposed surface or where it is below the ground-water level it is "thoroughly cemented by calcite" (Ginsberg, 1957, p. 96). The restriction of this solution-deposition process to limestones of initially high permeability is probably related both to their accessability to ground-water and to the free movement of solutions through the pore system. Maxwell (1960) has recently experimentally demonstrated the greater effectiveness of flowing solutions over static ones during compaction of a quartz sand by solution and redeposition.

How far do the ions migrate before redeposition? Is the distance to be measured in microns or feet? These are problems still to be solved. Much must depend on the distribution and quantities of aragonite and calcite as well as on the rate of movement and chemical composition of the solution, and variations in temperature and pressure. What does appear certain is that a great deal of calcite cement must have been derived locally from molluscan shells, many of which have disappeared. There is also the further possibility that, in a permeable limestone, the dissolved molluscan carbonate may be carried right away from its parent sediment, so leading to a major development of secondary porosity.

The Cavity Stage in Pleistocene Limestones: A Postscript

More than a year after this paper had been submitted the author was shown a collection of thin sections of Pleistocene limestones from Bermuda, by Gerald Friedman, in the laboratories of the Pan American Petroleum Corporation, Tulsa, Oklahoma. Here, for the first time since the concept of the empty micrite envelope had been worked out (on the basis of fabrics in fully cemented Carboniferous and Jurassic limestones), the author saw cavities in all stages of solution and redeposition. In these limestones the molluscan aragonite had begun to dissolve while the skeletal grains were still only lightly cemented with calcite about their points of contact. Where the micrite envelopes were empty, the cementation of the primary pores was no more advanced. Filling of the envelopes with drusy calcite was also well advanced or complete before the primary pores were filled.

The stages of fabric evolution agree well with Friedman's mineralogical data (1964). These indicate a change from a sediment of mixed aragonite and high-magnesium calcite to a fully cemented limestone of nearly pure low-magnesium calcite. In the field, the least altered material was splashed by sea spray. The most altered limestones were inland and only wetted by rain water.

REFERENCES

American Geological Institute, 1960, *Supplement to the Glossary of Geology and Related Sciences:* Washington, D.C., 72 pp.

Bathurst, R. G. C., 1958, Diagenetic fabrics in some British Dinantian limestones: *Liverpool Manchester Geol. J.*, v. 2, pp. 11–36.

________ 1959*a*, Diagenesis in Mississippian calcilutites and pseudobreccias: *J. Sed. Petrol.*, v. 29, pp. 365–376.

________ 1959*b*, The cavernous structure of some Mississippian *Stromatactis* reefs in Lancashire, England: *J. Geol.*, v. 67, pp. 506–521.

Bøggild, O. B., 1930, The shell structure of the mollusks: *K. Danske Vidensk. Selsk. Skrifter, Naturvidensk. og Mathem. Afd., 9. Raekke,* II, v. 2, pp. 231–326.

Brown, P. R., 1961, *Petrology of the Lower and Middle Purbeck Beds of Dorset:* Ph.D. thesis, University of Liverpool.

Clark, P. S., 1957, A note on calcite-aragonite equilibrium: *Am. Mineralogist,* v. 42, pp. 564–566.

Folk, R. L., 1959, Practical petrographic classification of limestones: *Am. Assoc. Petrol. Geologists Bull.*, v. 43, pp. 1–38.

Ginsburg, R. N., 1957, Early diagenesis and lithification of shallow-water carbonate sediments in south Florida: in *Regional Aspects of Carbonate Deposition,* Soc. Econ. Mineralogists Paleontologists Special Publication n. 5, pp. 80–99.

Jamieson, J. C., 1953, Phase equilibrium in the system calcite-aragonite: *J. Chem. Phys.*, v. 21, pp. 1385–1390.

________ 1957, Introductory studies at high-pressure polymorphism to 24,000 bars by X-ray diffraction with some comments on calcite—II: *J. Geol.,* v. 65, pp. 334–343.

Johnston, J., H. E. Merwin, and E. D. Williamson, 1916, The several forms of calcium-carbonate: *Am. J. Sci.*, v. 41, pp. 473–512.

Lander, J. J., 1949, Polymorphism and anion rotational disorder in the alkaline earth carbonates: *J. Chemistry Physics,* v. 17, pp. 892–901.

MacDonald, G. J. F., 1956, Experimental determination of calcite-aragonite equilibrium relations at elevated temperatures: *Am. Mineralogist,* v. 41, pp. 744–756.

Maxwell, J. C., 1960, Experiments on compaction and cementation of sand: *Geol. Soc. Am. Mem. 79,* pp. 105–132.

Newell, N. D., 1942, Late Paleozoic Pelecypods: Mytilacea: *University of Kansas Publication,* State Geol. Survey of Kansas, v. 10, pt. 2, pp. 1–115.

Piveteau, J., 1952, *Traité de Paléontologie,* Tome II, Paris, Masson et Cie., 785 pages.

Turner, F. J., 1949, Preferred orientation of calcite in Yule marble: *Am. J. Sci.*, v. 247, pp. 593–621.

Skeletal Durability and Preservation

by Keith E. Chave *Lehigh University, Bethlehem, Pennsylvania*

Introduction

Paleontologists and paleoecologists deal with fossil assemblages. In almost every geological situation at least part of the original life assemblage has been lost. It is common to accept the fact that the soft parts of organisms normally are missing from the fossil record. It is also common to assume, perhaps without being conscious of it, that all or most of the mineralized skeletal parts are preserved. The data presented in this chapter suggest that this is generally not warranted.

Laboratory experiments, aimed at testing the resistance of various types of skeletal materials to destructive forces, have been carried out. Field studies on Bermuda, Campeche Bank, and elsewhere have been used to check the validity of the results. Quantitative and qualitative data have been obtained which indicate wide ranges of skeletal durability under differing types of physical, chemical, and biological attack. Physical destructive processes have been studied in the laboratory by use of tumbling barrels. Studies of chemical destructive forces have been limited to experiments on the solubility of skeletal materials in aqueous solutions. Biological destruction of skeletal materials has been observed and described by many writers, but no significant quantitative work has, to date, been reported upon.

Physical Destruction

In nature, physical destruction of skeletal materials is largely limited to depositional environments. Under marine conditions, most of this destruction probably takes place in shallow water and is accom-

This research has been supported by the Petroleum Research Fund of the American Chemical Society.

plished by the action of waves and strong currents. The actual breakup of skeletons is, for the most part, due to particle-against-particle abrasion. Laboratory studies of the resistance of skeletal parts to physical destruction have been carried out using tumbling barrels to simulate the effects of waves and currents and provide the particle-against-particle abrasion. Some of the results of these experiments have been reported (Chave, 1960).

Three series of experiments were performed. In the first, skeletal parts were placed in a one-and-one-half gallon porcelain tumbling barrel, with chert pebbles and tap water adjusted to pH 8 with $NaHCO_3$ and tumbled at the relatively slow rate of 30 rpm. Periodically the contents of the barrels were sieved, weighed, and examined microscopically, and then returned to the barrel for further tumbling. Some of the results of these experiments are shown in Figures 1 and 2.

The figures illustrate the percentage of skeletal carbonate larger than 4 mm as a function of tumbling time on a log scale. Initially, all samples were larger than 4 mm. The most durable form tested was the compact intertidal and supratidal snail, *Nerita*. After 183 hours of tumbling the shells were somewhat worn but nevertheless specific identification was still possible. The least durable forms

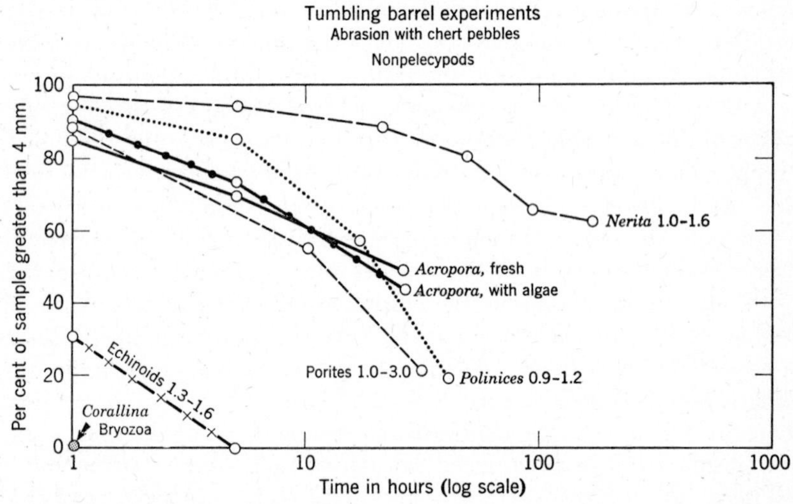

Fig. 1 Durability of nonpelecypods. Percentage of original sample remaining larger than 4 mm after various periods of time in the tumbling barrel. Numbers following skeletal name are range of size of specimens in inches.

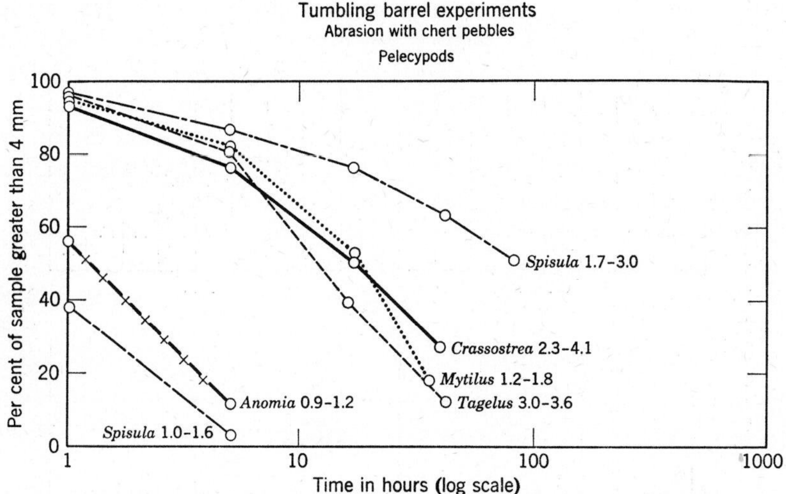

Fig. 2 Durability of pelecypods (see caption to Fig. 1).

tested were filamentous calcareous algae and bryozoa, which were reduced to unrecognizable particles in less than one hour. Intermediate in durability were various pelecypods, gastropods, corals, and echinoids. *Acropora cervicornis,* the staghorn coral, both clean and encrusted with lithothamnioid algae, was tumbled in order to determine if the encrustation influences durability; apparently it does not.

A second series of experiments was carried out using silica sand in place of chert pebbles; otherwise the conditions were the same as in the previous experiment. In these runs, the rates of skeletal destruction were slower than with the chert pebbles, but the relative rates were much the same. In one experiment, a mixture of typical shallow-water skeletal types from Corona del Mar, California, was tumbled with silica sand. Some of the results of this experiment are shown in Figure 3. The skeletons and their original weights, were: *Mytilus,* a mussel, 48 gm; *Aletes,* a colonial gastropod, 23 gm; *Haliotis,* an abalone, 17 gm; *Tegula,* a turban snail, 9 gm; various species of small limpets, 6 gm; *Strongylocentrotus,* an echinoid, 8 gm; *Piaster,* a starfish, 6 gm; and *Corallina,* a red calcareous alga, 7 gm. At the end of 40 hours the echinoids, starfish, and algae were no longer present in the greater than 2 mm class, yet the mollusks were only slightly worn. At the end of the 183-hour experiment, two of the mussels were nearly whole, but had holes near the hinge; the third was in

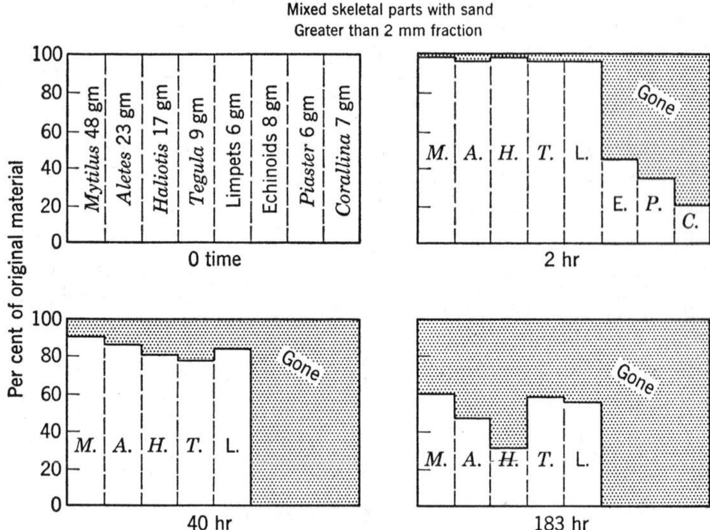

Fig. 3 Physical destruction of skeletal assemblage from Corona del Mar, California. Percentage of original sample larger than 2 mm after 2, 40, and 183 hours of tumbling.

several pieces. The *Aletes* colony was reduced to half-size, but was easily recognizable. The abalone was broken in several pieces. *Tegula* and the limpets were worn but probably could have been identified as to species.

In the third series of experiments, skeletal parts were tumbled alone in the water, abrasion being caused by skeleton-against-skeleton contact. Again a wide range of durabilities was observed. The order of destruction was somewhat different from the previous experiments because the size and weight of the skeletal parts affected the force of impact, and therefore the durability.

Although experiments on the resistance of skeletal materials to physical destructive forces are still in progress, several conclusions appear valid. First and foremost, the durability of skeletal materials varies widely, more widely than with other types of sedimentary mineral grains. Second, skeletal mineralogy does not exert a clear influence on physical durability. The most durable form studied, *Nerita,* is composed of calcite and aragonite. The next most durable are calcitic *Crassostrea,* mixed calcitic and aragonitic *Mytilus,* and aragonitic *Polinices, Spisula* (large size), *Tegelus,* and several corals.

The least durable are calcitic *Anomia,* echinoids and *Corallina,* and aragonitic bryozoa and *Spisula* (small size).

The third conclusion that can be reached is that the size of the skeletal part has some effect on physical durability, but it is not a controlling factor. For instance, specimens of *Anomia, Mytilus,* and *Spisula* of approximately the same size and weight performed quite differently in the tumbling barrel. This is illustrated in Table 1. *Mytilus* is clearly the most durable form. On the other hand, "large *Spisula*" (1.7 to 3.0 in.) is much more durable than the smaller representative of the same genus (1.0 to 1.6 in.), as seen in Figure 2.

Apparently the major factors controlling the resistance of skeletal materials to physical destruction are the microarchitecture of the shell and the disposition of organic matrix among the crystals of carbonate. Dense, fine-grained skeletons are the most durable—*Nerita, Spisula, Mytilus,* etc. Of intermediate durability are the hard, somewhat porous structures of the corals and the organic-rich, coarsely crystalline shells of the oysters. The least durable forms are those with much openwork and organic matrix—echinoderms, bryozoa, algae, etc.

It appears, from the data presented, that in shallow, agitated environments, complex life assemblages of skeletal types can be modified by physical abrasion to produce a simple assemblage of durable skeletons which may be preserved in the fossil record. The final assemblage may not be a good representation of the life assemblage or of the environment from which it came. An example of what appears to be the result of these processes, from the geologic record, is illustrated in Plate 19 of the *United States' Geological Survey, Professional Paper 195* (Woodring et al., 1940). The illustration shows a slab of coarse sandstone containing fairly well-preserved robust gastropods, *Neverita* and *Olivella,* and fragments of less robust pelecypods, *Anadara* and *Volsella.* No other fossils are evident, although it appears probable that the life assemblage from which this fossil assemblage was derived contained other more fragile forms. Paleoeco-

TABLE 1. *Weight percentage of original shell material larger than 4 mm after being tumbled with chert pebbles*

Genus	Number of Specimens	Average Weight (gm)	Time Tumbled (hours) 1	5	17	36
Mytilus	18	1.1	95.7	82.1	51.3	17.3
Spisula	18	0.9	38.3	2.7	....	....
Anomia	14	0.9	61.0	1.1	....	....

of unstable carbonate minerals are significantly more soluble in natural waters than those composed of the stable form. Thus, mineral stabilization may occur by solution and either dispersion of the dissolved ions or redeposition as stable calcite. Stabilization by this mechanism could prevent a great deal of skeletal material from being preserved in the geologic record.

It has been suggested that aragonite and magnesium calcite are being dissolved on the sea floor (Chave, 1962). The importance of this process, in terms of volume of skeletal material, is not known. Solution of skeletons in sedimentary rocks after uplift appears to be a significant mechanism of destruction of fossil evidence. If the enclosing sediments are firm at the time solution takes place, a cast mold will be preserved. If, on the other hand, solution occurs in an unconsolidated sediment, evidence for the existence of the fossil may be lost.

An interesting example of what appears to be the effect of solutional removal of shell material by ground water occurs in the upper Navesink formation of the Upper Cretaceous of New Jersey. At Nutt Creek (Stop 5, second day, *1st Annual Atlantic Coastal Plain Field Trip Guidebook*, 1960), the fauna collected by the writer and 12 graduate students included:

Exogyra costata — *Choristothyris plicata*
Exogyra cancellata — *Paranomia* sp.
Ostrea mesenterica — *Belemnitella americana*
Gryphaea convexa — pelagic Foraminifera
Pecten sp. — ostracodes

Also included were a few poorly preserved casts and molds of gastropods and other pelecypods.

The fossil fauna contains representatives of all modern taxonomic groups which deposit stable, calcitic skeletons, with the exception of the barnacles and the pelagic algae. The original mineralogy of the belemnites is unknown. There are here no representatives of taxonomic groups which today deposit unstable minerals. The rock from which the fossil assemblage was collected is quite friable; thus casts and molds are rare. It seems very likely that this Upper Cretaceous fossil assemblage from New Jersey is the "insoluble residue" of a much larger, diverse fauna and flora, most of which has left no record.

It is interesting to note that the only Foraminifera represented, to any extent, at this locality are pelagic. Thus paleoecologic interpretation based upon a pelagic:benthonic foraminiferal ratio would place this shallow-water oyster-bank fauna in the deep sea. The enigma appears to result from the fact that pelagic Foraminifera have tests of low solubility calcite, and benthic Foraminifera have tests of more soluble magnesium-calcite and occasionally aragonite.

It appears that a life assemblage of skeletal materials can be drastically altered by solution in natural waters, producing a strangely biased fossil assemblage. Destruction of the skeletal remains, in this case, is controlled by original mineralogy. Erroneous paleoecologic interpretations may be made of such assemblages.

Biological Destruction

Biological destruction of skeletal materials occurs mainly in depositional environments. Destructive processes include the dropping of shells on rocks by sea birds; the gnawing activities of fish, crabs, and other animals; boring activities of sponges, algae, pelecypods, and snails; burrowing activities of sediment-feeding worms, mollusks, and echinoderms; and bacterial destruction of organic integuments within calcareous skeletons. The effects of many of these processes have been discussed by Ginsburg (1957).

There are essentially no quantitative data in the literature on the importance of biologic destructive processes in nature. Little is known, even qualitatively, about the ecologic factors controlling biologic destruction. Many of the activities of sediment feeders and burrowers are impressive to observe. Sediment ingestion by holothurians, for instance, is quantitatively enormous, (Crozier, 1918; Mayor, 1924; Ginsburg, 1957; and others). Nonetheless, the only quantitative data available that indicate significant effects of holothurians on mineral grains are two poorly described experiments by Mayor. Crozier, on the other hand, after qualitative observations of holothurians concluded that the effect of passage of sediment through the gut was quite small. Actually, it would appear that enzymatic extraction of organic nutrients from carbonate sediments at a low pH would be a very inefficient process. A large amount of energy would be required to maintain a low pH, even locally, within the gut. It appears most probable that organic nutrients are obtained from the sediments at a pH of about 8, and therefore the only possible effect on the sediment would be mechanical abrasion during the passage through the animal.

Burrowing worms, mollusks, and echinoderms, as well as such browsing forms as parrot fish, process large amounts of skeletal sedimentary material to obtain food. At the present time, it is not clear whether these activities have a major role in the destruction of skeletal materials, a minor one, or none at all. Likewise, the boring activities of mollusks, sponges, and algae have never been investigated quantitatively. Thus the over-all importance of these processes is not known.

Processes of biologic destruction of skeletal materials are readily observed in many natural environments. Their significance in terms of the overall problem of skeletal preservation and fossilization, however, is unknown. This field is ripe for quantitative investigation.

Summary

The fossil record does not provide a complete picture of a life assemblage or an environment. Soft parts are, of course, commonly destroyed early. In many depositional and postdepositional environments, mineralized hard parts are also lost from the record.

Skeletal materials exhibit a wide range of durabilities. Calcareous skeletal parts are destroyed by physical processes in the high-energy environments of shallow water. Physical durability is controlled by the microarchitecture of the shell. Chemical solution may occur in both depositional and postdepositional environments. Chemical durability is controlled by skeletal mineralogy. Biological durability is complex, and at present not understood.

Paleoecologic interpretations of fossil assemblages from rocks representing high-energy depositional environments and from rocks of high permeability are difficult because of selectivity of destruction of skeletal elements. Paleoecologic interpretations of assemblages from relatively impermeable rocks or representing low-energy environments may, in many cases, be more satisfactory.

At best, paleoecological interpretations are difficult and the factors of selective destruction should be kept in mind in order that valid interpretations might be made.

REFERENCES

Bøggild, O. B., 1930, Shell structure of mollusks: *Danske Vidensk. Silsk.*, v. 9, pt. 2, pp. 235–326.

Chave, K. E., 1952, A solid solution between calcite and dolomite: *J. Geol.*, v. 60, pp. 190–192.

________ 1954, Aspects of the biogeochemistry of magnesium, Pt. 1: Calcareous marine organisms: *J. Geol.*, v. 62, pp. 266–283.

________ 1960, Carbonate skeletons to limestones: Problems: *Trans. N. Y. Acad. Sci.*, ser. II, v. 23, pp. 14–24.

——— 1962, Factors influencing the mineralogy of carbonate sediments: *Limnol. and Oceanog.*, v. 7, pp. 218–233.

Chave, K. E., K. S. Deffeyes, R. M. Garrels, M. E. Thompson, and P. K. Weyl, 1962, Observations on the solubility of skeletal carbonates in aqueous solutions: *Science,* v. 137, pp. 33–34.

Crozier, W. J., 1918, The amount of bottom material ingested by holothurians: *J. Exptl. Biol.,* v. 26, pp. 379–383.

Ginsburg, R. N., 1957, Early diagenesis and lithification of shallow-water carbonate sediments in south Florida: Regional aspects of carbonate deposition, *Soc. Econ. Paleontologists and Mineralogists,* pp. 80–100.

Graf, D. L., and J. R. Goldsmith, 1955, Dolomite-magnesian calcite relations at elevated temperatures and CO_2 pressures: *Geochim. Cosmochim. Acta,* v. 7, pp. 109–128.

Harker, R. I., and D. F. Tuttle, 1955, Studies of the system CaO-MgO-CO_2: *Am. J. Sci.,* v. 253, pp. 274–282.

Jamieson, J. C., 1953, Phase equilibrium in the system calcite-aragonite: *J. Chem. Phys.,* v. 21, pp. 1385–1390.

Lowenstam, H. A., 1954, Factors affecting aragonite-calcite ratios in carbonate secreting marine organisms: *J. Geol.,* v. 62, pp. 284–322.

Mayor, A. G., 1924, Causes which produce stable conditions in the depth of the floors of the Pacific fringing reef flats: *Carnegie Inst. Wash.,* v. 340, pp. 27–36.

Meigen, W., 1903, Beitrage zur Kenntnis der Kohlensauren Kalk: *Naturu. Gesell. Frieburg,* v. 13, pp. 1–55.

Woodring, W. P., R. Stewart, and R. W. Richards, 1940, Geology of the Kettleman Hills oil field, California: *U. S. Geol. Surv. Prof. Paper 195,* 170 pp.

Preservation of Primary Structures and Fabrics in Dolomite

by R. C. Murray *Shell Development Company (A Division of Shell Oil Company), Exploration and Production Research Division, Houston, Texas*

ABSTRACT

Several mechanisms serve to illustrate that dolomitization does not universally destroy all primary structures and fabrics and that the nature of the dolomitizing water may determine, in part, the degree of preservation or apparent preservation obtained.

During dolomitization, the growth of new crystals within a limestone commonly shows a strong tendency to replace carbonate and to avoid pre-existing void space. This preference for growth by replacement as opposed to growth as cement has been interpreted as indicating that the dolomite grew by use of locally derived carbonate ion. Preference for replacement by dolomite causes the preservation of original cavities in organisms, fossil molds formed prior to dolomitization, and interparticle voids in cement-free or slightly cemented carbonate sands. This preference for replacement thus reproduces the original fabric or structure in dolomite. Organisms that resist dolomitization in early stages, such as crinoid parts, may be preserved as excellent molds by dissolution of the skeletal material as part of the dolomitization process. Internal structure of both skeletal and nonskeletal particles is sometimes preserved as inclusions within replacement dolomite crystals. Excellent preservation is sometimes achieved because of differences in dolomite crystal size, orientation, and clarity.

Zoned dolomite crystals exhibiting clear rims and cloudy centers may be misinterpreted as a replaced carbonate-pellet sand fabric.

The writer gratefully acknowledges the generous assistance given by his colleagues at Shell Development Company during the formulation of these ideas and preparation of the manuscript. He is especially indebted to F. J. Lucia, R. J. Dunham, R. J. Stanton, J. L. Wilson, R. Rezak, and K. S. Deffeyes.

These clear rims are believed to result from excess dissolution of $CaCO_3$ by volume over precipitation of dolomite in the immediate area of the growing dolomite rhomb. Such excess dissolution should occur during *local-source* dolomitization.

Introduction

It is not uncommon to find statements in the literature that suggest that the growth of replacement dolomite in carbonate rock causes total obliteration of primary organic and inorganic structures and fabrics. This is certainly true in some examples. Indeed, it would be unrealistic to expect that a rock subjected to any alteration process would emerge with as clear a record of original features as the original material. However, it is also clear that many of the original or predolomitization features are often preserved in dolomite, thus permitting the gathering of data useful in reconstructing paleoecologic and other aspects of depositional environments. This point is amply documented by many dolomitized specimens, both organic and inorganic, that may be found in any study collection, and by many classic paleoecologic studies of carbonate rock bodies which include abundant dolomite; for example, the Niagaran reefs of the Great Lakes area (Lowenstam, 1950), the Permian reef complex (Newell et al., 1953), and the Ellenburger group of central Texas (Cloud and Barnes, 1948) illustrate such studies. It is doubtful that, had these authors been given their choice, they would have chosen to have had their rocks altered by extensive growth of replacement dolomite. In each study, the authors have recognized the limitations placed on the study by whatever loss of preservation had taken place. However, because of some preservation of original features, it has been possible to make contributions to our knowledge of original carbonate sediments and sedimentary environments. This preservation has commonly been in the form of delicately preserved fossils or fossil molds and sedimentary structures and fabrics.

The purpose of this paper is to examine, and advance interpretations for, some of the common mechanisms by which some primary features are preserved or appear to be preserved in dolomite. The discussion has been divided into sections on skeletal remains and inorganic sedimentary structures. This distinction is used only to separate the examples; the fact is recognized that the cause of preservation may be more dependent on the conditions of dolomitization than on the origin of the feature.

Preservation of Skeletal Remains

Selective Replacement of Skeletal Material with Preservation of Organic Voids

Colonial organisms, such as tabulate corals and bryozoans, that build skeletons of calcium carbonate are commonly dolomitized with a distinct preference for replacement of the original carbonate. Dolomite has grown by replacement in existing calcite or aragonite and has not grown as new crystals in existing void spaces. This type of preservation is especially good when the cavity is considerably larger than the dolomite rhomb size. In the tabulate corals, the cavity within the corallite is commonly preserved as a void, with only terminations of crystals that began growth within the skeleton penetrating into the original cavity. Such a preference for replacement produces a fairly accurate gross reproduction of the organism. The preference for dolomite to grow by replacement of existing carbonate and to

1 inch

Fig. 1 Syringopora: *This completely dolomitized colony exhibits growth of dolomite within the sediment between the corallites. The body chambers and corallites are very well preserved as voids.*

Fig. 2 Favosites: *The skeleton has been completely dolomitized, with preservation of the original voids. These voids occupy more than half the volume of the specimen.*

avoid the growth of new crystals in pre-existing void space has been interpreted (Murray, 1960) as indicating that the dolomite grew by utilizing a local source of carbonate ion. Specifically, if dolomitization is accomplished by a water relatively low in total CO_2 with respect to Ca and Mg, as described by Weyl (1960), local utilization of carbonate in volume-for-volume replacement should occur. Furthermore, growth of a replacement dolomite rhomb should be accompanied by dissolution of calcium carbonate beyond the volume of the rhomb. This excess dissolution provides the carbonate necessary for growing a solid dolomite crystal. The excess carbonate is necessary because dolomite requires 12 to 13% more carbonate for a given volume than calcite, and because the solid dolomite rhomb often occupies a volume that had some pore space and thus was deficient in carbonate. Under these conditions, the rhomb should grow where that carbonate is available, namely, within pre-existing calcite or aragonite by replacement and not within the larger void space as new crystals. Dolomite cement does occur both as overgrowths on earlier crystals and sometimes as new crystals. However, in the writer's experience, the latter is relatively uncommon. There are many spectacular examples of pre-existing void space preserved after dolomitization.

Paleozoic examples of this type of preservation in corals are shown in Figures 1 and 2. Cullis (1904, p. 409, Figs. 62–64) discusses and illustrates several examples of this type of preferential replacement in the dolomitized corals found in Funafuti boring. His Figure 62 has the following caption:

> Coral substance converted into dolomite; cavities empty, except for a lining of clear dolomite crystals, separated from the recrystallised coral by a well-marked "dirt line."

Where calcite or aragonite cement has been deposited prior to dolomitization or where carbonate sediment is introduced into the colony, as in the case of *Syringopora* (Figure 1), this carbonate may also be replaced by dolomite.

Selective Replacement of Carbonate Rock Matrix with Preservation of Fossil Molds Developed Prior to Dolomitization

Dissolution of skeletal material, particularly of those organisms or parts of organisms that are more susceptible to solution alteration, may occur prior to dolomitization. Molds produced by selective dissolution are common in limestone. When a limestone with fossil molds is dolomitized, it is not uncommon for dolomite to grow within the existing rock and to avoid growth of new crystals as dolomite cement in void space. The evidence necessary to prove conclusively that the development of the mold predates the dolomitization is very difficult to obtain. Bathurst (1958) discusses the criteria used to identify calcite and aragonite void-filling cements and, as such, is a useful reference for workers attempting to establish this type of time relationship. If the mold is lined with a drusy calcite or aragonite mosaic which grew into pre-existing void space, and dolomite has replaced the drusy cement, the mold at least predates the dolomitization of the cement. This interpretation of the time relationship between mold and dolomitization is valid, because the mold had to exist at the time of deposition of the calcium carbonate drusy mosaic. If molds of a particular organism formed prior to dolomitization, similar molds should also exist in associated limestone beds. This would be true if the limestone which was dolomitized and that which was not were originally similar, and if both had been subjected to predolomitization leaching.

Many molds of brachiopods, gastropods, and cephalopods, commonly with internal casts of dolomitized sediment, exist. These internal casts of dolomitized sediment or the outer surface of the mold itself may be used for identification purposes. If formation of the mold by dissolution precede dolomitization, preferential growth of dolomite by replacement as opposed to growth as cement may permit preservation of the mold.

Selective Removal of an Organism that is Resistant to Dolomitization

Dissolution of skeletal material to produce molds may accompany dolomitization or may follow partial dolomitization. The latter case would require selective replacement of the rock by dolomite that avoided growth within a particular organism. The organism, still calcite or aragonite, would be available for later selective dissolution, leaving a mold in the dolomitized rock. This selective dissolution might be accomplished during exposure to weathering on an outcrop. This postdolomitization leaching may be poorly selective, producing poor preservation. The imperfect preservation may result from dissolution of some dolomite.

Perhaps the most common example of production of molds of fossils that selectively resist dolomitization is the preservation of crinoid columnals and calyxes in completely dolomitized rock. In such rocks, other skeletal debris, such as bryozoan material, which may be less resistant to dolomitization is commonly replaced. Murray (1960) and Lucia (1962) have noted that these single-crystal skeletal particles are observed in all stages of incomplete dolomitization and in associated limestone. Lucia has reported evidence for dissolution of lime mud that existed between crinoid particles with preservation of the crinoid particles as calcite in limestone associated with dolomite. However, in associated rocks that have been completely dolomitized, the crinoid particles either have been removed to form molds or have been replaced as single crystals of dolomite. The suggestion has been made that, in the early stages of dolomitization, the dolomite grows preferentially within carbonate mud between the particles with slight impingement of the crystals on the particles. In the later stages of local-source dolomitization, the calcite in some of the crinoid fragments is removed to provide carbonate for production of additional dolomite. The result is the preservation of these organisms as molds. These molds are marred only by internal surfaces of impinged rhombs. The preservation of these crinoid molds results from the fact that the dolomite avoids these single crystals in the early stages of dolomitiza-

Fig. 3 Crinoid Molds: These molds are found only in completely dolomitized crinoid-mud rock. The external surfaces of the columnals and internal casts of the axial canals are well preserved.

tion, and from the utilization of these particles as sources of carbonate to form the final additional dolomite. The result is the development of crinoid molds as part of the dolomitization process. The preservation is sometimes quite remarkable, with external surface detail readily available. Internal casts of axial canals are often preserved through dolomite replacement of lime mud that was deposited in these openings prior to dolomitization (see Figure 3).

Delicate Replacement of Skeletal Carbonate

Dolomite sometimes reproduces details of shell structure by delicate and subtle differences in crystal size, clarity, and crystallographic orientation (Figure 4). This appears to be especially true when the rock is replaced by relatively fine-size dolomite crystals. Specifically, the more important relationship is the size of the rhombs with respect to the size of the structure to be preserved. Many workers have observed, and have effectively used, this type of preservation where it exists. However, there appears to be little evidence for the cause of differences in crystal size.

Replacing rhombs tend to grow with their crystallographic axes oriented, within the limit of observation, coincident with those of the replaced calcite. This coincidence is observed in dolomite that has replaced drusy calcite or aragonite cement or single-crystal crinoid particles. Where fine dolomite replaces a relatively coarse drusy cement, the mass of dolomite often shows a suggestion of wavy extinction similar to that of the original cement. Crinoids are often replaced as single dolomite crystals, with the optic axis of the dolomite appearing coincident with that of the original calcite. If the orientation of the rhomb was controlled by an original calcite crystal in a lime mud, the orientation of the mass of rhombs may appear random. This would

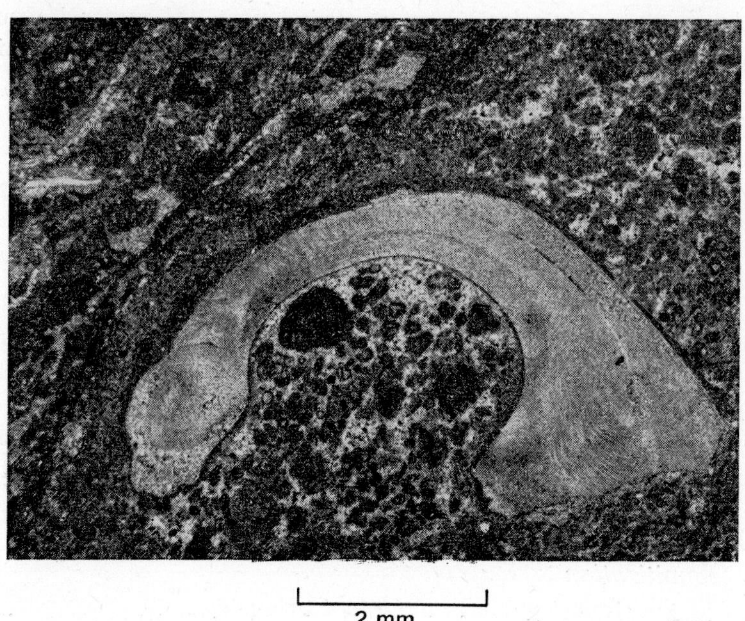

Fig. 4 Gastropod—Delicate Preservation: The organism has been replaced by very fine dolomite, with preservation of the original shell microstructure.

be true because the orientation of the original particles where the rhombs begin growth may be random. The subject of clarity of dolomite crystals and included material will be discussed later.

It cannot be assumed that if these delicate preservations do not exist in a dolomite, organisms were present and have been obliterated through dolomitization. Van Tuyl (1916, p. 323), in discussing the "paucity of organic remains" in dolomite observed that many ancient limestones are also nearly barren of organic remains. Indeed, rocks interpreted as having been deposited as lime muds with relatively few organic sand-size or larger particles are commonly dolomitized. Such observations cast further doubt on the all too common interpretation that organic remains once existed and have been obliterated by dolomitization when the dolomitized sediment may originally have been lime mud. This point becomes even more credible when delicate sedimentary structures, such as burrowing and lamination, are preserved or when limestone deposited as lime muds can be traced laterally into dolomite with continuity of bedding and structures.

It would, of course, be dangerous to interpret any dolomite apparently devoid of organic remains as having been deposited as an unfossiliferous lime mud. This interpretation in itself has significance with respect to original sedimentary environment. However, it would be equally dangerous to assume obliteration of organisms by dolomitization without careful study of the dolomite for the more subtle types of preservation of original structures and fabrics.

Preservation of Skeletal Material as Inclusions within Dolomite Crystals

Perhaps the most common example of this phenomenon is the preservation of internal structure patterns within dolomite crystals that have replaced echinoderm parts as single crystals (Figure 5). These "pseudomorphs" can be detected in thin section whenever their size is relatively large with respect to the dolomite rhomb size. Lucia (1962) used this type of preservation in reconstructing the original concentration of crinoid particles in dolomitized Devonian carbonates.

Preservation of Organic Remains in Chert Prior to Dolomitization

Delicate preservation of skeletal carbonate in replacement chert within dolomite has been noted and used by many workers. This preservation may be selective to the organism and may permit removal

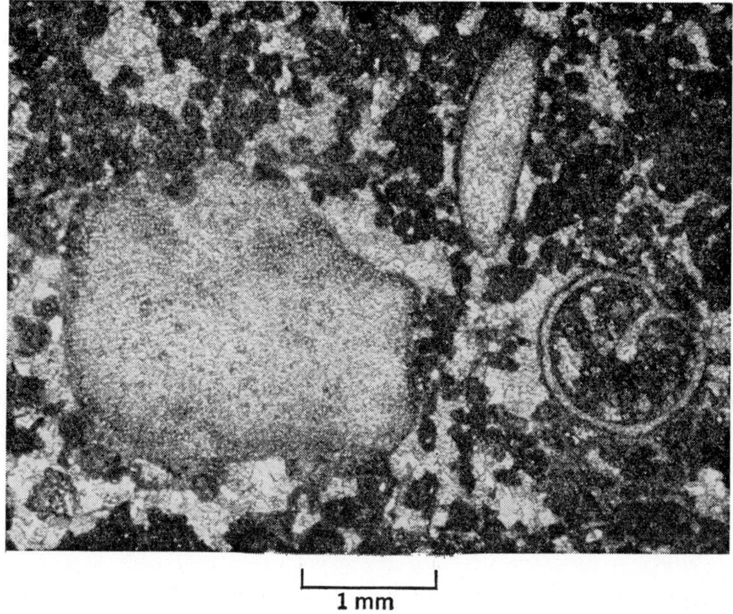

Fig. 5 Echinoderm Particle: The internal structure of this echinoderm part is well preserved within the single dolomite crystal.

of the organism by acid dissolution of the surrounding dolomite. In addition, there may be delicate preservation of the internal structure of the organism. In such cases it must be assumed that deposition of the chert preceded dolomitization, because preservation is more perfect in the chert than in the dolomite. Had dolomitization preceded silicification, preservation within the chert would be at best equal to that in the dolomite. In attempting to observe the original fabrics and structure in dolomite, it is often rewarding to search for small silica replacement patches. Caution must, of course, be exercised in interpreting the total rock on the basis of observations made in lenses of replacement chert. It is possible that the chert may be selectively replacing a specific organism or microfacies. Examination of the shape and boundary of the chert mass often proves helpful in eliminating this possibility.

Preservation of Inorganic Sedimentary Structures in Dolomite

Preservation of many inorganic sedimentary structures, and thus such environmental indicators as bedding, lamination, burrows, and mud cracks, often occurs in dolomitized limestone by subtle differences in crystal size, orientation, or clarity in much the same way as delicate preservation of organic structures. Two particularly interesting modes of preservation, discussed previously in section on *Preservation of Skeletal Remains*, are reproductions of original carbonate sand fabrics because of preference for replacement of the particles and any carbonate cement that may have existed at the time of dolomitization, and preservation of the internal structure of oolites as inclusions in single dolomite crystals.

Preservation of a Carbonate Sand Fabric

Analogous with the preservation of the tabulate coral skeletal pattern is the preservation of a carbonate sand fabric that has been only

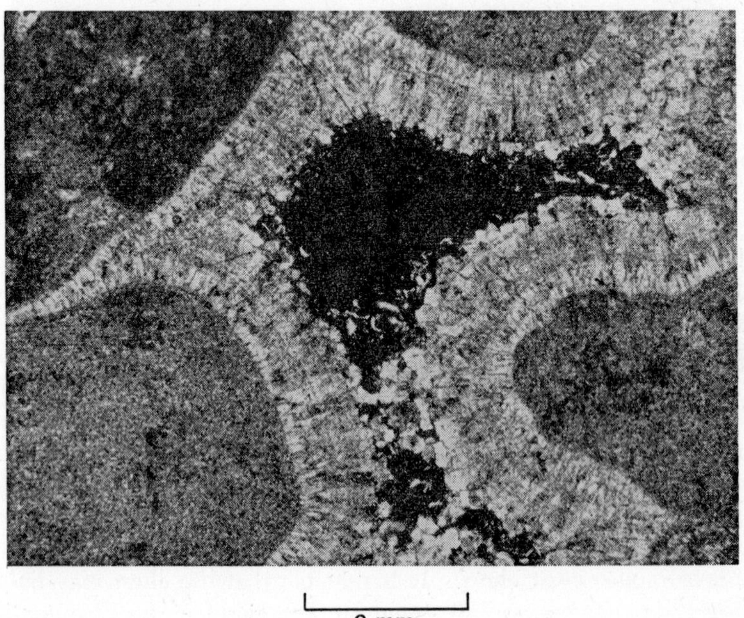

Fig. 6 Dolomitized Carbonate Pellet Sand: These particles and the incomplete drusy cement have been replaced by fine crystals of dolomite. The acicular pattern, so common in early $CaCO_3$ drusy cements, is preserved because of a tendency of the rhombs to grow with their crystallographic axes coincident with those of the replaced oriented cement. There are associated particulate sediments that have not been dolomitized and that still retain an acicular calcite drusy cement.

slightly cemented with calcite or aragonite prior to dolomitization (Figure 6). In such cases it is not uncommon to find the particles and early drusy cement replaced by dolomite and the interparticle void space preserved. Such a preference for replacement results in good preservation of the fabric of the rock. For example, an originally crossbedded carbonate sand may appear as a crossbedded dolomite. Without careful study, such a rock might be misinterpreted as having been deposited as a sand composed of dolomite grains. However, the grains are commonly replaced by several crystals which individually exhibit evidence of replacement of discrete original $CaCO_3$ particles. This type of preference for replacement of pre-existing carbonate with the retention of voids relatively larger than the crystal size of the replacing dolomite crystals may also be interpreted as indicating that the dolomite grew by utilizing locally derived carbonate.

Preservation of Carbonate Sand Particles as Inclusions in Dolomite Crystals

Outlines of particles and the internal structure of particles such as ooliths are sometimes preserved as inclusions within single dolomite crystals. Illing (1959, plate 1, fig. 5) and Folk (1959, plates 42–43) illustrate examples of this phenomenon. Figure 7 illustrates an oolite partially replaced by large dolomite rhombs with imperfect, but perceptible, preservation of the oolite rings as inclusions within the replacing rhomb. The inclusions have high birefringence and appear randomly oriented. Because they occur within the area of the oolith, they are assumed to be calcite or aragonite. Recognition of the identity of the particles and the original fabric of the rock where preserved as inclusions may permit interpretations of the original sedimentary environment.

Clear-Rimmed, Cloudy-Centered Dolomite Crystals

Figure 7 also illustrates a phenomenon commonly observed in dolomite—clear rims and cloudy centers. The cloudy center results from nondolomite inclusions, and, because of the preservation of the pattern of the oolite, these inclusions are interpreted as nonreplaced patches of oolite. The clear rim, despite the fact that it exists within the realm of the oolite and represents replaced oolite, is essentially devoid of visible included material. This phenomenon has been noted by many workers—for example, Cullis (1904, p. 408), Pettijohn (1957, plate 29D), Williams, Turner, and Gilbert (1954, fig. 119A), and Folk

(1959)—and commonly the term "zoned crystal" has been applied. These cloudy centers have sometimes been interpreted as original discrete particles of carbonate sand or silt, and the sediment has been interpreted accordingly. This is rather difficult to understand, considering the rhombic outline of the cloudy centers and the common observation of such zoned crystals existing as discrete porphyroblasts in lime mud and within individual particles such as the illustrated oolith.

When dolomite is studied in reflected light, the pattern produced by abundant dolomite crystals with clear rims and cloudy centers is sometimes mistaken for that produced by a carbonate-pellet sand deposited free of interstitial lime mud (Figure 8). The cloudy centers appear to be particles when the rhombic outline is obscured at low magnification.

The origin of these clear rims and cloudy centers offers an interest-

Fig. 7 Inclusions within a Dolomite Rhomb: This dolomite rhomb has grown partially within two ooliths and partially within the interoolith area. Inclusions within the interoolith part of the rhomb suggest that some clear calcite existed there prior to dolomitization and has been replaced. The rings of the oolith are reproduced crudely as inclusions within the ooliths. Note the clear rim on the rhomb within the area of the two ooliths.

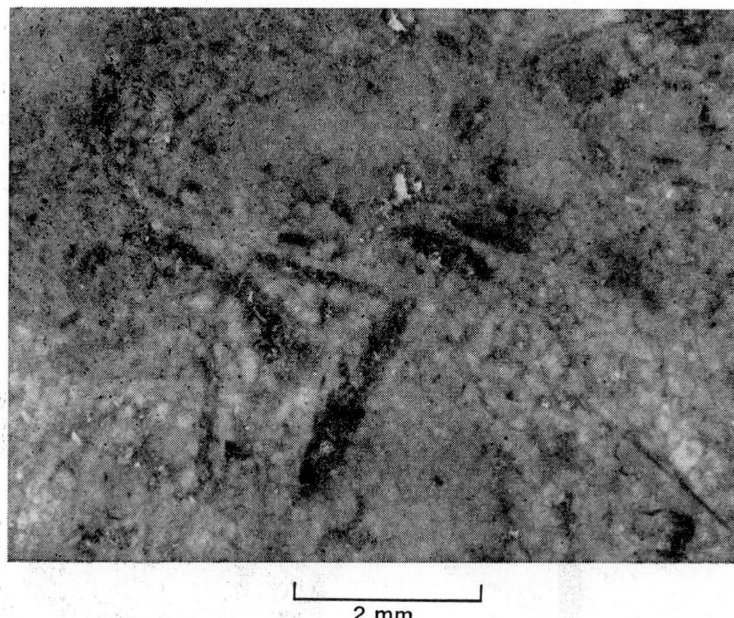

Fig. 8 Pseudocarbonate Sand Fabric in Dolomite: This granular-appearing fabric might be misinterpreted as a dolomitized carbonate pellet sand. The apparent grains are zoned dolomite crystals that have replaced a carbonate mud. The larger patches are grains of lightly pyritized skeletal material and represent particles that once floated within the mud. Note that the pseudo grains exist even within the pyritized skeletal particles.

ing problem: Why did the crystal fail to include parts of the original limestone during growth of the outer part of the crystal?

Dolomitization by use of a local source of carbonate (Murray, 1960; Weyl, 1960) suggests a possible hypothesis (see Figure 9). When a rhomb grows by replacement by using local-source carbonate, carbonate minerals must be dissolved locally outside as well as inside the volume of the final rhomb, thus providing the carbonate necessary for growing solid dolomite rhombs that will fill pore space previously existing within the volume of the rhomb and providing the carbonate necessary to offset the 12 to 13% volume difference. If this excess dissolution of calcite is concentrated in the volume immediately outside the rhomb at any stage in its growth, the calcite immediately outside the rhomb should acquire a higher porosity as rhomb growth progresses. Indeed, it is not unreasonable that ultimately, when the rhomb has achieved a certain size, a moat of void space might develop locally around the growing rhomb. This moat should progressively widen as growth progresses. Under such circumstances, the outer part of the rhomb should grow almost as micro-void-filling cement and thus clear of inclusions. If a complete moat were to form, the rhomb would fall to the bottom by gravity, giving asymmetric clear rims. Because of the small distance involved, projections of the calcite might extend across the moat at all times to the growing rhomb, thus keeping the rhomb centered. The conditions for forming a moat would not be met if compaction of the limestone kept pace with growth of the

Fig. 9 Hypothesis for the Origin of Clear Rims and Cloudy Centers in Dolomite Crystals: (1) Dolomite begins growth by replacement. The excess carbonate needed for the growth of the rhombs is supplied by dissolution af $CaCO_3$ beyond the limits of the rhomb. (2) Excess dissolution of $CaCO_3$ beyond the limits of the rhomb creates higher porosity immediately around the growing crystal. (3) Continued removal of $CaCO_3$ produces a very high porosity zone around the growing crystal. The inclusion-free rim forms because of lack of $CaCO_3$ available to be included. (4) The very high porosity zone continues to expand with continued crystal growth producing an early stage cloudy center and a late stage clear rim. Compaction of the nonreplaced limestone could destroy the high porosity zone remaining around the crystal when growth ceases.

rhomb. If this interpretation of the origin of clear rims and cloudy centers is true, and it is extremely difficult to test, the final stage of dolomite replacement occurs in local-source dolomitization without a single plane interface between the replacing and replaced phase, and some of the meaning of the word replacement is lost. Support for the hypothesis lies only in the fact that "local-source" dolomitization should produce such a phenomenon as clear rims and cloudy centers in replacement dolomite crystals, and such crystals are common in nature.

Later addition of dolomite in optical continuity on dolomite rhombs either within sucrose dolomite or on crystals that line voids may either enlarge earlier clear rims or produce clear dolomite rims on pre-existing cloudy crystals.

REFERENCES

Bathurst, R. G. C., 1958, Diagenetic fabrics in some British Dinantian limestones, *Liverpool and Manchester Geol. J.*, v. 2, pp. 11–36.

Cloud, P. E., and V. E. Barnes, 1948, The Ellenburger group of central Texas, *Univ. Texas Bur. Econ. Geol. Pub. 4621,* 473 pp.

Cullis, C. Gilbert, 1904, The mineralogical changes observed in the cores of the Funafuti borings, in *The Atoll of Funafuti,* Royal Soc. London, sec. XIV, pp. 392–420.

Folk, R. L., 1959, Thin section examination of pre-Simpson Paleozoic rocks, *Univ. Texas Pub. 5924,* v. 1, pp. 95–130.

Illing, L. V. 1959, *Deposition and Diagenesis of Some Upper Paleozoic Carbonate Sediments in Western Canada,* New York, World Petroleum Congress, sec. I, Paper 2.

Lowenstam, Heinz, A., 1950, Niagaran reefs of the Great Lakes area, *J. Geol.*, v. 58, pp. 430–487.

Lucia, F. J., 1962, Diagenesis of a crinoidal sediment: *J. Sed. Petrol.*, v. 32, pp. 848–865.

Murray, R. C., 1960, Origin of porosity in carbonate rocks, *J. Sediment. Petrol.*, v. 30, pp. 59–84.

Newell, N. D. et al., 1953, *The Permian Reef Complex of the Guadalupe Mountains Region, Texas and New Mexico—A Study in Paleoecology,* San Francisco, W. H. Freeman, 236 pp.

Pettijohn, F., 1957, *Sedimentary Rocks,* Second Edition, New York, Harper & Bros., 718 pp.

Van Tuyl, F. M., 1916, The origin of dolomite, *Iowa Geol. Surv. Ann. Report,* v. 25, pp. 251–421.

Weyl, P. K., 1960, Porosity through dolomitization: conservation of mass requirements, *J. Sed. Petrol.*, v. 30, pp. 85–90.

Williams, H., F. J. Turner, and C. M. Gilbert, 1954, *Petrography,* San Francisco, W. H. Freeman, 406 pp.

Statistical Approaches to Paleoecology

Factor Analytic Model in Paleoecology

by John Imbrie *Columbia University and American Museum of Natural History, New York*

Introduction

Purpose

Paleoecology is a complex subject, as anyone who has tried to make environmental interpretations of ancient fossiliferous rocks is aware. Advances in understanding come primarily from lines of approach exemplified by other papers in this volume—that is, by careful observation and theoretical analysis both of modern organisms and environments and of ancient fossils and rocks. If this is so then it is appropriate to ask whether or not it is reasonable, at this stage in the development of the discipline, to attempt the application of mathematical or statistical methods. The purpose of this paper is to demonstrate that it is precisely *because* of the complexity of the paleoecosystem (see p. 2) and our meager level of understanding of it that mathematical models are essential adjuncts to other approaches.

Owing to limitations of space and of the competency of this author, it is impossible to attempt here a general review of mathematical models as applied to paleoecology. Instead, after some general remarks on mathematical models, one particular model will be briefly described and a theoretical example analyzed.

The Role of Models

The raw data of any science are extraordinarily complex, and the prime task of science is to discover simple, general principles lying behind surface appearances. Newton's gravitational law is a classic example of the power of a simple concept to make clear a welter of

This research was supported by the Petroleum Research Fund of the American Chemical Society.

data (Figure 1). Simplifying concepts in geology commonly take a non-numerical form, but they are no less important on this account. A more fundamental and characteristic difference between theories in physics and geology (or ecology) concerns the identification of meaningful parameters. In the physical sciences, one knows *a priori* many of the quantities that must be specified—mass, force, charge, distance, temperature, pressure, etc.—while in the natural sciences this is rarely the case.

The term *model* is a currently fashionable name for a simplifying concept which is put forth rather more tentatively than a theory and with a greater realization of its incompleteness as a representation of nature. Lacking the dignity of a theory, it can serve as a trial balloon with less embarrassing consequences if punctured.

Any mathematical approach to nature implies a model. Such models are often of great importance in natural science in spite of their crudeness as approximations of reality. The normal curve is a case in point. This model frequency distribution, although never found in nature, nevertheless represents a conspicuous tendency. The normal curve is thus an essential item in the geologist's mental tool bag *even if no numerical observations are made.* Similarly, simplifying con-

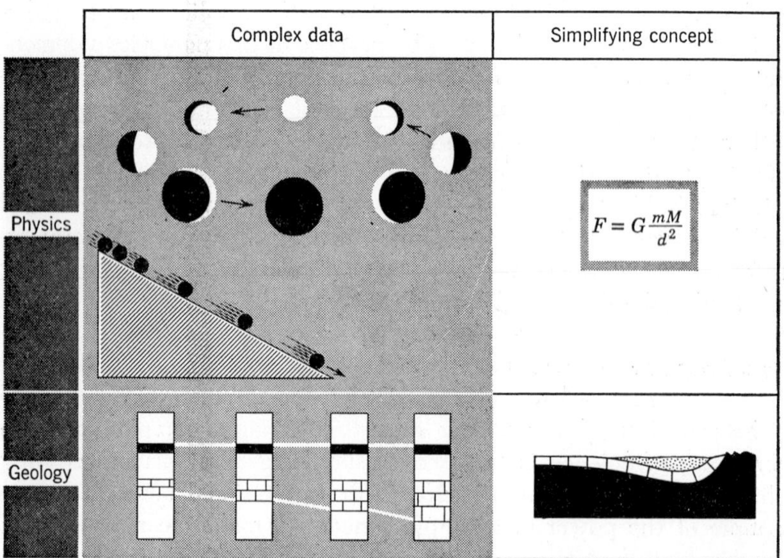

Fig. 1 The role of theories as simplifying concepts in physics and geology.

cepts such as the factor model outlined below represent important aids to thought about relationships in paleoecological data.

The Factor Model

Historical background

The origins of the model presented here go back to the early years of the present century when Charles Spearman (1904) and a school of investigators developed the essential concepts of factor analysis as a tool for psychometric research. Thurstone and a group of American workers added significantly to the theory and practice of factor analysis, notably by increasing its generality (1931), by rigorous organization and analysis (Thurstone, 1947; Holzinger and Harman, 1941), and by developing practical computing techniques (Harman, 1960).

The second source for this model is the theory of path coefficients developed for the solution of certain problems in genetics. The fundamental work in this field is that of Wright (1921). Li (1955) provides a lucid presentation and summary of the method.

Applicability of the Model

The mathematical model described in this paper is designed to aid in the interpretation of observational data, particularly in problems where (1) pertinent information is intrinsically numerical or can be appropriately coded in numerical form; (2) the volume of information is large; and (3) *a priori* knowledge of causal relationships is inadequate. These conditions are commonly found in paleoecology. Depending on the nature of the problem and the kind of data, the first condition, however, may be a severe limitation. This point is stressed in Figure 2 where two types of geological information (numerical and geometric) are distinguished. If the essential information is geometrical, factor analysis can be explicitly applied only if convenient, meaningful coding schemes are employed. If basic data are in numerical form, however, such as a table of species abundances, then the model is directly applicable.

Description of the Model

Observational data are taken to be numerical measurements of n paleoecological variables observed at each of N localities or in N field samples. The variables may be any combination of petrologic, chemi-

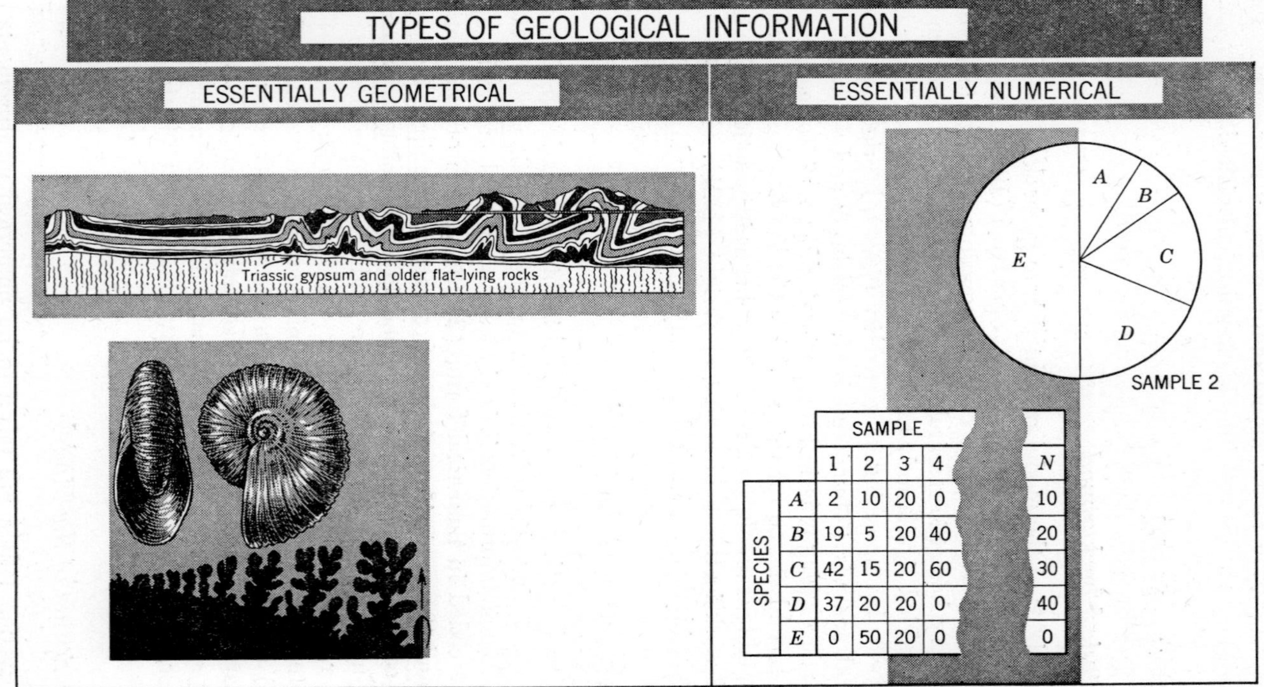

SPECIES		SAMPLE 1	2	3	4	N
	A	2	10	20	0	10
	B	19	5	20	40	20
	C	42	15	20	60	30
	D	37	20	20	0	40
	E	0	50	20	0	0

Fig. 2 Two contrasting types of data common in geology.

cal, or paleontological characteristics. These data are arranged in tabular form with n rows and N columns. In matrix notation, this is an $n \times N$ matrix $[x_{ji}]$, in which x_{ji} represents the jth variable at the ith locality ($j = 1, 2, 3, \ldots n; i = 1, 2, 3, \ldots N$).

The paleoecosystem of which the observations are a reflection is assumed to consist of m causal influences (or sets of causal influences) C_f ($f = 1, 2, 3, \ldots m$). These influences may be any combination of primary, penecontemporaneous, or postdepositional causes. They may, in addition, be either randomly related to each other or exhibit correlations due to common causes acting at a more remote level.

The notion of cause and effect is defined strictly as a mathematical concept: If $m - 1$ causes be held constant and a variation allowed in any one cause, then a proportional variation is observed in an effect x_j. Such a model does not exclude the possibility of numerous causal steps intervening between cause C_f and effect x_j in a minutely structured chain, hence this definition does no violence to nonmathematical formulations of the causal relation. All cause-and-effect relationships ultimately resolve into a simple "if *A* then *B*" relation (Reichenbach, 1954, p. 157).

Each variable x_j is assumed to be completely and linearly determined by the m causes C_f. The relative importance of the cause C_f on variable x_j is indicated by a coefficient c_{jf}. Thus,

$$x_j = c_{j1}C_1 + c_{j2}C_2 \cdots + c_{jf}C_f \cdots + c_{jm}C_m$$

The objective of a paleoecological study is thus threefold: (1) to determine m, the minimum number of causal influences needed to account for the observed variation; (2) to identify these causal influences, C_f; and (3) to specify for each variable the relative importance of each cause.

The linearity of the causal relation assumed above should be carefully noted. If the underlying relationships are in fact not linear, this will cause a discrepancy in proportion to the deviation from linearity. If the relationships are not linear but are monotonic, then some simple transformation of raw data can usually be found to solve the problem. In the case of nonmonotonic relationships, however, where a parabolic or other peaked function is involved, the problem demands a more elaborate transformation procedure. In empirical tests of the model it is surprising to find how useful a linear or log-linear model can be. At the present stage of development the possibilities of this simple model should be explored further before taking more elaborate schemes into account.

Numerical Example

In Figure 3 a hypothetical path model is shown with four causes ($m = 4$): *S, T, M,* and *D.* *S* is taken to be the average salinity measured at a number of localities over a marine basin; *T* is the mean temperature of the bottom water; and *M* the per cent of sand on the sea floor. *D* is taken as a diagenetic factor which acts on fossil shells and causes differential preservation.

The double-headed arrow indicates that causes *T* and *M* are correlated ($r = 0.84$) owing to a common control of *T* and *M* by depth. The correlation is not perfect, hence remote factors other than depth are operating on *T* and *M.* No other correlations occur among the four causes ($r_{ST} = r_{SM} = r_{SD} = r_{TD} = r_{MD} = 0$).

Note that other possible relationships could have been postulated among the four causes, including complete independence. Correlations among immediate causes S, *T, M,* and *D* imply a causal structure acting on a higher level (remote causes). A consideration of these relationships is an important part of the factor model, just as it is important in analyzing complex systems in nature where correlated causes are involved. Many discussions of causal relationships in ecology and paleoecology err by overlooking this feature.

Given the four causes and their interrelationships, the next step is to postulate a *causal scheme* relating the effect variables x_j to their immediate causes. Nine variables having a causal scheme indicated in Table 1 are postulated. Variable x_1, for example, is equally in-

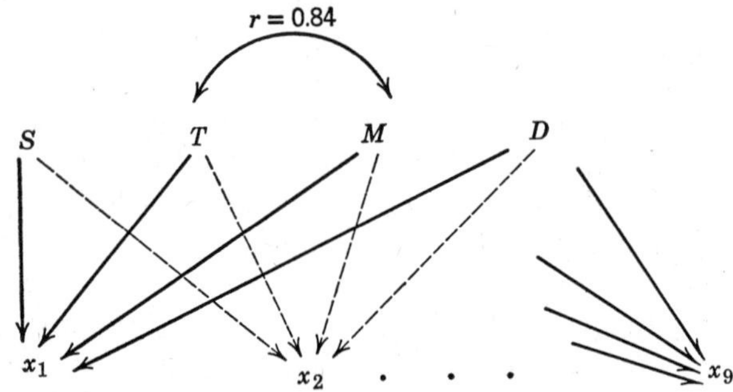

Fig. 3 Path model for the numerical example of this paper. S, *T, M, and D represent causes (salinity, temperature, sand, and diagenesis). Double-headed arrow indicates a correlation greater than zero (0.84) between T and M.* x_1, x_2, . . . x_9 *represent nine measurable effects. Arrows linking causes and effects symbolize causal influence.*

TABLE 1. *Causal scheme relating causes* S, T, M, D, *to nine variables dependent on them*

	x_1	x_2	x_3	x_4	x_5	x_6	x_7	x_8	x_9
S	0.25	0.40	0.10	0.50	0.70	0.10	0.00	0.10	0.00
T	0.25	0.30	0.20	0.20	0.10	0.10	0.10	0.80	0.50
M	0.25	0.20	0.30	0.20	0.10	0.70	0.10	0.10	0.50
D	0.25	0.10	0.40	0.10	0.10	0.10	0.80	0.00	0.00

fluenced by all four causes as specified by the entries in the table. As an equation,

$$x_1 = 0.25S + 0.25T + 0.25M + 0.25D$$

Variable x_2, however, has a different causal scheme:

$$x_2 = 0.40S + 0.30T + 0.20M + 0.10D$$

and is more strongly influenced by salinity than the other causes. Note that each species or petrographic character is completely explained by the four causes, but that each has a different causal pattern. In the path model (Figure 3) an arrow is used to represent a causal relation between a cause and an effect.

In the first four columns of Table 2 values of the causal influences are assumed for each of eight localities. These values were created arbitrarily, subject to two restrictions. First, they conform to the pattern of intercorrelations mentioned previously, with $r_{TM} = 0.84$ and other correlations equal to zero. Second, the scale of each causal variable is adjusted by a linear transformation so that its variance is equal to unity. Although this step is not necessary, it makes the results of computations easier to understand.

From the first four columns of Table 2 and the assumed causal structure given in Table 1, the last nine columns corresponding to the nine variables are calculated.

Application of Factor Analysis to the Numerical Example

Up to this point in the discussion we have assumed the role of an all-knowing paleoecological gremlin. Knowing the variances of each cause and each effect, and the causal schemes among the causes and linking the causes with the effects, such a gremlin could construct a *path coefficient model.* In such a model a number is assigned to each

TABLE 2. *Data for test example on causes* S, T, M, D *and nine variables. Decimal point is assumed between first and second digit of each five-digit sequence*

	S	*T*	*M*	*D*	1	2	3	4	5	6	7	8	9
Loc. 1	31110	04000	08000	27347	17614	17979	17250	20690	25712	11846	23078	07111	06000
Loc. 2	02745	08000	04000	20678	08856	06366	11346	05840	05189	05942	17742	07074	06000
Loc. 3	36600	10000	08500	20678	18944	21408	16481	24068	29538	12678	18392	12510	09250
Loc. 4	25620	14000	01500	20252	15343	16773	13913	17935	21509	07037	17752	13912	07750
Loc. 5	12810	20000	22000	15367	17544	17061	18028	16342	14704	20220	16494	19481	21000
Loc. 6	22875	26000	29500	20678	24763	24918	24609	24605	23630	27605	22092	26038	27750
Loc. 7	28365	28000	21000	01150	19629	24061	15196	24098	24870	20452	05820	27336	24500
Loc. 8	22875	34000	25500	39276	30413	28377	32448	27265	25890	27465	37371	32038	29750

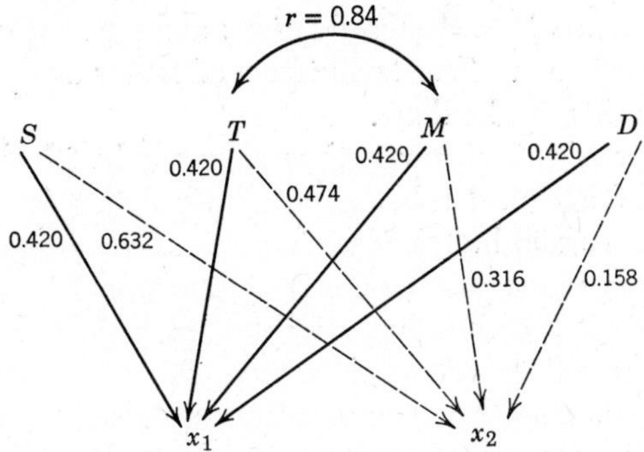

Fig. 4 Path coefficient model for two variables (x_1 and x_2) in numerical example. Symbols as in Fig. 3, except that path coefficients are placed along each path to indicate their relative importance.

path linking a cause and an effect—a path coefficient—which specifies the relative strength of the relationship. For procedures see Li (1955, Chap. 12). In this example, 36 path coefficients would be required. The eight path coefficients involved in variables x_1 and x_2 are illustrated in Figure 4. Given such a path model we can calculate the correlation that will be observed between effects x_1 and x_2. The correlation between any two effects is equal to the sum of the path coefficients along all possible paths linking the two effects. Each such path will here be a composite path consisting of either two or three steps; the coefficient along each composite path is the product of path coefficients along separate segments of the path. Verbally this sounds complicated, but by reference to Figure 4 it can be seen that the application of this rule amounts to a visualization of the causal links connecting each pair of effects. For the pair in question, x_1 and x_2,

$$r_{12} = (0.420)(0.632) + (0.420)(0.474) + (0.420)(0.316) + (0.420)(0.158) + (0.420)(0.840)(0.316) + (0.474)(0.840)(0.420) = 0.94$$

The main purpose in pointing out this relationship is to emphasize that if we are given a causal scheme, correlations among all of the effects are completely determined.

As the number of really knowledgeable paleoecological gremlins is rather small, the reader may well wonder how the ordinary scientist can apply the path model to a real situation. In the preceding paragraph, for example, we are given a causal scheme from which the correlations among effects can be calculated. The empirical problem is exactly the reverse: given the correlations among effects, we wish to derive a causal scheme. The techniques of factor analysis provide a means by which this can be done.

The remainder of this paper is thus concerned with demonstrating the derivation of a causal scheme from raw data using factor techniques. Two cases will be taken up in turn. *Case 1* assumes that the paleoecologist has made measurements proportional to all those contained in Table 2. For the nine variables this would be no problem. For the four immediate causes, however, we must assume that the scientist in question has been unusually astute, not only in guessing what the underlying causes are but in finding observable properties exactly proportional to them. We further assume that he does not know for certain either the number or the identity of the causes. *Case 2* will assume that he has measured only the nine variables. The justification for considering *Case 1* is to demonstrate that even if the investigator is able to measure rock properties linearly related to the actual causes, a mathematical model is needed to clearly demonstrate his success and to evaluate the true relative importance of each cause. A step-by-step procedure under *Case 1* is given below.

STEP 1. Calculate from the raw data of Table 2 a matrix of correlation coefficients. An extract from this 13×13 matrix is given in Table 3. Note first the intercorrelations among the four causes. Only one correlation is greater than zero, as postulated in the causal scheme. Also, note the correlations between x_1 and other elements in the table. From our causal scheme we know that x_1 is in fact equally controlled by all four causes—and yet the correlation x_1 with causes S, *T*, *M*, and *D* are respectively 0.420, 0.772, 0.772, and 0.420. The

TABLE 3. *Extract of correlation matrix for numerical example. Entries are product moment correlations computed for each pair of causes and variables*

	S	*T*	*M*	*D*	x_1	x_2	x_3	x_4
S	1.000	0.000	0.000	0.000	0.420	0.632	0.158	0.784
T	0.000	1.000	0.840	0.000	0.772	0.739	0.714	0.577
M	0.000	0.840	1.000	0.000	0.772	0.714	0.739	0.577
D	0.000	0.000	0.000	1.000	0.420	0.158	0.632	0.157
x_1	0.420	0.772	0.772	0.420	1.000	0.941	0.941	0.878
x_2	0.632	0.739	0.714	0.158	0.941	1.000	0.771	0.975
x_3	0.158	0.714	0.739	0.632	0.941	0.771	1.000	0.678
x_4	0.784	0.577	0.577	0.157	0.878	0.975	0.678	1.000

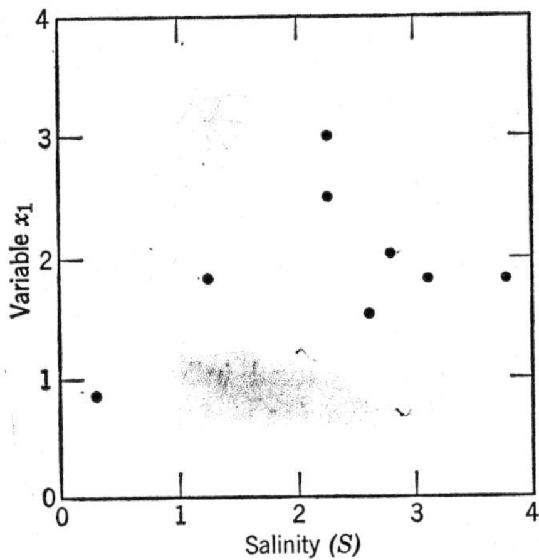

Fig. 5 Relationship between variable x_1 and cause S.

high correlations of the variable with T and M are due to the correlation between the causes T and M. Here is a useful caution to the interpretation of correlations in paleoecology, whether they are expressed in numerical form *or intuitively comprehended in the field.* In considering the relation between any effect and an assumed cause we must consider the possibility that other causes are correlated with the assumed one. Note that if no measurement of M were taken, the correlation r_{1T} would remain unchanged.

Another point of interest in the table is the low level of the correlation between x_1 and cause S. The observed correlation (0.420) is a statistical generalization of the random-appearing relationship plotted in Figure 5. We must beware of assuming that no causal relation exists even though observed correlations are low. In this particular case it is worthwhile to note that with a sample size of 8 the correlation in question is not significantly different from zero. This points up an essential difference between a mathematical and a strictly statistical model.

STEP 2. Perform an orthogonal factor analysis on the correlation matrix. The procedures involved here are algebraically complex, but are well described elsewhere (see Harman, 1960). Computer programs are available for performing an entire analysis from raw data to finished product. The present example was run on an IBM 7090 in less than three minutes. As there are various varieties of factor analysis possible, it is appropriate to mention here the system used in this study. The principal components method was employed, using highest correlations as initial communality estimates. Eight iterations were automatically performed to converge on the true values. Four orthogonal factor axes accounted for 100% of the variance. Four factors were therefore rotated by the varimax criterion. The varimax matrix is given in Table 4.

Input to these calculations is the raw data, and no assumptions are made as to the number of influences (factors) or as to the identity of the casual variables. The factor analytic system employed here correctly discovered that four causal influences are sufficient to account for the observed variance ($m = 4$). In addition, the varimax matrix (Table 4) provides a means of identifying the four vectors (variables) which lie at the extremes of the vector configuration in m-space—that is, those which are statistically the most independent. These four extremes are correctly identified as (causes) *S*, *T*, *M*, and *D*. The procedure by which this is done is explained elsewhere (Imbrie, 1963).

STEP 3. Having identified the most independent variables (in this case, *causes*) the next step is to resolve each of the other nine vectors

TABLE 4. *Rotated (varimax) factor matrix for numerical example. Entries are projections of each variable on orthogonal reference axes* B_1, B_2, B_3, *and* B_4. h^2 = *communality = sum of squares of elements in each row*

	Factor Axes				
	B_1	B_2	B_3	B_4	h^2
S	−0.088	0.995	0.044	0.004	1.000
T	0.957	0.088	−0.052	−0.271	1.000
M	0.950	0.085	−0.053	0.295	1.000
D	−0.058	0.039	−0.998	−0.003	1.000
x_1	0.739	0.507	−0.444	0.010	1.000
x_2	0.689	0.704	−0.171	−0.033	1.000
x_3	0.702	0.250	−0.665	0.053	1.000
x_4	0.520	0.840	−0.154	0.010	1.000
x_5	0.168	0.980	−0.108	0.007	1.000
x_6	0.935	0.215	−0.173	0.225	1.000
x_7	0.175	0.059	−0.983	0.000	1.000
x_8	0.956	0.200	−0.047	−0.210	1.000
x_9	0.994	0.090	−0.055	0.012	1.000

TABLE 5. *Oblique projection matrix. Tabled values are projections of variables on oblique axes* S, T, M, D

	S	*T*	*M*	*D*
S	1.000	0.000	0.000	0.000
T	0.000	1.000	0.000	0.000
M	0.000	0.000	1.000	0.000
D	0.000	0.000	0.000	1.000
x_1	0.420	0.420	0.420	0.420
x_2	0.632	0.474	0.316	0.158
x_3	0.158	0.316	0.474	0.632
x_4	0.784	0.314	0.314	0.157
x_5	0.956	0.137	0.137	0.137
x_6	0.126	0.126	0.877	0.126
x_7	0.000	0.122	0.122	0.973
x_8	0.113	0.898	0.113	0.000
x_9	0.000	0.522	0.522	0.000

representing variables into the four vectors representing the assumed causes and lying obliquely at the extremes of the configuration. The oblique projection matrix (see Imbrie, 1963) given in Table 5 shows the projection of each of the nine variables onto each of the four assumed causes. The entries in this matrix are algebraically identical to the path coefficients that could have been calculated from the known causal structure. In addition, each row in this table is an objective statement of the relative importance of each cause in influencing each variable. Note, for example, the causal structure calculated for variable x_1. It is equally influenced by each cause—as is in this case known to be true. For convenience, each row can be summed and each element in the row expressed as a fraction of that sum. This is done in Table 6, which thus represents precisely the causal structure originally postulated.

Our hypothetical, astute paleoecologist at this stage would be able to congratulate himself on having discovered a causal scheme which will account precisely for all of the variance in his table of data. In addition, he knows that no more than four causes are necessary to account for the data, and can evaluate accurately the relative importance of each cause.

Case 2 is a more realistic model in which the investigator has only ordinary sagacity. Here we assume he has measured the nine vari-

TABLE 6. *Oblique projection matrix (Table 5) recalculated to express each entry as per cent of total in row*

	S	*T*	*M*	*D*
S	100	00	00	00
T	00	100	00	100
M	00	00	100	00
D	00	00	00	100
x_1	25	25	25	25
x_2	40	30	20	10
x_3	10	20	30	40
x_4	50	20	20	10
x_5	70	10	10	10
x_6	10	10	70	10
x_7	00	10	10	80
x_8	10	80	10	00
x_9	00	50	50	00

ables but has not measured variables directly proportional to the real causes. The procedure is identical to that above except that a 9×9 correlation matrix is computed. The tabled entries in this matrix are of course identical to the corresponding elements in the 13×13 matrix previously calculated. Further, the number of dimensions (factors) needed to account for 100% of the variance in this case is still four. An orthogonal factor analysis would pick out the four most extreme (independent) variables of the vector configuration. These are variables x_5, x_6, x_7, and x_8 corresponding to the now unknown causes S, *M*, *D*, and *T*, respectively (see Table 1).

Having identified the extreme variables, the paleoecologist now reviews the nature of these variables and from all available evidence postulates a causal structure. He may test this postulate by seeking measurable variables likely to be more closely proportional to the underlying causes. In any case, he will have an objective measure of the complexity of the paleoecosystem under study—that is, he will know that $m = 4$, and can guard against overexplaining or underexplaining his data.

Factor Model in the Real World

The numerical example just explained was designed to illustrate in a concrete way some theoretical implications of the factor model in paleoecology. The relationships postulated in it are assumed to operate precisely, and influences other than the four assumed causes are not considered. Random error is eliminated. Considering the realities of the fossil record and the imperfection of our recording techniques, this simple-minded model can hardly be expected to work perfectly in the real world. The question for future work to determine, therefore, is the extent to which the factor model approximates reality.

Unpublished studies on materials from the Great Bahama Bank indicate that the model fits this relatively simple modern ecosystem quite well. Results of application of the model to data from the Florena shale (Permian) in Nebraska, Kansas, and Oklahoma (see Imbrie et al., 1959), are encouraging. Thirty-one variables were measured on 74 samples, including abundance data on fossil groups, petrographic measures such as the frequency of burrows, and the composition of the rock in terms of major minerals and oxides. Approximately 60% of the variance was explained with $m = 5$. Key variables identified as the most independent of the 31 are: crinoids, burrows, fusulines, dolomite, and oncolites. What ultimate influences or sets of influences do these key variables reflect? Some hints can be found by noting those variables which tend to associate closely with each key variable. These reaction groups (associations) are tabled below.

Group 1	Group 2	Group 3	Group 4	Group 5
crinoids	burrows	fusulines	dolomite	oncolites
Derbyia	*Euomphalus*	corals	SO_4	echinoids
clams				*Composita*
subulitid snails				
Bryozoa				

Other indications come from noting the geographic and stratigraphic distribution of samples dominated by each reaction group. Information other than that used in calculation can, of course, also be considered. Cephalopods, for example, were not numerically tabulated in this study but are known to be associated with Group 2.

From a consideration of the lines of evidence just indicated, the five Florena influences are tentatively identified as follows:

GROUP 1. Shallow, prodelta, nutrient-rich waters overlying a marl bottom.

GROUP 2. Quiet, deeper waters with unrestricted access to open water and a marl bottom.

GROUP 3. Shallow, nutrient-poor, carbonate-bottom shelf-lagoon with restricted circulation but with salinities near normal.

GROUP 4. Hypersaline, marl-bottom shelf-lagoon.

GROUP 5. Turbulent, clay-free, subtidal shoal.

REFERENCES

Harman, H. H., 1960, *Modern Factor Analysis*, University of Chicago Press, Chicago, 469 pp.

Holzinger, K. J., and H. H. Harman, 1941, *Factor Analysis*, University of Chicago Press, Chicago, 417 pp.

Imbrie, John, Leo Leporte, and D. F. Merriam, 1959, Beattie limestone facies and their bearing on cyclical sedimentation theory: *Kansas Geol. Soc.*, 24th Field Conference Guidebook, pp. 69–78.

Imbrie, John, 1963, Factor and vector analysis programs for analyzing geologic data: *Tech. Rpt. No. 6, ONR Task No. 389–135*, 83 pp.

Li, C. C., 1955, *Population Genetics*, University of Chicago Press, chap. 12.

Reichenbach, Hans, 1954, *The Rise of Scientific Philosophy*, University of California Press, Berkeley and Los Angeles, 333 pp.

Spearman, Charles, 1904, General intelligence, objectively determined and measured: *Amer. J. Psychol.*, v. 15, pp. 201–293.

Thurstone, L. L., 1931, Multiple factor analysis: *Psych. Rev.*, v. 38, pp. 406–427.

——— 1947, *Multiple-factor analysis*, University of Chicago Press, Chicago, 535 pp.

Wright, Sewall, 1921, Correlation and causation: *J. Agric. Research*, v. 20, pp. 557–585.

Index